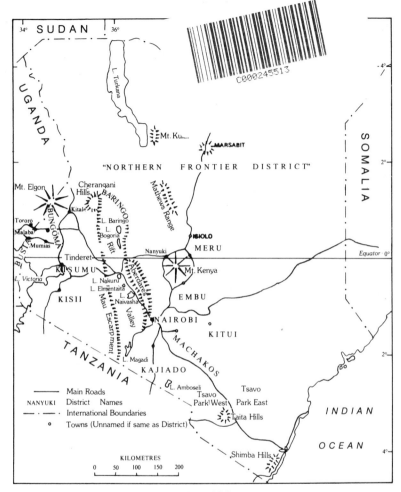

KENYA

Collins Guide to the
WILD FLOWERS
OF EAST AFRICA

Sir Michael Blundell, K.B.E.

COLLINS
8 Grafton Street
London W1

ACKNOWLEDGEMENTS

In producing this book I owe a great debt of gratitude to many kind friends and helpers. In particular to:

Ms Christine Kabuye and Mr Geoffrey Mungai of the Herbarium in Nairobi for generous help in identifying and classifying many of the plants illustrated. Especially I must mention Mr J. B. Gillett, now working at the Herbarium, The Royal Botanic Gardens, Kew, without whose enthusiasm, encouragement and unstinting research, the book would never have been produced. Also the numerous botanists at Kew who have helped me with difficult identifications, and the Director of Kew for allowing me to use the invaluable information available in the authoritative *Flora of Tropical East Africa*.

I am also indebted to Mr Nigel Pavitt, Mr Peter Davey and Mr Tim Campbell for allowing me to use their photographs and for going into the remoter places of East Africa from the coast to more than 4250m (14,000ft) to secure the illustrations. Mr Pavitt, in particular, has helped me greatly with the text and format of the book.

Inevitably a book with so many colour illustrations is expensive to produce and I am indebted to the following for generous financial support:

Mr A. Blundell; East African Breweries Limited; East African Natural History Society; Heublein International Management Corporation; Kenya Horticultural Society; Kenya Wine Agencies Limited; Mr H. F. Oppenheimer; Sir Peter Tapsell, M.P.

I must also thank Mrs Susan Goodwin for her tireless work in typing and correcting the manuscript and Mrs Marcelle Blundell for help in arranging and checking it; Dr A. D. Q. Agnew and the publishers, the Oxford University Press, for allowing me to use material contained in *Upland Kenya Wild Flowers*, and Dr Grey-Wilson for information contained in his book *Impatiens of Africa*; Mr Richard Moss for his clear and concise maps.

Finally, mention must be made of Mr Crispin Fisher and Mrs Gilly McWilliam at Collins Publishers for much help, advice and patience while the book was in course of preparation.

CONTENTS

PREFACE

I have long felt the need for a book which would give the resident of, or traveller in East Africa an introduction to the beautiful wild flowers of the region; a book which would not demand a training in botany but be as approachable for the general reader as for the expert botanist. I have therefore set out to present the beauty of our wild flowers primarily through colour photographs, which will provide an invaluable guide to recognition of the various species. A description of each plant, presented in reasonably simple language and concentrating on the type of growth and leaf form of the individual species, provides a text to complement the illustrations. I have included not only descriptions of every plant portrayed, but also of many allied species.

It is obvious that a single volume of this size cannot include every one of the thousands of plants which occur in East Africa; indeed most of the grasses and sedges and many of the trees and bushes would not be considered flowers by many people. I have therefore selected for illustration those that will most commonly be seen, with some description of their most noticeable relatives. Also included are some of the rarer and more unusual species as these are exciting to find and interesting to see.

The illustrations have been arranged according to colour in a sequence from white to yellow and through orange to red, purple and blue. The species text is in taxonomic order, family by family. To aid identification a simple key based upon conspicuous features is included to guide readers to broad groups of families.

Photographic Credits

P. Bally: 427, 428.   **G. R. Van Someron:** 117.

Tim Campbell: 5, 7, 9, 27, 28, 31, 35, 41, 68, 71, 101, 136, 149, 153, 162, 163, 165, 171, 186, 187, 199, 209, 213, 230, 248, 251, 261, 273, 278, 302, 303, 311, 321, 323, 327, 347, 383, 412, 418, 422, 430, 444, 452, 468, 472, 477, 498, 508, 513, 519, 525, 534, 536, 542, 548, 553, 563, 577, 583, 589, 606, 611, 632, 634, 646, 656, 678, 732, 744, 773, 774, 776, 798, 799, 801, 805, 806, 818, 825, 848, 849, 864.

Peter Davey: 1, 3, 4, 8, 13, 21, 24, 49, 50, 70, 77, 78, 80, 96, 97, 102, 125, 130, 131, 145–8, 161, 166, 167, 173–5, 178, 181, 185, 190, 198, 204, 208, 215–18, 220, 227, 232, 234, 235, 239, 249, 252, 257, 267, 269, 271, 272, 279, 283, 293, 300, 304, 315, 329, 338, 348, 350, 356, 360, 365, 376, 385–7, 389–91, 405, 423, 432, 435, 442, 446, 451, 460, 465, 476, 479, 497, 501, 506, 511, 517, 521, 530, 531, 533, 535, 541, 543, 559, 592, 593, 602, 605, 614, 636, 640, 668, 673, 679, 681, 689, 704, 705, 730, 733–5, 737, 745, 757, 763, 769, 770, 786, 804, 810, 811, 813, 819, 855.

Nigel Pavitt: 2, 6, 10–12, 14–20, 22, 23, 25, 26, 29, 30, 32–4, 36–40, 42–8, 51–67, 69, 72–6, 79, 81–95, 98–100, 103–16, 118–24, 126–9, 132–5, 137–44, 150–2, 154–60, 164, 168–70, 172, 176, 177, 179, 180, 182–4, 188, 189, 191–7, 200–3, 205–7, 210–12, 214, 219, 221–6, 228, 229, 231, 233, 236–8, 240–7, 250, 253–6, 258–60, 262–6, 268, 270, 274–7, 280–2, 284–92, 294–9, 301, 305–10, 312–14, 316–20, 322, 324–6, 328, 330–7, 339–46, 349, 351–5, 357–9, 361–4, 366–75, 377–82, 384, 388, 392–404, 406–11, 413–17, 419–21, 424–6, 429, 431, 433, 434, 436–41, 443, 445, 447–50, 453, 454–9, 461–4, 466, 467, 469–71, 473–5, 478, 480–96, 499, 500, 502–5, 507, 509, 510, 512, 514–16, 518, 520, 522–4, 526–9, 532, 537, 538–40, 544–7, 549–52, 554–8, 560–2, 564–76, 578–82, 584–91, 594–601, 603, 604, 607–10, 612, 613, 615–31, 633, 635, 637–9, 641–5, 647–55, 657–67, 669–72, 674–7, 680, 682–8, 690–703, 706–729, 731, 736–43, 746–56, 758–62, 764–8, 771, 772, 775, 777–85, 787–97, 800, 802, 803, 807–9, 812, 814–17, 820–4, 826–47, 850–4, 856–63.

Jacket: front bottom right by Peter Davey; others by Nigel Pavitt.

INTRODUCTION

The Flora of East Africa

No one knows how many species of flowering plant occur in East Africa. There are certainly some which have not yet been named scientifically, and there are some which are confined to single specific regions only. There are cases in which a single species has been given more than one scientific name, so that the number of species appears to be higher than it really is; and there is also dispute over whether certain forms have specific status. Nevertheless, when the botanists working on the *Flora of Tropical East Africa* (*FTEA*) complete their work (which may well be not before the end of the century), we shall probably find that over 11,000 species of flowering plant occur in the region.

The East African flora is particularly interesting because of the wide range of ecological and climatic conditions encountered in the area. The two major factors governing distribution and growth are rainfall and altitude, and recognition of plants can often be assisted by a knowledge of the zones in which they are likely to be found. The zones may be broadly defined as follows:

Alpine zone above 3650m (12,000ft).

Highlands including moorlands, higher rainfall forest and upland grassy plains; altitude *c.* 1800–3650m (6000–12,000ft), rainfall above *c.* 1000mm (40in).

Moister bushed woodland and grassland medium to higher rainfall areas; altitude *c.* 1100–2000m (3600–6500ft), rainfall 625–1000mm (25–40in).

Drier bushed woodland and grassland medium dry to medium rainfall areas; altitude *c.* 760–1800m (2500–6000ft), rainfall 400–625mm (16–25in).

Dry bushland low rainfall areas; altitude generally below 1060m (*c.* 3500ft), rainfall 250–400mm (10–16in).

Arid bushland or dwarf shrub grassland rainfall below 250mm (10in), altitude generally below 760m (2500ft).

It should be noted that the **coastal zone**, where the moisture index is rarely less than 10, and the conditions are warm and tropical with a rainfall of 1000mm (40in) upwards, is an area extending inland all along the coast for an approximate distance of 16–24km (10–15 miles). After this the drier bushed woodland and dry bushland zones are predominant.

True deserts – areas devoid of plants, except in specially favoured spots – do not exist in East Africa, although there are semi-deserts in the north of Kenya where only scattered herbs and shrubs are found, which, although leaving much of the surface of the ground bare, maintain a network of roots beneath. Dry bushland, where there is usually a fair amount of vegetation, especially after the infrequent rains, is sometimes wrongly called desert because it can support only a very sparse human population.

5

The Ecological Zones of East Africa

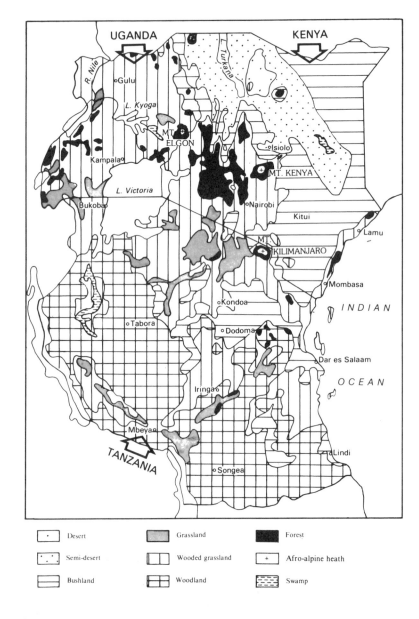

Desert

Semi-desert

Bushland

Grassland

Wooded grassland

Woodland

Forest

Afro-alpine heath

Swamp

The East African region does not have true rain forest except possibly in the Usambara Mountains, but the forest can be divided into areas of higher rainfall (more than 1000mm p.a.), where considerable cloud and mist persist; and areas known as dry forests which, although evergreen, have rainfall of around 750mm p.a. Examples of the former can be found on Mount Kilimanjaro, the Ruwenzoris, Mount Elgon and Mount Kenya, and of the latter in Langata (Nairobi National Park), the Chyulu Hills and parts of the Nyeri District below 2000m (6500ft). It should always be remembered that as altitude increases, the effect of rainfall is proportionately enhanced. Moving westwards in Kenya and Tanzania, the mean night temperature tends to rise with the mellowing effect of the great bodies of water in Lakes Victoria and Tanganyika. It may happen that plants in the eastern districts will be found at slightly higher altitudes in the west. Again, plants in the more southerly areas may extend their range to lower altitudes than in the north due to the movement of the sun and its effect on mean temperatures. The altitude ranges given in this book are based on collection notes attached to specimens in the East African Herbarium, Kew and elsewhere, as well as from personal observation. They must be taken as an indication only, as few were recorded with accurate altimeters, and further study may well reveal an extended range of individual species. The normal range may also be altered by more localized factors. For instance, where a cool stream flows at the bottom of a narrow gorge with limited sunshine, plants from higher altitudes may well extend their range down the stream to lower levels; similarly in the upper regions, on warm hillsides facing the full effect of the morning or afternoon sun, the opposite may occur, a plant becoming established some quite considerable height above its normal altitude. The altitudes given, therefore, are intended as a guide only and the conversions from metric to imperial measures are not to exact but to approximate, easily comprehended ranges.

Many of the brightly-coloured, orange and red flowers in East Africa, such as the Aloes, *Leonotis*, and most of the Loranthaceae are particularly attractive to birds such as the Sunbirds (*Nectarinea*) which are able to distinguish these colours. Many East African plants also have an unusually generous supply of nectar compared with those of more temperate areas such as Europe and North America, and support an above-average population of bees.

Enthusiastic plant and flower lovers have sometimes been guilty of indiscriminate and unwise uprooting and collecting, which has done considerable damage to species such as some of the Orchids, *Caralluma*, *Adenium obesum* (Desert Rose), *Cyrtanthus* and the Cycads. Where a house is being built, a road widened or a forest cut down, an attempt at moving a plant may save it, but they are otherwise best left in the wild where they have made their homes. Many of the more rare and beautiful plants will not easily tolerate or accept a change in environment or soil conditions. They die. Far better to leave them where they have chosen to develop on their own so that everyone visiting or seeing the area can enjoy them.

Notes on the Text

Where the name of a species has one or more other names in brackets after it, it signifies that the name has recently been changed by botanists, the old name being recorded for reference purposes in brackets. Examples are: *Cordia africana* (*C. holstii*, *C. abyssinica*) and *Scadoxus multiflorus* (*Haemanthus multiflorus*).

Where a plant has not as yet been given a scientific name or when a scientific name has not as yet been definitely established, I have adopted from the Editor of the *Flora of Tropical East Africa* the practice of designating it as a Species 'A' or Species 'B' etc., e.g. *Bidens* species A. It must be realized that when new plants are discovered in a region like East Africa, botanists hesitate to name them specifically until they have researched the botanical records of other countries – a process which may take time – in order to satisfy themselves that the plant has not already been named.

Where a plant is recorded from the photograph as a species only, e.g. *Dyschoriste* sp., *Vernonia* sp., it means that, herbarium material being unavailable, it was impossible to make an exact identification from the photograph only. I have included them in these instances, however, as the general picture of the flower will help the reader to a generic if not specific identification.

Altitude figures, both in metres and feet, are meant to be an indication only of the altitude range. Neither they nor the conversions from metres to feet can possibly be precise. The reasons for this are fully explained in the introduction. Metric figures for sizes of flowers and inflorescences may be taken as accurate, conversions are to the nearest convenient fraction. For readers requiring precise conversions and for use with other texts giving only one form of measurement, conversion tables are given on page 17.

Where a plant is not tolerant of salt carried in the air from the sea, the altitude is shown as 1m (3ft) upwards.

The abbreviations which appear in the texts are:

FTEA = *Flora of Tropical Africa*
UKWF = *Upland Kenya Wild Flowers*
KTS = *Kenya Trees and Shrubs*

Where species are recorded as 'A', 'B' etc., the names are those in *Upland Kenya Wild Flowers*.

Place Names and Localities

The following place names are in Kenya:

Kisii, Kisumu, Western Kenya, Elgon, Kitale, Cheranganis, Tinderet (which refers generally to the area from Maji Mazuri above Eldama Ravine, Anabkoi to Eldoret and west to Lessos, Londiani, Tinderet Mountain, Mteitei Valley), Mau, Rift Valley, Aberdares, Baringo, Kajiado, Machakos, Magadi, Embu, Meru, Nyambeni Hills, Mount

Kenya, Mathews Range, the Ndotos, Turkana, Isiolo, Nanyuki, Nyeri, Kitui, Narok, Loita Hills (near the Maasai Mara area), Kericho, Limuru, Nairobi, Taita Hills, Sokokwe forest near Malindi.

Lamu, Malindi, Mombasa are coastal ports which are not recorded on our maps. Plants growing near them are recorded as 'in coastal areas or regions'.

The following place names are in Tanzania:

The district Maasai will include Moshi, Arusha, Mounts Kilimanjaro and Meru, Ngorongoro Crater, Mbulu, Serengeti, Mount Hanang. Tanga includes Lushoto, the Usambara and Pare Mountains and Mount Kumazi. Morogoro region includes the Uluguru Mountains which are a notable floral enclave, Mpwapwa, Kondoa includes Dodoma. Lake areas include Bukoba, Mwanza, Musoma, Shinyanga. The ports of Tanga, Dar-es-Salaam and Lindi are not shown, as plants growing at or near them are recorded as 'in coastal areas'. Pemba Island and Zanzibar are specifically mentioned where appropriate.

The following place names are in Uganda:

The northern region includes Gulu, Kitgum and West Nile. The Imatong Mountains are in this region and are partly in Uganda and partly in southern Sudan, south of Juba. The eastern region includes Jinja, Tororo, Mbale, Mount Elgon, Lake Kioga, Soroti. The western region includes Kigezi, Kabale, Mbarara, Ankole, Fort Portal and Lake Albert. Buganda includes Kampala, Masaka, Mengo and Entebbe. Karamoja with Mount Moroto and Mount Debasien are in the eastern region.

In general, the maps are designed to indicate areas only, without obscuring them with too much detail. There are forest islands in Taita Hills in Kenya; in the Uluguru Mountains, near Morogoro; south-east of Mbeya; on the eastern shores of Lake Tanganyika (near Gombe Stream) and near Bukoba in Tanzania; and a famous island 'of afro-alpine vegetation' in the Ruwenzori Mountains in Uganda, all of which are important to botanists. Limitations of space prevent their presentation on the maps but they are noted here for the interest of botanists and flower-lovers.

Finally, it should be understood that where a wide, general area is mentioned as the locality in which a given species is found, the specific locality is determined by the ecological zone or type of habitat recorded in the text referring to the species. A plant recorded with a habitat in dry, rocky outcrops in *Acacia-Commiphora* woodland, for instance, will not normally be found in upland forest areas and *vice versa*.

Many of the species here are also found in West, Central and South Africa, and in Angola, e.g. *Calodendrum capense* and *Nymphaea caerulea* (*N. capensis*), but for the purposes of this book, the distribution mentioned refers generally to the tropical and subtropical countries of the Eastern Africa region as a whole.

Identifying Plants

The illustrations and the descriptions in this book will help you to identify the flowers found in East Africa. The photographs have been arranged by colour, which is one immediate approach to identification, although plants can appear in several colour forms and more careful study will frequently be required. The colour index guides you to both listed and unlisted species arranged in order of family under each colour heading. The text describes where a particular species may be found, altitude, size and overall appearance, leaf and flower structure, and other pertinent features by which it may be recognized. Try to recognize the features of the various families. The key following, and linked with the contents list guides you to particular family groups. Use this in conjunction with the colour index. Allow for habitat requirements which will further restrict the possibilities. Carefully study the leaf shape and arrangement and the formation and placing of the flowers. Positive identification will not always be possible to specific level, but in attempting it you will gain a deeper understanding of East Africa's plants.

For a detailed investigation to determine the family to which a plant belongs a hand lens (a ×10 magnification is most suitable) and a mounted needle for opening up flowers are very useful. The keys to families in *Upland Kenya Wild Flowers* and *Some Common Flowering Plants of Uganda* may then be consulted. The first is now difficult to obtain but the latter is readily available in Nairobi. For more detailed reference sources, see *Further Study* on page 442.

If other methods of naming plants fail, the Botanist in Charge, East African Herbarium, Box 45166, Nairobi, Kenya (situated behind the National Museum), is prepared to name properly dried specimens if details of place of collection etc. are supplied and if the Herbarium is allowed to retain the specimens. If a plant is found in an area or at an altitude from which it has not previously been recorded, or with a previously unrecorded African name or use, an annotated specimen serves as a valuable and welcome permanent record for the Herbarium.

The Naming of Plants

English names do not exist for most of the plants in this book, and to manufacture them would be difficult and wrong. If there is an English specific name (e.g. Pyjama Lily, Fireball Lily, Desert Rose) it is given in the text, and similarly with family names (e.g. Malvaceae, the Hollyhock family). There are African vernacular names for many plants but they do not necessarily differentiate between species within a genus to the degree necessary to meet modern botanical requirements, and because of the many different peoples in East Africa, each plant might well have up to a dozen local names.

To avoid the confusion of different local and linguistic differences in naming plants, every species of plant is known internationally by a scientific name usually consisting of two Latin words. The first word, which is given a capital letter, identifies the genus to which the plant belongs; the second word indicates the species and is usually a Latin adjective that gives more specific information: it may be the latinized name of the botanist who first located and described the plant, e.g. *fischeri*, *hildebrandtii* or *battiscombei*, or it may give some vital clues as to the plant's characteristics, e.g. *multiflorus* (many-flowered); *repens* (creeping); *foetida* (evil-smelling), or an indication of its locality, as with *Lobelia keniensis* (of Kenya) and *Notonia abyssinica* (of Abyssinia). Occasionally a word of Greek origin creeps into the specific name, as in *Acacia xanthophloea* from the Greek for yellow bark or skin. This method of naming plants is called the binomial system.

There may be a third name after the specific name to indicate a subspecies or variety within the species, e.g. *Senecio* (genus) *johnstonii* (species) ssp. *battiscombei*; or *Aeschynomene* (genus) *cristata* (species) var. *pubescens*. Each subspecies normally occupies its own distinct area; the various subspecies of *S. johnstonii* occur on different East African mountains. A variety may co-exist with other varieties of the species.

Groups of related genera are placed together in families, whose names are usually formed by adding -*aceae* to the basic part of the name of the genus considered to be typical of the family. Thus Ranunculaceae stands for '*Plantae ranunculaceae*' – plants resembling *Ranunculus*. A few of the first families to be recognized by botanists are exceptions to this rule; e.g. Palmae and Gramineae are the classical Latin names for palms and grasses, while the Cruciferae – Cross-bearers' – have flowers in which the four petals form a cross. These families have alternate names – Arecaceae, Poaceae, Brassicaceae – for use by those who think that all family names should be formed on a single plan.

Groups of related families are called orders whose names usually end in -ales. Thus the order Cycadales embraces the related families Cycadaceae, Zamiaceae and Stangeriaceae. When dealing with a large number of families, botanists arrange them in a natural sequence so that, as far as possible, similar families are together, and the position of a family in the sequence gives some indication of its characteristics. The present book is arranged according to the system proposed in 1926 and 1934 by the Kew botanist J. Hutchinson.

Botanical names are derived from geography, habitat, habits, leaf and flower characteristics, colours, smell, other plants, appearance. Each of the examples given in the list overleaf is in the masculine form; each will change according to whether the name of the flower is masculine, feminine or neuter. For example: *atlanticus* will become *atlantica* for feminine and *atlanticum* for the neuter; *campestris* will become *campestre* in the neuter. Some, such as *bicolor*, *macrobotrys* (large-clustered), *repens* or *pubescens*, remain the same for all genders. In some, such as *campestris*, the male and female are the same, only the neuter changing to *campestre*.

affinis   related to another species
alatus   winged
alpinus   growing in alpine zones
amabilis   lovely
amoenus   charming, pleasing
angustifolius   narrow-leaved
aquaticus   of water or by water
arboreus   tree-like
argenteus   silvery
argutus   sharp
aurantiacus   orange
aureus   golden
australis   southern
bellus   pretty
bicolor   two-coloured
borealis   northern
caeruleus   blue
campanulatus   bell-shaped
campestris   growing in flat areas
capensis   of the Cape (South Africa)
citriodorus   lemon-scented
coccineus   scarlet
communis   common, occurring in plenty
concolor   of the same colour
coriaceous   leathery
crassifolius   thick-leaved
deciduus   dropping the leaves
discolorus   two-coloured
edulis   edible
fastigiatus   erect or upright
flavus   pale yellow
floridus   free-flowering
foetidus   evil-smelling
formosus   handsome
fragrans   sometimes strong-smelling
fragrantissimus   with very strong, sweet
  smell
fruticosus   shrubby
glabrous   without hairs
glaucus   sea-green, blue-grey
grandiflorus   large-flowered
graveolens   smelling unpleasantly
heterophyllus   variable-leaved
himalaicus   of the Himalayas
hirsutus   hairy
hispanicus   of Spain
humilis   low-growing
incanus   grey down
insignis   outstanding
lacteus   milky-white
laevigatus   smooth and polished
latifolius   broad-leaved
lilacineus   lilac-coloured
liliiflorus   like a lily
littoralis   of sea shores
lusitanicus   of Portugal
luteus   yellow

macrophyllus   large-leaved
macropetalus   large-petalled
maculatus   spotted, bleached
marginatus   margined
mollis   soft
moschatus   musk-scented
nanus   dwarf
nitidus   shining
nudiflorus   without leaves (of flowers)
nutans   nodding
occidentalis   western
odoratus   sweet-scented
odoratissimus   very sweet-scented
orientalis   eastern
palustris   of swamps and marshes
paniculatus   flowering in panicles
parvifolius   small-leaved
parviflorus   small-flowered
parvus   small
pauciflorus   few-flowered
pendulus   weeping, hanging down
pictus   painted or coloured
platyphyllus   broad-leaved
polyanthus   many-flowered
praecox   early
procerus   very tall
procumbens   creeping
prostratus   flat, hugging the ground
pulchellus   beautiful
puniceus   crimson
racemosus   with flowers in racemes
repens   creeping and rooting
reticulatus   veined, as in a net
rubus   red
rupestris   of rocks or cliffs
salicifolius   willow-leaved
sanguineus   blood-red
sativus   sown, planted or cultivated
sempervirens   always green, evergreen
sinensis   of China
speciosus   showy
spicatus   flowers in spikes
splendens   glittering or shiny
stellatus   star-like, starry
suavolens   sweet-scented
suffruticosus   woody at base
sylvaticus   of woods
tomentosus   with short, dense hairs
triflorus   flowers in threes
tulipiferus   bearing flowers like a tulip
umbellatus   flowers in umbels
velutinus   velvety
vernalis   coming in the spring
versicolor   variously-coloured
viridis   green
vulgaris   common

SYSTEMATIC LIST
of Seed Plant Families in East Africa

Arranged in the sequence of J. Hutchinson, *Families of Flowering Plants, Dicotyledons 1926, Monocotyledons 1934.* Transverse broken lines indicate marked breaks in affinity; thus **19.** Papaveraceae is much more closely related to **20.** Fumariaceae, than to **18.** Piperaceae.

The names of families represented in East Africa by alien species only are placed in brackets.

An asterisk * after a family name indicates that this family has been published in *The Flora of Tropical East Africa,* ** published in two parts, *(1) to be published in two parts of which one has not yet (1986) appeared.

In one or two families, e.g., Elatinaceae and Ranunculaceae, the number of genera or species differs from those recorded in *FTEA*, as research since the publication date of the relevant volume has updated the position.

GYMNOSPERMS:
Total four genera,
twelve species, all woody

	Genera	Species	
1. Cupressaceae*	1	1	
2. Cycadaceae*	2	7	see page 18
3. Podocarpaceae*	1	4	

DICOTYLEDONS:
Archichlamydeae
(petals free or absent)

	Genera	Species	
4. Annonaceae*	27	92	trees, shrubs & lianes
5. Monimiaceae*	1	1	upland forest tree
6. Lauraceae	4	6	trees and a parasitic twiner
7. Hernandiaceae*	3	6	lowland trees and lianes
8. Myristicaceae	3	4	forest trees
9. Ranunculaceae*	7	30	see page 18
10. Ceratophyllaceae*	1	2	submerged aquatics
11. Nymphaeaceae	1	28	see page 20
12. Cabombaceae*	1	1	aquatic
13. Berberidaceae*	1	1	upland shrub
14. Menispermaceae*	10	30	mostly twiners
15. Aristolochiaceae*	2	5	see page 20
16. Rafflesiaceae	1	1	parasite
17. Hydnoraceae	1	2	see page 21
18. Piperaceae	2	14	see page 21
(19. Papaveraceae*)	1	1	see page 22
20. Fumariaceae*	2	2	upland herbs
21. Turneraceae*	6	15	see page 22
22. Capparaceae*	11	90	see page 23
23. Moringaceae*	1	7	woody in dry country
24. Cruciferae*	21	53	see page 29
25. Violaceae*	3	20	see page 30
26. Resedaceae*	2	3	see page 31
27. Polygalaceae	4	50	see page 31

SYSTEMATIC LIST

	Genera	Species	
28. Crassulaceae*	7	46	see page 33
29. Vahliaceae*	1	3	herbs
30. Droseraceae*	1	5	insectivorous herbs
31. Podostemaceae	3	5	aquatic, on rocks
32. Hydrostachyaceae*	1	3	aquatic
33. Elatinaceae*	2	4	upland herbs and shrublets
34. Caryophyllaceae*	16	28	see page 35
35. Aizoaceae*	14	26	see page 36
36. Portulacaceae	4	16	see page 37
37. Polygonaceae*	7	43	see page 38
38. Phytolaccaceae*	3	4	see page 40
39. Chenopodiaceae*	9	20	herbs or shrublets, often halophytic
40. Amaranthaceae*	25	89	see page 41
41. Basellaceae*	1	2	subsucculent twiners
42. Linaceae*	3	10	see page 43
43. Zygophyllaceae*	3	10	see page 44
44. Geraniaceae*	3	17	see page 45
45. Oxalidaceae*	2	20	see page 47
46. Balsaminaceae*	1	70	see page 48
47. Lythraceae	7	39	see page 52
48. Sonneratiaceae*	1	1	a mangrove
49. Oliniaceae*	1	1	upland forest tree
50. Onagoaceae*	3	13	see page 52
51. Trapaceae*	1	1	floating aquatic
52. Montiniaceae*	1	2	lowland forest shrubs
58. Haloragaceae*	3	3	aquatic or terrestrial herbs
54. Callitrichaceae	1	1	upland herbs in wet places
55. Thymelaeaceae*	7	31	see page 53
56. Nyctaginaceae	3	10	see page 54
57. Proteaceae	2	18	see page 55
58. Dilleniaceae*	1	5	see page 56
59. Pittosporaceae*	1	6	small upland trees
(**60.** Bixaceae*)	1	1	softly woody shrub
61. Cochlospermaceae*	1	1	rhizomatous suffrutex, Uganda
62. Flacourtiaceae*	21	45	see page 56
63. Canellaceae*	1	3	forest trees
64. Tamaricaceae*	1	2	shrubs near dry country streams
65. Passifloraceae*	8	54	see page 56
66. Cucurbitaceae*	28	116	see page 57
67. Begoniaceae	1	18	see page 61
68. Caricaceae*	1	1	forest tree
69. Cactaceae*	2	5	see page 62
70. Theaceae*	3	3	upland forest shrubs
71. Ochnaceae	5	16	see page 62
72. Ancistrocladaceae	1	1	lowland liane
73. Dipterocarpaceae	1	9	trees and shrubs in Tanzania
74. Myrtaceae	2	20	trees and shrubs
75. Lecythidaceae*	2	3	lowland trees and shrubs
76. Melastomataceae*	17	79	see page 64
77. Combretaceae*	5	74	see page 65
78. Rhizophoraceae*	5	14	trees, shrubs and mangroves
79. Guttiferae* including Hypericaceae*	9	33	see page 67
80. Tiliaceae	7	107	see page 68
81. Sterculiaceae	15	75	see page 70
82. Bombacaceae	2	4	see page 74
83. Scytopetalaceae*	1	1	small tree in upland forest
84. Malvaceae	14	137	see page 74
85. Malpighiaceae*	6	18	see page 80

	Genera	Species	
86. Erythroxylaceae*	2	7	lowland shrubs
87. Ixonanthaceae*	3	3	trees and shrubs
88. Euphorbiaceae	71	494	see page 81
89. Escalloniaceae*	1	1	upland forest shrub
90. Rosaceae*	11	50	see page 86
91. Dichapetalaceae	2	16	woody
Leguminosae:			
92. Caesalpinioideae*	44	150	see page 89
93. Papilionoideae**	103	945	see page 95
94. Mimosoideae*	21	125	see page 122
95. Hamamelidaceae*	1	1	see page 126
96. Myrothamnaceae*	1	1	shrublet on sunny rocks
97. Buxaceae*	1	1	forest shrub
98. Salicaceae*	2	2	woody, near water
99. Myricaceae	1	4	woody
100. Casuarinaceae*	1	1	coastal tree
101. Ulmaceae*	4	10	woody
102. Moraceae	11	82	mostly woody
103. Urticaceae	15	41	herbs or softly woody
(104. Cannabaceae*)	1	1	hash
105. Aquifoliaceae*	1	1	upland forest tree
106. Celastraceae	9	53	see page 126
107. Brexiaceae*	1	1	woody
108. Icacinaceae*	6	12	see page 127
109. Salvadoraceae*	3	4	trees and shrubs
110. Olacaceae*	6	9	woody
111. Opiliaceae*	2	3	woody, often lianes
112. Viscaceae	3	8	see page 127
113. Loranthaceae	12	98	see page 128
114. Santalaceae	3	20	root semi-parasites, herbs or shrubs
115. Balanophoraceae	2	2	root parasites
116. Rhamnaceae*	11	23	see page 132
117. Vitaceae	6	127	see page 132
118. Rutaceae*	14	46	see page 133
119. Simaroubaceae	4	6	woody
120. Balanitaceae	1	8	see page 134
121. Burseraceae	3	70	see page 134
122. Meliaceae	11	40	see page 135
123. Sapindaceae	25	55	see page 136
124. Melianthaceae*	1	2	upland forest trees or shrubs
125. Anacardiaceae*	9	42	see page 137
126. Connaraceae*	9	16	lowland trees, shrubs or lianes
127. Cornaceae*	1	1	upland forest tree
128. Alangiaceae*	1	2	forest shrubs
129. Araliaceae*	3	16	upland and savanna forest
130. Umbelliferae	34	85	see page 139

DICOTYLEDONS:
Metachlamydeae or
Gamopetalae (petals united)

	Genera	Species	
131. Ericaceae	4	23	see page 140
132. Ebenaceae	2	32	trees and shrubs
133. Sapotaceae*	13	46	trees and shrubs
134. Myrsinaceae*	5	10	trees and shrubs
135. Loganiaceae*	6	36	trees and shrubs
136. Oleaceae*	5	38	see page 141
137. Apocynaceae	29	85	see page 142
138. Asclepiadaceae	54	231	see page 143

15

SYSTEMATIC LIST

	Genera	Species	
139. Rubiaceae* (1)	102	631	see page 149
140. Caprifoliaceae*	1	1	see page 157
141. Valerianaceae*	2	4	montane herbs
142. Dipsacaceae*	4	8	see page 157
143. Compositae	125	877	see page 158
144. Gentianaceae	11	45	see page 180
145. Primulaceae*	5	20	see page 181
146. Plumbaginaceae*	3	11	see page 182
147. Plantaginaceae*	1	6	upland herbs
148. Campanulaceae* (including Lobeliaceae*)	7	80	see page 182
149. Sphenocleaceae*	1	1	herb in lowland swamps
150. Goodeniaceae*	1	2	see page 185
151. Hydrophyllaceae	1	3	herbs in wet places
152. Boraginaceae	12	65	see page 186
153. Solanaceae	9	65	see page 188
154. Convolvulaceae*	22	170	see page 191
155. Scrophulariaceae	52	184	see page 374
156. Orobanchaceae*	2	4	see page 379
157. Lentibulariaceae*	2	24	aquatic, or nearly so, capture small animals
158. Gesneriaceae	4	45	see page 380
159. Bignoniaceae	8	13	see page 381
160. Pedaliaceae*	8	16	see page 382
161. Acanthaceae	56	390	see page 384
162. Verbenaceae	13	123	see page 397
163. Nesogenaceae*	1	1	lowland herb, S.E. Tanzania
164. Cyclocheilaceae*	1	1	shrublet in N.E. Kenya
165. Labiatae	38	288	see page 400

MONOCOTYLEDONS

	Genera	Species	
166. Butomaceae*	1	1	marsh herb
167. Hydrocharitaceae	8	23	see page 410
168. Alismataceae*	7	8	aquatic and marsh herbs
169. Triuridaceae*	1	1	saprophyte
170. Juncaginaceae*	1	1	marsh herb
171. Aponogetonaceae	1	7	aquatic, fresh water
172. Zosteraceae	1	1	marine aquatic
173. Potamogetonaceae	1	7	aquatic, fresh water
174. Ruppiaceae	1	1	aquatic, fresh water
175. Zanichelliaceae	3	6	marine aquatic
176. Najadaceae	1	4	aquatic, fresh water
177. Commelinaceae	11	111	see page 411
178. Flagellariaceae*	1	1	climbing lowland herb
179. Xyridaceae	1	19	herbs in boggy places
180. Eriocaulaceae	1	25	see page 415
181. Musaceae	1	1	tall herb
182. Zingiberaceae	4	37	see page 416
(183. Cannaceae)	1	1	tall herb
184. Marantaceae*	5	7	tall forest herbs
185. Liliaceae	25	241	see page 417
186. Tecophilaeaceae*	2	4	herbs, in Tanzania
187. Pontederiaceae*	3	4	aquatic
188. Araceae*	15	39	see page 425
189. Lemnaceae*	5	8	minute, free floating aquatic
190. Typhaceae*	1	3	tall marsh plants
191. Amaryllidaceae*	7	23	see page 425
192. Iridaceae	12	53	see page 427

	Genera	Species	
193. Dioscoreaceae*	1	19	twiners, flowers very small
194. Agavaceae	2	34	see page 430
195. Palmae*	8	12	palms
196. Pandanaceae	1	10	screw pines
197. Hypoxidaceae	2	8	see page 430
198. Velloziaceae*	1	8	woody herbs on sunny rocks
199. Taccaceae*	1	1	lowland herb
200. Burmanniaceae	2	4	saprophytes
201. Orchidaceae** (1)	71	696	see page 431
202. Juncaceae*	2	8	upland herbs, rushes
203. Cyperaceae	29	445	sedges
204. Gramineae***	185	860	grasses

There are twenty-two main families of flowering plants in East Africa; twenty of them are included in this book and named below. The Gramineae (grasses) and the Cyperaceae (sedges) are not illustrated or described in the book. Once the family characteristics have been mastered, anyone studying the region's flowers will be able to assign to the correct family 75 per cent of the plants likely to be encountered; it is, therefore, well worth learning the descriptions given under the Family Name:

Capparaceae, Amaranthaceae, Cucurbitaceae, Combretaceae, Tiliaceae, Malvaceae, Euphorbiaceae, Leguminosae (Caesalpinioideae, Papilionoideae, Mimosoideae), Asclepiadaceae, Rubiaceae, Compositae, Convolvulaceae, Scrophulariaceae, Acanthaceae, Labiatae, Commelinaceae, Liliaceae, Orchidaceae.

Conversion Guide

Inches to Millimetres
1in =25.4mm
⅛in = 3.175mm
¼in = 5.08mm
¼in = 6.350mm
½in =12.700mm
¾in =19.050mm

Inches to Centimetres
1in =2.54cm
3in = 7.620cm
6in =15.240cm
8in =20.320cm
10in =25.400cm
12in =30.480cm

Feet to Metres
1ft =0.30m
5ft = 1.524m
10ft = 3.048m
50ft =15.240m
100ft =30.480m
500ft =152.400m
1000ft =304.800m

Millimetres to Inches
1mm =0.039370in
25mm=c. 1in
40mm=1.575in
60mm=2.362in
80mm=3.150in
90mm=3.543in
100mm=3.937in

Centimetres to Inches
1 cm =0.39in
5cm=c. 2in
10cm= 3.937in
30cm=11.811in
50cm=19.685in
100cm=39.370in

Metres to Feet
1m =3.28ft
5m = 16.404ft
10m = 32.808ft
50m = 164.042ft
100m = 328.084ft
500m =1640.420ft
1000m =3280.840ft

DIRECTORY OF SPECIES

1. Cycadaceae

The Cycadaceae are a very ancient plant family. Examples have been found in fossil forms millions of years old. They and the Ginkgo are the only seed plants in which the male gametes are mobile, like those of ferns, mosses and algae. There are ten genera among the cycads consisting of more than 100 species which are scattered about the tropics and subtropics. They all have massive unbranched stems, pinnate leaves, naked ovules (usually in cones) and very large seeds. There are only two genera in East Africa: *Encephalartos* with three or four species and *Cycas* with one species found on the coast.

Encephalartos tegulaneus **Plate 1**
A cycad with a cylindrical stem growing up to 7.6m (25ft) and up to 30cm (1ft) in diameter which is covered with scars of abscissed leaves and scale leaves in alternating zones. Scale leaves are lanceolate-acuminate to linear 15cm (6in) long. Other leaves are linear-oblanceolate, up to 1.5m (5ft) long and 30cm (1ft) wide. The male cone is nearly cylindrical, tapering abruptly at the apex and gradually at the base, 35cm (14in) long and 10cm (4in) wide. The scales on the cone overlap like roof tiles. The female cone is slightly smaller and wider – up to 15cm (6in). This cycad is found in dry or medium dry areas at 1500–2100m (4700–6900ft), only in Kenya, on rocky hills or in cedar, *Phoenix* or *Euphorbia* forest near,springs, in the Mathews Range and neighbouring mountains.

E. hildebrandtii Not uncommon in drier forest belts and in bush in coastal districts. The Brazil-nut-like kernel may be boiled, dried and ground for use as flour and the pith of the stem also provides food in time of famine. Male cone size: 20–50cm (*c.* 8–20in) long, 5–9cm (2–3½in) diameter. Female cone: 28–60cm (*c.* 11–24in) long, 15–25cm (*c.* 6–10in) diameter. Altitude range 1–300m (3–1000ft). Coastal areas of Kenya; Tanga, Morogoro, Zanzibar (Tanzania); all regions of Uganda except Buganda; no record elsewhere.

DICOTYLEDONS

2. Ranunculaceae
THE BUTTERCUP FAMILY

A medium-sized, mainly temperate family of herbs or, rarely, climbers; often more or less poisonous. Leaves are usually alternate, with sheathing bases, usually divided. Sepals and petals (if present) free, stamens numerous, spirally arranged; carpels one to many. Thirty species in seven genera in East Africa.

Anemone thomsonii   **Plate 29**
A rhizomatous silky-tomentose perennial with much-dissected leaves, the ultimate segments oblong-dentate, sepals white or pale pink. Single-flowered, the flowering stem with a silky appressed indumentum, dense near the involucre and below the flower. Flower 2.5–6.5cm (1–2¾in) in diameter. A locally common plant in moist or boggy (often rocky) situations on peat soil. Altitude range 2700–3900m (8850–12,900ft). Elgon, Cheranganis, Aberdares, Tinderet and Mt Kenya (Kenya); Kilimanjaro (Tanzania); Mbale – Elgon (Uganda); also in Ethiopia. The only species in East Africa.

NB There are three varieties: *A. thomsonii* var. *thomsonii* with leaf segments cuneately broadly elliptic or oblate, more or less deeply lobed or segmented with the ultimate lobes or segments 1–5mm (up to ⅕in) broad and recorded on Elgon (Kenya). *A. thomsonii* var. *angustisecta* with leaves extremely dissected with ultimate segments linear and very narrow (0.5–0.75mm) (under ⅕in) broad, recorded only at Mbulu (Mt Hanang) in Tanzania. *A. thomsonii* var. *friesiorum* with segments of basal leaves cuneately obliquely ovate-elliptic or oblong-elliptic, more or less deeply lobed, ultimate lobes (not teeth) 4–8mm (⅙–⅓in) broad. Recorded as endemic in the Aberdares (Kenya); Tanzania and Uganda, no record; also southern Sudan (Imatong Mts) and Zaire.

Clematis brachiata *(C. hirsuta)*   **Plates 30 & 714**
The African equivalent of the Old Man's Beard of European hedgerows, this is a climbing plant of some magnificence. Each leaf has five to seven rounded to ovate leaflets and panicles of creamy white flowers grow on long stems. It can often be seen crowning the tops of small trees and large shrubs with a mass of flowers, followed by the fluffy seed heads of the type which gave Old Man's Beard its name. Flower 22–50mm (⅞–2in) across. It is widespread from 1000–2100m (3280–7000ft) in forest glades and edges, and wooded grassland in areas of medium rainfall, though it can also be seen on lava at Kibwezi (Kenya). One of seven species in East Africa. Widespread in Tanzania, Uganda and from Ethiopia to Mozambique.

C. simensis   **Plate 161**
Grows in similar conditions to *C. brachiata* at forest edges and roadsides in upland rain forest. It is a shrubby climber, though it can be a strong liane. The dark, shiny, green leaves have up to five leaflets and are larger and more oblong-elliptic than *C. brachiata*, making it immediately distinguishable. Flower 20–36mm (⅞–1⅜in) fully open. Sepals 7–16mm (¼–⅝in) long. Altitude range 1600–3250m (5250–10,650ft). Throughout Kenya upland forests; Maasai, Shinyanga, Tanga, Mbeya, Iringa (Tanzania); all regions of Uganda except northern; also Sudan, Ethiopia, Eritrea, south to Zimbabwe, Mozambique.

Delphinium macrocentron   **Plate 824**
The commonest of the four *Delphinium* species in East Africa, growing up to 2m (6½ft) high. It has three to ten flowers, with blue or metallic green sepals and an ascending stout spur, which are borne in erect spikes. The colour of this arresting and beautiful flower, *c.* 3cm (1⅜in) across, can range from dark blue to an unusual turquoise, moss green shade. In the right conditions (in wetter, cooler districts such as Limuru and Kericho) this delphinium can be grown easily from seed as a garden plant, but thrives best with strong competition from other bush-like plants. Found over a wide range in East Africa from 1650–3900m (5400–12,750ft), including upper plateau of Kilimanjaro and Mt Elgon (Kenya).

D. leroyi Rare; very similar to *D. macrocentron* but with white flowers, *c.* 6cm (¼in) across. Altitude 1400–1900m (4600–6250ft) (Kenya); West Mporotos, Rungwe (Tanzania); Mbale (Uganda); also southern Sudan, eastern Zaire to Malawi.

D. wellbyi Another beautiful and scented species with an open, wide flower with blue to pale blue sepals and an ascending spur. Flower 4.5cm (1¾in) across. Common in Ethiopia; only recorded in Kenya on grassland in Nyambeni Hills in Meru at *c.* 1800m (6000ft); Tanzania and Uganda, not known; elsewhere, Ethiopia only.

Ranunculus multifidus   Plate 252
A perennial herb sometimes growing along the ground and propagating by producing roots at the nodes or tip of the stem. It has numerous yellow flowers and its leaves may be bi- or tri-sected. Flower 1cm (⅜in) across. This is the commonest 'buttercup' in tropical Africa and is found at streamsides and, growing as a weed, at the sides of tracks and roads in upland rain forest and moorland from 1200–3250m (4000–10,750ft).

3. Nymphaeaceae
THE WATERLILY FAMILY

A small family spread over the whole world with only some thirty-five species. They are aquatic perennials with floating leaves which may be heart-shaped or have the stem attached to the lower surface. Sepals are free, petals may often pass gradually into the stamens, which are free. One genus in East Africa with eight species.

Nymphaea caerulea (*N. capensis*)   Plate 825
This waterlily, which is common in East Africa, is blue, but the centre of the ray-like flower is often orange-yellow tinged with red. Flower 6–20cm (2⅜–7¾in) across. Altitude range 1–2680m (3–9000ft). All regions of Kenya and Tanzania; all regions of Uganda except northern; also Ethiopia, Somalia, southern Sudan south to Mozambique, Zimbabwe.

N. lotus   Plate 31
A hairless waterlily with a tuberous rhizome and floating rounded leaves. Its flowers are white or cream. Flower 10–18cm (4–7in) across. Altitude always below 1200m (4000ft). It is an uncommon species which can be found in Lake Victoria and Lake Jipe and has also been recorded in one or two pools in the coastal regions and in a marsh in Turkana (Kenya); all regions of Tanzania except Mpwapwa, Kondoa; all regions of Uganda except northern; also Ethiopia, Somalia, southern Sudan south to Mozambique, Zimbabwe.

4. Aristolochiaceae

Herbs or shrubs, often climbers, with alternate, simple exstipulate leaves, often cordate at base; flowers bisexual, usually zygomorphic, solitary, axillary, often evil-smelling. Sepals often produced in a long tube, often asymmetrically three-lobed above; no petals, stamens six – many, fused to the style, ovary inferior with six carpels, with the styles connate into a column above; seeds numerous with much endosperm. Five species in two genera in East Africa.

Aristolochia bracteata (*A. bracteolata*)   **Plate 540**
A prostrate or erect rhizomatous glabrous herb with orbicular leaves; flowers dark mauve to cream-coloured and solitary. Flower: perianth tube 17–23mm (¾–1in) long; limb 20–22mm (⅘in) long. Altitude range 290–900m (950–2950ft). This is a rare plant and so far has only been recorded in South Horr on the Loilengalani road and from the Marsabit district, but not the mountain (Kenya); Tanga (Tanzania); northern region of Uganda; also in Sudan, Somalia. It should be looked for in rather dry areas.

5. Hydnoraceae

This is a very small family of parasites which lack chlorophyll and grow on the roots of trees and shrubs forming a pseudo-rhizome. The pseudo-rhizome is warty and may be simple or branched, round or angled; leaves and scale leaves are absent. Flowers large and solitary; calyx fleshy and thick, three–four-lobed with the margins meeting; three to five stamens are inserted on the calyx tube and unite to form a ring around the stigma; anthers are numerous and lack stalks; the stigma is rudimentary or stalkless; the ovary is inferior and uni-locular, with many apical or parietal placentas, and ovules are numerous. Berry-like fruits are produced underground with a great many small seeds in a glutinous pulp. These plants sometimes reveal their presence by an evil smell. They are probably more common than is generally supposed. Two species in one genus in East Africa.

Hydnora abyssinica (*H. johannis*)   **Plate 541**
A parasite with the underground pseudo-rhizome cylindrical or obscurely angled and completely covered with warts. The flower is large with a very strong, unpleasant smell; the calyx is very fleshy and four-lobed with the inner surface cream to the apex and bright red and bristly below. Flower 13–14cm (5–5½in) long. It is usually found growing on the roots of acacia trees at 90–1500m (300–4900ft) and is perhaps more common than is generally thought, since it is only visible when in flower. All regions of Kenya and Tanzania except Southern Highlands and southern (Songea); all regions of Uganda except eastern (Jinja, Lake Kioga); also Sudan, Ethiopia, Somalia (there are related species south to Mozambique, Zimbabwe).

6. Piperaceae
THE PEPPER FAMILY

Herbs, sometimes shrubby and climbers; leaves entire, alternate or opposite, stipulate or not, often fleshy. Inflorescence a spike usually with crowded flowers. Flowers bisexual or unisexual, subtended by a peltate bract; perianth absent (in East African species). Fruit an indehiscent berry. Fourteen species in two genera in East Africa.

PIPERACEAE

Piper capense   **Plate 162**
A tall soft shrub or herb, with broad-ovate to orbicular, cordate, sparsely tomentose
leaves and solitary whitish spikes, the fruits exceeding the bracts and the lamina
aromatic when crushed. Flower spike 3cm (1½in) long. Altitude range 1500–2750m
(5000–9000ft). A common undergrowth plant of wetter highland forests and
recorded throughout Kenya; all regions of Tanzania; all regions of Uganda except
northern; also in Ethiopia, Zaire and south to Mozambique, Zimbabwe, Cape.

P. guineense A soft shrubby climber with ovate leaves and solitary spikes, fruits
stalked. Flower spike 6.5cm (*c.* 3in) long. Altitude *c.* 1500m (5000ft). It is a rare
plant in Kenya, only found in Kakamega Forest, climbing by means of adventitious
roots near the nodes. Lake areas, Tabora (Tanzania); western region, Buganda
(Uganda); also Sudan, Ethiopia, Zaire, Zambia.

P. umbellatum A soft shrub similar to *P. capense* from which it differs in being
glabrous, and in having orbicular, hardly acuminate leaves and spikes in axillary
umbels of three to six; the fruits also not exceeding the bracts. Flower spike 4.5cm
(1¾in) long. Altitude range 1500–2750m (5000–9000ft). Common in wetter forests
and recorded in Nyambeni Hills and western region of Kenya. Maasai, Tanga,
Morogoro, Tabora, Mbeya, Songea – one record Zanzibar only (Tanzania); western and eastern regions, Buganda (Uganda); also Sudan, Ethiopia, Zaire, Zimbabwe, Mozambique.

7. Papaveraceae
THE POPPY FAMILY

This is a rather small family of some 200 species found mainly in northern temperate areas. They often contain poisonous or medicinal substances, such as opium.
The sap or juice is white or yellow. Solitary flowers on a long stalk have two or three
sepals, four to six free petals, numerous stamens and a superior ovary with
numerous ovules, fruit and capsules. The single species recorded in East Africa is
introduced, not indigenous.

Argemone mexicana   **Plate 253**
An erect herb with yellow flowers which produces yellow latex. Leaf bases circle the
stem and the roughly oblong leaves are white-veined. Flower 5cm (2in) across. It is
a weed of waste, dry places, roadsides and abandoned old cultivated ground,
which was introduced to East Africa from America under the name 'Mexican
Poppy'. Altitude range from 1–1800m (3–5900ft). Widespread in Kenya; Mwanza,
Arusha, Tabora (Tanzania); Ankole, Mengo, Kampala (Uganda).

8. Turneraceae

Herbs, shrubs or trees with simple usually exstipulate alternate leaves; flowers
bisexual, regular, often dimorphic, solitary to numerous, mostly axillary in racemes,
panicles or cymes; calyx tubular, five to numerous, teeth imbricate, five petals and

stamens both inserted on the calyx-tube; ovary superior; three styles; stigma apically divided; fruit a three-valved capsule. Fifteen species in six genera in East Africa.

Streptopetalum serratum   **Plate 254**
A caulescent heterophyllous annual up to 0.4m (1½ft) tall. Stem shortly pubescent and more or less densely setiferous, setae short, yellow and swollen at base. Leaves narrowly elliptic, entire and tapering below into a short petiole, glabrous or pubescent on both surfaces, and shortly setiferous on midrib, and sometimes on nerves, below. Lower leaves, margin symmetrically and bluntly pinnatifid or pinnatilobed, apex acute; upper leaves, margin above bluntly serrate, apex acute. Flowers one to nine, petals yellow or orange, 13–16mm (½–⅝in) long, 2–4mm (1/12–⅛in) across. Altitude range 510–1830m (1675–6000ft). Found in sandy soil among rocks in bushland and thorn scrub, in grassland and by roadsides. Northern Frontier areas, Baringo (Kenya); Shinyanga, Mpwapwa (Tanzania); Karamoja (Uganda); three species in East Africa; also in Sudan, Ethiopia, Zambia, Zimbabwe (south-west border only).

9. Capparaceae

A medium-sized, mainly tropical family of shrubs or small trees or, less often, herbs. Their leaves are alternate, simple or palmate. Flowers are bisexual and usually four in number with sepals, petals and stamens all free, the latter often numerous. The ovary is superior and usually borne on a stalk (the gynophore). East Africa has ninety-one species in eleven genera.

BOSCIA
Trees or shrubs; leaves simple, entire, coriaceous; flowers small, racemose, or fascicled, sometimes collected into terminal panicles; four sepals, valvate, free to base; no petals, six to twenty stamens, free; single-celled ovary; fruit globose. Eight species in East Africa.

Boscia coriacea   **Plate 163**
An evergreen, very twiggy shrub or small tree up to 7m (23ft) tall; young twigs glabrous or minutely puberulous and glabrescent. Leaves petiolate; blade elliptic or lanceolate-elliptic, usually narrow, more rarely broad, generally 6cm (2.5in) long and c. 2cm (¾in) broad, apex attenuate, sharply mucronate, base cuneate, rigid and leathery, pale glaucous greyish-olive-green, glabrous. Midrib very pronounced beneath. Inflorescence a terminal or axillary, short, dense, pale yellowish-green, many-flowered raceme up to 3cm (1¼in) long. Flowers pale yellow or greenish-yellow, about 6mm (¼in) across, variously described as sweet-smelling or unpleasant. Sepals ovate-elliptic to elliptic-oblong, 3mm (⅛in) long; receptacle rim prominent with an uneven thick edge. Altitude range 150–1500m (500–5000ft). Found in deciduous bushland, semi-desert scrub, and grassland with scattered trees and recorded in Northern Frontier areas, Kajiado, Magadi, Kwale and Kibwezi (Kenya); Maasai, Pare, Lushoto (Tanzania); Karamoja (Uganda); also in Sudan, Ethiopia and Somalia.

   NB This species has five synonyms: *B. teitensis*; *B. pungens*; *B. xylophylla*; *B. somalensis* and *B. paolii*.

B. mossambicensis   Plate 164

A dense, twiggy shrub or small tree up to 10m (33ft) tall, often with a rather flat crown. Leaves alternate and clearly spaced on old and new twigs (or rarely, fascicled, outside East Africa); petiolate. Blade narrowly elliptic to oblanceolate or more rarely obovate, c. 5.5cm (2⅛in) long and 1.2–1.8cm (c. ½–1¾in) broad, usually acute and sharply mucronate, though sometimes rounded and obtuse, narrowed towards the base but often rounded at the very base; smooth on the margin, leathery, pale green, glabrous with the midrib markedly depressed above and prominent pale green beneath. The inflorescence is an axillary, many-flowered raceme, with yellowish-green filaments, yellow or cream anthers, and fleshy, green or purple sepals, glabrous or thinly pubescent outside. Inflorescence 4–7cm (1⅝–2¾in) long; sepals 4.5–6mm (⅛–¼in) long. Altitude range 630–1500m (2150–4900ft). Found in deciduous woodland, bushland and thicket and grassland with scattered trees. Recorded in Meru, northern areas, Kajiado and Kitui (Kenya); Nzega, Shinyanga, Iringa (Tanzania); no record in Uganda; also Ethiopia, Somalia, southern Zaire, Zambia and Zimbabwe.

CADABA

Shrubs with simple leaves. Flowers in racemes or corymbs; four sepals in two series, the outer enclosing the inner; four or no petals, clawed; stamens more or less adnate to the gynophore; ovary one- or two-celled on a long gynophore to whose base a curious tubular or ligulate nectarial appendage is attached. Fruit linear, cylindrical, sometimes dehiscing into two valves. Thirteen species in East Africa.

Cadaba farinosa   Plate 165

A slender, much branched and rather densely twiggy and tangled shrub with arching branches up to 5m (16½ft) tall or, more rarely a tree up to 8m (26ft). Young twigs farinaceous with small white sessile scales, or with stalked scales or spreading glandular or eglandular hairs, sometimes all intermixed, becoming glabrous with age. The scales on the leaves and other parts are waxy in appearance and may be a protective secretion or device. Leaf-blade elliptic to roundly elliptic, sometimes obovate or obovate-oblong 5–50mm (⅛–2in) long, and 3–30mm (⅛–1¼in) wide, apically mucronate, sometimes minutely so, rounded, emarginate or obtuse, farinaceous, especially when young. Inflorescence a rather dense but few-flowered shortly subcorymbose raceme. Petals 10–13mm (⅜–½in) long, creamy yellow or dirty pink, blade narrowly lanceolate-elliptic, long-clawed. Altitude range 0–1700m (0–5600ft). Found in deciduous bushland, grassland with scattered trees and desert scrub, riverine vegetation and sometimes on anthills (Kenya); Maasai (Tanzania); Acholi, Bunyoro, Mbale (Uganda); also in Sudan, Ethiopia, Eritrea, Somalia, Zaire.

   NB There are two subspecies: C. farinosa ssp. farinosa, in which the scales are sessile or very shortly stipitate, recorded in Northern Frontier areas, Kajiado and coast – Lamu (Kenya); Maasai (Tanzania); all regions of Uganda; also Ethiopia, Eritrea, Somalia. C. farinosa ssp. adenotricha in which the scales are largely stipitate, the stalks being of various lengths. The glandular hairs are usually very small. Found in Meru, Kajiado, Voi River (Kenya); Musoma, Buha, Morogoro (Tanzania); Ankole, Busoga, Masaka (Uganda).

C. longifolia   A slender shrub up to 5m (16½ft) tall with black bark. Twigs glabrous or extremities mealy. Leaves pale green, leathery, linear-oblong or lanceolate or elongate-oval to 6.25cm (2½in) long and 1.25cm (½in) broad, apex obtuse or sub-acute, often mucronate; the midrib often prominent beneath. Flowers in short terminal corymbs which are up to 5cm (2in) long. Four petals narrowly elliptic, reddish, *c.* 16mm ($\frac{3}{5}$in) long, with long claws and longer than the green sepals. Altitude 450m (*c.* 1500ft). Northern Province in dry bushland (Kenya); Tanzania and Uganda, no record; also in Sudan, Somalia, Eritrea, Ethiopia.

C. mirabilis **Plate 32**
An erect shrub up to 3m (10ft) tall with rigid coriaceous, oblong-elliptic, ovate or suborbicular leaves; rounded or obtuse at the apex (sometimes retuse) varying to subacute or apiculate, the base rounded to subcordate. The leaves are fleshy, glabrous, and abundantly glandular-hairy, especially when young. The inflorescence a short corymb up to 5cm (2in) long; petals wrinkled and white or cream in colour, *c.* 15mm ($\frac{3}{5}$in) long; appendage 1.5–2cm ($\frac{3}{5}$–$\frac{4}{5}$in) long, bright golden yellow; five stamens. Altitude range 300–1500m (1000–5000ft). Found in northern districts in semi-arid areas and recorded from Lake Turkana to Meru (Kenya); Tanzania and Uganda, no record; also in Sudan, Ethiopia, Somalia.

C. rotundifolia A shrub with puberulous shoot tips. Leaves coriaceous, glabrous, very broadly ovate to elliptic or suborbicular, up to 3.75cm (1$\frac{1}{2}$in) in diameter, with two pairs of principal lateral nerves from the base. Flowers in terminal racemes, no petals, outer sepals 7–8mm (*c.* $\frac{1}{3}$in) long; appendage 2cm ($\frac{4}{5}$in) long, clawed. Altitude range 450–500m (1500–1650ft). Found in Turkana and common on sandy soils (Kenya); Tanzania and Uganda, no record; also in Sudan, Ethiopia, Eritrea, Somalia.

C. ruspolii A twiggy evergreen shrub up to 2m (6$\frac{1}{2}$ft) tall. Twigs reddish-brown, pubescent, especially when young. Leaf obovate-oblong or elliptic, 2.5–5.5cm (1–2$\frac{1}{5}$in) long, and 1.4–2.5cm ($\frac{1}{2}$–1in) broad, leathery with a wavy margin, scaly on both surfaces; apex obtuse to acuminate, base broadly narrowed to subcordate. Inflorescence a short subcorymbose raceme. Petals white, 7–12mm ($\frac{1}{4}$–$\frac{1}{2}$in) long; the outer sepals 5–6mm ($\frac{1}{4}$in) long, somewhat keeled. Altitude range 180–1020m (600–3350ft). Found in deciduous bushland and grassland with scattered trees, in low to medium rainfall areas, and recorded in Namanga, Taita Hills, Northern Frontier areas and Tana River (Kenya); in similar habitats in north-eastern Tanzania; Uganda, no record; also in Ethiopia.

Capparis cartilaginea **Plate 33**
A spreading shrub, dull grey-green overall, which grows up to 2.4m (8ft). Its leaves are somewhat fleshy, ovate to rounded, but with a sharp-pointed apex and with small, backward-curving stipular spines. The flowers are *c.* 7cm (2$\frac{3}{4}$in) across, white ageing to mauve, with numerous stamens ageing to deep red. It is found in coastal areas and northern and north-eastern regions of Kenya, on coral, rocks, sand and stony ground from sea level to 1800m (6000ft). Six species in East Africa. Maasai near Munduli, Loliondo and Lindi (Tanzania); no record in Uganda; also Sudan, Ethiopia, Somalia, Middle East.

CLEOME

Annual or perennial herbs; leaves petiolate, alternate, simple or digitately three to nine foliolate; flowers more or less zygomorphic, in terminal racemes; four sepals; four petals, equal or unequal, often long-clawed; stamens free; ovary single-celled; fruit a capsule with two dehiscing valves, smooth or longitudinally nerved. Twenty-one species in East Africa.

Cleome allamannii **Plate 638**
An annual, glandular or hairless, sticky plant with five to seven foliolate, narrowly

CAPPARACEAE

linear leaves, several of them with a conspicuous yellow patch. Its pink to magenta or mauve flowers form graceful racemes. Petals 15–30mm (¾–1⅛in) long. It is found in sandy or rocky soil in dry bushland where there is no cultivation, at 100–600m (300–2000ft). Northern and eastern Kenya; Tanzania and Uganda, no record; endemic.

C. angustifolia   Plate 255
A slender, glaucous, erect herb, with three to nine foliolate leaves and filiform-linear leaflets; petals unequal, yellow, mauve at the base. Inflorescence up to 30cm (12in) long; petals 1–2cm (⅜–¾in) long. This is a handsome and distinct species found in bushland, grassland and semi-desert scrub with a tendency to become a weed on stony ground. Altitude range below 1150m (3600ft). Aberdares (low altitudes), Magadi and Kajiado (Kenya); Maasai (Tanzania); Uganda, no record; also in Ethiopia, Mozambique.

C. hirta   Plate 715
An annual or short-lived perennial glandular herb with five to nine foliolate leaves and linear leaflets; four petals, purple or pink, paler towards the base; equal or unequal and often long-clawed. Inflorescence 10–30cm (4–12in) long; petals 1–1.8cm (⅜–¾in) long. Altitude range 1–1800m (3–5900ft). A common plant of open woodlands and grasslands, becoming a weed at roadsides and in cultivated ground below 1640m (5400ft). It is much more widespread, with a higher altitude range, than *C. allamannii*, and grows in wetter areas and into cultivated and disturbed places. Kitale, western regions, Baringo, Rift Valley, Magadi, Kajiado, Nairobi, Machakos, Nanyuki and lower areas of Mt Kenya (Kenya); all regions of Tanzania and Uganda; also Ethiopia, Zaire, Malawi, Zimbabwe, Mozambique.

C. monophylla   Plate 554
An annual herb, erect or spreading up to 1m (3ft) tall and very variable. Stem rather abundantly covered with rather short glandular and longer eglandular hairs. Leaves simple, very variable; blade usually lanceolate or oblong, more rarely ovate or linear-lanceolate, pubescent on both surfaces with hairs like those of the stem. Inflorescence up to 30cm (12in) long; petals pink or mauve but sometimes yellow; six stamens; sepals 3–5mm (⅛–¼in) long. A common plant in grassland, deciduous woodland, bushland or on lake shores, and often a weed of cultivated and disturbed ground. Altitude range 30–2100m (100–6900ft). Widespread from western Kenya to Machakos and Elgon to Kajiado (Kenya); all regions of Tanzania and Uganda; also in Somalia south to Zimbabwe, Mozambique.

NB An unusual form is found near Dodoma in Tanzania, in which the leaves are remarkably small and ovate, probably an adaptation of the normal form to dry season conditions.

C. parvipetala   Plate 555
An annual or short-lived perennial herb, low-growing and bushy. Stem woody below, the branches brown and woody, except towards extremities, densely covered with short glandular hairs, glabrescent below. Leaves petiolate, usually five-foliolate; leaflets elliptic to obovate-elliptic, usually less than 7mm (¼in) long, rarely up to 15mm (⅜in) long; rather densely glandular-hairy. Inflorescence dense, 10–15cm (4–6in) long; petals, 4–11(17)mm (⅛–⅔(¾)in) long, pink or mauve, the upper pair yellow-spotted; seven stamens. Found in deciduous bushland and semi-desert scrub on rocky or bare ground. Altitude range 900–1020m (2950–3450ft). Northern Frontier and Turkana – Lodwar (Kenya); Tanzania and Uganda, no record; also in Sudan.

26

C. usambarica   Plate 639

An annual herb, branched and erect, up to 1m (3ft) tall, stem glabrous or with a few scattered, stalked glands. Leaves petiolate, three- to five-foliolate; leaflets rhombic-elliptic, acute, the margins sometimes serrulate or at least ciliolate, otherwise glabrous. Inflorescence up to 40cm (16in) long, bracts very small, simple or trifoliolate. Petals 1–2cm ($\frac{2}{5}$–$\frac{3}{4}$in) long, long-clawed, pink or magenta, the upper pair yellow-spotted. Found in lowland rain forest, bushland and thicket, rocky ground, margins of swamps and streamsides, becoming a weed in cultivated ground. Altitude range 5–1800m (15–5900ft). Northern Frontier areas, Narok and Kwale (Kenya); Lushoto district, Usambara Mountains, Tanga area (Tanzania); also Zanzibar, southern Sudan, Ethiopia.

Crateva adansonii   Plate 166

A savannah tree, 4$\frac{1}{2}$–9m (15–30ft) high – sometimes to 15m (50ft). Bark pale brown. Leaves trifoliolate, pale green, tufted at the ends of branches. Leaflets ovate-lanceolate, up to 10cm (4in) long and 3.75cm (1$\frac{1}{2}$in) broad; apex long-acuminate, base cuneate. Flowers precocious, in creamy-flowered corymbs at or near the end of the twigs; four pale green sepals; four petals, 1.25–2cm ($\frac{1}{2}$–$\frac{3}{4}$in) long, all on one side of the flower, white or creamy-yellow, sometimes with lilac tips; stamens 2–2.5cm ($\frac{3}{4}$–1in) long, pale lilac. Found in savannah woodland. Altitude range 600–1400m (1950–4600ft). Only species in East Africa. Northern Frontier districts and Samburu (Kenya); Shinyanga, Musoma, Tabora (Tanzania); Uganda, all regions; also Sudan, Ethiopia, Somalia, Rwanda, Zaire, Zambia.

Gynandropsis gynandra   Plate 34

A tall annual with egg-shaped to elliptic leaflets. The flowers have white, pale pink or lilac petals. It is an easily recognisable weed, common on cultivated ground and by roadsides throughout East Africa from 1–2400m (3–7900ft). It is closely related to *Cleome allamannii*, from which it can be distinguished by the insertion of the stamens on the stalk – the gynandrophora – well above the base of the petals. Petals 10–20mm ($\frac{2}{5}$–$\frac{4}{5}$in) long. One species in East Africa.

MAERUA

Unarmed trees or shrubs; leaves simple or trifoliolate, often with minute bristly stipules; flowers axillary, solitary or fascicled or in terminal racemes or corymbs. four sepals, with a more or less persistent tube; nought or four petals, inserted in mouth of calyx tube; stamens indehiscent, free; ovary one- or two-celled; fruit baccate. Thirty-one species in East Africa.

Maerua edulis (*Courbonia glauca*)   Plate 167

A bushy shrub which grows to 2.4m (8ft), with leathery, ovate or rounded leaves, their bases rounded or heart-shaped with an impressed pattern of veins on the underside. The solitary, axillary flowers are white with a wavy, feathery appearance, often closing slightly during the heat of the day. Stamens 15–30mm ($\frac{3}{5}$–1$\frac{1}{5}$in) long. It is found at altitudes up to 1850m (6000ft). Freshly sliced pieces of root thrown into muddy water will clear the mud away. All regions of Kenya and Tanzania; all regions of Uganda except Buganda; also Ethiopia, southern Somalia, eastern Zaire, Malawi, Zambia, Mozambique.

M. endlichii   Plate 168

An evergreen shrub up to 3.5m (11$\frac{1}{2}$ft) tall with ascending and spreading branches, glabrous except for the margins of the sepals. Leaves are disposed along the twigs in fascicles, petiolate and simple, obovate-oblong to elliptic, narrowed at apex to an acute point, or truncately rounded and sometimes emarginate, shiny, dark green with the midrib prominent beneath. Twigs grey, often arising at right-angles. Inflorescence a short corymbose raceme or the one or two flowers in the axils of the clustered leaves. Flowers white; petals 2–3mm ($\frac{1}{12}$–$\frac{1}{8}$in) long; stamens 1–2cm ($\frac{3}{8}$–$\frac{3}{4}$in) long, seventeen to twenty in number. Found in deciduous bushland and grassland with scattered trees and shrubs; altitude range 650–1800m (2100–5900ft). Northern Frontier areas, the Mathews Range, Baringo, Embu and Magadi (Kenya); lake areas, Maasai, Tanga, Mpwapwa, Kondoa (Tanzania); Uganda, no record; also in Zambia.

M. kirkii   Plate 35
A shrub or tree, growing to 4.5cm (15ft) in height with erect branches. Its leathery leaves are obovate-oblong, 10cm (4in) long and 5cm (2in) wide with the apex rounded and sharply pointed, and the base obtuse or subcordate, the upper surface rough and the lower covered with short hairs. Its green-white flowers, with black centres, are carried in dense, level-topped, many-flowered racemes; stamens c. 3cm (1$\frac{1}{8}$in) long. It is found in semi-arid, warm districts of Kenya from 100–1300m (300–4250ft). Tanga, Mpanda, Morogoro (Tanzania); Uganda, no record; also Zambia, Zimbabwe, Malawi, Mozambique, eastern Zaire.

M. subcordata (*Courbonia subcordata*)   Plate 169
A much-branched shrub growing up to 2m (6ft). Its egg-shaped to rounded leaves are usually stiff and leathery with slightly prominent veining on both sides and more or less rounded or broadly wedge-shaped at the base. Its roots, like those of *M. edulis*, can be used for clearing muddy water. Colour of flower, greenish-yellow; filaments c. 2cm ($\frac{3}{4}$in) long. Altitude range 100–1200m (300–4000ft). Open grassland throughout Kenya; Moshi, Lushoto (Tanzania); Karamoja (Uganda); also in Somalia, Sudan, Ethiopia.

M. triphylla   Plate 170
An erect or scandent shrub or small tree, 5–7.5m (16–24ft) tall. Twigs glabrous or pubescent. Leaves simple or one to three foliolate. The inflorescence is a simple or branched corymbose raceme; sepals 5–9mm ($\frac{1}{5}$–$\frac{1}{3}$in) long, hairy or glabrous outside, with the margin generally white-pubescent; petals obovate, 3–5mm ($\frac{1}{8}$–$\frac{1}{5}$in), clawed, whitish or greenish in colour. Altitude range 650–1400m (2100–4600ft). It is found in grassland with scattered trees, the edges of thickets and deciduous bushland and sometimes on termite mounds, and recorded in coastal and lacustrine regions throughout East Africa; also Sudan, Ethiopia, Somalia, Rwanda, Zaire.

M. parvifolia (*M. trichophylla*)   A bushy shrub occasionally up to 3m (10ft) tall. Branches glabrous, foliage densely papillose. Leaves simple, very small, linear to oblanceolate, 6mm ($\frac{1}{4}$in) long, bunched on knotty twigs. Flowers small, greenish-yellow, pedicels and receptacles long and pilose; sepals 5mm ($\frac{1}{5}$in) long, 3mm ($\frac{1}{8}$in) wide; stamens 12mm ($\frac{1}{2}$in) long. Altitude range 900–1650m (2950–5400ft). Found on Magadi road and in the south of Kenya; lake areas, Maasai, Tabora, Mpwapwa, Kondoa, Mbeya, Iringa (Tanzania); northern and possibly western Uganda; also Sudan, Malawi, Zambia, Zimbabwe, Mozambique.

THYLACHIUM
Shrubs; leaves alternate, simple or trifoliolate; flowers large in corymbose racemes; calyx split transversely on expanding; no petals; stamens indefinite; ovary unilocular; fruit a many-seeded berry. Four species in East Africa.

Thylachium africanum   **Plate 171**
A shrub or small tree up to 7m (23ft) in height or, rarely, a dwarf shrub from
15–25cm (6–10in) high, with tuberous roots. Stems branched, or several slender
unbranched stems arising from the thickened rootstock, smooth or rough with light
grey, fissured bark. Leaves glabrous, one to three foliolate, or with simple leaves
intermixed. Leaflets elliptic, ovate, linear to lanceolate or oblanceolate 3–10cm
(1½–4 in) long and 0.6–5.3cm (¾–2⅛in) wide, with a somewhat revolute margin,
sometimes undulating, coriaceous. Inflorescence a terminal loose corymbose
raceme with one to twenty or more flowerheads; buds 7–14mm (¼–½in) diameter
before opening. Stamens spreading, wavy, up to 3–6cm (1½–2⅜in) long, white.
Found in deciduous woodland, and thicket, grassland with scattered trees, riverine
forest and old cultivated areas. Altitude range 25–1550m (80–5200ft). Northern
Frontier areas, Leroghi Plateau, Kitui, Tsavo West and Taita Hills (Kenya); all
regions of Tanzania; Uganda, no record; also in Malawi, Zimbabwe, Mozambique.

T. thomasii   A shrub, sometimes scandent, or a small tree from 1–4m (3–13ft) tall,
with large tuberous roots. Young twigs terete, glabrous or shortly hispid. Leaves
simple; blade variable in size and shape, suborbicular, elliptic, ovate or obovate,
with the margin slightly revolute, coriaceous or slightly fleshy, somewhat scabrous,
3–9cm (1½–3½in) long, 2–7cm (¾–2¾in) wide. Inflorescence a one to ten flowered,
loosely corymbose raceme; buds glabrous or minutely punctiform, up to 11mm (⅜in)
diameter; stamens spreading and wavy, up to 3cm (1⅛in) long. Found in deciduous
woodland and bushland, secondary scrub and strands near the sea, sometimes on
termite hills; altitude range 1–1000m (3–3280ft). Kitui, Lamu, Kwale district near
Mackinnon Road (Kenya); Tanzania and Uganda, no record; also in Somalia.

10. Cruciferae (Brassicaceae)
THE CABBAGE FAMILY

Herbs, or occasionally shrubs with alternate exstipulate leaves; inflorescence
racemose usually without bracts; four sepals and petals; six stamens, the two outer
shorter than the four inner; ovary bilocular, each loculus with two parietal placen-
tae, the septum between usually membraneous; single style; stigma two-lobed or
capitate; fruit usually a capsule or not uncommonly indehiscent, never fleshy.
Mainly a Mediterranean family including many weeds which occasionally appear in
East Africa as rare casuals. Fifty-four species in twenty-one genera in East Africa.

Farsetia stenoptera   **Plate 36**
An erect annual covered with white medifixed hairs with linear to narrow-lanceolate
leaves, twisting when not turgid, yellow or livid to red; corolla tube c. 13mm
(½in) long; corolla lobes c. 9mm (⅜in) long. A common plant of dry country and rather
variable. Altitude range 500–1700m (1650–5650ft). The flowers open at night and
are seldom seen to advantage in sunlight, rather like *Silene burchellii*. One of seven
species in East Africa. Rift Valley, Baringo, Nanyuki, Magadi, Machakos and
Kajiado (Kenya); lake areas, Maasai, Tanga, Mpwapwa, Kondoa (Tanzania);
northern region (Uganda); also Sudan, Ethiopia, southern Somalia.

Raphanus raphanistrum   **Plate 172**
An erect annual with unswollen taproot; leaves pinnatifid with the terminal lobe the
longest. Flower c. 18mm (¾in) long; petals yellow, mauve or white, often dark-

veined; fruit ridged, constricted and dehiscent between the seeds with a beak up to four times as long as the distance between constrictions. An uncommon weed, probably not persistent and introduced from southern Europe. Altitude range 15–2750m (50–9000ft). One other species in East Africa. Tinderet, Mau, Aberdares, Kitale, Rift Valley (Kenya); Tanga, Morogoro, Mbeya, Iringa (Tanzania); Uganda, no record; widely introduced elsewhere.

11. Violaceae
THE VIOLET FAMILY

Herbs, shrubs or trees with alternate, or (rarely) opposite stipulate, simple leaves; flowers regular or zygomorphic, bisexual, solitary or in racemes; five sepals, free; five petals, free, the anterior one often with a spur projecting between adjacent sepals; five stamens, all similar, or the anther pair with appendages projecting into the spur; filaments free or united; ovary superior, sessile, suborbicular; style simple and stigma undivided; fruit a capsule. Twenty species in three genera in East Africa.

Hybanthus enneaspermus   Plate 716
A very variable, hairy herb or shrub with linear-lanceolate to entire-elliptic serrate leaves and red or pink-spurred flowers, c. 1cm (⅜in) across, and seeds longitudinally ribbed, pitted and glabrous. It is extremely variable but usually found as a linear-leaved strigose-hairy annual up to 25cm (10in) tall, with pink flowers in disturbed dry or sub-desert bush. Altitude range 20–1500m (65–4900ft). Not common. Magadi, Nairobi, Kajiado in dry, disturbed country, and western regions although this is not sub-desert country (Kenya); all regions of Tanzania except Songea; all regions of Uganda except Buganda; also widespread in tropical Africa.

Viola abyssinica   Plate 556
A creeping, hairy, perennial herb with pointed leaves, hairy between the veins above and sepals which are hardly appendiculate. It is very similar to V. eminii but is found at lower altitudes and is also more rampant and often has erect flowering stems. Flowers solitary blue to violet, 10mm (⅜in) long. Found creeping among rocks and on wettish acid or peaty soils in the open or along forest paths, and streamsides. Altitude range 1800–2850m (6000–9500ft). Aberdares, Elgon, Cheranganis, Mau and Mt Kenya (Kenya); Maasai, Shinyanga, Tanga, Tabora, Morogoro, Mbeya, Iringa, Songea (Tanzania); all regions of Uganda except Buganda; also in Ethiopia, southern Sudan, Zaire, south to Mozambique, Zimbabwe.

V. eminii   Plate 557
A creeping, hairy, perennial herb with subcordate leaves, rounded at the apex and glabrous or only slightly hairy along midrib above (cf. V. abyssinica). Flowers solitary, blue to violet, 12mm (½in) long. A common violet creeping often amongst rocks or on peaty soil, in the open or along forest paths and streamsides. Altitude range 2500–3700m (8300–12,300ft). Elgon, Cheranganis, Aberdares and Mt Kenya (Kenya); Maasai, Shinyanga, Morogoro (Tanzania); all regions of Uganda except Buganda; also in Zaire, Rwanda, Burundi.

12. Resedaceae

Usually herbs; rarely trees or shrubs; leaves alternate, simple or divided, stipulate; inflorescence racemose and terminal; flowers bisexual (rarely unisexual), usually zygomorphic; four to six, usually five sepals, free; four to five petals, sometimes up to seven, free, often divided or fringed; nectary disc often present, at least on one side; stamens definite or indefinite, often ten to fifteen; anthers splitting longitudinally, facing inwards, two-celled; ovary superior of five (two to six) free or slightly connate carpels which often never completely close; the pollen tube growing through the carpel wall; fruit a capsule or of follicles. Four species in two genera in East Africa.

Caylusea abyssinica   **Plate 173**
An annual or short-lived perennial herb with linear-lanceolate, often undulate leaves and long racemes of whitish flowers; anthers salmon-coloured or orange, turning yellow when mature; petals up to 3.5mm (c. ⅛in) long. Common in disturbed places in grassland, but not found in driest or highest areas. Allied to the European Mignonette. Altitude range 1200–3000m (3900–9950ft). Western to eastern Kenya; Maasai, Shinyanga, Moshi, Mpwapwa, Kondoa, Morogoro, Mbeya, Iringa (Tanzania); Acholi, Karamoja, Kigezi (Uganda); also Ethiopia, Eritrea.

13. Polygalaceae

Herbs or woody climbers, shrubs and trees; leaves alternate, simple, entire, exstipulate; flowers zygomorphic, bisexual, usually in racemes; five sepals, the two posterior laterals often enlarged and petaloid; three to five petals, free or connate, the lower petal often forming an appendaged keel; five to eight stamens, with filaments united in a slit tube, rather similar to those of the Papilionoideae; anthers dehiscing by apical pores; ovary of two carpels; seeds usually arillate. (Species of *Polygala* may be easily mistaken for members of the Papilionoideae.) Fifty-five species in four genera in East Africa (all but five in *Polygala*).

Polygala abyssinica   **Plate 717**
A glabrous or sparsely hairy annual with linear leaves and loose racemes of white or flushed purple flowers, lateral wing of flower 0.8cm (⅓in) long, 0.5cm (⅛in) wide. Locally common and found in dry grassland at medium altitudes, 300–2600m (1000–8650ft). Mau, Aberdares, Rift Valley, Nanyuki, Machakos and Kajiado (Kenya); Maasai, Shinyanga (Tanzania); northern region – Gulu (Uganda); also in Sudan, Ethiopia.

P. albida   An erect puberulous annual with linear to elliptic-oblong leaves and short racemes bearing crowded green or white flowers; enlarged calyx lobe 5×3mm (⅕×⅛in). A fairly common *Polygala* often found as a weed of fields and roadsides; altitude range 1500–2300m (4900–7500ft). Cheranganis, Kitale, western regions, Kisii, Baringo and Kajiado (Kenya); all regions of Tanzania except Morogoro; all regions of Uganda; also Sudan, Ethiopia, Burundi, Zaire, Malawi, Zambia, Zimbabwe, Mozambique.

P. amboniensis   Plate 718

A glabrescent annual or short-lived perennial herb, leaves oblong-linear, flowers not very colourful, green and pink, or purple, 3mm ($\frac{1}{8}$in) long. A common plant of drier bushland from the coast to medium altitudes; altitude range 1–1000m (3–3280ft). Rift Valley, Magadi, Machakos (Kenya); Tanga, Morogoro, Songea (Tanzania); probably absent from Uganda; elsewhere, no record.

P. erioptera
An annual or short-lived perennial, with linear-oblong leaves and axillary clusters of white or red flowers; internal wing of flower 0.5cm ($\frac{1}{4}$in) long, 0.3cm ($\frac{1}{10}$in) wide. Fairly common in rocky areas of bare soil in the dry grasslands of Kenya, especially on shallow soils; altitude range 100–2000m (330–6660ft). Western region, Elgon, Kisii, Rift Valley, Magadi, Machakos, Nairobi (Kenya); all regions of Tanzania except Tanga, Mpwapwa, Kondoa; all regions of Uganda except Buganda; also Sudan, Ethiopia, Eritrea, Somalia south to Zimbabwe, Mozambique.

P. liniflora
An erect annual up to 0.3m (1ft) high, with narrow linear alternate leaves. Flowers pinkish, wings yellow, flushed pink with greenish veins, keel pale magenta, sometimes reddish, and the flower itself looks 'pea-like'; size of flower c.7mm ($\frac{1}{4}$in) long. Altitude range 20–1400m (65–4600ft). Found in dry country, gravelly ridges, open bushland with *Acacia* and *Commiphora* trees, dwarf scrubland and in sparse grass cover in Kenya; all regions of Tanzania except Mbeya, Iringa; northern, eastern regions of Uganda; also in Somalia, Zaire.

P. petitiana
A glabrous or glabrescent annual, with linear to narrow-elliptic leaves and elongated racemes of yellowish-green to dull purple flowers; enlarged calyx lobe 4×2mm ($\frac{1}{6}$×$\frac{1}{12}$in). The most easy to recognize of the annual erect *Polygala*. It grows in grassland, often on shallow soil, but not in dry bush areas or the highland forest zones; altitude range 1300–2600m (4250–8500ft). Widely recorded from Machakos westwards to Kisii and Kitale areas (Kenya); all regions of Tanzania and Uganda; also in Ethiopia, Eritrea, Rwanda, Burundi, Zaire, Malawi, Zambia, Zimbabwe, Mozambique.

P. sadebeckiana
Perennial herbs or shrubs erect or decumbent, with elliptic to oblong leaves and axillary racemes of eight to twelve (rarely more) orange-red to red flowers; lateral wing of flower 0.8cm ($\frac{1}{3}$in) long, 0.5cm ($\frac{1}{4}$in) wide. This name is applied to an uncommon but widespread group of plants which include erect or trailing red-flowered plants at forest edges and grassland, as well as prostrate, orange-yellow-flowered on bare grassland. Eventually two species may be recognized. Altitude range 20–2200m (60–7330ft). Mau, Aberdares, Kitale, Nanyuki, Machakos and Nairobi (Kenya); lake areas, Maasai, Tanga (Tanzania); northern and western regions of Uganda; also in Ethiopia, Somalia, Malawi, Mozambique.

P. sphenoptera   Plate 719

A perennial or annual shrubby herb, suffruticose or trailing with linear, oblong or elliptic leaves, sometimes with revolute margins (especially in dry land areas) and lateral axillary or extra-axillary, short, loose racemes of purple or pinkish-white flowers; enlarged calyx lobe 7×7mm ($\frac{1}{4}$×$\frac{1}{4}$in). This is an extremely variable species which grows in dry bushland, grassland and upland grassland as well as along paths and clearings in the wetter highland forests. It appears to intergrade from one form to another, according to the habitat, from Magadi to the Cheranganis (Kenya). Dry grass and bushland forms have narrow, revolute-margined leaves; while forms from wetter areas have broad, elliptic, acuminate leaves and often a trailing habit.

Altitude range 300–2500m (c. 1000–8200ft). Throughout Kenya; all regions of Tanzania except Songea; all except western region of Uganda; also Ethiopia, Zaire south to Mozambique, Zimbabwe.

P. stenopetala   Plate 558
A perennial herb, sometimes an annual, or shrublet about 1.5m (4½ft) tall; erect, stems slightly winged, glabrous. Leaves linear, grasslike and pointed at the apex. Flowers blue or greenish with purple-brown veining; wings c. 7mm (c. ¼in) long. Found in wooded grassland or occasionally burnt areas; altitude range 1–450m (3–1500ft). Kwale district at the coast (Kenya); Tanga, Morogoro, Mbeya, Iringa, Songea (Tanzania); probably absent from Uganda; elsewhere, no record.

14. Crassulaceae
THE STONECROP FAMILY

A fairly large family of herbs or shrublets with succulent leaves, found mainly outside the tropics, usually in rather dry places. Their flowers are regular with four to five petals and sepals, either free or united, the calyx being persistent. The stamens are free and as many, or twice as many, as the petals. The fruit consists of four or five free or almost free follicles; the seeds minute. Forty-five species (of which one may not be native) in seven genera in East Africa.

Crassula alba   Plate 174
An erect herb, probably biennial, with a rosette of lanceolate, fleshy basal leaves and opposite leaves on the stem. Corymbs of closely clustered small white flowers are held on single stems springing from the base; each inflorescence 5–10cm (2–4in) across. A locally common plant of dry, rocky grassland at altitudes from 1400–4500m (4600–14,750ft). From north to south in the central highland areas and from the Cheranganis and Mau to Kajiado and Machakos (Kenya); Shinyanga, Bukoba, Mwanza, Mbeya (Tanzania); western region of Uganda; also Ethiopia, Zimbabwe, Mozambique.

C. alsinoides   A creeping or prostrate plant with elliptic, acute, unmarked leaves and solitary pink or white flowers which are borne on stems with linear leaves. Flower c. 6mm (¼in) across. Locally common in temporary water pools around Nairobi (Kenya); Maasai, Tanga, eastern region, Mbeya, Songea (Tanzania); western region and eastern – Jinja, Lake Kioga (Uganda); also Ethiopia, Somalia, Zaire, Zambia, Malawi, Mozambique.

Crassula granvikii   A soft perennial herb with a trailing base and tufted erect stems having linear leaves and a small tight bunch of pinkish flowers at the end. At higher altitudes the flowers are very small but in lowland forms can be very robust. Flower size c. 2–3mm (c. ⅛in) across. However, the leaves are often obtuse and not linear. It is a plant of considerable tolerance. Altitude range 1500–4500m (4900–14,750ft). Widespread in Kenya; lake areas, Maasai, Tanga, Morogoro, Mbeya, Iringa (Tanzania); all regions of Uganda except Buganda; also Sudan, Ethiopia.

CRASSULACEAE

C. pentandra var. phyturus   Plate 175
A low-growing, soft but woody herb or plant, trailing at the base, with erect stems
and succulent triangular-ovate or lanceolate leaves. The leafy shoots shown in the
photograph are c. 6mm ($\frac{1}{4}$in) across. The flowers are pinkish-white in dense axillary
clusters. Altitude range 2000–4000m (6600–13,100ft). Common in stony upland
grassland over a wide area (Kenya); lake areas, Maasai, Tanga, Morogoro (Tanzania); Uganda – all regions except Buganda; also Sudan, Ethiopia.

Cotyledon barbeyi   Plate 438
An erect, many-stemmed shrub with obovate to oblanceolate fleshy leaves;
inflorescence glandular; flowers large, pendulous and red, 22–25mm (c. 1in) long.
Locally common and conspicuous in dry, stony bushland, especially on small hills;
altitude range 950–2400m (3100–7900ft). Only species in East Africa. Mau, Narok,
Nanyuki, Rift Valley, Machakos, Nairobi and Kajiado (Kenya); lake areas, Maasai,
Tanga (Tanzania); Uganda, no record; also in southern Arabia, Sudan, Ethiopia,
Somalia and south to Mozambique and Zimbabwe.

Kalanchoe citrina   Plate 256
An erect, pubescent, weak perennial with oblanceolate to ovate, deeply dentate
leaves, and a small dense corymb of yellow flowers; lobes 5–7mm ($\frac{1}{5}$–$\frac{1}{4}$in) long;
corolla tube 10–12mm ($\frac{2}{5}$–$\frac{1}{2}$in) long. Found in dry rocky bushland; altitude range
1000–2100m (3280–6900ft). Baringo, Machakos and Baragoi (Kenya); no record
in Tanzania; northern regions – Gulu (Uganda); also in Ethiopia, Somalia.

K. densiflora   Plate 257
An erect, hairless herb with a dense terminal corymb of yellow flowers. Flower size
c. 6mm ($\frac{1}{4}$in) across; corymb c. 10cm (4in) across. The stalked leaves (which are
succulent, as with all Kalanchoe) are rounded to ovate and crenate. This is the
commonest Kalanchoe species and is found in disturbed places from 1800–2725m
(6000–9000ft). Elgon, Tinderet, Mau, Aberdares, Rift Valley, Embu, Machakos,
Nairobi and Kajiado (Kenya); Maasai, Tanga, Morogoro, Mbeya, Iringa (Tanzania);
all regions except Buganda (Uganda); also Zaire (Ruwenzori Mts), Sudan (Imatong
Mts), Ethiopia.

K. glaucescens   Plate 415
A hairless perennial, trailing at the base and with erect stems, with obovate to
ovate-elliptic, stalked leaves and small terminal corymbs of salmon-yellow to
yellow flowers; corolla tube c. 11mm ($\frac{2}{5}$in) long. It is a locally common plant found in
stony bushland from 400–2000m (1300–6550ft). Recorded in Mumias, Narok,
Baringo, Rift Valley and Machakos districts (Kenya); all regions except Mbeya,
Njombe and Songea (Tanzania); all regions except northern (Uganda); also
Ethiopia, Somalia, Sudan, Rwanda, Burundi, Zaire.

K. lanceolata   Plate 258
An erect, glandular, down-covered annual with a dense corymb of yellow to
orange-red flowers. Its obovate to oblong, succulent leaves are entire or dentate
and almost hairless. Flower size c. 11mm (c. $\frac{2}{5}$in) long. It grows to 1m (3$\frac{1}{2}$ft) in height
and is locally common in dry country from 200–2100m (650–6900ft). Mt Elgon,
Kitale, Mumias, Baringo, Rift Valley, Magadi, Machakos, Kajiado and Nairobi
districts and Voi, Tsavo and inland coastal areas at altitudes slightly lower than K.
densiflora (Kenya); all regions of Tanzania except Morogoro; all regions of
Uganda; also Sudan, Ethiopia, Somalia, south to Zimbabwe, Mozambique.

K. lateritia An ascending, glandular, down-covered, weak perennial with obovate, crenate, succulent leaves and rather small corymbs of bright red flowers. Flower c. 15mm (⅝in) across; corolla tube 9–12mm (⅓–½in) long. It is found in bushed grasslands in western Kenya in Kitale and Mumias districts and near the coast at altitudes up to 1800m (5900ft); all regions of Tanzania; no record in Uganda; also Zaire, Rwanda, Malawi, Zimbabwe, Mozambique.
NB Classified as Sp 'A' in *UKWF*.

K. pumila   **Plate 720**
A bushy plant growing to 0.7m (2ft) high, with closely set obovate leaves notched on upper margin, purplish-brown and covered with white bloom. Flowers pitcher-shaped, red-violet in colour. A native of Madagascar, cultivated in gardens but found in the wild. Its status as a native of East Africa is undetermined, and no specimen is present in the East African Herbarium.

K. schweinfurthii (*K. rohlfsii*)   **Plate 416**
An erect glandular pubescent, weak, perennial with ternate leaves bearing lanceolate to ovate leaflets and a dense terminal corymb of yellow flowers. Flower 1cm (⅜in) long. Altitude range 1350–2000m (4400–6550ft). A locally common plant found in rocky grassland, especially in the Rift Valley, also recorded in Machakos and Kajiado (Kenya); lake areas, Maasai, Mpwapwa, Kondoa, Morogoro (Tanzania); western region of Uganda; also Rwanda, Ethiopia, Malawi, Zimbabwe, Mozambique.

Sedum ruwenzoriense   **Plate 259**
A trailing or erect, softly woody, small shrub with blunt, cylindrical leaves and diffuse terminal cymes, yellow in colour. Flower c. 9mm (⅓in) across. Altitude range 3050–3900m (10,000–12,800ft). It is common in rock crevices in the moorland and lower alpine zones. High Cheranganis, Aberdares and Mt Kenya (Kenya); Tanzania, no record; all regions of Uganda except Buganda; also southern Sudan, Ethiopia, Zaire and Rwanda.

S. meyeri-johannis Similar in all respects to *S. ruwenzoriense* except for its trailing habit. Flower c. 9mm (⅓in) across. Locally common as an epiphyte in highland mist zones. Cheranganis, Aberdares, and Mau (Kenya); Maasai – Mt Kilimanjaro (Tanzania); eastern region – Mt Elgon (Uganda); also Zaire.

15. Caryophyllaceae

Mostly herbs, with simple, opposite stipulate or exstipulate leaves; flowers mostly bisexual, regular, in cymose inflorescences; five sepals, free or connate; five petals, free (sometimes absent); five or ten stamens, free; ovary of two to five connate carpels; ovules on a free central placenta; fruit a capsule; seed curved. Thirty-two species in sixteen genera in East Africa.

Silene burchellii   **Plate 721**
A perennial herb with linear acute leaves and racemes of three to nine flowers; petals reddish, pale pink, cream or purple. The flowers bisexual (rarely unisexual) with five sepals, connate at the base; five petals with a narrow claw (in the calyx

tube); ten stamens; calyx tube 1.1–2.5cm ($\frac{2}{5}$–1in) long. The plant is short-hairy, not viscid. The commonest *Silene* in Kenya, though not abundant. The petals open at night and remain open during the following morning only, becoming darker and curling towards midday. The plant can grow from medium-altitude grasslands right up to the moorlands of the alpine zone; altitude range 1500–4050m (4900–13,300ft). Elgon, Cheranganis, Mau, Aberdares, Mt Kenya and in Kitale, Rift Valley, Nairobi and Kajiado (Kenya); all regions of Tanzania; all regions of Uganda except Buganda; also Sudan, Ethiopia, Eritrea, Somalia, Rwanda, Burundi, southern Zaire, Zambia, Zimbabwe, Mozambique, South Africa.

S. macrosolen A perennial herb similar to *S. burchellii*, but larger in all its parts and completely glabrous, though the inflorescence has viscid patches on the peduncle, pedicels and rachis; calyx tube 3.2–4.4cm (1$\frac{1}{4}$–1$\frac{3}{4}$in) long. Rare, only found in fairly well-watered but high-altitude grassland. Altitude range 1800–3300m (6900–10,100ft). Aberdares, Mt Kenya, Rift Valley (Kenya); Maasai, Tanga, Mpwapwa, Kondoa (Tanzania); Uganda, no record; also Sudan, Ethiopia.

16. Aizoaceae

This is a large family which is very well represented in South Africa, where there are hundreds of species related to *Mesembryanthemum*. They are annual or perennial herbs or shrublets, rarely shrubs. The leaves are simple and the flowers regular. There are no petals – what look like petals, as, for instance, in Delosperma, are staminodes. There are twenty-six species in East Africa covering fourteen genera.

Delosperma oehleri   **Plate 640**
Originally described by Engler in 1909 from a specimen collected by Oehler and Jaeger in northern Tanzania, this species was not found again until rediscovered by the photographer Peter Davey at 1950m (6400ft) on a quartzitic hill in Narok district (Kenya), when our photograph was taken. The magenta of the petal-like staminodes was not recorded by the original collectors. Flower *c.* 12mm ($\frac{1}{2}$in) across. One of three species in East Africa. Maasai, Ndaesekera Mts (Tanzania); Uganda, not recorded; endemic.

D. nakurense A shrubby, low-growing perennial with unstalked, fleshy, thick, almost succulent leaves and pink, sometimes whitish flowers. Flower *c.* 2cm ($\frac{4}{5}$in) across. It likes to grow in well-drained, crumbly, rocky ground or among rocks in dry bush and grassland at altitudes 1500–2100m (5000–7000ft). Locally common in parts of the Rift Valley and occasionally elsewhere (Kenya); Maasai, Olmerungu, Lushoto, Handeni (Tanzania); Uganda, endemic.

Mollugo nudicaulis   **Plate 37**
A glabrous annual with a rosette of spathulate leaves and a dichotomous or sub-umbelliform scape of pinkish or red flowers. Flower 3mm ($\frac{1}{8}$in) across. This is a small and easily overlooked annual of shallow soils in lower-altitude grassland; altitude range 60–1860m (300–6200ft). Widespread, not common. Mau, Kisii, Narok, Baringo, Rift Valley and Nairobi (Kenya); all regions of Tanzania except Mbeya, Iringa; all regions of Uganda; also throughout tropical Africa.

17. Portulacaceae

A rather small, mainly herbaceous family found in most parts of the world. Its leaves are entire and often rather succulent. There are two sepals and five (sometimes four or six) petals and from five to many stamens. The ovary is superior and unilocular with one or more ovules attached to the base. Sixteen species in four genera in East Africa, with much research still to be done.

Calyptrotheca somalensis   **Plate 176**
A suberect shrub up to 3m (10ft) tall, with succulent stems with a greenish sap springing from very large, fleshy rootstocks. Leaves fleshy, broadly oblanceolate, apex rounded or acuminate, margin entire, base narrow-cuneate. Flowers greenish in short fascicles up to 2.5cm (1in) long, terminating the branchlets; petal 1.25cm ($\frac{1}{2}$in) long, 0.8cm ($\frac{1}{3}$in) wide. Filament white. Found in *Acacia-Commiphora* scrubland; altitude range 600–900m (2000–3000ft). Mandera, Moyale and Mackinnon Road areas (Kenya); Tanzania and Uganda, no record; also in Ethiopia, southern Somalia.

Portulaca foliosa   **Plate 495**
An annual or robust perennial herb or low shrub with subterete glaucous leaves and golden to white stipular hairs. Flowers usually solitary, with pinkish sepals and yellow to orange petals; size of flower 1cm ($\frac{1}{3}$in) across. Very similar in appearance to *P. kermesina*. Found in stony dry grassland and scrubland at medium altitudes with a wide ecological tolerance; altitude range 1200–2200m (4000–7100ft). Kisii, Narok, Baringo and Machakos (Kenya); all regions of Tanzania except Mpwapwa, Kondoa, Songea; all regions of Uganda except eastern; also in Zambia, Mozambique.

P. grandiflora   **Plate 260**
A spreading semi-succulent herb with lanceolate leaves. Size of flower *c.* 2cm ($\frac{3}{4}$in) across. This is not a wild species in Kenya, but a garden escape, which appears to be spreading, and has been recorded on the Magadi road from Nairobi and near Juja in Kenya. Altitude range 1150–1500m (3500–5000ft). It is illustrated here as visitors may find it and wish to know the species; it may also spread further afield and become more commonplace, like *Tagetes minuta* and *Lantana camara*.

P. kermesina   **Plate 261**
A branched, fleshy perennial with slightly tapering leaves of a dull grey-green and with numerous long (usually over 5mm/$\frac{1}{5}$in) hairs at the base of the leaf. The usually solitary flowers are yellow, 1cm ($\frac{2}{5}$in) across. Found in dry, sandy or stony soils in drier areas; altitude range 1200–2200m (4000–7100ft). Central, southern and Rift Valley districts (Kenya); lake areas (Tanzania); northern (Gulu) and eastern (Jinja, Lake Kioga) regions (Uganda); elsewhere, sporadic from Eritrea to Cape.

P. oleracea   A glabrous annual with numerous spreading branches bearing alternate obovate-spathulate leaves with inconspicuous stipular hairs; flowers yellow in terminal clusters. Flower *c.* 1.2cm ($\frac{1}{2}$in) across. A widespread *Portulaca* found as a nitrophilous weed in gardens, cultivation, railway tracks and roadsides. The flowers open only for a short time in the morning. Altitude range 5–2040m (16–6800ft). Elgon, Kitale, western Kenya, Baringo, Rift Valley, Machakos, Nairobi and Kajiado (Kenya); all regions of Tanzania except Mpwapwa, Kondoa; all regions of Uganda except Buganda; also Ethiopia, Eritrea, south to Mozambique; widespread in most warm countries.

P. parensis   A low annual or perennial herb with fleshy leaves and numerous long, silvery, stipular hairs; flowers, yellow, often solitary, 1 cm (⅓in) across. Grows as an erect herb up to 5cm (2in) tall. Stipules mostly broadened at the base and up to 7mm (⅓in) long, silvery-white in colour. Four to six petals, imbricate, free or connate up to halfway. Stamens as many and opposite to the petals, sometimes more numerous. The most easily recognizable of the *Portulaca*, but is rarely seen and has only been recorded in Kenya on Suswa Mountain on rocky ridges at 1800m (6000ft). Our photograph was taken on the Magadi road, however, so it would be helpful if any other record is reported to the Herbarium, c/o The National Museum, Nairobi. Altitude range 350–2100m (1160–7000ft). The original type was gathered in the Pare Mts, Tanga region (Tanzania); Uganda and elsewhere, not recorded.

P. quadrifida   **Plate 262**
A prostrate annual herb up to 30cm (12in) long; stems slender, often rooting at the nodes; leaves opposite up to 10mm (⅜in) long but often less, variable in shape and size, lanceolate to elliptic-oblong, apex usually acute. Flower *c.* 2cm (¾–1in) across. Stipular hairs numerous, whitish. Usually four petals, yellow or orange, rarely pink or purplish, almost free. Eight to twelve stamens. A common plant in stony, dry grassland and scrubland at medium altitudes, 1200–2100m (4000–7000ft), and often a weed in cultivated land and roadsides. Elgon, Aberdares, Kitale, Kisii, Narok, Rift Valley, Machakos and Nairobi (Kenya); all regions of Tanzania except Tabora and Songea; northern and western regions of Uganda; also Malawi, Zimbabwe, Mozambique.

Talinum caffrum   **Plate 263**
A glabrous perennial herb from a thickened fleshy root with usually oblanceolate, elliptic-lanceolate or linear leaves and axillary yellow flowers. Size of flower 12mm (½in) across. Found in open grassland or bushland below 1800m (6000ft). One of three species in East Africa. Narok, Magadi, Nanyuki, Machakos and Kajiado (Kenya); all regions of Tanzania except Mpwapwa, Kondoa, Songea; northern (Gulu) and western regions (Uganda); also in Ethiopia and southern Sudan to Mozambique, Zimbabwe, Cape.

T. portulacifolium   **Plate 641**
A hairless perennial herb or small shrub with obovate to oblanceolate, fleshy leaves and long terminal racemes of many flowers, purple to purple-pink; pedicels recurved when in fruit. Flower *c.* 12mm (½in) across. Common in dry bushland at 9–1650m (30–5900ft) in Kenya; all regions of Tanzania except Tabora, Songea; all regions of Uganda; also Ethiopia and Somalia south to Mozambique, Zimbabwe, Cape.

18. Polygonaceae
THE DOCK FAMILY

A medium-sized, cosmopolitan family of herbs, shrubs or climbers and, very rarely, trees. Their leaves are usually alternate and the base often sheathing. Flowers are small and often unisexual; the regular, three- to six-lobed perianth is often persistent (remaining after the normal time of withering); there are five to nine stamens and a superior ovary with only one ovule, fruit a nutlet. Forty-three species in East Africa distributed through seven genera.

Oxygonum sinuatum An almost hairless annual with elliptic to oblanceolate or obovate leaves bearing one to three pairs of shallow-lobed or entire pink flowers. Flower c. 5mm (c. ¼in) across. It is rare at the coast and is found generally in waste places from 1–2100m (3–7000ft). It is the commonest *Oxygonum* and has unpleasant prickly fruits. All regions of Kenya, Tanzania and Uganda; also Sudan, Ethiopia, Zaire southwards.

Polygonum afromontanum An almost hairless scrambling or trailing plant with elliptic leaves and axillary clusters of few pink flowers. Altitude range 2100–3150m (c. 7000–10,300ft). Fairly common at the tree line on Mt Kenya, Aberdares (Kenya); Mts Oldiani, Hanang only (Tanzania); Uganda and elsewhere, not known.

P. convolvulus A climbing, twining, almost hairless annual herb with ovate acuminate or triangular hastate leaves and fascicles of pink flowers in racemes or borne axillary. Flower c. 5mm (c. ⅛in) across. Becoming noticeable in cultivated arable areas, 1700–2200m (5500–7200ft) in Kenya, Tanzania, Uganda and elsewhere; an introduced weed from Europe.

P. pulchrum A softly hairy perennial herb with narrow-lanceolate entire leaves, often with longitudinal undulations. The inflorescence is a raceme of one to five pink flowers. Flower c. 5mm (c. ¼in) across. It is a locally common waterside plant from 0–2100m (0–7000ft) and often found around artificial dams in most districts of Kenya, Tanzania and Uganda; widespread in subtropical and tropical Africa

P. salicifolium   **Plate 2**
An erect, almost hairless annual with elliptic, almost sessile leaves and a terminal group of slender, interrupted racemes of pink or white flowers. Flower c. 5mm (c. ¼in) across. It is a common waterside plant from 1–2400m (3–8000ft) in Kenya, Tanzania (Zanzibar, Pemba Is.) and Uganda; also Ethiopia, Eritrea, Rwanda, Burundi, Zaire, south to Mozambique.

P. senegalense An erect, variable hairy perennial like a soft shrub in general appearance; the stems are more or less covered with conspicuous slightly inflated brown sheaths. The leaves are lanceolate, acute, hairless or covered with dense, white, soft hairs, and the inflorescence is a raceme of pink or white flowers, c. 5mm (⅛in) across. It is a common herb of river and streamside and marshes; altitude range 45–3000m (150–10,000ft). There are two distinct forms of this species between which intermediates occasionally occur; var. *senegalense* is almost hairless except for the glands, while var. *albotomentosum*, which is much less common, is covered with dense, soft, white hairs. Widespread in Kenya, Tanzania (except Songea) and Uganda (except eastern); also throughout tropical Africa.

P. setulosum   **Plate 722**
A roughly hairy perennial herb with lanceolate-ovate or elliptic leaves and inflorescence of one to five racemes, terminal, composed of pink flowers, 5mm (⅛in) across. It is a common waterside plant, often growing at higher altitudes, 1050–2750m (3500–9000ft), than the other species of *Polygonum*. Elgon, Mau, Aberdares, Kitale, western Kenya, Kisii, Narok, Rift Valley and Nairobi (Kenya); all regions of Tanzania and Uganda; also in Sudan, Rwanda, Burundi, Zaire, Zambia.

POLYGONACEAE

Rumex usambarensis   Plate 642
A weak shrub, sometimes almost a climber, with oblong-elliptic leaves with a
pointed tip and outward-pointing lobes at the base. The flowers are carried as a
complex red panicle c. 7.5cm (3in) across. It is a beautiful plant, common at
900–2400m (3000–7900ft). Often seen alongside roads and invading newly
cleared woodland around Nairobi (Kenya); Maasai, Tanga, Tabora, Mbeya, Iringa
(Tanzania); all regions of Uganda except northern; also Malawi, Zaire.

R. abyssinicus Ranges from 730–3300m (2400–10,800ft). It prefers wetter
places and in its lower altitudes is confined to stream banks and sides but higher in
its range it replaces R. usambarensis. It has large leaves like those of the European
docks; flowers green in colour. Flower panicle up to 40cm (15in) long; 25cm (10in)
wide. Widespread except Mpwapwa, Kondoa (Kenya and Tanzania); all regions of
Uganda except eastern; also throughout highlands of tropical Africa.

R. bequaertii The most common and widespread dock in Kenya. It has an erect
raceme of greenish-brown clustered flowers, panicle 80cm (c. 30–32in) long, 30cm
(c. 12in) wide, and large leaves like those of the two preceding species, and is also
found in wetter places and often at higher altitudes than R. usambarensis, from
690–3700m (2300–12,300ft). Maasai, Tanga, Morogoro, Mbeya, Iringa, Songea
(Tanzania); all regions of Uganda except northern; also Ethiopia and south to
Zimbabwe, Mozambique.

R. ruwensoriensis Sparsely covered with short, soft hairs. It has large oblong-
lanceolate leaves, similar to those of European docks, and greenish-yellow·to
brownish-red flowers. Flower panicle up to 40cm (15¾in) long, 19cm (7½in) across. It
is the common dock on the Aberdares and Mt Kenya and is often found along
streamsides, from 1950–3700m (6500–12,300ft). Morogoro, Mbeya, Iringa (Tanzania); western, eastern regions of Uganda; also in the mountains of Zaire.

19. Phytolaccaceae

A rather small, mainly tropical family which has alternate leaves and regular
flowers. Ovaries may have one to many carpels, each with an ovule. Four species
in three genera have been recorded in East Africa.

Phytolacca dodecandra   Plate 177
A climbing, scrambling or more or less erect shrub with bluntly ovate-elliptic leaves
narrowing to a prominently and ultimately recurved mucronate tip, cuneate or
cordate at the unequal-sided base and long, trailing racemes of pedicellate white or
cream, long-staminate, scented flowers. Short-staminate flowers a yellowish-
green; raceme 15–30cm (6–12in) long; sepals 2–3mm (1/12–1/8in) long. It is a local
plant of bushland and cleared forest at medium altitudes, 500–2400m
(1640–7900ft), and though often found as a low trailing shrub it can grow as a
strong climber in riverine forest. Elgon, Aberdares, Rift Valley, Taita Hills, Nairobi
and Turkana (Kenya); all regions of Tanzania and Uganda; also widespread in
tropical Africa and Madagscar.
  NB This is a notoriously poisonous plant which causes many deaths among
cattle and sheep, which eat the soft, juicy leaves when grass is scarce in times of
drought. The fruits contain saponins and are used, especially in Ethiopia, as a

substitute for soap. This kills the water snails in pools used for washing clothes and thus reduces the incidence of Bilharzia.

20. Amaranthaceae

A rather large family of herbs, shrublets or, occasionally lianes found throughout the tropics and warm-temperate regions. The small flowers are often surrounded by chaffy bracts. The perianth usually has five free, stiff, chaffy segments with a stamen opposite each segment uniting at the base to form a cup. The uni-locular ovary is superior and usually has one central, basal ovule; the fruit is usually dry, rarely fleshy. There are eighty-nine species known in East Africa from all parts except the high mountains; they belong to twenty-five different genera but are often hard to tell apart.

Achyranthes aspera   **Plate 643**
An annual or perennial, tomentose or pubescent herb or shrub with ovate-obtuse to lanceolate-acute leaves and long spikes of reddish-purple flowers. A most variable plant: the var. *aspera* has larger flowers, more than 5.5mm (*c.* ¼in) long, and the bract longer than the bracteole and grows as a shrub along forest edges and waste places. The var. *sicula* has smaller flowers, less than 5mm (⅕in) long, and the bract shorter than the bracteole, and mainly grows west of the Rift Valley at forest edges. It also has an annual form which is a field weed. Altitude range 1–3000m (1–9850ft). Both widespread in Kenya; all regions of Tanzania and Uganda; also found in a great variety of habitats except in very dry country, in most warm countries.

Amaranthus hybridus ssp. **cruentus**   **Plate 644**
An erect, glabrous annual with rhombic cuneate leaves and terminal, axillary spike-like racemes. It is the commonest *Amaranthus* in its altitude zone. The inflorescence is red or a slightly winey-red colour, 30×15cm (12×6in). In *A. hybridus* ssp. *hybridus*, which is the typical ssp. in Kenya, there is a purple variant very similar to ssp. *cruentus*. Commonly found in cultivation on disturbed ground; altitude range 1200–2400m (4000–8000ft). Throughout Kenya including the Chyulu Hills; Maasai, Tanga, Mpwapwa, Kondoa, Mbeya, Iringa, Songea (Tanzania); eastern region and Buganda (Uganda); widespread elsewhere.

   NB Like several of the eleven species of *Amaranthus* found in East Africa, this is eaten as a pot herb resembling spinach, and is a very valuable component of the rural African diet.

Centemopsis gracilenta   **Plate 645**
An erect annual or short-lived perennial up to 1.6m (5ft) high. Stem wiry, tough and strongly striate. Leaves linear to linear-filiform up to 9.5cm (*c.* 4in) long with revolute margins, sessile, sharply mucronate at apex. Inflorescence carmine to pink or whitish, spiciform, conical at the tip and elongating in fruit. Flowers solitary in axil of bracts; each individual flower 4mm (⅙in) long. Found in deciduous woodland, along roadsides, on dry, shaded banks by ditches; a weed of cultivation, always in sandy soil. Altitude range 50–2270m (170–7300ft). Coastal bushland and Kitui (Kenya); Tabora, Mpwapwa, Kondoa, Mbeya, Iringa (Tanzania); Uganda, no record; also in Somalia, Zaire, Malawi, Zambia, Zimbabwe, Mozambique.

C. kirkii
Plate 646

An erect, sparsely-downed annual or short-lived perennial able to exist under a variety of conditions. It has linear sessile leaves and reddish spikes of two-flowered cymes; inflorescence c. 3cm (1⅜in) long. Common in dry bushland at 100–1980m (300–6300ft). Eastern region, Machakos, Nairobi and Kajiado (Kenya); all regions of Tanzania except lake areas; Uganda, no record; also Ethiopia, Zambia, Malawi, Mozambique, Zimbabwe.

Cyathula cylindrica
Plate 178

A scrambling perennial herb covered in soft hairs with lanceolate to ovate leaves and solitary, cylindrically uninterrupted, grey to slightly straw-coloured terminal spikes; inflorescence 2cm (⅞in) in diameter. Its trailing habit and usually hanging, grey-silver racemes make it easy to identify. Rather uncommon in Kenya; found in wetter, high-level forests at 1290–3050m (4300–10,000ft); all regions of Tanzania except southern (Songea); all regions of Uganda except Buganda; also Sudan, Ethiopia south to Mozambique, Zimbabwe. Ten other species in East Africa.

C. orthacantha
Plate 179

An erect, pubescent to tomentose annual with ovate-elliptic or orbicular leaves and pedunculate terminal racemes of almost sessile cymes. Flower whitish, 13mm (½in) across. An uncommon annual of disturbed drier areas often in Acacia bushland; altitude range 610–1400m (2000–4600ft). Kisii, Baringo, Magadi, Nanyuki and Kajiado (Kenya); all regions of Tanzania except southern (Songea); northern region of Uganda (Gulu); also in Sudan, Ethiopia, Zambia, Zimbabwe.

C. polycephala (C. schimperiana)
Plate 180

A hair-covered or woolly herb with ascending or erect stems and ovate-elliptic, heart-shaped or rounded leaves. The terminal inflorescence is leafless and crowded with pedunculate cymes which are spaced out so that each may develop into a separate, straw-coloured ball, c. 22mm (¾in) across. Altitude range 1500–2700m (5000–9000ft). It is a common weed of upland grassland (Kenya); Maasai, Mpwapwa, Kondoa (Tanzania); Uganda, no record; also Ethiopia, Zaire, Rwanda.

Digera muricata
Plate 647

An erect, often very tall annual which is usually unbranched below, with linear to lanceolate leaves and long terminal spikes of purple flowers in the form of cymes, the sterile flowers of each cyme forming green wings. Flower c. 4mm (¼in) long. It is found in dry places, often on stony or sandy soil in grassland, at 5–1500m (16–5000ft). Only species in East Africa. Kisii, Baringo, Nanyuki, Machakos, Magadi and Kajiado, and in dry, low-altitude areas such as the Northern Frontier districts (Kenya); lake areas, Maasai, Tanga, Mpwapwa, Kondoa, eastern region (Tanzania); northern region of Uganda; also Sudan, Ethiopia.

Gomphrena celosioides
Plate 181

A perennial herb covered with soft hairs, and having prostrate or ascending branches, and obovate to elliptic leaves. Its white terminal spikes are pedunculate. Inflorescence c. 12mm (½in) across. It came originally from South America but has spread as a weed during the present century in the tropics and subtropics, and is now common at the sides of roads and over most of East Africa at altitudes up to 2130m (7000ft). All regions of Kenya and Tanzania; all regions of Uganda except western; also widespread in tropical Africa as an alien weed.

Pupalia lappacea Very similar to *Cyathula*, from which it differs in having alternately arranged cymes in the raceme, more highly developed sterile flowers with stellate hooks in fruit and no staminodes. It is an annual or perennial, prostrate, scrambling or erect herb with elliptic or ovate leaves and terminal, erect or pendulous racemes of grey-white flowers with well-spaced, alternate cymes on short peduncles. Flower (in dry country): sepal, 3.5–5mm (⅛–¼in) long. It is an annoying plant which produces highly adhesive burrs, especially in dry country. They stick on all clothing. Widespread at 1–1900m (3–6200ft). All regions of Kenya, Tanzania and Uganda (except Buganda), and widespread in tropical Africa.

Sericocomopsis hildebrandtii   Plate 182
A much-branched, canescent, bushy shrub with obovate to spathulate leaves and terminal racemes of sessile cymes; each flower 5mm (¼in) across. The inflorescence is white, which distinguishes it from *S. pallida*, which has grey inflorescences. It is often confused with *Cyathula cylindrica*, but can be distinguished by the absence of hooks on the cymes. A common shrubby amaranth of dry thornbush country, especially on fine soils. One of two species in East Africa. Altitude range 150–1820m (500–6000ft). Narok, Baringo, Rift Valley, Magadi, Nanyuki, Machakos and Kajiado (Kenya); lake areas, Maasai, Tanga (Tanzania); northern region of Uganda (Gulu); also in southern Ethiopia.

S. pallida   Plate 183
A much-branched, bushy shrub with white stellate hairs on ovate-elliptic leaves and terminal racemes of well-separated, pedunculate, alternate greyish cymes. Inflorescence 2.5–9cm (1–4in) long, 1.5–2.25cm (⅔–1in) across. A common shrub of dry thorn bush, deciduous bushland, rocky and disturbed places in shallow, often calcareous soils; altitude range 100–1220m (328–3900ft). Baringo, Kajiado, Northern Frontier areas, Embu, Kitui, Coast Nyika (Kenya); Maasai, Tanga (Tanzania); Uganda, no record; also in Ethiopia, Eritrea, Somalia.

21. Linaceae
THE FLAX FAMILY

Herbs, shrubs or trees with simple, mostly stipulate, alternate or opposite leaves; inflorescence mostly a terminal or axillary cyme; flowers regular, bisexual, four to five sepals, free or connate below, imbricate, persistent; petals as sepal number, free or connate, fugacious, contorted in bud, often clawed; stamens generally as sepal number. Ovary superior, three- to five-celled. Seed a capsule or drupe, splitting along the line of junction of the carpels. Ten species in three genera in East Africa.

Linum volkensii   Plate 264
An erect herb up to 90cm (c. 3ft) high, annual or perennial, often woody at the base, glabrous in all parts. Stems, terete, obscurely longitudinally ridged. Leaves all alternate, linear-lanceolate to linear, apiculate or sharply acuminate, margin scabrid-setulose. Inflorescence a terminal loose corymbose cyme of pentamerous yellow flowers, often fading white, occasionally purple-veined, sepals with midrib prominent in basal half, pedicel 1–11mm (to ⅜in) long, five petals, generally rounded. Found in upland grassland, in marshes and by streams; altitude range

1300–2750m (4250–9000ft). Three other species in East Africa. Widespread in Kenya; Maasai, Tanga, Morogoro, Mbeya, Iringa, Songea (Tanzania); all regions of Uganda except Buganda; also in Ethiopia, eastern Zaire, Malawi, Mozambique.

22. Zygophyllaceae

A small family, recorded mainly in warm and arid regions, with leaves usually compound, flowers regular with four or five free sepals and petals and usually twice as many stamens. The ovary is superior with the fruit splitting into two or more one-seeded portions at maturity. There are some ten species, covering three genera, known in East Africa.

Tribulus cistoides   **Plate 265**
A creeping perennial with opposite and paripinnate leaves bearing four to seven oblong to oblong-lanceolate leaflets, with yellow or cream-coloured flowers, 15–25mm ($\frac{3}{8}$–1in) across. One of six species in East Africa. A plant of dry, arid and warm zones with sandy soils found up to 800m (2600ft) in Kenya, although rare above 910m (3000ft); also recorded in coastal regions of Tanzania and from Eritrea to Mozambique.

T. terrestris   **Plate 266**
Much more widely spread and common at 0–2300m (0–7700ft), growing on sandy soils, waste ground near human habitations, roadsides and cultivated land. Its small, star-like, yellow flowers project from the axils above the strictly opposite and oblong lanceolate leaves. Flower 6–9mm ($\frac{1}{4}$–$\frac{3}{8}$in) across. The seed husks are spiked and irritatingly attach themselves to stockings. Amongst the Akamba people it used to be a test of manhood for young warriors to walk across a threshing floor covered with these spiked fruits without showing signs of pain. It is easily recognized along roadsides on sandy furrows and folds in National Parks such as Buffalo Springs and Tsavo West (Kenya); all regions of Tanzania and Uganda; also widespread in Africa.

T. zeyheri ssp. **macranthus**   **Plate 267**
An annual or biennial, hirsute herb with all vegetative parts covered with stiff, spreading hairs; branches prostrate up to 60cm (2ft) long, internodes cylindrical and up to 8cm ($3\frac{1}{4}$in) long; five to six pairs of leaflets, ovate. Flowers large, 30–50mm ($1\frac{1}{2}$–2in) across, pedicel 20–40mm ($\frac{4}{5}$–$1\frac{3}{5}$in) long. Eight to twelve sepals, densely hairy, deciduous, petals lemon yellow, ten stamens, ovary globular. Found on sandy beaches, dry plains and along roads; altitude range 0–1500m (0–4900ft). Recorded in Northern Frontier areas, Taita district (Kenya); also south tropical Africa. Ssp. *macranthus* is a robust form of *T. zeyheri* with stiff, spreading hairs, internodes longer and leaves larger, 2–5cm ($\frac{4}{5}$–2in) long, and is much confused with *T. cistoides*.

23. Geraniaceae

THE CRANESBILL FAMILY

A medium-sized, mainly herbaceous family containing only five genera, found in most temperate and subtropical regions but absent from the humid tropics. Its leaves are often palmately veined or lobed; sepals and petals are free and usually five in number, stamens twice as many; the ovary is superior, beaked, with three to five loculi, and one or two pendulous ovules in each loculus. The fruit splits into several tailed, and usually single-seeded, mericarps. There are seventeen species in East Africa belonging to three genera.

Geranium aculeolatum   Plate 38

A perennial trailing herb rooting at the nodes with sharp, reflexed prickles and palmately-lobed leaves. The flowers are almost always in pairs and white or mauve in colour, c. 16mm ($\frac{5}{8}$in) across. Altitude range 1200–3050m (4000–10,000ft). It is found in montane forests and moist places such as stream sides and marshy sides of valleys and sometimes as a weed in cultivated places (Kenya); all regions of Tanzania except lake areas, Mpwapwa, Kondoa; western and eastern regions of Uganda; also Ethiopia, Sudan, Zaire, Malawi, Mozambique.

G. arabicum ssp. arabicum   Plate 723

A perennial herb, diffusely branched or ascending, occasionally tufted; stems somewhat woody, stoloniferous, creeping and scrambling, longitudinally grooved, pilose or pubescent, with short reflexed, appressed hairs. Leaves usually opposite, but sometimes in basal rosettes, especially the radical ones, occasionally pinkish-red on the lower surface. Inflorescence usually two-flowered, the flowers rarely solitary by reduction. Petals obovate or spathulate, obtuse or retuse, white or purple (rarely pale purple) with conspicuous red veins, 6–10mm ($\frac{1}{4}$–$\frac{2}{5}$in) long, 2–3mm (c. $\frac{1}{8}$in) wide. Altitude range 1100–3950m (300–12,900ft). Found in upland rain forest, bushland, grassland, and moor, often in moist places by streams or in marshes. Aberdares, Elgon, Kiambu, Machakos, Chyulu Hills (Kenya); all regions of Tanzania except Mpwapwa, Kondoa; all regions of Uganda except Buganda; also widespread in tropical African highlands.

NB Ssp. *arabicum* illustrated differs from the species in that the leaf lamina is divided for about three-quarters of the radius, each lobe rhombic in outline and incised.

G. kilimandscharicum   Plate 724

A perennial prostrate stoloniferous herb, sometimes up to 40cm (15$\frac{3}{4}$in) long; stems frequently tufted, sometimes creeping or scrambling, longitudinally grooved, pilose or hispid, the main stem woody below; prostrate branches sometimes rooting at the nodes. Leaves opposite, but the basal ones sometimes in a rosette, frequently pinkish-red on the lower surface. (The rosette is more common in dwarf plants.) Flowers generally solitary pink-red to light pink, mericarps pilose; petals 5–9mm ($\frac{1}{5}$–$\frac{1}{3}$in) long, 3–5mm ($\frac{1}{8}$–$\frac{1}{5}$in) wide. Altitude range 3200–4400m (10,800–14,400ft) and 2100–2400m (7000–7900ft) in Iringa and Mbeya (Tanzania). Found only in the alpine belts of high mountains in upland moors, on rocky and dry ground with open vegetation, along stream banks and less often in upland grassland or upland rain forest. Elgon, Mt Kenya (Kenya); Maasai (Mt Kilimanjaro), Mbeya, Iringa (Tanzania); eastern region of Uganda (Elgon); not known elsewhere.

NB In the illustration, the flower is above the leaves of another species: in *G.*

GERANIACEAE

kilimandscharicum the lobes are palmate and are divided nearly to the midrib, as in the leaf on the extreme right-hand bottom corner.

G. ocellatum   Plate 648
An ascending, diffusely-branched, annual herb with spreading hairs or glands and rounded, palmatisect leaves. Its paired flowers are pink with dark, almost black-purple, centres, c. 14mm (⅜in) across. Altitude range 1000–2900m (3300–9500ft); generally found in shade, as in caves, or along hill slopes or forest edges, but also as a weed in cultivated ground. Elgon, Tinderet, Rift Valley and Kitale (Kenya); Moshi, Pare, Morogoro (Tanzania); Karamoja, Kigezi, Busoga (Uganda); also from Ethiopia to Zimbabwe and east Cameroun.

Monsonia angustifolia   Plate 39
An annual with smaller mauve or white flowers; petals 7–15mm (¼–⅜in) long. Widespread and often found on cultivated ground and damp grassland, at 400–2200m (1300–8500ft). Kenya uplands; Musoma (Serengeti), Mpwapwa, Mbeya (Tanzania); Karamoja, Toro, Ankole (Uganda); also Somalia to Zimbabwe, Mozambique.

M. longipes   Plate 184
A profusely branched perennial with up to five bright yellow or lemon flowers (also occasionally white); petals 15–25mm (⅝–1in) long. Appears to be limited to 800–2200m (2600–8500ft). Nairobi and Rift Valley areas (Kenya); lake areas, Maasai, Mbeya, Iringa (Tanzania); Uganda, no record; also Ethiopia.

M. ovata   Plate 268
An erect perennial plant with fleshy roots. The flowers, usually in pairs, are yellow or white, c. 2cm (⅝in) across, and the leaves are opposite to each other on the stem. Found in open plains with acacia trees or wooded grassland on sandy and stony soils. 800–1500m (2600–5000ft). Rift Valley, Machakos and Magadi districts (Kenya); Mbulu, Moshi, Pare (Tanzania); Uganda, no record; also in Zimbabwe.

M. senegalensis   Plate 725
An annual, prostrate to decumbent, or sometimes erect herb, branching from an often woody base. Stems frequently with short alternating lateral shoots in one of the axils of the apparently opposite leaves; internodes 0.5–4cm (¼–2in) or more long. Vegetative parts covered with short often gland-tipped hairs (sometimes recurved). Leaves alternate, but at every node the leaf is apparently opposite a shoot. Lamina ovate, acute at the apex, margin serrate or dentate to repand-dentate, the base cordate. Inflorescence usually of solitary axillary flowers; petals obovate, 9–12mm (⅓–½in) long, 5–8mm (¼–⅓in) wide, the apex truncate or shallowly lobed, pink with dark veins. Stamens greenish-yellow. Found in deciduous woodland and semi-arid grassland, often on rocky ground, lava outcrops or in dry sandy places; altitude range 200–2100m (660–6900ft). Tsavo West, Turkana, Kajiado and Magadi (Kenya); Maasai, Mbeya, Iringa (Tanzania); Uganda, no record; also in southern Sudan, Ethiopia, Eritrea, Somalia, south to Zimbabwe, Mozambique.

Pelargonium alchemilloides   Plate 40
A perennial herb covered with short, soft hairs, with a slightly tuberous rootstock, and leaves alternate below and opposite towards the apex, orbicular and five- to seven-lobed. The flowers, from five rarely, and more normally seven, to as many as sixteen per peduncle with five white petals, though occasionally these are pink or dark red; flower c. 2cm (⅝in) across. It is found along slopes of hills and mountains in

grassland and savannah woodland extending up to the edges of montane forest, at 700–2800m (2200–9200ft). Elgon, Kitale, Rift Valley, Nanyuki, Machakos, Nairobi and Kajiado (Kenya); Maasai, Tanga, Tabora (Tanzania); northern and western regions of Uganda; also Sudan, Ethiopia, Eritrea, Mozambique.

P. whytei **Plate 559**

A down-covered to almost hairless herb which lies along the ground except for the upturned tip of the stem (and occasionally with groups of stems rising at the same level). Its leaves are rounded, variously dissected and opposite. There are two to five flowers per peduncle, usually with four petals which are pink with red veins and seven antheriferous filaments; flower *c.* 12mm (½in) across. Although previously only recorded with four petals, this photograph, taken at 2100m (6900ft) on the Gilgil West Road (Kenya), clearly shows five petals. In certain areas, the flower may be variable in this respect. Found in Kenya in drier parts of montane forest belt, in grassland regions and ericaceous habitats at 1200–3500m (3800–11,500ft). Western Usambara, Rungwe, Njombe (Tanzania); Mbale – Elgon, Karamoja (Uganda); also from Ethiopia to Malawi, Zaire, Zambia.

24. Oxalidaceae

A smallish family of herbs, and in rare cases shrubs or trees, which is well represented in South Africa and South America. Leaves are alternate and usually trifoliate; flowers regular with five free sepals and petals, usually ten stamens and with a superior ovary and a capsule fruit. There are twenty-one species in East Africa belonging to two genera.

Oxalis corniculata **Plate 269**

An annual or perennial, much-branched herb with stems creeping but sometimes ascending and frequently rooting at the nodes. The flowers are yellow in one- to six-flowered pseudo-umbels, or solitary, 7mm (¼in) across. It is a common weed in cultivated or disturbed ground, lawns and roadsides and is sometimes found in sub-alpine grassland. It is very variable both in mode of growth, size and the pubescence of its parts, and there are forms with purple or purple variegated leaves. Widespread in its altitude range from 10–2950m (30–9700ft), especially in western and central Kenya; all regions of Tanzania except Mpwapwa, Kondoa; all regions of Uganda; also in Zanzibar, widespread in tropical Africa.

Two varieties also occur in East Africa:

a) *O. corniculata* var. *corniculata*, with creeping or ascending stems and leaflets up to 15mm (⅗in) long and 20mm (⅘in) wide, usually thinly punctulate only underneath; capsule over 5mm (⅕in) long. Found in similar areas to *O. corniculata*, flowers yellow in colour, 5mm (⅕in) across.

1b) *O. corniculata* var. *repens*, with creeping or prostrate stems rooting at almost every node; leaflets very small, up to 4mm (⅙in) long and 5mm (⅕in) wide, thickly punctulate on both sides, capsules globose, very short and rarely longer than 3–4mm (⅙in). Flower yellow, 5mm (⅕in) across. Found in forest glades and moorlands; altitude range 2400–4100m (7900–13,450ft).

O. latifolia   Plate 649
The common oxalis, grows from small bulbils or runners and is a common and pestilential weed in all gardens in East Africa but it is not indigenous: it was introduced from America. The leaves and peduncle arise directly from a small oval bulbil or from runners. The flowers are in five- to over twenty-flowered pseudo-umbels and a light pink-purple in colour with a green throat. The leaves are trifoliolate in form. Altitude range 1–2520m (3–8250ft). Widespread in eastern Africa from Ethiopia to Mozambique and Zimbabwe.

O. radicosa   A perennial herb with usually thin stems arising from a thick tuberous mainstock, 5mm ($\frac{1}{4}$in) across. Stems erect or ascending, not rooting at the nodes, somewhat angular, loosely pubescent with spreading hairs, more densely so at the nodes and young parts. Leaves alternate or rarely fasciculate; leaflets very variable in size, usually softly hairy on both sides; ciliate at margins. Sepals linear-lanceolate up to 5mm ($\frac{1}{4}$in) long, often tinged with purple. Petals usually appearing pinkish in bud, sometimes with reddish markings on the throat and greenish at base, 10mm ($\frac{2}{3}$in) long. Found in forest clearings, grassland, rocky slopes; a weed in cultivated land and on roadsides. Altitude range 300–2400m (1000–7900ft). Elgon, Kitale, Cheranganis and Nairobi (Kenya); all regions of Tanzania except Songea; all regions of Uganda; also in Somalia south to Zambia, Malawi, Mozambique.

O. obliquifolia   Plate 726
A bulbous plant with a vertical rhizome and the leaves trifoliolate in form. The single pink or purple flowers on short erect stalks sometimes have a yellowish base, 10–23mm ($\frac{3}{8}$–$\frac{7}{8}$in) long. Found in shallow soils at 600–3170m (2000–10,400ft), it occasionally appears as a weed in cultivation and at roadsides. Mau, Tinderet, Kitui, Kisii, Baringo and Nairobi districts (Kenya); Mbulu, Kahama, Mbeya (Tanzania); Acholi, Karamoja (Uganda); also Sudan, Ethiopia, Zaire, Zambia, Malawi, Zimbabwe, Mozambique.

25. Balsaminaceae

A family found in all tropical and subtropical regions, composed almost wholly of *Impatiens*, of which the best known are the 'Busy Lizzies'. There are seventy species in East Africa, all of the same genus. More information from *Impatiens of Africa* by C. Grey-Wilson.

Impatiens burtonii   Plate 41
A prostrate, decumbent, or more or less erect perennial up to 2m (6$\frac{1}{2}$ft) tall, though often less; stems rooting at the lower nodes, glabrous or pubescent above, or glabrescent. Leaves spirally arranged; lamina ovate to ovate-oblong or elliptic-lanceolate, the base rounded to subtruncate or cuneate; the apex usually shortly acuminate, more rarely subobtuse; finely pubescent above and beneath, or glabrous beneath. Lateral veins three to ten pairs, margin more or less crenulate. Flowers in axillary fascicles of one to three, epedunculate, white or pale pink; lateral united petals 13–33mm ($\frac{1}{2}$–1$\frac{1}{3}$in) long, dorsal petal c. 8mm ($\frac{1}{3}$in). This is one of the most widely spread *Impatiens*, ranging from the Camerouns to East Africa, and is closely allied to *I. polyantha*, *I. quisqualis*, *I. shirensis* and *I. leedalii*, but it is

distinguished from these by its more finely veined leaves, the narrow lateral sepals, in the rather different shape of the lower sepal and spur, and the fact that both the lower sepal and spur are nearly always finely pubescent. There also appear to be a number of synonyms – *I. eminii*, *I. meyeri-johannis*, *I. kerkhoveana*, *I. brevicalcarata*, *I. stuhlmannii* etc. There are also a number of varieties. Altitude range 800–3350m (2600–11,800ft). Found in moist, often densely shaded places, upland rain forest, and forest margins, scrub bamboo thickets, in ravines, wet ditches, along riversides and on the edges of swampy areas. Flowers throughout the year. Found mainly in western and south-western Kenya; western Tanzania; widespread in Uganda; recorded throughout the Camerouns.

I. fischeri   Plate 496

A tuberous rooted perennial up to 1.25m (*c.* 4ft) tall, glabrous, stems thin and sappy, rather poorly branched, leaves spirally arranged, ovate to oblong or broadly elliptic, the apex acute or acuminate, the base rounded or shortly cuneate, margin crenate-dentate, or crenulate, lateral veins eight to twelve pairs. The inflorescence is a two- to five- (sometimes six-) flowered raceme. Flowers dark red or scarlet; lateral united petals 17–18mm ($\frac{3}{4}$in) long; upper petals 6–7×3–4mm ($\frac{1}{4}×\frac{1}{8}$in) oblong to oblong-ovate; lower petal 11–14×8–10mm (*c.* $\frac{1}{2}×\frac{1}{3}$in), broadly and rather obliquely oblong or oblong-elliptic. A common plant of wet highland forest; altitude range 2050–3100m (6700–10,500ft). Found in moist shaded places in rain forest often in dense shrubby or swampy areas, along river margins or in bamboo thickets. Flowers through most of the year, but seldom profusely flowering. Aberdares and Mt Kenya (Kenya); not known elsewhere.

NB The lower sepal gradually tapers into a 29–40mm ($1\frac{1}{6}$–$1\frac{3}{8}$in) long incurved spur, slightly swollen at the tip.

I. hochstetteri   Plate 727

An erect to procumbent annual or perennial, stems 20–50cm (occasionally to 70cm) ($7\frac{3}{4}$–20in) long, often rooting at the lower nodes, glabrous. Leaves spirally arranged, generally with a slender petiole, ovate to ovate-lanceolate, elliptic or elliptic-oblanceolate, often membraneous, the apex sub-acute, acuminate or cuspidate, the tip 4×2.5mm ($\frac{1}{6}×\frac{1}{10}$in), the base cuneate, sparsely pubescent or glabrous, above and below, lateral veins four to nine pairs, margin crenate or crenate-dentate. Flowers axillary, solitary or in fascicles of two to three (sometimes four), also sometimes on a reduced peduncle; whitish, pale mauve or pale pink, often with a small white or pale yellow dot towards the base of the lateral united petals. The lower sepal shallowly navicular, abruptly constricted into a 16–34mm ($\frac{2}{3}$–$1\frac{3}{8}$in)-long, curved filliform spur, often slightly thickened at the tip. This species is extremely variable as regards the size of the various parts. Variation in leaf-shape and size is very prominent and much of this can be attributed to habitat conditions, those growing in damper shadier places having longer, thinner textured leaves. The species is the most widely distributed of all the African *Impatiens*, having been recorded from the Red Sea Hills to the southern Drakensberg mountains in South Africa. It is easily recognized by its rather small flowers, in which the upper petal of the lateral united pairs are much reduced and sometimes almost obsolete; lateral united petals 8–19mm ($\frac{1}{3}$–$\frac{3}{4}$in) long; dorsal petal 6–7×6–7mm ($\frac{1}{4}×\frac{1}{4}$in) when flattened (shallowly cilliate); lower sepal 5–8mm ($\frac{1}{5}$–$\frac{1}{3}$in) long. The lower petal of the lateral united pair has a distinct ligulate appendage. Altitude range 100–2800m (328–9200ft). Found in moist, usually shaded places, in lowland or upland forest, forest fringes, tracksides, river beds and rocks, riverine forest belts, irrigation channels and occasionally around cultivated fields, rarely in rock crevices, sometimes forming large colonies. Flowers throughout the year, widespread as above.

There are four recognized subspecies:

a) *I. hochstetteri* ssp. *jacquesii*: leaf lamina narrowly elliptic at least six times as long as broad. Eastern Zaire.

b) *I. hochstetteri* ssp. *hochstetteri*: leaf lamina not more than four times as long as broad. Distribution as above. See Plate 728.

c) *I. hochstetteri* ssp. *angolensis*: flowers pale pink or mauve, upper petals of lateral united pair 5×2.5mm ($\frac{1}{5}$×$\frac{1}{10}$in) entire or emarginate. Angola only. united pair 5×2.5mm ($\frac{1}{5}$×$\frac{1}{10}$in) entire or emarginate. Angola only.

d) *I. hochstetteri* ssp. *fanshawei*: flowers mauve-purple, upper petal of lateral united pair 2×2.5mm ($\frac{1}{12}$×$\frac{1}{10}$in) entire. North-western Zambia.

I. hoehnelii   Plate 650

A rather weak, straggling perennial up to 30cm (12in) tall, stems weakly branched, more or less procumbent, rooting at the lower nodes, the upper half usually upright, glabrous or sparsely pilose on the youngest parts. Leaves spirally arranged, rarely subopposite. Flowers solitary, pale pink or mauve. The upper and lower petals with a narrow sinus between them, rarely overlapping; the upper petal transversely semi-elliptic, the lower petal transversely oblong but somewhat drawn out towards the tip. Dorsal petal 8–11 to 12–16mm ($\frac{1}{3}$–$\frac{1}{2}$ to $\frac{1}{2}$–$\frac{2}{3}$in); lateral united petals 13–28mm ($\frac{1}{2}$–1$\frac{1}{8}$in) long; lower petal 12–24mm ($\frac{1}{2}$–1in) long. Central and southern areas of Kenya, in moist shaded places, upland rain forest, bamboo thickets, along stream margins and in swampy or marshy terrain; so far not recorded elsewhere.

I. nana   Plate 729

Weakly-branched annual, perhaps perennial, herb, generally 30–80cm (12–31in) tall. Stems green or reddish, rooting at the lower nodes, usually rather densely pubescent at the apices but gradually glabrescent with age. Leaves spirally arranged, subopposite or in verticels of three to four (but their lower leaves always spirally arranged) sessile, subsessile or the lower leaves with a petiole 1.2–2.2cm (c. $\frac{1}{2}$–1in) long, lamina ovate to elliptic-lanceolate or narrowly oblanceolate, the base cuneate to somewhat attenuate, apex acute to shortly acuminate, lateral veins five to fourteen pairs, margin serrate to serrate-denticulate. Flowers solitary, axillary or in fascicles of two to three, pink to purplish, the lateral united petals with a dark magenta spot towards the base, the spur whitish. Bracts subulate, inconspicuous, lateral sepals linear-lanceolate, acute or shortly acuminate; lower sepal navicular, abruptly constricted into a curved filiform spur 14–25mm ($\frac{1}{2}$–1in) long; dorsal petal suborbicular, emarginate, dorsally with a narrow crest terminating in a short acute point. Dorsal petal 8–11mm ($\frac{1}{3}$–$\frac{1}{2}$in) long, 12–16mm ($\frac{1}{2}$–$\frac{2}{3}$in) broad; lateral united petals 15–21mm ($\frac{3}{5}$–$\frac{5}{6}$in) long. Ovary usually finely pubescent; fruit narrowly fusiform. Found in moist, usually shaded places in upland rain-forest, along forest fringes, road- and tracksides, river margins, by cultivated ground and in marshy places. Altitude range 450–3000m (1475–9800ft). Taita Hills (Kenya); Arusha, Lushoto, Kilosa and Morogoro districts (Tanzania); not known elsewhere.

I. niamniamensis   Plate 439

A hairless, woody herb which, if supported, can reach over 2m (6$\frac{1}{2}$ft) in height. Its leaves are ovate-lanceolate and its flowers are red or red and yellow, c. 14mm ($\frac{2}{3}$in) long, with small petals and a big spur. A rare plant, it is found in wet forests at 700–2250m (2300–7500ft). Western Kenya; Bukoba (Tanzania); south-western Uganda; also in Rwanda, Burundi, Zaire, southern Sudan.

I. meruensis ssp. **cruciata** **Plate 651**
A decumbent to erect perennial growing to *c.* 1m ($3\frac{1}{4}$ft) tall, sometimes scrambling over supporting vegetation. The stems are simple to moderately branched, usually densely covered with short soft hairs when young but becoming hairless when old. The leaves are long, slender, generally hairless and spirally arranged; the flowers are pale to deep pink in colour, sometimes slightly mauvish, *c.* 25mm (1in) across (sometimes much reduced in size during drought). The upper petal of each lateral united pair with a slight purplish blotch towards the base. Altitude range 1100–3630m (3600–12,000ft). Common in central and southern Kenya in shaded places in forests or along pathways and the banks of rivers and streams; Tanzania, not known; Elgon, Mt Kadam (Uganda); not known elsewhere.

I. pseudoviola An annual or short-lived perennial growing up to 30–40cm (11–16in) tall. Stems normally erect, simply or moderately branched and hairless, sometimes covered with fine hairs though becoming hairless below. Leaves are spirally arranged or occasionally subopposite, and ovate to ovate-rhomboid or ovate-elliptic, acute or shortly acuminate and the base shortly cuneate; hairless or covered with fine hairs above and below. The flower is single, *c.* 2cm ($\frac{4}{5}$in) across, though occasionally two or three together appear, violet pink or purplish in colour with a violet or yellow spot towards the base of the united lateral petals. It is found in damp shady places, upland rain-forest amongst small herbs and mosses, sometimes on decaying tree trunks or stumps and the sides of streams and dry waterfalls. Altitude range 1550–3200m (5100–10,500ft). Widespread in central and southern Kenya, sometimes forming large colonies; Mts Meru and Kilimanjaro (Tanzania); not known elsewhere.

I. sodenii **Plate 730**
An erect, hairless herb 1–3m (3–10ft) tall, branched or unbranched from the base only with ten to fifteen elliptic to oblanceolate leaves in each whorl. Its nearly equal petals form a flat white, pink or slightly red, almost rounded outline. Flower *c.* 35mm ($1\frac{2}{5}$in) across. It is locally common in escarpment zones, near waterfalls and streams and in misty situations at 1000–2700m (3250–8800ft). Much transplanted into gardens, it can now be seen in many parts of Kenya; northern and eastern regions of Tanzania; Uganda and elsewhere, no record.

I. tinctoria An upright glabrous perennial to 2m ($6\frac{1}{2}$ft) tall with a large, swollen, tuberous rootstock at or just below the soil surface. Leaves spirally arranged, petiolate or subsessile, the petiole rather slender with a few short-stipitate or almost sessile glands in the upper half. Inflorescence, a flowered raceme rarely subumbellate. Flowers white, the lower lateral petals often veined or spotted pink or purple towards the base. Lateral united petals 20–55mm ($\frac{4}{5}$–$2\frac{1}{5}$in) long; upper petal 6.15×2.5mm ($\frac{1}{4}$–$\frac{3}{5}$×$\frac{1}{10}$in); lower petal 18–50×16–46mm ($\frac{3}{4}$–2in×$\frac{2}{3}$–$1\frac{3}{4}$in). Altitude range 1500–3630m (5000–12,000ft). Found in damp, generally shaded places, upland rain-forest, forest fringes, shrub-filled gullies, stream margins and shady banks, throughout East Africa; also central and north-east Africa (e.g. Red Sea Hills).

NB *I. tinctoria* is a variable species with four recognizable subspecies in East Africa which are often related to particular areas; the most important is:

I. tinctoria ssp. **elegantissima** **Plate 731**
Altitude range 1800–3630m (5900–12,100ft). Throughout western Kenya from Elgon to Kisii and in the Aberdares, but forms in the east, i.e. around the Aberdares,

have shorter spurs; Tanzania, not known; northern region, Elgon (Uganda); not known elsewhere.

26. Lythraceae

Herbs, subshrubs, shrubs or trees with opposite, rarely whorled or alternate leaves, mostly stipulate; inflorescence a cyme, very rarely a panicle or flowers solitary; flowers mostly regular, bisexual, four to eight to numerous; sepals connate into a tube, valvate, petals free, inserted towards the top of the calyx-tube, and alternating with calyx-lobes, crumpled in bud, sometimes absent; stamens four to eight inserted in the calyx-tube below the petals; ovary superior two- to six-celled, rarely single-celled, with numerous axile ovules in each loculus; fruit a capsule, with lidded, valvular or irregular dehiscence. Seeds small. Thirty-nine species in seven genera in East Africa.

Lythrum rotundifolium   Plate 565
Subprostrate herb rooting at the nodes; leaves oblong-elliptic, obovate or suborbicular, 5–20mm ($\frac{1}{5}$–$\frac{4}{5}$in) long, 4–11mm ($\frac{1}{6}$–$\frac{1}{2}$in) wide. Flowers shortly stalked in the leaf axils; calyx tube about 4mm ($\frac{1}{6}$in) long; four petals, elliptic, mauve, 6–8mm ($\frac{1}{4}$–$\frac{1}{3}$in) long; eight stamens. Found in wet places, chiefly on volcanic soils, between 1700 and 3050m (5700–10,200ft). Western and central Kenya; Ngorongoro, Usambara, Mbeya, Runjwe, Njombe areas (Tanzania); northern and south-western Uganda; also Sudan (Imatong Mts), Ethiopia, eastern Zaire, Rwanda.

Lawsonia inermis   Plate 185
An erect, many-stemmed shrub up to 3$\frac{1}{2}$m (12ft) in height, sometimes spiny. Leaves opposite, glabrous, elliptic or obovate up to 3.75cm (1$\frac{1}{2}$in) long, apex acute often apiculate, base cuneate, midrib depressed on upper surface, petiole short. A dye (henna) is obtained by crushing the leaves and adding lemon juice to the strained liquid. The white flowers are sweet-scented, c. 4mm ($\frac{1}{6}$in) across, and borne in long panicles. Calyx with short top or saucer-shaped tube, four ovate, acute and mucronate lobes and a ring on top of the tube on which the usually four stamens alternating with the petals are fixed. Fruit a capsule 5mm ($\frac{1}{5}$in) in diameter. Altitude range 1–1000m (c. 3–3300ft). Coast Province, riparian in the northern and north-eastern districts (Kenya); Tanga, eastern region, Songea (Tanzania); northern region of Uganda; also Senegal to Somalia and south to Mozambique.

27. Onagraceae

Herbs, rarely shrubs or trees, with alternate or opposite or rarely whorled, stipulate or exstipulate, simple leaves; flowers solitary and axillary or sometimes aggregated into panicles or racemes, usually bisexual, regular (rarely irregular); sepals valvate, two to seven, mostly four; petals free as many as sepal number, very rarely fewer, in one to two rows; ovary inferior, mostly four-celled. Style simple, fruit a capsule, rarely a nut or berry. There are twelve species in two genera in East Africa.

Epilobium stereophyllum   Plate 652
A stoloniferous herb usually less than 1m (3ft) high, usually pubescent and with
sessile ovate to ovate-lanceolate, sometimes lanceolate or oblong leaves, obtuse
or subacute at apex. Flowers pink or mauve; petals obovate, 8–15mm ($\frac{1}{3}$–$\frac{3}{5}$in) long;
sepals 5–10mm ($\frac{1}{5}$–$\frac{2}{5}$in) long. A fairly common plant of swampy places, in upland
moors, grasslands and on moist ground along streams and rivers. It is variable (in
the length of the indumentum) and there are a number of synonyms, and two
varieties: E. stereophyllum var. stereophyllum and E. stereophyllum var. kiwuense.
Altitude range 2700–3660m (7850–11,900ft). Elgon, Cheranganis, Limuru, Aberdares and Kitale (Kenya); Kilimanjaro (Kibo), Pare Mountains (Tanzania); Kigezi
district, Elgon (Uganda); also in Ethiopia, Zaire, Rwanda and Burundi.
    NB Var. kiwuense has been recorded down to 1750m (5700ft) and has a lower
high-altitude limit – 2740m (c. 8000ft). This plant is a relative of the English Willow
Herb.

28. Thymelaeaceae

A small family, commonest in Africa, of perennial herbs with woody rootstock,
shrublets, shrubs or small trees, usually with a tough fibrous bark. The flowers are
regular, the lower part of the calyx remaining around the ovary in fruit (so that the
fruit appears to be inferior), the upper part being tubular and petaloid. Small real
petals appear at the mouth of the calyx tube or are absent. Fruit has one seed, an
achene or drupe. There are thirty-one species in East Africa belonging to seven
genera.

Gnidia involucrata   Plate 270
A perennial herb or undershrub, unbranched to much branched, up to 1m (3ft) or
more with a woody rhizome. Stems and branches, glabrous, green to reddish,
sometimes brownish. Leaves sessile, or shortly petioled, linear to elliptic, obtuse to
acute, glaucous but sometimes glabrous. Inflorescence a terminal or axillary flower
head. Flowers orange-red or pinkish to red, four-merous (rarely five-). The pedicel
has a brush of silky hairs; calyx tube densely pubescent above the articulation.
Petals obovate to spathulate and fleshy, 1–1.5mm (under $\frac{1}{12}$in) long, 0.3–1.2mm
(under $\frac{1}{12}$in) wide; calyx tube 8–12mm ($\frac{1}{3}$–$\frac{1}{2}$in) long, lobes 2–3mm ($\frac{1}{12}$–$\frac{1}{8}$in) long,
0.5–2mm (c. $\frac{1}{12}$in) broad. Found in open and wooded grassland, often in areas
where burning takes place, also in deciduous bushland and woodland; altitude
range 1000–2700m (3000–8850ft). West Suk, Machakos, Kajiado, Chyulu Hills,
Taita Hills, Northern Frontier areas (Kenya); all regions of Tanzania; northern
region of Uganda; also Ethiopia, Sudan, Zaire south to Zimbabwe, Mozambique.
    NB A very variable species, especially in the degree of branching, which appears
to be related to seasonal variations and the degree of burning.

G. subcordata (Englerodaphne subcordata)   Plate 42
A much-branched shrub up to 3.5m (11$\frac{1}{2}$ft) high. Branches slender, glabrous; bark
dull or purplish grey. Leaves opposite; leaf blade ovate or suborbicular, apex acute,
rounded or truncate, base rounded or truncate, sometimes subcordate, 10–25mm
($\frac{2}{5}$–1in), sometimes to 35mm (1$\frac{2}{5}$in), long, membraneous green above, glaucous-
green beneath, glabrous or with occasional hairs along midrib beneath. Inflorescence a terminal four- to six-flowered bracteate fascicle. Flowers greenish-white,

white or cream, four-merous, shortly pedicelled. Eight petals, somewhat fleshy lobes, linear-spathulate, emarginate or toothed. Calyx tube 9–12mm ($\frac{1}{3}$–$\frac{1}{2}$in) long; petal lobe c. 3mm ($\frac{1}{8}$in) long. Found in upland dry evergreen forest and associated bushland, *Acacia* woodland and wooded grassland; altitude range 1400–2400m (4600–7875ft). Recorded in all regions except Northern Frontier (Kenya); Maasai, Tanga, Mpwapwa, Kondoa (Tanzania); northern region (Uganda); also in Sudan.

29. Nyctaginaceae

Herbs, shrubs or climbers, and, rarely, trees with alternate or opposite simple leaves without stipules. Inflorescences are usually cymose, with bracts; there are usually five fused and petaloid sepals forming a sheath around the ovary in fruit; petals are rounded, stamens may be single or many, with the filaments often fused into a cup at the base. The ovary is single-celled with a style and capitate stigma and with one erect ovule. The fruit remains closed when ripe, the seed having some endosperm and a straight or curved embryo. Ten species in three genera in East Africa.

Commicarpus grandiflorus An erect or prostrate, densely glandular, pubescent perennial herb to 40cm (15in) tall (the entire plant with sticky glandular hairs, and raised glands in several whorls on fruiting calyx). Leaves ovate to suborbicular and flowers purple, 6mm ($\frac{1}{4}$in) across, in whorls: five sepals, tubular at base, spreading into the purple limb above. This is a sharply defined species, extremely sticky all over, and found in drier bushland; altitude range 850–1750m (2800–5750ft). Baringo, Machakos and Kajiado (Kenya); lake areas, Maasai, Shinyanga, Tanga, Mpwapwa, Kondoa (Tanzania); all regions except eastern Uganda; also in Sudan, Ethiopia and Somalia.

NB In *Upland Kenya Wild Flowers (UKWF)*, this species is called *C. boissieri*, which does not occur in East Africa.

C. helenae *(C. stellatus)*   **Plate 826**
A perennial, pubescent (sometimes glandular), trailing herb with ovate leaves and white flowers (occasionally pale pink), 2–3mm ($\frac{1}{12}$–$\frac{1}{8}$in) across. A common plant found in dry bush country; altitude range 1800m (6000ft) and below. Especially in eastern districts – Magadi, Machakos, Kajiado, but also in Baringo (Kenya); lake areas, Maasai, Shinyanga, Tanga, Morogoro (Tanzania); northern and western regions (Uganda); also Sudan, Ethiopia, Somalia, Botswana.

C. pedunculosus   **Plates 653 & 654**
A trailing plant or herb, sometimes with scrambling branches up to 50cm (20in) in length, with purple-magenta flowers; inflorescence c. 25mm (1in) across, each flower c. 5mm ($\frac{1}{8}$in) across. It is common in thickets and riverine areas in dry territories up to 2100m (6900ft). Eastern districts, Narok, Rift Valley, Nanyuki, Embu, Machakos, Nairobi and Kajiado (Kenya); lake areas, Maasai, Shinyanga, Mpwapwa, Kondoa (Tanzania); northern and western regions (Uganda); also Sudan, Ethiopia, Rwanda.

C. plumbagineus Plate 43
A shortly pubescent trailing herb, sometimes scrambling or with ascending branches up to 30cm (1ft) long with ovate to suborbicular leaves and white or cream flowers and stalked glands on the fruit. Inflorescence 25mm (1in) across; each flower 5mm (⅕in) across. It is similar to *C. pedunculosus*, but the latter has magenta flowers, and is often found in wetter areas. *C. plumbagineus* favours drier areas and appears to be more common in the Rift Valley. Found in thickets and riverine areas up to 2100m (6900ft). Western districts, Kisii, Baringo, Rift Valley, Embu, Machakos and Kajiado (Kenya) – it appears to favour central to western Kenya, while *P. pedunculatus* is more common from central to eastern Kenya; all regions except southern – Songea (Tanzania); all regions of Uganda; also Somalia, Ethiopia, Zaire south to Zimbabwe, Mozambique.

30. Proteaceae

A medium-sized family of evergreen trees, shrubs or plants with a woody rootstock which produces herbaceous branches every year, found mainly in southern Africa and Australia. They are hard-leaved, have a perianth of four valvate segments, often united at the base, four stamens, a superior ovary and are usually uniovulate. Members of this family prefer altitudes above 2250m (7500ft) and acid, often rocky soils. The national emblem of South Africa is a *Protea*; and one species, *Grevillea robusta*, the Silver Oak, is much planted in the Nairobi area, often as a windbreak in coffee plantations. Eighteen species in two genera in East Africa.

Protea kilimandscharica Plate 440
A relative of the better-known South African *Proteas*. It grows up to 4½m (15ft) in height, at altitudes of 2700–3650m (9000–12,000ft) in mountain savannah. The whitish-looking leaves and branches are hairless and smooth; and the head of white flowers, up to 5cm (2in) across. Northern Frontier areas including Turkana and West Suk, Rift Valley and Central Province (Kenya); Maasai, Shinyanga, Mbeya, Iringa (Tanzania); northern region of Uganda.
NB This species is sometimes recorded as *P. caffra* ssp. *kilimandscharica*.

P. gaguedi (*P. abyssinica*) Plate 186
A shrub or tree up to 5m (15ft) high, branchlets pilose when young. Leaves lanceolate to narrowly-oblong-lanceolate, 10–15cm (4–10in) long and about 2cm (¾in) broad, apex obtuse, base slightly tapered. Flower heads up to 10cm (4in) diameter; perianth white, 2cm (⅘in) long, densely hairy; stamens and styles pinkish; bracts 3.75cm (1½in) long. Widespread and often in colonies on stony, infertile soil; altitude range 2150–3350m (7000–11,000ft). Northern Frontier areas including Turkana and Suk, Rift Valley, western region and Kajiado (Kenya); all regions of Tanzania except lake areas; all regions of Uganda except Buganda; also Ethiopia to Mozambique, Zimbabwe.
NB This species is more widely spread than *P. kilimandscharica*, whose altitude range is slightly higher and the flower heads much smaller.

31. Dilleniaceae

A widespread Australian and Asian family with only one genus represented –
Tetracera, with five species in East Africa.

Tetracera boiviniana   **Plate 44**
A much-branched shrub up to 6m (20ft) high. Leaves alternate, elliptic to obovate to
10cm (4in) long, margin denticulate or serrate, lamina grey-tomentose beneath,
dark green above with nerves impressed. The sweet-scented flowers are white or
rose, and borne in few-flowered terminal cymes; flower 2.5cm (1in) in diameter.
Five sepals, silky outside, five petals, stamens numerous and carpels free, densely
hairy or glabrous, dark red when ripe. A coastal shrub in thicket and savannah
country; altitude range 50–370m (50–1200ft). Kwale district – Diani and Shimba
Hills (Kenya); Lushoto, Korogwe, Tanga, Uzuramo district, Dar-es-Salaam (Tanzania); also coastal areas in Mozambique.

32. Flacourtiaceae

A medium-sized tropical or subtropical family of trees or shrubs. Their leaves are
usually alternate and stipules often absent. Flowers are regular, stamens often
numerous; ovary superior and unilocular; fruit a hard capsule or berry which
remains closed when ripe. Forty-five species in twenty-one genera in East Africa.

Oncoba routledgei   **Plate 187**
A shrub or small tree up to 8m (26ft) tall with spiny branches and dark green, glossy
leaves which are often wine-red when young. The flowers are fine and waxy, rather
like those of the *Camellia*, c. 6cm (2½in) across. The leaves are elliptic or elliptic-
oblong, with finely serrate margins and an acute apex. The fruit is large, woody and,
when ripe, yellow and of 75mm (3in) diameter. Altitude range 900–2440m
(3000–8100ft). Most upland forests (Kenya); Arusha, Lushoto, Morogoro (Tanzania); Ankole, Kigezi, Mbale – Bugisu (Uganda); also in Ethiopia and Zaire – Lake
Albert.

O. spinosa   Closely related to *O. routledgei* and has similar leaves and fruit, but its
flowers are not so fine and impressive. Found in similar habitat in Kenya at
20–1800m (70–6000ft); Mwanza, Moshi, Singida and Zanzibar (Tanzania); western Nile, Kigezi, Mbale – Bugisu (Uganda); also widespread Senegal to Ethiopia
and south to Mozambique.

33. Passifloraceae
THE PASSION FRUIT FAMILY

Herbaceous or weedy climbers with tendrils and usually palmately-lobed stipulate,
alternate leaves; flowers bisexual, usually in racemes or solitary, usually with a

receptacular tube surrounding the base of the ovary; five sepals, free; five petals, free, or absent often with a corona in one to two series; five stamens, ovary of three carpels; three styles; stigmas capitate; fruit a berry or baccate capsule. Fifty-three species in eight genera in East Africa.

Adenia venenata   A climber or a small shrub, the branches growing from the top of an enormously extended, rounded, tapering woody trunk; leaves orbicular to broadly ovate, in outline shallowly to deeply three- to five-lobed (occasionally seven-); lobes with rounded apex, leaf blades grey to glaucous beneath, base cordate, top obtuse or rounded, three-nerved from near base, margin entire. Inflorescences mostly on short shoots, rarely in the axils of normal leaves; petals 3–6mm ($\frac{1}{8}$–$\frac{1}{4}$in). Flowers yellow, male larger than female, petals oblong-lanceolate, slightly obtuse, three- to five-nerved in male, one- to three-nerved in female. Found in wooded grassland, deciduous woodland and bushland; altitude range 0–1500m (0–4900ft). Northern districts, Baringo, Lake Bogoria, Lamu and Tsavo (Kenya); Bukoba, Mwanza, Shinyanga (Tanzania); West Nile, Bunyoro, Teso (Uganda); also Sudan, Ethiopia, Somalia.

Passiflora subpeltata (*P. edulis*)   **Plate 45**
A climber up to 15m (50ft) in height or length, perennial, glabrous, stems sometimes more or less angular. Leaf blades three-lobed up to three-fourths, rarely unlobed, suborbicular to broadly ovate in outline, base acute to cordate, three-nerved from base, suborbicular, lobes elliptic to oblong, top acute, shortly acuminate, margins serrate. Inflorescence single-flowered. Flowers white, corona threads purplish towards base, 4–7cm (1$\frac{3}{8}$–2$\frac{3}{4}$in). Bracts and bracteoles ovate, acute forming an involucre. Fruit yellow or purplish. Found as an escape from gardens or cultivation in forest edges and disturbed ground; altitude range 0–2500m (0–8200ft). Nairobi, Machakos, Mau, Kericho and Limuru – Kieni forest (Kenya); Maasai, Tanga, Morogoro, Mbeya, Iringa (Tanzania); Buganda (Uganda); elsewhere, widely cultivated. This climber is not an indigenous wild plant, probably originating in Brazil, and is much cultivated for its fruit, but escapes are found in the wild and it is included here for clarification. In *UKWF* it is named as *P. eichlerana*.

34. Cucurbitaceae
THE CUCUMBER FAMILY

A medium-sized family, which includes the gourds, cucumbers, marrows and melons, found throughout the tropics and subtropics but rare in temperate countries. These are prostrate or climbing herbs with tendrils, in rare cases they are rather woody. Their flowers are white, yellow or greenish and unisexual, the sexes often being borne on separate plants. The floral receptacle forms a cup or tube to the rim of which the five free sepals and five free or connate petals are attached. There are five basic stamens but they are often closely joined in pairs with the fifth free, giving the appearance of only three. The ovary is inferior and the fruit usually a berry but sometimes hard-shelled or, rarely, dry. There are eighty-three species in Kenya covering twenty-three genera.

Cephalopentandra ecirrhosa   **Plate 497**
A perennial glabrous climber from a hemispherical or elongate fleshy tuber projecting above the soil surface; sessile leaves of two types, one deeply pinnatifid with

acute lobes, the other shallowly lobed, the lobes rounded and all leaves more or less elliptic in outline. Flowers yellow or cream; male corolla lobe 12–28mm ($\frac{1}{2}$–1$\frac{1}{10}$in) long, 8–13mm ($\frac{1}{3}$–$\frac{1}{2}$in) broad; female corolla lobe 26mm (1in) long, 12mm ($\frac{1}{2}$in) broad. Found in dry semi-desert bushland, on sandy soil; altitude range 45–1090m (150–3600ft). Only in Northern Frontier districts, Meru and on the Bura–Ilara road at Km 23 (Kenya); Tanzania, no record; Karamoja (Uganda); also in Ethiopia, Somalia. Illustration shows the fruit.

Citrullus colocynthis   Plate 3
A perennial trailing herb with somewhat woody tuberous rootstock; stems angled, shortly hairy when young becoming scabrid. Leaf elongate-ovate, distinctly scabrid-hairy underneath, smooth above except on the nerves, palmately-deeply three- to five-lobed. Flower petals greenish-yellow, 8–9mm ($\frac{1}{3}$in) long, 4–6mm ($\frac{1}{6}$–$\frac{1}{4}$in) broad. The fruit on a stalk up to 55mm (2$\frac{1}{4}$in) long, smooth, green longitudinally striped or mottled with yellow or rather uniform yellow when ripe, 50–120mm (2–5in) in diameter or more. Found in semi-desert, bushland and grassland; altitude range 600–770m (1800–2300ft). Northern Frontier areas, such as Lake Turkana, Lysamis and Marsabit (Kenya); Tanzania and Uganda, no record; elsewhere, no record from Ethiopia south to Mozambique, but known in tropical and subtropical North Africa.

NB The wild ancestor of the Water Melon, *Citrullus lanatus*, also occurs in East Africa.

Coccinia adoensis   Plate 271
A climber or trailer up to 3m (10ft) tall or long; rootstock, perennial and woody, as well as root tubers; strigose-pubescent on all parts. Stems annual, leaves ovate in outline, divided into seven oblong or even linear lobes. Two to twenty-two male flowers in solitary or unbranched racemes, on long peduncles, co-axillary with a long pedicillate solitary flower. Corolla golden-orange to apricot-orange or salmon-coloured (rarely tinged purplish, with brown veins outside); corolla (male) 13–30mm ($\frac{1}{2}$–1$\frac{1}{5}$in) long, 7–14mm ($\frac{1}{4}$–$\frac{1}{2}$in) broad; (female) 12–18mm ($\frac{1}{2}$–$\frac{2}{3}$in) long, 7–10mm ($\frac{1}{4}$–$\frac{2}{5}$in) broad. Female flowers solitary. Found mainly in highland *Acacia* grassland; altitude range 500–2140m (1650–7000ft). Common in north-west Kenya, rare near Nairobi, Elgon, Cheranganis, Tinderet, Mau, Aberdares, Kitale, western districts, Machakos and Kajiado (Kenya); all regions of Tanzania except Tanga; all regions of Uganda; also Ethiopia south to Zimbabwe and Mozambique.

C. grandis   Plate 4
A perennial climber or trailer up to 20m (65ft); rootstock tuberous; young stems green, herbaceous, angled, glabrous except at nodes, becoming white-dotted when older; perennial eventually, woody and subterete with thin, greyish or brownish, papery bark. Leaf blade broadly ovate to subpentagonal or orbicular in outline, more or less cordate at base, entire or sinuate and often with distinct reddish glandular teeth, glabrous, punctate, 34–115mm (1$\frac{1}{3}$–4$\frac{2}{3}$in) long, shallowly to deeply-palmately three- to five-lobed. Lobes variable, shallowly triangular, broadest at the base, ovate to rhombic in outline; corolla lobe (female) 21–32mm ($\frac{4}{5}$–1$\frac{1}{4}$in) long, 7–13mm ($\frac{1}{4}$–$\frac{1}{2}$in) wide; (male) 14–20mm ($\frac{1}{2}$–$\frac{4}{5}$in) long, 10–16mm ($\frac{2}{5}$–$\frac{3}{5}$in) wide. Tendrils simple. Male flowers solitary or paired (rarely three to four), receptacle tube expanded above, slightly glandular-hairy internally, lobes triangular to lanceolate or lanceolate-spathulate, often red-tipped. Corolla campanulate, pale yellow or pale apricot-orange, green-veined, lobes united in lower half, sometimes red-tipped. Female flowers solitary on 4–25mm ($\frac{1}{6}$–1in) long stalks, receptacle tube cylindrical, lobes filiform, lanceolate or triangular, also often red-tipped. Fruit

fleshy, red when ripe except in small green area around stalk. Found in deciduous bushland, woodland and wooded grassland, dry evergreen forest and evergreen woodland; altitude range 1–1680m (3–5500ft). Uncommon. Northern Frontier areas, Turkana, coast, western districts and Central Province (Kenya); Tanga, Pangani, Morogoro, Songea (Tanzania); all regions of Uganda; also in Sudan, Somalia, possibly Ethiopia.

Cucumis sp. **Plate 272**
Trailers or climbers without a swollen rootstalk and often with stiff hairs, tripalmate leaves and simple tendrils. The flowers are yellow and like those of the melon or cucumber, as are the leaves. The photograph shows an unidentified species from near the Chalbi Desert. Fruit *c.* 55mm (2⅕in) long.

C. aculeatus A common species with spiny, yellow, hooked hairs on stem ridges; petal (male) 6–9mm (¼–⅜in) long, petal (female) 8–13mm (⅓–½in) long. Found in grassland or bushland at 1100–2200m (3600–7200ft) over much of eastern and central Kenya; Mbulu, Dodoma, Iringa (Tanzania); Ankole (Uganda); also eastern Zaire, Rwanda and southern Ethiopia.

C. prophetarum **Plate 273**
A yellow-flowered perennial which is hairy but not spiny. Petals (male) 5–6mm (*c.* ¼in) long; petals (female) 5–8mm (*c.* ¼in) long. Common in Kenya in bushland and semi-arid *Commiphora* country at lower altitudes, 0–2020m (0–6750ft). Lake areas, Moshi, Tanga – Lushoto (Tanzania); northern region – Karamoja (Uganda); also eastern Zaire, north-eastern tropical Africa, Arabia.

C. dipsaceus Distinguished by its stiff, almost prickly, spreading hairs and leaves which are hardly lobed at all. Petals (male) 5–10mm (⅕–⅖in) long; petals (female) 6–15mm (¼–⅗in) long. Also common in Kenya in dry bushland at lower altitudes, 420–1800m (1400–6000ft). Moshi, Lushoto, Iringa (Tanzania); Karamoja (Uganda); also Ethiopia, Somalia.

Lagenaria abyssinica Similar to *L. sphaerica* (below), but the petiole glands are small, tubular, and point downwards. Flower white with green nerves, opening in the evening; petals (male) 23–45mm (1–1⅞in) long, 18–35mm (¾–1⅖in) broad, female flowers slightly smaller. Found in bushland riverine forest to subalpine bamboo zones, and wherever there are trees in its altitude range of 1350–2700m (4500–9000ft). Elgon, the Cheranganis, Mau, Aberdares, Nyambeni Hills, Kitale, Nairobi, Narok and Kajiado (Kenya); Maasai, Morogoro, Mbeya, Iringa (Tanzania); western region of Uganda; also Sudan, Ethiopia, eastern Zaire.

L. sphaerica **Plate 46**
A deciduous climbing herb with bifid tendrils similar to *L. abyssinica* but with robust conical glands at junction of petiole with lamina, projecting at right angles to the petiole. Flowers paired, rarely solitary; petals white or creamy white with green veins, clawed with expanded rounded rim. Petals (male) 24–53mm (1–2in) long, 15–35mm (⅗–1⅖in) broad; (female) 22–60mm (9⁄10–2⅖in) long, 12–38mm (½–1½in) broad. Fruit large, 73–100mm (3–4in) round, deep green with pale green or yellowish transverse streaks, dots and patches; shell hard and flesh whitish. Found in riverine and ground-water forest, thicket and old cultivations, in drier districts; altitude range 0–1650m (0–5400ft). Western region, Embu and Machakos (Kenya); all regions of Tanzania except Mbeya and Iringa; all regions of Uganda; also from Somalia to South Africa.

Momordica boivinii **Plate 274**

A climbing or trailing herb up to 2m (6½ft) in length, from a perennial tuberous rootstock; the stems annual, glabrous or pubescent. Leaf-blade ovate, cordate; apiculate or acute, sometimes densely hairy beneath often subglabrous, and somewhat three-lobed with short triangular lateral lobes. One to six flowers, petals orange-yellow or bright orange, the two outer petals with scales at the base; petals (male) 13–15mm (½in) long, 6–9mm (¼–⅓in) broad; (female) 8–10mm (⅓in) long, 5–6mm (⅕–¼in) broad; obtuse. The fruit resembles a long, 23–100mm (1–4in), rather weak, thin, cucumber 4–9mm (⅙–⅓in) broad, very slightly ribbed and either glabrous or densely hairy. Found in deciduous bushland, thickets, woodland and wooded grassland; altitude range 0–1600m (0–5250ft). Northern Frontier and coastal areas, Tana River, Embu (Kenya); lake areas, Maasai, Tabora, Mbeya, Iringa (Tanzania); northern region of Uganda; also southern Ethiopia south to Zimbabwe, Mozambique.

M. calantha A monoecious, pubescent climber with bifid tendrils. Flower pure white or tinged orange-cream, black at the centre. Petal (male) 20–25mm (⅘–1in) long, 5–10mm (⅕–⅖in) broad; female very slightly smaller. Altitude range 600–1800m (2000–6000ft). It is an uncommon plant but found on forest margins near Nairobi and also recorded in Aberdares and on Mt Kenya (Kenya); Maasai, Tanga, Morogoro (Tanzania); Buganda (Uganda); elsewhere, not known.

M. foetida **Plate 47**

A dioecious, pubescent, perennial climber or trailer with a woody rootstock, simple or bifid tendrils and stems spotted with dark green; leaves simple or divided. The large flowers white, cream, yellow, or orange, often with black or orange spots of colour on sepals or petals; male flowers usually subumbellate, rarely solitary, often with a prominent suborbicular sheathing bract; petal 17–35mm (⅔–1⅖in) long, 9–27mm (⅖–1in) broad; female petals similar. When crushed the plant has a nasty foetid smell. This is the common *Momordica* of forest edges, cultivated and disturbed places in wetter regions in all upland areas; altitude range 0–2300m (0–7550ft). Western Kenya to Machakos and Kitale to Kajiado (Kenya); all regions of Tanzania and Uganda; also widespread in tropical Africa and south to Zimbabwe, Mozambique.

M. friesiorum **Plate 417**

A perennial with tuberous rootstock, climbing or trailing up to 4m (13ft) long. Leaves pedately three to five foliolate, middle leaflet the largest, elliptic, ovate-lanceolate, ovate or broadly ovate, obtuse or subtruncate at the base, acuminate, slightly apiculate at apex, subentire and remotely denticulate to distinctly sinuate-toothed, almost glabrous to markedly pubescent, 27–130mm (1–5in) long. Lateral leaflets similar but smaller with blunted apices, sometimes lobed on the outer side at the base. Tendrils bifid, rarely simple. Male flowers five to fifteen subumbellate on a 40–80mm (1½–3⅕in) long peduncle. Receptacle tube cylindrical below, campanulate above, like the lobes, dark brownish-green to purplish or almost black, sometimes green with darker nerves; lobes broadly triangular or triangularly-acuminate; corolla pale yellow or pale orange-yellow with darker throat and a dark purple or black eye. Receptacle tube *c.* 10mm (⅖in) long, lobes 3–12mm (⅛–½in) long, corolla petals 12–15mm (½–⅗in) long. Found in upland rain-forest and upland evergreen heathland, especially on the margins and in clearings; altitude range 1500–2600m (4900–8500ft). Naivasha, Muranga, Ngong Hills (Kenya); Uluguru Mountains, Mbeya, Songea (Tanzania); Mbale (Uganda); also in Ethiopia.

M. pterocarpa   A dioecious pubescent perennial climber with a tuberous rootstock and rather weak, sometimes bifid, tendrils. The receptacle tube of male flowers is short, 7mm ($\frac{1}{4}$in) long. Male flower petals 15–32mm ($\frac{3}{8}$–1$\frac{1}{4}$in) long; female petals *c.* 20mm ($\frac{4}{5}$in) long. Both have the outer two petals with scales at the base. So far only found in the triangle bordered by Kikuyu–Ngong–Thika (Kenya); Tanga, Tabora, Morogoro, Mbeya, Iringa (Tanzania); northern and western regions of Uganda; also Sudan, Ethiopia, Eritrea, eastern Zaire, Malawi, Mozambique.

M. rostrata   A climber up to 7m (23ft) long; rootstock tuberous, visible above ground and tapering upwards into the stems, dark green or brownish with scattered paler lenticels, 15–20cm (6–8in) across. Young stems green, herbaceous, glabrous except for hair tufts at the nodes, soon becoming woody with smooth or slightly rough, grey or brownish bark. Leaves five to twelve foliolate, deciduous; terminal leaflet elliptic, ovate or suborbicular, equal-sided and cuneate, slightly apiculate, sinuate-toothed or dentate, 11–47mm ($\frac{1}{2}$–1$\frac{1}{2}$in) long, 10–28mm ($\frac{2}{5}$–1in) broad; lateral leaflets smaller, rather more rounded and somewhat unequal-based. Tendrils simple. One to fourteen male flowers, subumbulate, subtended by a very small pale green-white pubescent bract. Flowering stems often almost leafless, receptacle tube brownish-green, broadly campanulate, lobes pale green, hairy at the margin; petals recurved in upper third, rich orange-yellow but three with a dark greenish to brownish-purple basal patch, two with incurved scales inside at the base. Male petals 7–13mm ($\frac{1}{4}$–$\frac{1}{2}$in) long, 4–8mm ($\frac{1}{6}$–$\frac{1}{3}$in) broad; female petals *c.* 8mm ($\frac{1}{3}$in) long, *c.* 4mm ($\frac{1}{6}$in) across. Female flowers solitary (rarely paired), ovary 12–14mm ($\frac{1}{2}$in) long with eight slight longitudinal ridges. Found in deciduous bushland, thicket, woodland and wooded grassland; altitude range 15–1650m (50–5400ft). Northern Frontier areas, Kajiado, Magadi, Rift Valley and Machakos (Kenya); lake areas, Maasai, Tanga, Mpwapwa, Kondoa (Tanzania); northern region (Uganda); also in southern Ethiopia.

Peponium vogelii   **Plate 275**
A climber growing locally in rocky places and on forest edges. In the less humid areas its leaves are narrowly acute-lobed, in upland forest areas in zones of higher rainfall the leaf lobes are broad and obtuse with dense hairy stems. The flowers are 4–8cm (1$\frac{1}{2}$–3$\frac{1}{8}$in) across, and have white or pale yellow petals; the fruit is bright red when ripe. It can be a short or a tall climber according to conditions and is found at altitudes 80–2440m (260–8100ft). Most parts of Kenya except very dry conditions; Arusha, Songea and Zanzibar (Tanzania); Kigezi, Busoga, Masaka, Sese Islands (Uganda); also from Ethiopia to Ghana and Zaire to Mozambique, Seychelles, Angola.

35. Begoniaceae

A family almost confined to the moist tropics which consists mainly of one very large genus – *Begonia*. Succulent herbs or soft shrubs, rarely climbers; leaves alternate, simple or compound, stipulate, usually asymmetric. Flowers unisexual, regular, the males with two sepals, nought to five petals and numerous stamens, females without stamens, with an inferior (two-) three (four-)-locular ovary with axile placentation. Three stigmas, often twisted and divided. Fruit a capsule or berry; seeds very numerous, minute. One genus with eighteen species in East Africa.

Begonia meyeri-johannis   **Plate 48**
A dioecious, woody forest climber, glabrous except for the lower leaf veins and petioles, with simple ovate to suborbicular acuminate asymmetric leaves; flowers, in loose axillary cymes, white tinged pink; sepals 15–20mm ($\frac{3}{4}$–$\frac{4}{5}$in) long. A common plant in the wetter and wettest highland forest; altitude range 1550–2400m (5000–8000ft). Mau, Aberdares, Mt Kenya, Nyamberi Hills and Limuru – Kieni forest (Kenya); Kilimanjaro, Usambara, Uluguru and Rungwe Mts (Tanzania); western region – Ruwenzori volcanoes (Uganda); also in eastern Zaire, Rwanda, Burundi.

36. Cactaceae

A medium-sized American family of stem succulents with only one genus in the Old World. Normally they have tufts of spines or bristly hairs and virtually no leaves. Petals and stamens are usually numerous, the ovary inferior and the fruit a berry. In East Africa there is only one native genus, the epiphytic *Rhipsalis*, but there are three or four introduced species of *Opuntia*.

Opuntia vulgaris   **Plate 441**
Commonly known as the Prickly Pear and not truly wild in East Africa, this species was introduced from Central America for use as a hedge plant in ranching country. In other countries it has become a major menace, covering large tracts of land, but in East Africa has generally been kept under control by local conditions. Flowers yellow, 22–30mm ($\frac{7}{8}$–1$\frac{1}{5}$in) across, often tipped with red; the fruit is the shape or size of a large egg, soft, green and covered with unpleasant spiny bristles. Found in open bushy places below 1700m (5700ft) in central and south-eastern Kenya; Pangani, Rufiji, Mafia Island and Zanzibar (Tanzania); Uganda, no record.

37. Ochnaceae

A rather small tropical and subtropical family of trees, shrubs and herbs with simple alternate leaves and rather distinctive stipules. The flowers are usually five in number with free sepals and petals and stamens often numerous. The superior ovary often has more or less free carpels. There are sixteen species in five genera in East Africa.

Ochna holstii   **Plate 276**
A tree up to 24m (80ft) high and 0.3m (1ft) in diameter with a smooth, grey, brittle bark, slashed pink. Leaves lanceolate or oblong-lanceolate, up to 10cm (4in) long and 3cm (1$\frac{3}{5}$in) broad with closely serrulate margins, acute apices and cuneate bases. Six to ten yellow flowers, *c.* 2cm ($\frac{4}{5}$in) across, in short stoutish corymbs at the end of short lateral twigs. Sepals at flowering time up to 1.25cm ($\frac{1}{2}$in) becoming purple-red, rigid and enlarging in the fruit. Altitude range 1400–2300m (4500–7650ft). Widespread in higher *Podocarpus* forests in western Kenya, also Nairobi and Machakos (Kenya); all regions of Tanzania except lake areas; Imatong

Mountains and Mbale – Elgon (Uganda); also recorded in Sudan, Zaire to Mozambique, Zimbabwe.

O. inermis   Plate 498
A shrub, leaves small, broadly elliptic to rotund up to 2.5cm (1in) long, margins minutely serrulate or serrate. Flowers yellow becoming dark red, 10mm (⅜in) across (sweet-scented like primroses), usually solitary at the ends of short twigs. Closely allied to O. ovata. Found in drier woodland bush; altitude range 230–1425m (750–4750ft). Northern Frontier districts, Taita Hills (Kenya); Tanzania, not known; northern region of Uganda; elsewhere, Limpopo Valley.

O. insculpta
A shrub or small tree growing to 9m (30ft) with hairless, papery, oblong-elliptic leaves with their apex acuminate, margins finely-spiny denticulate and base broadly cuneate. Their veining is pinnate with the midrib pronounced beneath. Yellow flowers, 25mm (1in) across, are carried in short, few-flowered racemes which terminate in very short branchlets. This species is found in several forests between 1200–2200m (4000–7200ft). Especially common at Marsabit (Kenya); Maasai, Shinyanga, Tanga (Tanzania); Buganda (Uganda); also southern Ethiopia.

O. mossambicensis   Plate 277
A much-branched shrub up to 3m (10ft) in height. Leaves coriaceous, obovate-oblong to 18cm (7in) long and 7.5cm (3in) broad, apex rounded, margin serrulate, base acute to cuneate, petiole 3mm (⅛in) long. Up to ten flowers, yellow, rather large, in dense terminal and axillary cymose corymbs, as long or larger than the leaves, anthers opening by pores and pedicels jointed near base. Corymb c. 18cm (7in) long or longer, c. 30mm (1⅛in) across. Altitude range 1–700m (3–2300ft). Coastal forest and scrubland (Kenya); Tanga, Morogoro, Songea (Tanzania); Uganda, no record; also in southern Somalia and northern Mozambique.
NB In the genus *Ochna* the petals are always yellow.

O. ovata   Plate 278
A hairless shrub or, less often, a small tree. Leaves are ovate to oblong or lanceolate-elliptic with net-like venation, especially in age, their apex may be obtuse or acute, margins are evenly serrate and tend to be spiny. A few bright yellow-green flowers, c. 12mm (½in) across, are grouped together in racemes on short axillary shoots which are often produced before the leaves have expanded. Common in less arid bushland and on the margins of forest around Nairobi and elsewhere in central Kenya at 600–1900m (2000–6200ft), uncommon elsewhere. Lake areas, Tanga, Tabora, Mpwapwa, Kondoa, Morogoro, Songea (Tanzania); Uganda and elsewhere, no record.

O. thomasiana   Plate 442
A large shrub up to 4.5m (15ft) in height. The leaves are subsessile, coriaceous, elliptic or ovate-elliptic, 32–82mm (1¼–3¼in) long and 12–32mm (½–1¼in) wide. Apex acute, margins spinulose-serrate, the bristle-like teeth, 6mm (¼in) apart, becoming much longer and gland tipped near the base. The leaf base normally cordate but sometimes cuneate. Flowers yellow, in few-flowered racemes; sepals 8mm (⅓in) long; petals 12mm (½in) long. Coastal forest (Kenya); Tanzania and Uganda, no record; also southern Somalia.

38. Melastomataceae

Trees, shrubs or herbs, usually with stiff bristly hairs. Leaves simple, usually entire, opposite and decussate, exstipulate. Leaf veins parallel, diverging from the base and converging at the apex. Flowers regular. Calyx tubular. Petals, very often a rich purple, usually free with a corona between petals and stamens. Stamens the same or twice as many as petals, usually opening by a single apical pore. Ovary inferior or half inferior. Fruit a berry or capsule. The garden shrubs *Lasiandra* belong to this family. Seventy-nine species in seventeen genera in East Africa.

Antherotoma naudinii   Plate 732
Herb with square stems and ovate to lanceolate leaves with three to five parallel nerves and stiff bristly white hairs; flowers in condensed terminal dichasia; receptacle tube broadly fused to ovary to halfway or more; four to five sepals, persistent; four to five petals, 4mm (⅙in) long, 3.5mm (⅛in) wide, pink to purple; eight to ten stamens, all similar, all with two small lobes at the knee, ovary with a ring of bristles at the tip. Altitude range 300–2150m (1000–7000ft). A common plant in the west of Kenya, particularly in the northern area in short grass on shallow soils in damp places and in rock crevices and pavements and by lakes, rivers and ditches. Cheranganis, Mau, Kitale, western regions, Kisii (Kenya); Bukoba, Buha, Songea, Mbeya, Iringa (Tanzania); West Nile, Ankole, Teso (Uganda); also in Ethiopia, south to Zimbabwe, Mozambique.

Dissotis canescens   A pubescent perennial from a woody rootstock with oblong-linear leaves; inflorescence a long, leafy panicle of pedunculate (stalked) cymes of subsessile purple flowers. Petals 15mm (⅝in) long, 11mm (⅞in) wide; long stamens with anthers 8mm (⅓in) long, short stamens with anthers 7mm (¼in) long. It grows from 50–125cm (20–50in) tall – occasionally 180cm (70in). Common in burnt grassland; altitude range 800–1950m (2600–6400ft). Western regions, Cheranganis, Tinderet, Kisii, Elgon and the Kitale area (Kenya); lake areas, Tabora, Mpwapwa, Kondoa, Mbeya, Iringa, Songea (Tanzania); all regions of Uganda; also in Ethiopia, Zaire, south to Zimbabwe, Mozambique.

Dissotis or **Melastomastrum** sp.   Plate 655
This plant has not been recorded in *FTEA* and has not been traced: it may well be a new species. Photograph taken in Taita Hills.

D. speciosa   Plate 656
A woody herb or shrub up to 2.5m (*c.* 8ft) high; stem four-angled, branchlets densely appressed, pubescent. Leaf-lamina lanceolate, lanceolate-ovate, or narrowly oblong, apex subacute, base rounded to truncate, white, sericeous above at first, becoming appressed setucose, appressed pilose beneath. Inflorescence terminal, flowers solitary, more or less concealed at first by the leaves; flowers five-merous, bracts often reddish. Calyx tube cup-shaped, densely appressed sericeous-villous. Petals mauve to reddish purple, ten stamens, five large and five short. Petals 35–40mm (*c.* 1½in) long, 22–27mm (*c.* 1in) wide; calyx tube 12–14mm (*c.* ½in) long, 8–12mm (⅓–½in) diameter. Found in valley grassland and swampy places; altitude range 900–2250m (2950–7350ft). Elgon, Kitale, western regions, Kisii and Narok (Kenya); lake areas, Tabora, Mbeya, Iringa (Tanzania); eastern region, Mbale, Masaka, Mengo (Uganda); also found in Sudan, Zaire, Zambia, Mozambique.

D. senegambiensis **Plate 657**
An erect, bristly annual or perennial herb with lanceolate to linear or even ovate leaves; cymes almost sessile to pedunculate at the apices with short-stalked purple flowers in dense clusters. Petals 10–15mm ($\frac{2}{5}$–$\frac{3}{5}$in) long, 8–13mm ($\frac{1}{3}$–$\frac{1}{2}$in) wide. Altitude range 1050–2700m (3450–8850ft). This is the commonest *Dissotis* in Kenya and is widespread, usually on the sides of paths and in disturbed grasslands on basement complex rocks. It can be seen near hot springs and jets in the Rift Valley but is recorded throughout Kenya, especially in damp places (Kenya); lake areas, Tanga, Mpwapwa, Kondoa, Mbeya, Iringa (Tanzania); all regions of Uganda; also in Ethiopia and Sudan south to Mozambique.

39. Combretaceae

A medium-sized tropical and subtropical family of trees, shrubs and woody lianes with simple leaves lacking stipules. They have a calyx cleft into four or five parts and a matching number or no petals. Stamens are as many, or twice as many, as the sepals. The ovary is inferior and the leathery fruit, single-seeded and often winged, remains closed when ripe. There are seventy-four species in East Africa representing five genera; all but six species belong to the genus *Combretum*, with opposite or whorled leaves, petals and four- or five-winged fruits, or to *Terminalia* with alternate or clustered leaves, no petals and flat-winged fruits.

Combretum aculeatum **Plate 188**
A climbing and rambling shrub which grows up to 3m (10ft) in height with zig-zag branches. Its leaves are alternate or sub-opposite, ovate and covered in soft hairs; the petioles usually persist as curved spines which help the plant to climb. The white flowers have red anthers and are *c.*11mm ($\frac{2}{5}$in) across. Altitude range 9–1700m (30–5600ft). Coastal regions, Maasai, Northern Frontier, often in thickets on dried-out swampy soils, and in all the rather dry parts of Kenya; Moshi, Tanga, Lushoto (Tanzania); West Nile, Karamoja, Mbale (Uganda); also Sudan, Ethiopia, Somalia.

C. constrictum **Plate 499**
A scandent shrub with long straggling branches and scrambling by the enlarged and persistent petioles. Leaves usually alternate, obovate-elliptic up to 10cm (4in) long, apex shortly acuminate, base rounded, lamina covered with white dots above, glabrous beneath except on veins. Flowers scarlet in terminal heads up to 5cm (2in) in diameter, upper receptacle constricted above the enlarged base into a long tube enlarging upwards. Petals clawed, linear-lanceolate, fringed with minute hairs; 7–8mm ($\frac{1}{3}$in) long, 2.5mm ($\frac{1}{10}$in) wide; upper receptacle 10–15mm ($\frac{2}{5}$–$\frac{3}{5}$in) long, 7mm ($\frac{1}{3}$in) in diameter at apex, constricted in the middle for 4–7mm ($\frac{1}{6}$–$\frac{1}{3}$in) long. Fruit conical, five-angled, not winged. Found in damp localities; altitude range 0–1200m (0–3850ft). Machakos and coastal districts (Kenya); Pangani, Mpanda, Morogoro, Songea (Tanzania); Uganda, no record; also in Somalia, Mozambique.

C. exalatum **Plate 5**
A much-branched, bushy, scandent, deciduous shrub up to 5m (16$\frac{1}{2}$ft) high. Young branches densely tomentose but peeling to show a greyish-purple surface. Leaves opposite, lamina papyraceous, narrowly oblong-elliptic to obovate up to 13cm (5in)

long and 4cm (1⅝in) wide, apex rounded, sometimes retuse or even apiculate, revolute or folded inwards in times of drought, pubescent to glabrescent above, pubescent to tomentose beneath, often concealing the dense but not continuous silvery scales, eight to ten pairs of lateral nerves. Flowers yellow-green to yellow, lower receptacle tomentose. Petals 1.5mm long, 0.8mm wide. Fruit with very narrow wings. Common in *Acacia-Commiphora* bushland; altitude range 300–1000m (1000–3280ft). Machakos, Taita, Voi and Kibwezi (Kenya); Pare, Lushoto, Kilosa (Tanzania); Uganda, no record; also in southern Somalia.

C. mossambicense
Plate 500

A shrub or loose climber covered in soft, downy hairs with ovate-elliptic, rounded leaves and racemes of crowded flowers coloured pink, crimson, green or creamy-pink. The photograph shows unripe fruit which are *c.* 25mm (1in) long. Found in *Commiphora* bushland, especially along watercourses, at 600–1600m (2000–5300ft). Kajiado and coastal areas (Kenya); Shinyanga, Tabora, Dodoma (Tanzania); Acholi, Bunyoro, Murchison Falls (Uganda); also south to Malawi, Zaire, Mozambique, Zimbabwe, Zambia.

C. paniculatum
Plate 501

A twining, woody climber with opposite leaves and hairless or down-covered stems. Racemes of showy red flowers are borne in axillary panicles on pendulous non-twining branches. Inflorescence (branch illustrated) *c.* 35mm (1⅜in) long. This is a local and impressive plant whose bright flowers can often be seen in the middle and upper branches of sparsely-foliaged trees and found in or near riverine forest. 10–2000m (30–6700ft). Most of Kenya; Arusha, Pangani, Morogoro and Zanzibar (Tanzania); Ankole, Mbale – Tororo, Mengo (Uganda); also south to Mozambique, Zimbabwe from Ethiopia.

Terminalia brownii
Plate 542

A deciduous tree up to 15m (50ft), slashed brown, usually rather flat-topped, bole ashy grey. Young shoots and leaves tomentose. Leaves not crowded at the ends of the branches, elliptic-obovate to broadly obovate, 5–7.5cm (2–3in) long, 3.75–6.25cm (1½–2½in) broad, apex usually shortly apiculate, base cuneate. Flowers white, glabrous and evil-smelling; inflorescence up to 12cm (4¾in) long. Fruit broadly elliptic to ovate, purple-red with a faint glaucous bloom. Found in dry savannah and on mountain slopes in arid areas, often riparian; altitude range 700–2000m (2300–6560ft). Widespread in its habitat (Kenya); Maasai, Mpwapwa, Kondoa, Morogoro (Tanzania); all regions of Uganda except Buganda; also Sudan, Ethiopia, Somalia, eastern Zaire.

T. orbicularis
Plate 502

A shrub to 3m (10ft) high, though occasionally a small tree to 9m (30ft) high with a corky, rectangularly fissured bark. Leaves glabrous, rounded-elliptic to 3.75cm (1½in) long, spirally arranged on the spur shoots. Flowers with calyx crimson outside and cream within, borne on inflorescences arising from reduced branchlet cushions; peduncle lanate when young. Inflorescence 2.5–5cm (1–2in) long. Fruit large, 7.5cm (3in) diameter, bright red with wings orbicular, looking rather like Chinese lanterns from a distance. Found in dry *Acacia-Commiphora* bushland; altitude range 500–1800m (1640–6900ft). Northern Frontier districts, Taita Hills, Machakos, Tsavo National Parks (Kenya); Ethiopia and Somalia.

T. prunioides
Plate 658

A tall deciduous tree with grey, longitudinally fissured bark. Its branches tend to appear in tables, or layers, like those of the Cedar of Lebanon. Its leaves are obovate and wide with a wedge-shaped base, 5cm (2in) long and 25mm (1in) wide. The magnificent, but brief, display of white blossom is reminiscent of cherry or plum blossom – hence the specific name meaning 'like *Prunus*'. Each spike of blossom *c.* 56–80mm (2¼–3⅛in) long. The fruits are purplish-brown or red, elliptic-oblong in outline, apex obtuse, deeply emarginate or mucronate. Altitude range 30–1400m (100–4600ft). A native of the coast, eastern and northern provinces (Kenya); Lushoto, Tanga, Perani Forest (Tanzania); Uganda, no record; also Somalia and south to Mozambique, Zimbabwe, Zambia.

40. Guttiferae (Clusiaceae)

A medium-sized family of trees and shrubs, or much less often herbs, confined, except for the mainly herbaceous *Hypericum*, to the tropics. A yellow latex contained in glands or ducts is usually present. Flowers regular, usually hermaphrodite and with four or five free sepals and petals. Stamens numerous, often united in bundles. Ovary superior; styles free or united at the base or absent, the stigma sessile on the ovary. Nine genera with thirty-three species occur in East Africa. Among these, four, the largest of which is *Hypericum* with eleven species in East Africa, were formerly separated as the *Hypericaceae*.

Hypericum annulatum A member of the same family as the St John's Wort of European gardens, this minutely-haired perennial herb has ovate to lanceolate leaves and loose corymbs of flowers with much reduced glandular hairy bracts. In bud the flowers appear to be orange-red, but when open are yellow, *c.* 23mm (⅞in) across. Locally common on sandy grasslands at 1100–3600m (3600–12,000ft). Found in many districts – Tinderet, Mau, Aberdares and Mt Kenya in the higher altitudes and Rift Valley, Nanyuki, Machakos, Baringo and Kitale in the lower ones (Kenya); Maasai, Tanga (Tanzania); eastern region of Uganda; also northern Ethiopia, Eritrea.

H. revolutum   **Plates 279 & 280**
A shrub or tree up to 12m (40ft) high. Its lanceolate to oblong-lanceolate leaves are up to 25mm (1in) long and 6mm (¼in) broad, narrowing acutely to a clasping base with pinnate venation displaying linear and often translucent glands. Solitary yellow flowers, 4–5cm (1½–2in) across, are borne at the ends of branches, their stamens grouped in five bundles of about thirty each. It is a shrub of upland and dry evergreen forest bush, often riparian, at 1930–3290m (6500–11,500ft). Widespread (Kenya); Maasai, Tanga, Morogoro, Mpwapwa, Kondoa (Tanzania); all regions of Uganda except Buganda; also from Ethiopia, Rwanda, Burundi, Zaire to Zimbabwe, Mozambique, Madagascar and Comoro Is.

H. roeperianum   **Plate 281**
A shrub or small tree up to 4½m (15ft) in height. Leaves lanceolate or oblong-elliptic from 2.5–10cm (1–4in) long, acute narrowing to a clasping base; reticulation of tertiary veins with a translucent dot in each interstice. Flower bright yellow, up to 5cm (2in) in diameter, in few-to-many-flowered terminal corymbose cymes. Stamens in five bundles of about forty-five each bundle. It is found in dry evergreen forest, bushland and bamboo, often riparian; altitude range 1500–2900m

(5000–9800ft). Laikipia, Ngong and Mt Kenya (Kenya); Maasai, Kilimanjaro, Usambaras (Tanzania); northern and western regions of Uganda; also Sudan, Ethiopia.

41. Tiliaceae
THE LIME TREE or JUTE FAMILY

A medium-sized family of trees, shrubs or herbs, often with hairs in radiating clusters, found throughout the tropics and subtropics, with *Tilia*, the Lime tree, alone in temperate countries. Leaves are alternate and stipulate, the calyx usually have five valvate sepals and the petals are free. Stamens are more numerous than the petals, usually free, and spirally arranged with the ovary superior. 107 species in seven genera in East Africa.

Grewia bicolor   Plate 282
A much-branched shrub or tree up to 9m (30ft) tall. Leaves often asymmetrical, elliptic, elliptic-oblong, or lanceolate up to 7.5cm (3in) long, apex rounded or obtuse or slightly apiculate, margin serrulate (often minutely), base rounded or broadly cuneate, under-surface covered with a uniform whitish tomentum. Flowers yellow, 1.25cm ($\frac{1}{2}$in) in diameter, in two or more, flowered axillary cymes. Found throughout Kenya in dry savannah country; altitude range 1–1800m (3–6000ft). There is a form recorded in Taita and Ukambani (Kenya) with coarsely serrate leaves and twigs conspicuously lenticillate; all regions of Tanzania and Uganda; also in Ethiopia south to Mozambique, Zimbabwe.

G. lilacina   Plate 733
A shrub growing up to 1.8m (6ft). The leaves are obovate-oblong, the apex rounded and the margins closely crenate-serrate. The flowers are solitary, *c.* 18mm ($\frac{3}{4}$in) across, generally appearing before the leaves and pink, lilac or magenta in colour. Found at 750–1200m (2500–4000ft) in warm, semi-arid areas (Kenya); lake areas, Maasai, Shinyanga, Mpwapwa, Kondoa (Tanzania); Uganda, no record; also Ethiopia and Somalia.

G. similis   Plate 734
A shrub growing up to 1.8m (6ft) in height and sometimes climbing to 9m (30ft) or more. Its young shoots and inflorescence are down-covered. In all species of *Grewia*, some or all of the hairs are stellate. The leaves are elliptic, rounded to obtuse at the apex with margins finely serrulate and base rounded. The flowers are bright mauve, pink or magenta (very rarely white), *c.* 2cm ($\frac{3}{4}$in) across, in three- to six- or more flowered, terminal and axillary inflorescences, appearing when the tree is in leaf. It is widespread in all areas of Kenya with rainfall above 750mm (30in) from 600–2100m (2000–7000ft), but does not occur in dry areas. All regions of Tanzania except Songea; all regions of Uganda; also Ethiopia.

G. tembensis var. kakothamnos   Plate 49
A much-branched shrub with obovate or obovate-orbicular leaves; the leaves generally narrow to an acute or obtuse apex (but there are two forms – var. *kakothamnos* and var. *nematopus* – in which the apex is rounded); margins dentate-serrate. Flowers one to few in short axillary cymes, white with a purplish tinge; anthers yellow; sepals 6mm ($\frac{1}{4}$in) long; petals shorter than the sepals. Found

in dry bush ground and widely spread from 300–1800m (1500–6000ft). Var. *tembensis* has only been recorded in Turkana (Kenya). Var. *kakothamnos* is widespread in Kenya. All regions except Tabora and Songea (Tanzania); northern region – Gulu (Uganda); also Sudan, Ethiopia, Somalia.

G. tembensis var. **nematopus** **Plate 735**

A much-branched shrub with obovate or obovate-suborbicular leaves up to 3.75cm ($1\frac{1}{2}$in) long. The apex is rounded, margins dentate-serrate, the leaf glabrous, slightly pubescent, with three basal nerves and arched secondaries. Flowers one to few, on slender stalks 10–25mm ($\frac{2}{5}$–1in) long, white with a purple tinge. Petals, 3–4mm ($\frac{1}{8}$–$\frac{1}{6}$in) long, shorter than the sepals, 5mm ($\frac{1}{5}$in) long. Anthers yellow, filaments reddish. Altitude range 450–1800m (1500–6000ft). Var. *kakothamnos*, with almost sessile pinkish flowers on stalks under 5mm ($\frac{1}{5}$in) long, is more widespread in the same ecological zone; sepals 11mm ($\frac{2}{5}$in) long; petals 9mm ($\frac{1}{3}$in) long. Var. *nematopus* appears to be restricted to Machakos, Tsavo and Taita districts (Kenya); Maasai, Shinyanga (Tanzania); Uganda and elsewhere, no record.

G. tenax **Plate 50**

A shrub up to 2m ($6\frac{1}{2}$ft) in height. Its leaves are rounded to obovate, usually about 8mm ($\frac{1}{3}$in) long but occasionally reaching 5cm (2in). Their apex is rounded and margins more or less coarsely dentate-crenate. One or two white flowers, 2cm ($\frac{4}{5}$in) across, are borne on long, slender peduncles, jointed above the middle, green-yellow outside, white within, with sepals 12mm ($\frac{1}{2}$in) long. It is found in dry *Acacia-Commiphora* bushland up to 1500m (5000ft) in coastal, northern and southern districts (Kenya); Maasai, Shinyanga, Tanga (Tanzania); northern region of Uganda; also southern Sudan, Somalia, Zimbabwe, Limpopo Valley.

G. truncata **Plate 51**

A shrub or small tree up to 6m (20ft) tall. Leaves oblong or obovate-oblong to *c.* 18cm (7in) long and 10cm (4in) wide, apex truncate, obtuse or shortly acuminate, margins finely denticulate towards base, coarsely so near apex, base rounded, lamina three-nerved from base, subglabrous above, softly pubescent beneath. Flowers white, 2cm ($\frac{4}{5}$in) long, in few to many-flowered cymes. Petals circular. Found in bushland and woodland; altitude range 10–1000m (30–3300ft). Taita Hills, Kilifi and Tana River (Kenya); Maasai, Shinyanga, Tanga (Tanzania); Uganda, no record; also in Malawi, Mozambique.

G. villosa **Plate 418**

A shrub up to 3m (10ft) in height with young parts covered with silky hairs. Its rounded, sometimes broadly elliptic leaves are green and up to 10cm (4in) in diameter with the base often obliquely cordate, the margin serrate and the undersurface covered with grey down or weak, shaggy, long hairs and with prominent veins. The dull yellow flowers with reddish veins, *c.* 12mm ($\frac{1}{2}$in) across, have oblong petals, notched and much shorter than the sepals. The copper-coloured, hairy fruit is edible. Although nearly all the other species of *Grewia* have hermaphrodite flowers, this species has male and female flowers on separate plants. The flower in the photograph is female. *G. villosa* is common in dry bush country up to 1220m (4000ft), at the coast and in northern and southern districts (Kenya); Maasai, Shinyanga, Tanga, Mpwapwa, Kondoa, Mbeya, Iringa (Tanzania); northern and eastern regions of Uganda; also Ethiopia and Sudan, south to Zimbabwe, Mozambique.

Triumfetta brachyceras (*T. macrophylla*)   **Plate 283**
An erect, much-branched, down-covered, woody herb or shrub with ovate or lanceolate and often undivided leaves and large, sparsely-leaved terminal panicles of numerous cymes; flowers yellow, *c.* 8mm (⅓in) across; capsules with hooked prickles are 3–7mm (⅛–¼in) long. It varies considerably in leaf shape and size, and in habit, as it often behaves as a scrambler. It is the commonest *Triumfetta* in upland forest areas of Kenya and is often encountered at forest edges and along roadsides at 1300–2500m (4250–8200ft). Other species are much more common in lower, drier areas. Lake area, Maasai, Shinyanga, Tanga, Tabora, Mbeya, Iringa (Tanzania); all regions of Uganda except northern; also in southern Sudan, Ethiopia, eastern Zaire, Rwanda and Burundi.

T. flavescens   **Plate 284**
A down-covered shrub with branches often densely covered with small black spots or dots. Its leaves are ovate to rounded, somewhat angular or slightly tri-lobed. The yellow flowers, *c.* 15mm (⅝in) across, are loosely grouped in small clusters of cymes. Common in dry bush country at 910–1830m (3000–6000ft). Kisii, Rift Valley, Machakos, Kajiado, and especially Magadi (Kenya); Maasai, Shinyanga, Tanga (Tanzania); northern region of Uganda; also Ethiopia, Somalia, Sudan.

T. pilosa   An erect woody herb or small shrub with lanceolate to ovate-lanceolate leaves and loose terminal inflorescences of small yellow flowers crowded in leafy cymes at the nodes; capsule globose, mostly pilose with apically hooked prickles. Flower 15mm (⅝in) across when open, but usually closed. A locally common plant of forest margins and old cultivation from 5–1900m (16–6250ft). Aberdares, Kitale, Mumias, Embu, Kajiado (Kenya); Songea, Zanzibar (Tanzania); western region of Uganda; also Burundi, Zimbabwe.

T. rhomboidea   **Plate 503**
An erect pubescent herb or undershrub with ovate to ovate-lanceolate leaves, often three-lobed and deep red/yellow cymes in small crowded clusters at upper nodes; capsule with hooked glabrous prickles 1mm long; each flower in cyme very small – 1mm across. This is a polymorphic species and commonly occurs along paths and roadsides in upland forests, dry country and grassland; altitude range 5–2280m (16–7600ft). Often a weed of cultivation and recorded throughout East Africa except lake areas of Tanzania to northern Uganda; also throughout tropical Africa to South Africa.

T. tomentosa   A low shrub with brown woolly indumentum and ovate or lanceolate-ovate, sometimes slightly three-lobed leaves; cymes in crowded terminal panicles; capsule with slightly curved pilose or almost glabrous prickles 3–9mm (up to ⅓in) long. Flower *c.* 6mm (¼in) long, 4mm (⅛in) across. A common plant of forest clearings and old cultivations; altitude range 0–2100m (0–6900ft). Widespread throughout tropical Africa.

42. Sterculiaceae

A small, medium-sized, tropical and subtropical family of trees, shrubs, shrublets and herbs, usually with some stellate hairs. Their leaves are alternate and usually have stipules. The three- to five-lobed, valvate calyx is persistent. There may be up to five free petals, or none at all, forming a contorted corolla. Five to many stamens may be free, or more or less united, with the ovary superior. Seventy-five species in fifteen genera in East Africa.

DOMBEYA

There are eleven *Dombeya* species in East Africa, but there is still much work to be done on them; they are very variable and names cannot be said to have been finalized. All have white or pink apple-blossomy flowers massed in umbels. There is a small shrub-like species, *D. faucicola*, which is found round Nakuru (Kenya), with short ovate leaves (only 5cm/2in long and nearly as broad) which has only a two- to five-flowered inflorescence above the leaves. Flowers white with small petals 9mm (⅓in) long.

Dombeya burgessiae   Plate 52
A forest undershrub or small tree. Leaves denticulate, 15cm (6in) long and 10cm (4in) broad, pubescent above and beneath, occasionally almost glabrous, apex long-acuminate, base cordate (often with overlapping lobes). Flowers white or pink, usually in simple umbels; pedicels up to 10cm (4in) long. Sepals to 2cm (⅘in) long and 1cm (⅜in) broad; petals up to 1.25cm (½in) long and broad. At first sight, the umbels of flowers might remind a European visitor of *Philadelphus* or Mock Orange. Altitude range 1000–3000m (3300–9800ft). It is widespread in almost all drier upland forest (Kenya); lake areas, Maasai, Shinyanga, Tabora, Mbeya, Iringa, Songea (Tanzania); all regions of Uganda; also in Ethiopia, eastern Zaire, south to Zimbabwe, Mozambique, Natal.

D. kirkii   Plate 189
A much-branched shrub or small tree up to 9m (30ft) high. Bark smooth and light grey. Leaf-lamina 10cm (4in) long and 6cm (2⅜in) wide, ovate or rarely shallowly three-lobed, apex acuminate, base cordate, margin irregularly crenate-serrate, thinly pubescent on both sides. Flowers white, *c.* 10mm (⅜in) across, in many-flowered axillary panicles, pedicels 2cm (⅘in) long, densely pubescent with many short stellate hairs. Altitude range 600–2100m (2000–7000ft). Widespread in all semi-arid and arid areas throughout East Africa; also in Zaire, Rwanda, Mozambique, Zimbabwe.

D. rotundifolia   Plate 190
A tree, growing to 2–4.5m (6–15ft) in height in the savannah and on forest edges, this *Dombeya* has feathery, rounded to broadly ovate leaves which are sometimes obscurely lobed, cordate at the base and often densely covered with stellate hairs. Flowers, *c.* 18mm (⅔in) across, are borne in white or pinkish clusters and resemble cherry blossom. However, the petals persist for months and become brownish – in which state the tree is not very attractive. It prefers the altitude range 1370–2130m (4500–7000ft). Common in Kenya; lake areas, Maasai, Shinyanga, Tabora, Mbeya, Iringa (Tanzania); northern (Gulu) and western regions of Uganda; also Ethiopia, Zaire, Zambia, Zimbabwe, Mozambique.

D. torrida (*D. goetzenii*) A tree up to 15m (50ft) tall and bole up to 1.2m (4ft) in girth. Bark grey and smooth; a slash in the bark reveals yellow-brown or sometimes pink with white streaks. Branches pubescent when young, glabrous when older. Leaves dark green, usually with red nerves, denticulate, suborbicular to broadly ovate, rarely three-lobed, 12–35cm (5–14in) long and 9–25cm (3½–10in) broad, softly pubescent on both sides; long acuminate at the apex, deeply cordate at the

STERCULIACEAE

base, often with overlapping lobes at the base. The inflorescence is up to 30cm (12in) long, the final ramifications bearing umbels ten- to eighteen-flowered; flowers pale pink, deep red at the base of the staminal tube; petal 9–12.7mm (⅓–½in) long; sepal up to 12mm (½in) long. Altitude range 2100–2850m (7000–9500ft). This is a *Dombeya* found in highland forest throughout Kenya and is a splendid sight when in flower. All regions of Tanzania except lake and Mpwapwa, Kondoa areas; all regions of Uganda except northern; also Ethiopia, Zaire, Malawi.

Hermannia sp. A. (in *UKWF*)   Plate 285
A stellate-pubescent, much-branched shrub with simple, serrate oblong leaves with prominent venation and yellow flowers in panicles, five petals, five stamens opposite the petals; with sagittate anthers; five sepals, connate at base; flower 7mm (¼in) across. Altitude range 1200–2000m (3850–6550ft). One of fourteen species in East Africa. Common in Machakos area, in and bordering *Commiphora* woodland in sandy soils (Kenya). A little-known plant unlikely to be in Tanzania, Uganda or elsewhere.

H. exappendiculata   Plate 443
A loose, pubescent to grey-canescent shrub with smallish ovate-oblong leaves, broad stipules and large terminal, but loose-flowered panicles of yellow flowers, usually glandular-pilose on the rachis and calyx. Flower 8mm (⅓in) across. Altitude range 5–2000m (16–6560ft). Locally common in dry areas in *Commiphora* bushland (Kenya); Tanga, Morogoro, Songea (Tanzania); northern region of Uganda; also southern Somalia, Ethiopia.

H. kirkii   Plate 736
An erect, glandular-pilose, annual or rarely perennial, herb with narrow lanceolate to oblong, occasionally linear leaves; the flower petals pink-purple and usually twice as long as the calyx. It is similar to *H. viscosa* but in the latter the flowers are white with a pink base or pink and spreading, *c.* 10mm (⅜in) long, *c.* 6mm (¼in) across; the bracteoles clearly visible and the awns ascending; in *H. kirkii* the bracteoles are absent on the articulation of the fruit and the awns are spreading. Altitude range 200–1470m (650–4900ft). Widespread in northern countries and found in dry *Acacia* bushland, often in disturbed places in Kenya; lake areas, Maasai, Shinyanga, Mpwapwa, Kondoa, Mbeya, Iringa (Tanzania); northern Uganda; also Ethiopia south to Mozambique, Zimbabwe.

H. uhligii (*H. alhiensis*)   Plate 286
A grey-pubescent, upright or semi-prostrate shrub with oblong leaves and axillary panicles of five to fifteen yellow flowers. The *Hermannia* have stellate hairs and serrate leaves with prominent venation. The flowers have five sepals, connate at base, five petals, five stamens opposite the petals with sagittate anthers; petals 9mm (⅓in) long. *H. uhligii* is a common and conspicuous plant after the April–May rains in the dry grassland and bushland plains around Nairobi. The larger-flowered forms have been named *H. alhiensis*, but these really appear to grade into the small-flowered species which grow in exactly the same places. It is probably better to regard them all as *H. uhligii*. Altitude range 200–1850m (650–6050ft). Narok, Rift Valley, Magadi, Kajiado, Machakos and Nairobi (Kenya); lake areas (Musoma), Maasai, Shinyanga, Tanga (Tanzania); Uganda and elsewhere, no record.

Melhania angustifolia   Plate 287
An erect, woody annual or short-lived perennial up to 40cm (*c.* 17in) high. Branches virgate, young shoots rusty-tomentose later becoming grey-canescent in age.

Leaves ovate-elliptic, 5cm (2in) long, 4cm (1⅝in) wide, usually greyish. Inflorescence axillary one- to four-flowered; flowers yellow, 12mm (½in) across. Similar to *M. velutina*. Found among grasses on coral rocks, at the edge of cultivation, and in rocky situations; altitude range 1–1000m (3–3280ft). Recorded only on the islands of Zanzibar and Pemba, but the illustration was taken in the Taita Hills (Kenya), so the distribution is probably wider than so far recorded. Ten other species in East Africa.

M. ovata   **Plate 288**
A grey, canescent, woody herb or low shrub with ovate or suborbicular leaves and axillary groups of one to three yellow flowers, *c.* 15mm (⅜in) across. A common roadside weed in dry grassland, where it can be mistaken for a *Sida* at first glance; altitude range 5–1900m (15–6200ft). Rift Valley, Embu, Magadi and Kajiado (Kenya); Maasai, Shinyanga, Tanga, Mpwapwa, Kondoa (Tanzania); Uganda, no record; also southern Sudan, Ethiopia.

M. parviflora (*M. taylorii*)   **Plate 289**
An erect, annual or short-lived, perennial herb, branched from the base, incano-tomentose, up to 60cm (*c.* 28in) high. Leaves elliptic to almost orbicular, up to 7.5cm (3in) long and 4cm (1⅝in) wide, somewhat canescent, margins denticulate. Inflorescence axillary, one- to five-flowered; flowers lemon-yellow, 2cm (⅘in) across. Found in open areas in dry evergreen forest, especially in coastal areas on coral rocks; altitude range 10–600m (110–1950ft). Coastal areas (Kenya) and Somalia.

M. velutina A rusty-coloured, erect, woody annual or short-lived perennial, covered with soft, dense hairs. The leaves are ovate-elliptic with axillary groups of one to four yellow flowers, *c.* 15mm (⅜in) across. It is a common weed in the drier areas of Kenya, below 1830m (6000ft) and recorded in western Kenya and Kisii to Machakos, Nairobi and Kajiado in the east from 5–1900m (15–6200ft); all regions of Tanzania except Tabora and southern areas, Zanzibar; northern and western regions of Uganda; also Sudan, Ethiopia.

Sterculia rhynchocarpa   **Plate 444**
A small-branched tree up to 7.6m (25ft) high in dry rocky areas. The smooth, red-brown outer bark scales off as in a Plane tree, exposing a blue, green or reddish underbark. Leaves, small digitately nerved, and rather shallowly or obtusely lobed, 1.25–3.75cm (½–1½in) long and 1.25–5cm (½–2in) broad, pubescent or tomentose. Flowers, 9mm (⅓in) diameter, in short panicles with a yellow-green, campanulate perianth streaked with red, and producing a star-like collection of follicles up to 8.75cm (3½in) long; very closely tomentellous on the outside, roughened with prominent ridges and more or less conical warts and abruptly narrowing to a curved beak. In northern and eastern areas, such as Garissa and Mandera, the tree is more of a lowly branched shrub with numerous grey stems up to 1m (3ft) high, and spreading branches. Leaves small, pubescent, cordate in outline and very obscurely three-lobed. One to four flowers with campanulate, reddish-green tipped corollas. Altitude range 1–925m (3–3000ft). Coastal, northern and eastern areas and Machakos (Kenya); Tanga (Tanzania); northern region of Uganda; also in Ethiopia and Somalia. One of nine species in East Africa.

43. Bombacaceae

A small tropical family. Trees with digitate, stipulate leaves. Flowers hermaphrodite, without an epicalyx. Five petals, joined to the base of the staminal tube; five or more stamens, united below, anthers single-celled, ovary superior, five- to ten-celled, ovules numerous, style simple. Fruit a capsule or nut. Four species in two genera in East Africa.

Adansonia digitata   **Plate 54**
Commonly known as the Baobab Tree. A deciduous tree of vast girth whose obesity is manifest early in life. Bark smooth and grey, branches stout and stiff; leaves digitate, leaflets oblong up to 7.5cm (3in) long, acuminate, entire or sinuous at margin, downy on lower surface. Leaves on young plants simple. Flowers large, white, solitary, pendulous and axillary, c. 13cm (5½in) across; petals c. 7mm (c. ¼in) long. Calyx cup-shaped, five-cleft; five petals, leathery and ultimately reflexed. The flowers are attractive and sometimes missed by travellers. The leaves are used as a vegetable by African peoples, and the fruit, which is edible, also makes a cooling drink. A useful fibre can be made from the bark and the fruit cases make water dippers. A red dye is obtainable from the roots. Found in medium-rainfall areas and recorded throughout its altitude range, up to 1200m (4000ft) (Kenya); all regions except lake areas (Tanzania); never recorded in Uganda; also in southern Sudan, Ethiopia, Somalia south to the Limpopo Valley.

44. Malvaceae
THE MALLOW, HOLLYHOCK or COTTON FAMILY

A large family of herbs or shrubs or, less often, trees, usually with stellate hairs, which is found throughout the world and includes the Hollyhock of British cottage gardens. Leaves are alternate, often palmately veined and have stipules. Flowers are regular, usually rather showy and often with an epicalyx of bracts outside the calyx. The five petals are usually attached to the base of the staminal tube and fall off as one unit. Stamens are numerous, their filaments united to form a tube around the styles. The ovary has several carpels which often separate in the fruiting stage (mericarps). There are about 137 species in fourteen genera recorded in East Africa. The four genera most often met may be distinguished as follows:

Epicalyx absent:
Fruit splitting into mericarps:
Mericarps usually indehiscent, single-seeded   *Sida*
Mericarps dehiscent, two to three-seeded   *Abutilon*
Fruit a capsule   *Hibiscus*

Epicalyx present:
Fruit a capsule   *Hibiscus*
Fruit of indehiscent mericarps   *Pavonia*

Abutilon grandiflorum   **Plate 191**
A soft woody shrub with short dense pubescence; leaves usually sub-orbicular and cordate, the stipules strap-shaped and often curved. Flowers yellow-gold, 35mm

(1⅜in) across, solitary and opening in mid-afternoon (cf *Hibiscus cannabinus* whose flowers tend to close and droop after midday); mericarps up to twenty, acutely pointed but hardly awned, with the lateral glabrous area rounded at the top but not pointed. Altitude range 700–1600m (2300–5250ft). About thirteen species in East Africa. Drier parts of Kajiado and western regions (Kenya); Bukoba, Shinyanga, Mwanza, Morogoro, Songea (Tanzania); Buganda (Uganda); also Zaire, Zimbabwe, Madagascar.

A. hirtum   Plate 445
An erect, sparsely-branched, woody herb with ovate to rounded leaves. The orange-yellow flowers *c.* 4cm (1½in) across, are grouped usually in loose terminal panicles at the end of the brown branches and sometimes have a dark purple-red spot at the base. This species is found is dry *Acacia-Commiphora* bushland and grassland from 300–1800m (1000–6000ft) in Kenya; Moshi, Tanga, Mpwapwa, Kondoa (Tanzania); northern region (Gulu) of Uganda; also widespread in the tropics.

A. longicuspe   Plate 737
A perennial shrub with dense grey down on stems and leaf undersides, bearing rounded, cordate leaves. The flowers are rather smaller than *A. hirtum*, *c.* 25mm (1in) in diameter, and often hang down like crumpled bell tents. They are mauve, lavender or lilac with a darker centre and are borne in conical, terminal panicles. This is a common plant of upland forest edges at 1500–2750m (5000–9000ft). Elgon, Tinderet, Mau, Aberdares, Mt Kenya, Narok, Machakos and Nairobi regions (Kenya); all districts of Tanzania except Maasai; all districts of Uganda except Buganda; also Ethiopia to Zimbabwe, and Mozambique.

A. mauritianum   Plate 290
A soft, woody shrub with short, dense down and longer-spreading hairs, its leaves usually rounded and cordate. Solitary yellow-gold flowers *c.* 3cm (1⅛in) across, with more than twenty mericarps, each tapering acutely at the top into a hairy bristle and with the lateral hairless area also pointed at the top. The commonest member of the genus generally found in Kenya at altitudes up to 2000m (6500ft); Shinyanga, Bukoba, Mwanza, Moshi, Tanga, Lushoto, Morogoro (Tanzania); western districts and eastern region of Uganda; also widespread in tropical Africa to Zimbabwe and Mozambique.

A. rehmannii (*A. braunii*)   Plate 192
A shrublet up to 2m (6½ft) high, sparsely hairy, leaves cordate at base, acuminate at apex, margin toothed. Flowers deep yellow to orange, *c.* 3cm (1⅛in) across. Found in dry grassland and *Acacia* woodland. Altitude range 675–2050m (2167–8800ft). Lake Naivasha (Crescent Island) and Amboseli National Park (Kenya); lake areas, Maasai, Tanga region, Mpwapwa, Kondoa (Tanzania); Uganda no record; also in Rwanda, Zimbabwe.

HIBISCUS
About sixty-four species in East Africa. *Hibiscus aponeurus, H. flavifolius, H. fuscus, H. micranthus* and *H. pycnostemon* belong to a section 'Bombycella' which has rather small flowers and seeds covered with long silky hairs. In this section are also other scarlet-flowered species apart from *H. aponeurus*, viz. *H. crassinervius* in a few northern mountains; *H. hildebrandtii, H. zanzibarica* and *H. migeodii* in coastal regions.

Hibiscus aethiopicus
Plate 291

A low-growing perennial herb with elliptic long leaves (in rare cases three-lobed) and large, ornamental single yellow flowers, 5cm (2in) across, which appear only after the rains. It is a common plant which grows in shallow soil or hard clay grassland at 1200–2100m (4000–7000ft). Throughout central areas from Kajiado and Narok to Kitale (Kenya); all areas of Tanzania except southern; all areas of Uganda; also Eritrea, Ethiopia, southern Sudan, Malawi, Zimbabwe, Mozambique.

H. aponeurus
Plate 504

An erect, short-lived perennial with an often dense covering of yellowish to occasionally brownish hairs. Its leaves are oblong to ovate, its crimson flowers solitary and axillary, 25mm (1in) across. It is common in dry grassland throughout East Africa at 610–1950m (2000–6400ft); also in Sudan, Zaire and north Mozambique.

H. calyphyllus
Plate 446

A shrub with ovate-cordate, simple or shallowly three-lobed leaves. The yellow flowers, with a deep maroon patch at the base of each petal, are large, c. 9cm (3½in) across, and solitary on short pedicels. It is an occasional shrub in lowland dry woodland and evergreen woodland at 900–1800m (3000–6000ft) over most of East Africa; also throughout tropical Africa (but not in very dry areas).

H. cannabinus
Plates 193 & 738

A locally common erect annual. Its hairy stems also carry small spines. Leaves rounded, three- to seven-lobed. Pendulous flowers, c. 6cm (2⅜in) across, grey, grey-purple, purple or bright yellow with maroon or purple base; grouped in loose terminal racemes similar to those of H. calyphyllus but slightly smaller and, when yellow with a maroon base, maroon is smaller and more central. They generally open up to midday; in the afternoon they hang limply. Found throughout East Africa at 600–2100m (2000–7000ft) in dry grassland, although in semi-arid areas it is often found on the edges of moist places and intermittent water-courses; also Ethiopia, Zimbabwe, Mozambique; widespread in the tropics, often as a weed sometimes cultivated as a fibre plant.

H. sp. D (in UKWF)
Plate 505

Similar to H. vitifolius, but an erect herb with larger leaves and red/pink flowers with longer petals (to 7cm (2¾in)) and longer staminal tube (to 2.5cm (1in)) on pedicels articulated below the middle. Altitude range 20–1200m (65–3850ft). It replaces H. vitifolius in dry Commiphora woodland (e.g. Tsavo West and East) and at the coast, but has been recorded in Machakos and Kajiado districts (Kenya); Tanzania and Uganda, no record; also in southern Somalia.

H. flavifolius
Plate 55

Similar to H. aponeurus, but more robust. Ovate-rounded leaves and cream or white flowers, c. 22mm (⅞in) across. Fairly common in dry rocky grassland at medium altitudes, 1250–1950m (4100–6400ft) in the Mumias, Narok, Rift Valley, Machakos and Kajiado districts (Kenya); widespread in Bukoba, Mwanza, Shinyanga, Moshi (Tanzania); northern region (Gulu), West Nile (Uganda); also Ethiopia.

H. fuscus
Plate 56

An erect, sparsely-branched herb, woody up to 2–4m (6–13ft) in height, with brownish-black, stellate hairs on the stem, pedicels and calyx and colourless hairs on the leaves. The leaves are ovate-triangular, simple or (rarely) three-lobed. The white flowers, *c.* 3–4cm (1½–1½in) across, are usually solitary and appear in the axils. A common plant in disturbed ground or old cultivated fields, where it usually has small flowers. In natural rocky grassland, especially in the Rift Valley, it appears in a more branched form with flowers which are usually larger and pink or pale mauve in colour. Found over the whole of East Africa at 1250–2300m (4000–7500ft); also Ethiopia, Zaire, Malawi, Zimbabwe, Mozambique.

H. ludwigii (*H. macranthus*)   **Plate 292**
Usually small with erect branches, this shrub is sometimes larger and trailing. It has sharp irritant hairs which break off in the skin. The generally solitary flowers are yellow with a maroon base; they droop and are never fully open; closed flower *c.* 6cm (2⅜in) long. A common *Hibiscus* found at 1520–2440m (5000–8000ft) in Kenya, often in cleared forest grassland; throughout Tanzania except Songea; western, eastern regions, Buganda (Uganda); also Ethiopia, Malawi, Zimbabwe. babwe.

H. lunariifolius   **Plate 293**
Usually a small shrub with erect branches but sometimes longer and trailing; the whole plant is covered with frequent sharp irritant hairs which break off in the skin. Its leaves are ovate-triangular to pentagonal and sometimes obscurely lobed. The drooping flowers, *c.* 77mm (3in) across, are in leafless racemes or solitary; their yellow petals have a maroon base and never fully open. It is similar to *H. ludwigii*, except that its leaves are usually smaller, and it is found in dry areas, especially in rocky country at 1070–1680m (3250–5250ft). Mumias, Kisii, Rift Valley, Magadi and Kajiado districts (Kenya); Shinyanga, Mwanza, Moshi (Tanzania); eastern and Buganda regions (Uganda); also in Zimbabwe, India.

H. micranthus A stiff, slender, loosely pubescent perennial shrub with oblong to ovate leaves; flowers axillary and solitary; petals white becoming pink or pink with paler base. *H. micranthus* is a very variable species, and it has now been recognized that two different taxa have been confused under the name *H. micranthus* in East Africa. These are now treated as two separate species whose ranges overlap and which probably hybridize, thus making true identification difficult. Thus race one is now called *H. micranthus s.str.* and race two *H. pycnostemon.* Details as below:
H. micranthus *s.str.*   Calyx lobes short-triangular, shorter than or no longer than the tube. Staminal tube never more than 4mm (⅛in) long with stamens at base; flower up to 14mm (⅜in) across. Found in dry bushland and coastal areas; altitude range 1–1400m (3–4600ft). Throughout Kenya except in Rift Valley; all regions of Tanzania except Tabora; all regions of Uganda except Buganda.

H. pycnostemon (*H. pospischilii*)   **Plate 739**
Calyx lobes longer than the tubes, staminal tube always more than 4mm (⅛in) long with naked base and stamens only at apex. Flower: 0.6mm (¼in) across. Mostly found in inland dry grassland and rocky bushland; altitude range 600–1700m (1950–5575ft). Throughout Kenya and Tanzania; western and eastern Uganda. The flowers of both species are always white or pinkish, fading to a definite pink, but never scarlet or red as in *H. aponeurus. H. pycnostemon* is very close to the South African *H. meyeri* which is an older name.

H. sidiformis   **Plate 294**
An erect, tomentellous annual with orbicular, crenate, simple lower leaves and palmately tri-foliolate upper leaves; petals white or yellow. Flower *c.* 3cm (1⅛in)

across. A rare plant found in dry country, altitude range 500–900m (1640–2950ft), and recorded *only* in Kajiado and Baringo (Kenya); Moshi, Tanga, Tabora, Kigoma, Central Province, Southern Highlands (Tanzania); Uganda, no record; also Ethiopia to Zimbabwe to Mozambique, Madagascar.

H. trionum   Plate 194
A stellate-hispid herb with orbicular, deeply three- to seven-palmatilobed leaves, flowers solitary, axillary, petals white or yellow with a dark crimson spot at base. Flower 3cm (1¼in) across, 2.5cm (1in) long. An uncommon weed found in disturbed places in dry country; altitude range below 2250m (7500ft). Throughout a wide area from west to east in Kenya; lake areas, Moshi, Mpwapwa, Kondoa (Tanzania); Gulu, West Nile (Uganda); also widespread from southern Europe to South Africa.

H. vitifolius   Plate 295
Like the preceding two species, this plant has irritant hairs, shallow yellow flowers, c. 6cm (2⅜in) across, with a contrasting maroon base and three to five lobes. In many districts at 1220–2440m (4000–8000ft), it is common at the edges of forest in areas with little rainfall. Widespread in East Africa, tropical Africa and Asia.

PAVONIA
Shrubs or rough herbs with cordate, lobed or entire leaves; epicalyx present, or five to six bracts, often connate at base, petals variable in colour, staminal columns (in East Africa) glabrous with stamens at the apex with five carpels and ten stigmas, fruit of five single-seeded mericarps, often ornamented or appendaged. Twenty-five species in East Africa.

NB In East Africa and from Arabia to South Africa there is a group of closely related *Pavonia* species in which the five bracts of the epicalyx are large and broad and hide the true calyx, so that they look like the calyx and it appears as if there is no epicalyx. These species have, in the past, been classified together as '*P. patens*' but the type of this name has now been found to be an *Abutilon* and not a *Pavonia*. The species once united as '*P. patens*' are now treated as four or five distinct species of which two are *P. gallaensis* and *P. glechomifolia* (see below).

Pavonia gallaensis   Plate 296
A shrubby plant from 0.5–1m (1½–3ft) tall. Flower (corolla) c. 3cm (1⅜in) across. Found in bushed grassland, and open *Acacia-Commiphora* bushland. Altitude range 1500–1800m (4900–5900ft). Nanyuki, Machakos, Embu, Kitui, southern Turkana, Baringo, Kajiado, Magadi (Kenya); lake areas, Maasai (Tanzania); Uganda, no record; also Ethiopia.

P. glechomifolia   Plate 447
A rather sparsely stellate-pubescent trailing or erect shrub with ovate to orbicular cordate leaves and solitary flowers, petals yellow with or without a dark spot at base; corolla c. 3cm (1⅜in) across. Long narrow epicalyx bracts and warty fruit. Found in dry *Commiphora* woodlands and semi-desert scrub; altitude range 90–2300m (300–7500ft). Tsavo West, Baringo, Rift Valley, Magadi, Machakos and Kajiado (Kenya); Tanga (Tanzania); northern Uganda; also Ethiopia, Somalia.

P. propinqua   Plate 298
A stellate-pubescent shrub with oblong or ovate rounded leaves and solitary flowers, 30mm (1¼in) across; petals yellow usually turning pink with age. Locally common in dry *Commiphora* or *Combretum* country; altitude range 15–1250m (50–4100ft). Magadi, Machakos, Kajiado and Isiolo (Kenya); Maasai (Tanzania);

northern region of Uganda; also in Ethiopia and Somalia.

P. urens   Plate 740
A soft, usually rather hairy shrub which grows on the edges of upland forest and along the sides of streams and water-courses in drier areas. Flowers clustered or single, varying in colour from pink to mauve and white, 2–4cm ($\frac{4}{5}$–1$\frac{3}{5}$in) across. Strong, flexible ropes are made from the stems and branches by some of Kenya's pastoral people. Widespread in Kenya at 1220–2740m (4000–9000ft); all regions of Tanzania except Songea; all regions of Uganda; also Ethiopia, Sudan, Zaire to Mozambique.

P. zeylanica   Plate 299
A short-lived perennial or annual covered with hairs on all its parts. The leaves are rounded and three- to five-lobed. Solitary pale yellow or cream flowers, c. 15mm ($\frac{3}{5}$in) across. Common in dry *Acacia-Commiphora* bushland at 45–1070m (150–3500ft) after rains in Kenya; Maasai, Tanga, Morogoro (Tanzania); Uganda, no record; also Ethiopia, Somalia.

Sida acuta An erect, short-lived, sparsely pubescent perennial with short-petiolate, lanceolate-oblong leaves and solitary cream or pale yellow flowers, 6mm ($\frac{1}{4}$in) across, with five petals. Altitude range 5–1200m (16–3900ft). One of about eighteen species in East Africa. Found amongst cultivation in dry coastal districts and in western areas influenced by Lake Victoria, Nyanza (Kenya); all regions of Tanzania; western, eastern Uganda; also widespread in tropical Africa, south to South Africa.

S. cordifolia   Plate 300
An erect, woody, pilose annual with ovate, cordate or rounded leaves and solitary or often fascicled pale yellow flowers, 8mm ($\frac{1}{3}$in) across. Altitude range 10–1500m (33–5000ft). Found as a weed in the warmer parts of Kenya where rainfall is 750mm (30in) or more; all regions of Tanzania and Uganda; also widespread in tropical Africa.

S. 'cuneifolia'   Plate 301
A confusing group of wiry shrublets with small narrow leaves and small yellow flowers about 8mm ($\frac{1}{3}$in) across. Common in the upland grasslands of East Africa, especially where they are overgrazed. Called *S. cuneifolia* until 1985 when the true species was found to be confined to India, while the African material represents the following five closely-related species.

a) **S. schimperiana** Closely related to *S.* sp. A in *UKWF*, found in upland grassland from 1200–2400m (4000–8000ft). Recorded in Northern Frontier areas, Turkana, Rift Valley, Nairobi, Nyeri, western Kenya and Kajiado (Kenya); lake areas, Maasai, Shinyanga, Tanga (Tanzania); eastern region of Uganda.

b) **S. tenuicarpa** This is the species recorded as *S. cuneifolia* in *UKWF*. Altitude range 1300–2100m (1500–7000ft). Common near Nairobi and widespread in Kenya (a specimen found at 50m (160ft) in the coastal area of Kenya was probably brought down in flood waters); Maasai, Shinyanga (Tanzania); western and eastern regions of Uganda.

c) **S. shinyangensis** Only recorded in Tanzania at 1000–1300m (3300–4500ft) in the Shinyanga area.

d) **S. masaica** Recorded under the name Sp. A in *UKWF* as the form with larger leaves. Flower 8mm (⅓in) across. Altitude range 1500–1700m (4900–5600ft). Nairobi district, Rift Valley, Nairobi, Nyeri and Kajiado (Kenya); lake area (Tanzania); Uganda, no record.

e) **S. tanaensis** At 100–225m (330–750ft) near the Tana River (Kenya); also in Somalia.

S. ovata   **Plate 195**
A densely pubescent, shrubby, short-lived perennial or woody annual with ovate elliptic leaves and solitary pale or orange-yellow flowers 6mm (¼in) across. A common species, widespread in dry grassland areas at 15–2000m (50–6600ft). Highland districts throughout Kenya; lake area, Maasai, Mpwapwa, Kondoa, Morogoro (Tanzania); all regions of Uganda; also in Ethiopia, south to Zimbabwe, Mozambique.

S. rhombifolia An erect, short-lived perennial with ovate-elliptic or rhombic leaves and yellow flowers, *c*. 1cm (⅜in) across, in axillary racemes, though sometimes solitary. Common and widespread from 900–2500m (2950–8200ft), especially in places disturbed by man, throughout most parts of East Africa except Central Tanzania; widespread in tropical Africa.

Thespesia populnea   **Plate 302**
A shrub or small tree up to 9m (30ft) high. Leaves ovate-cordate, 12cm (5in) long, with acuminate apices, entire margins, and the blade more or less covered with minute, sessile, peltate scales: petioles long. Flowers large, with an epicalyx of three to five segments falling quickly. Calyx densely clothed with sessile scales outside. Corolla broadly campanulate, 5cm (2in) or more in diameter, bright light yellow (rarely cream) turning reddish in the afternoon, the centre red to dark maroon. Widespread in coastal areas on saline sands behind mangroves in tropical Africa. More common in Tanzania than in Kenya. Two species in East Africa.

Urena lobata   **Plate 741**
An erect, tomentose herb with orbicular to oblong, simple to shallowly three-lobed leaves. The fruit is globose. Pink flower 2cm (¾in) across. Altitude range 1200–2100m (3850–6900ft). Common in disturbed ground and cultivation in western regions – Kitale, Bungoma, Mumias, Nandi Hills and Kisii (Kenya); all regions of Tanzania except Maasai; all regions of Uganda; also from Ethiopia to Zimbabwe.

45. Malpighiaceae

A small to medium-sized, tropical or subtropical family of woody climbers or less often, trees, shrubs or shrublets, mainly in America. Flowers are mostly regular and five in number with ten stamens and a superior ovary, usually trilocular. Styles are free or joined below. There are eighteen species in East Africa belonging to six genera.

Caucanthus albidus   **Plate 196**
An erect or scrambling shrub with masses of sweetly-scented, creamy-white flow-

ers c. 1cm (⅜in) across, which are often conspicuous in dry bushland after rain at altitudes of 180–600m (600–2000ft). The winged fruit is distributed by the small whirlwinds or 'dust devils' which frequently travel across this dry country. Northern and eastern areas of Kenya; Tanzania and Uganda, no record; also in Ethiopia and Somalia.

Triaspis niedenzuiana (*T. erlangeri*)   **Plate 57**
A small, attractive, semi-erect or scandent shrub (sometimes twining with ends of branches) up to 3m (10ft) in height; younger stems and inflorescences more or less covered with somewhat stiff short hairs, older ones glabrescent. Leaves petiolate; lamina from an ovate or broadly elliptic (rarely ovate-lanceolate) rounded, sometimes cuneate, base, obtuse or subacute, older ones more or less densely pubescent, especially beneath. Flowers in loose, few-flowered corymbs terminating leafy annual branches. Petals pure white, lilac or pinkish, oblong or oblong-ovate, more or less spoon-shaped, shortly fimbriate at edges near base, clawed, lateral wing distinctly retuse at apex, dorsal wing reduced. Flower 1–1.25mm (⅜–½in) diameter; petal c. 4mm (⅛in) long. Found in deciduous bushland, sometimes on stony hillsides or rocky outcrops, also in poor montane scrub; altitude range 500–1350m (1500–4400ft). Northern Frontier areas (Moyale), Machakos, Taru plains, Isiolo (Kenya); Pare Mts (Tanzania); Uganda, no record; also Ethiopia, Somalia.

46. Euphorbiaceae

A very large, mainly tropical family of herbs, shrubs and trees. Leaves are usually stipulate, flowers unisexual, monoecious or dioecious. Petals are usually absent and the ovary trilocular. Inflorescence 3–6cm (1⅛in–2⅜in) long; flower under 2mm (₁₂in) across. There are about 494 species in East Africa belonging to seventy-one genera of which seven are alien.

Acalypha volkensii   **Plate 506**
A loose-trailing, softly woody plant with simple, serrate leaves and very narrow, axillary racemes of hairless red flowers. Common in upland grassland and forest margins at 800–2700m (2600–8850ft) (Kenya); lake areas, Maasai, Tanga (Tanzania); eastern region of Uganda; also southern Sudan, Ethiopia, Somalia.

Argomuellera macrophylla   **Plate 197**
A small tree up to 3m (10ft) tall with almost sessile oblanceolate-elliptic leaves up to 38cm (15in) long and 10cm (4in) wide, apex acuminate, base long-alternate, margins serrate or subentire. Flowers glomerulate in spike-like racemes. Male flowers with three or four reflexed sepals 0.5cm (⅛in) long, numerous stamens and bright yellow-orange receptacles. Found in mist zones in hill country; altitude range 1500–2000m (5000–6600ft). Two species only in East Africa. Taita Hills, Emali Hill, Machakos and Mathews Range (Kenya); lake areas, Maasai, Tabora (Tanzania); all regions of Uganda; also in Ethiopia, eastern Zaire south to Zimbabwe, Mozambique.

Croton dichogamus   **Plate 198**
A savannah shrub or tree up to 12m (40ft) tall with a pyramidal crown. Young branches densely covered with pale brown overlapping scales. Leaves ovate-

lanceolate to elliptic-lanceolate, broad, glabrous above, densely covered with silvery scales below, apex obtuse or slightly pointed. Flowers yellow, the female flower at the base of the short (to 6cm (⅔in) long) racemes, the male at the top. Altitude range 550–2000m (1800–6560ft). One of twenty-three species in East Africa. Found in dry bush and dry marginal forest (Kenya); lake areas, Maasai, Tanga, Mpwapwa, Kondoa, Morogoro (Tanzania); eastern region of Uganda; also in Ethiopia, Rwanda.

C. megalocarpus
Plate 303

A tree usually 6–12m (20–40ft) high, though sometimes to 24m (80ft). Bark grey. The wood has a strong spicy flavour like pepper. Leaves with a pair of stalked glands at the base of the lamina, crenulate, broadly ovate, usually 7.5–15cm (3–6in) long and 3.75–10cm (1½–4in) broad, acuminate, three to seven-nerved at the base, shortly stellate-puberulous at first on both surfaces but becoming nearly glabrous, sometimes tomentose throughout life. Inflorescence (male) up to 25cm (10in) long, (female) less than 10cm (4in) long. Flowers yellow-white, sweetly scented, normally dioecious or at least on separate shoots, sometimes a few females accompanying the males. Altitude range 625–2000m (2000–6500ft). Widespread in higher rainfall areas, occasionally reaching a size suitable for timber in wetter forest areas and recorded throughout its habitat conditions (Kenya); all regions of Tanzania except Mpwapwa, Kondoa, Mbeya, Iringa; western region of Uganda; also in Malawi, Mozambique.

Dalechampia scandens var. cordofanus
Plate 6

A twining perennial with three- to five-lobed palmatifid leaves, bracts subtending inflorescence often acutely three-lobed at tip; ovate yellow fruit surrounded by nine to twelve stiff-spreading calyx lobes. Flower cream; inflorescence including bract 3–4cm (1½–1½in) across. A common plant in disturbed *Commiphora* bushland in dry country, often growing by roadsides or around habitations. The sepals in fruit develop extremely irritating hairs. The male flowers are without disc or petals, female flowers with eight to twelve sepals becoming enlarged in fruit and an entire stigma. Altitude range 10–1400m (33–4600ft). Magadi, Machakos and Kajiado (Kenya); all regions except lake areas, Songea (Tanzania); northern region of Uganda; also in Sudan, Ethiopia, Somalia. There are two varieties of this species: var. *cordofanus* as above and var. *hildebrandtii* common at the coast (Kenya); Tanga, Morogoro, Songea (Tanzania); Zanzibar.

EUPHORBIA

An abundant genus, trees, shrubs or herbs more or less succulent with a toxic milky latex. Leaves simple, alternate or opposite, flowers much reduced to single stamens (male) and single gynoecium (female), crowded in a corymbose head or capitulum with linear bracts called a cyathium; cyathia solitary or arranged in dichasial cymes, each with one central female flower and many peripheral male flowers; involucre of cyathium regular, bearing one to five glands and five scale teeth; fruit a capsule with three single-seeded loculi. About 158 species in East Africa.

Euphorbia cryptospinosa
Plate 659

An erect shrub to 2m (6½ft) high, usually subscandent. Stems solitary, cylindrical, longitudinally sulcate, branching is alternate, opposite or fasciculate, spines present or absent. Leaves very small, deltoid, keeled, 1–15mm (to ⅝in) long, usually deciduous. Inflorescence a cyme; involucre sessile, 3mm (⅛in) across; both male and female flowers sub-globose, shortly pedicellate, brownish-yellow to deep scarlet. Found in thorn bushes where it resembles dead twigs except when in flower; altitude range 30–1350m (100–4500ft). Northern, north-eastern areas and in coastal hinterland (Kenya); elsewhere only in Somalia.

E. cuneata   Plate 304
A much-branched shrub up to 3m (10ft) tall with alternate, spine-tipped branches. Leaves glabrous, linear-cuneate to spathulate, 2.5cm (1in) long and 1.25cm ($\frac{1}{2}$in) wide, persistent at flowering time. Involucre, 0.3cm ($\frac{1}{8}$in) in diameter, in an umbel-like cyme or two to three in a cluster. At first sight may be easily mistaken for a *Commiphora*. The copious white latex seen when a stem or leaf is cut or broken is the easiest way to identify it as a *Euphorbia*. Altitude range 10–1700m (33–5660ft). A very variable species, of which several varieties are recognized. Found in northern districts and coast province where it is sometimes used as a hedge plant in coastal districts (Kenya); Maasai, Tanga, Morogoro, Songea (Tanzania);, Uganda, no record; also in Ethiopia, Somalia, Sudan.

E. gossypina   Plate 507
A fleshy-stemmed shrub often trailing over trees with oblong, acute, ephemeral leaves; inflorescence of umbellate cyathia which are white-woolly within. Yellowish-green flower *c*. 7mm ($\frac{1}{4}$in) across. Locally common in rocky bushland on shallow soils, altitude range 50–2100m (165–6900ft). Aberdares, Narok, Rift Valley, Nanyuki, Machakos and Nairobi (Kenya); Maasai (Tanzania); northern region of Uganda; also in southern Somalia.

E. graciliramea   Plate 305
A small, prostrate herb with succulent cylindrical stems, which grows from a woody rootstock. The brownish-yellow flowers have a faint purplish tinge, and on each spine shield form two small spines and one large one. The flower is really a group of reduced flowers *c*. 7mm ($\frac{1}{4}$in) across. Locally common at altitudes of 900–1650m (3000–5500ft). In the Narok, Rift Valley, Magadi, Nanyuki, Nairobi and Kajiado districts and it is also seen in the Maasai Mara area (Kenya); lake areas, Maasai, Mpwapwa, Kondoa (Tanzania); Uganda and elsewhere, not known.
   NB It may be eventually classified as a subspecies of *E. triaculeata*.

E. heterochroma   Plate 448
A much-branched, thorny leafless succulent bush with procumbent and ascending stems up to 2m (6ft) high. Branches four-angled (sometimes five), variegated green, with margins more or less sinuate-toothed. Spines very short up to 3mm ($\frac{1}{8}$in) long, diverging in pairs with or without a pair of minute prickles at base. Flower, a cyme, sessile or subsessile with three or four yellow involucres; cythia 2–3mm (*c*. $\frac{1}{12}$in) across. Found in bushland in dry rocky country; altitude range 100–1100m (325–3600ft). Baringo, Magadi, Machakos and Kajiado (Kenya); Maasai, Tanga (Tanzania); Uganda and elsewhere, not known.

E. kibwezensis   Plates 7 & 306
A tree growing to 6m (20ft) or more with a cylindrical bole surmounted by a crown of curved ascending limbs or branches. The branches are grey-green and hairless, three- to four-angled, though occasionally flat, and constricted into segments of varied shape, 5–20cm (2–8in) long and 5–7.5cm (2–3in) in diameter, the angles wing-like, very thin and unevenly toothed and wavy. The flowering eyes are yellow and carried in pairs, just above the spine. Flowers in cluster 6–7mm ($\frac{1}{4}$in) across. The fruit or seed is red, *c*. 20mm ($\frac{4}{5}$in) across. This is a tree of semi-arid and arid areas in thicket bush and on rocky shores. Altitude range 400–1600m

(1300–5250ft). It is sometimes found in dry situations near coast or lake shores (Kenya); Maasai, Tanga (Tanzania); Uganda and elsewhere, no record.

NB *E. nyikae* (Plate 508) is a closely-related species and not a synonym. *E. kibwezensis* is closely related to other species such as *E. bussei* from southern Tanzania, of which it may eventually be classified as a variety.

E. uhligiana
Plate 307

A succulent spiny perennial with densely tufted four-angled stems, up to 80–100cm (2–3ft) long, spreading from a thick fleshy root. Spines up to 13mm ($\frac{1}{2}$in) long in pairs, often united for 1–2mm at the base. Cyathia 2.5–4.5mm ($\frac{1}{10}$–$\frac{1}{6}$in) across. On stony slopes in open deciduous bushland, 435–1550m (1450–5200ft) above the sea in the Maasai areas of Kenya and Tanzania and Lushoto district (Tanzania); unknown elsewhere. Closely related to *E. stapfii* and the new species seen in plate 544.

E. rivae
Plate 543

A perennial with a swollen, fleshy rootstock and short prostrate branches, sparsely hairy, bearing orbicular leaves. Flower reddish-pink, *c.* 3mm ($\frac{1}{8}$in) across. Altitude range 700–1800m (2300–5900ft). Found locally in shallow soils and particularly common round Nairobi (Kenya); Tanzania and Uganda, no record; also in southern Sudan, southern Ethiopia.

E. schimperiana
Plate 449

An erect annual or short-lived perennial with usually narrow, elliptic leaves and deltoid triangular clasping bracts, glabrous or hairy on all parts, involucral glands with a central, crescent-shaped or oval body abruptly joined to a filamentous horn at each end. Cyathia 5mm ($\frac{1}{5}$in) across, in large, branched, leafy inflorescence. The commonest mountain *Euphorbia*, growing by roadsides and forest edges; altitude range 1100–3000m (3600–9850ft). Widespread in Kenya; all regions of Tanzania (except lake areas) and Uganda; also Sudan, Ethiopia, Malawi, Mozambique.

E. stapfii A spiny succulent shrub up to 2m (6$\frac{1}{2}$ft) high, branching from the base and sometimes rebranching above; branches four to five angled, slightly constricted at varying intervals, with spine shields sometimes united into continuous dark brown or greyish margins. Leaves rudimentary, scale-like, ovate and acute at apex. Cymes solitary from each flowering eye, sessile. Involucre greenish-yellow, *c.* 4.5cm (*c.* 2in) diameter. Close to *E. heterochroma* in some forms. Found in *Commiphora* scrub or old lava flows, and plains of lava boulders in soft damp mud; altitude range 375–2010m (1250–6600ft). Recorded in Embu, Machakos, Kajiado, Narok, coast dry hinterland (Kenya); Maasai, Tanga (Tanzania); northern region of Uganda; elsewhere, probably Zimbabwe, Zambia.

Euphorbia (New Species)
Plate 544

A sturdy, much-branched, leafless, spiny succulent shrub up to 2.5m (*c.* 8ft) tall with a milky somewhat poisonous latex. Branches four to five (six)-angled; 2–3mm (*c.* $\frac{1}{8}$in) thick. Flower cyathia 5mm ($\frac{1}{5}$in) across. Closely related to *E. stapfii*. Found in open deciduous woodland on rocky slopes; altitude range 900–1760m (2950–5775ft). Recorded only in northern regions, Tsavo, Machakos, Embu, Kitui coast hinterland (Kenya).

E. tescorum   A much-branched, thorny, leafless, succulent bush with milky latex, stems procumbent and ascending, to 2m (6ft) high. Branches four-angled (sometimes five), variegated green with margins more or less sinuous-toothed. Spines very short, 4mm (⅛in) long, diverging in pairs, spine shields continuous or interrupted. Cymes sessile or subsessile with three or four yellow involucres 2mm (¹⁄₁₂in) long. Very similar to *E. heterochroma*. Found growing on lava screes and at edges of scrub desert, altitude range 390–1300m (1300–4350ft). Kajiado, Taita Hills, Mwatate bush, Magadi (Kenya); Tanzania, no record; northern region of Uganda; also in southern Ethiopia.

Monadenium stapelioides   **Plate 545**
A herb with short, fleshy tuberculate perennial stems arising from a tuberous rootstock; leaves elliptic to obovate; caythia in pairs with a reddish involucral gland and pale whitish bracts; 5cm (2in) long. Altitude range 1800–2400m (6000–8000ft). Locally common in dry rocky screes and cliffs and dry grassland. Narok, Baringo, Rift Valley, Magadi and Nanyuki (Kenya); Maasai (Tanzania); Uganda and elsewhere, no record.
   NB The *Monadeniums* are a curious group of plants which occur rarely in dry country. Readers interested in succulent plants should consult the late P.R.O. Bally's monograph of this African genus in which all species are beautifully illustrated, mostly in colour. About thirty-five species in East Africa.

Ricinus communis   **Plate 546**
A tall, annual or perennial herb sometimes branching above with large five to nine palmatisect leaves; panicles terminal; capsules often softly prickly. Flowers red and green, 6mm (¼in) across. Widely cultivated (as castor oil) and spontaneous in dry country. One species in East Africa. Widespread in Kenya and tropical Africa. Altitude range 600–2000m (2000–6550ft). Recently palaeontologists have found some fossil fruits 300,000 years old in the Omo Valley in south-western Ethiopia, so it is certainly native in Africa.

Tragia brevipes   A climbing herb, sometimes woody at base with stinging hairs, especially on the fruits, and ovate to suborbicular, acuminate, cordate leaves. Flower *c*. 2mm (¹⁄₁₂in) long. Fairly common at edges of upland dry forest; this plant is one of the principal stingers of Kenya in upland areas. Altitude range 300–2340m (1000–7800ft). Twenty-two other species in East Africa. Widespread (Kenya); lake areas, Maasai, Tabora, Mpwapwa, Kondoa, Mbeya, Iringa (Tanzania); all regions of Uganda; also Ethiopia, northern Somalia, Malawi, Zambia, Zimbabwe.

T. impedita   **Plate 199**
A monoecious, pubescent erect or sub-erect shrub or herb to 1m (3ft) high, with stinging hairs. Leaves shortly petiolate, leaf blade ovate-lanceolate, acute at apex and shallowly cordate at base, margins serrate. Inflorescence up to 10cm (4in) long, leaf opposed, male flowers, occurring towards end of inflorescence, 3mm (⅛in across; female ones lower down, 1.5cm (⅜in) across. Flowers creamy-yellow. Female flowers with densely hairy calyx. Found in rough grassland, on stony hilltops, in *Acacia-Combretum* scrub, river banks and roadsides; altitude range 390–2000m (1300–6670ft). Nairobi, Nanyuki, Embu, Machakos, Kajiado, Rift Valley (Kenya); Maasai, Mpwapwa, Kondoa (Tanzania); not known elsewhere.

T. insuavis   **Plate 200**
A climbing or trailing perennial herb with stinging hairs especially on the stems and with ovate, cordate, often almost glabrous leaves. Flower *c*. 2mm (¹⁄₁₂in) long. It is a

rather uncommon plant in dry bushland and very variable; altitude range 640–1330m (2130–4430ft). Narok, Kajiado, Magadi and Machakos (Kenya); lake areas, Mpwapwa, Kondoa, Mbeya, Iringa (Tanzania); Uganda and elsewhere, no record.

47. Rosaceae
THE ROSE FAMILY

A large family, found mainly in temperate regions. Leaves are usually alternate, often divided and with stipules present. Flowers are usually perigynous with the receptacle forming a cup or saucer around the pistil with the sepals, petals and stamens attached to its rim, or occasionally to the inferior ovary. Petals are free and stamens often numerous and there may be one or many, more-or-less free carpels. Fifty species belonging to eleven genera are found in East Africa.

Alchemilla cryptantha A creeping herb, producing basal rosettes of shortly stalked ephemeral leaves and with long, often slender stolons rooting at the nodes, and covered with long, whitish or yellowish hairs. Leaves reniform, five-lobed, variably densely covered with long hairs on both surfaces, sometimes nearly glabrous; lobes broadly rounded to broadly obovate, normally shallow not reaching beyond the base of the lamina, the sides entire, the terminal teeth unequal (or the central ones smaller). Flowers axillary, usually one to two together, more or less concealed by the stipules, either subsessile or on filiform pedicels up to 8mm (⅓in) long; calyx-lobe 0.75mm long. Elongated, cymose inforescences rarely developed. Pedicels as hairy as the stems. It is similar to *A. kiwuensis* but the basal rosette is often absent and the leaves are more shallowly lobed. Locally common in alpine and montane grassland; altitude range 1300–4050m (4250–13,300ft). Elgon, Cheranganis, Tinderet, Aberdares, Mt Kenya, Kitale and Narok (Kenya); Moshi (Mt Loitokitok), Lushoto (Tanzania); Acholi (Imatong Mts), Kigezi, Mbale (Uganda); also widespread from Sudan, Eritrea, Ethiopia, to Zimbabwe, Mozambique.

A. fischeri   **Plate 8**
A trailing herb with rosettes of deeply-lobed hairy leaves, lobes obovate and rounded at the apex. The inflorescence is a small panicle formed of small masses of nearly stalkless, whitish flowers, 2mm (₁⁄₁₂in) across. Leaves: c. 10cm (4in) across. It is common in *Philippia* woodland at altitudes 2350–3380m (7600–11,100ft). Aberdares (Kenya); Maasai (Tanzania); Uganda, no record; also in southern Ethiopia.

A. johnstonii   **Plate 9**
A low, straggling shrub with prostrate stems and erect or procumbent branches, often dominant in carpet-like masses; sometimes with small and densely congested leaves. Stems woody but sometimes herbaceous (soft) at the extremities, rooting rather frequently at the nodes, usually reddish-brown, covered (often thickly) with long, ascending, more or less spreading, whitish hairs, rarely glabrous. Leaves, petiolate, often leathery, circular to reniform in outline three to five lobed (sometimes seven), 5–40mm (⅕–1⅗in) long, and usually broader than long; lobes often up to 1cm (⅜in) deep, obtuse or rounded, entire or dentate at apex, sometimes appearing emarginate, often markedly folded along the midrib. Inflorescence usually short, simple or branched, pedicels sparsely hirsute with long ascending hairs.

Flowers greenish-yellow, calyx lobe 1.5–2mm ($\frac{1}{12}$in) long. Found in upland moor, moist bamboo-thicket, moor grassland on damp ground and often in bogs; altitude range 2400–4200m (7875–13,775ft). Cheranganis, Aberdares (Kinangop), Mt Kenya (Kenya); Moshi (Kilimanjaro), Morogoro, (Tanzania); Toro (Ruwenzori), Kigezi, Mbale (Uganda); also in the Virunga Mts.
   NB *A. johnstonii* is a very variable species and there are twenty-five synonyms recorded in *FTEA*.

A. rothii   Plate 10
A rather stout species with a stocky central tuft of leaves and long creeping stolons. Stems variably shaggy with spreading or more or less deflexed pale brown hairs. Leaves round in outline, seven to nine lobed, 2.7–5cm (1–2in) in diameter, the basal sinus usually narrow, often closed, or nearly so, and covered on both sides with white or brownish hairs, often very soft and silky white, sometimes sparse on the upper surface; lobes very shallow often no more than 2mm ($\frac{1}{12}$in) deep so that the leaves often appear undivided. The leaves terminally very broadly rounded to truncate and dentate with nine to thirteen subacute teeth. Inflorescence often much exceeding the leaves and up to 22cm ($8\frac{1}{2}$in) long; panicles usually open but sometimes the inflorescence is dense; colour yellow. It is very similar to *A. cyclophylla* but has more hairy and rounded leaf lobes and usually a branching inflorescence. In the *Flora of Tropical East Africa* (*FTEA*), they are deemed the same. Found in heath and bamboo zones on higher mountains or hills, altitude range 2700–4000m (8850–14,400ft) in Elgon, Mau, Aberdares and Mt Kenya (Kenya); Tanzania, no record; Karamoja (Mt Debasien), Mbale – Elgon (Uganda); also in Ethiopia.

Hagenia abyssinica   Plate 450
A tree which grows to a height of about 15m (50ft). Its bark is dark red-brown and flakes off irregularly; leaves reddish when young and flowers pendant. The female inflorescence, 30–50cm (12–20in) long, is reddish and more bulky than the male which is orange-buff or white with a more plume-like appearance. It yields a powerful medicine for dealing with intestinal worms and in Ethiopia, where the tree is called Kosso, is much valued on this account. Found between 2400–3600m (8000–12,000ft) in all the moist uplands of Kenya, especially at the upper margin of montane forest, where it is often dominant. Arusha, Usambara Mts, Mbeya (Tanzania); Acholi, Imatong Mts, Kigezi, Mbale – Elgon (Uganda); also from Ethiopia through eastern Zaire to Malawi, Zimbabwe, and Zambia.

Rubus friesiorum   Plate 742
A sub-erect pubescent to tomentose shrub with tri-foliate leaves, dark green above, whitish below, and a cylindrical inflorescence of pinkish flowers with glabrous or hairy drupes; petal 1.2–1.6cm ($\frac{1}{2}$–$\frac{5}{8}$in) long. The prickles are red, variable in number, decurved, up to 3mm ($\frac{1}{8}$in) long, basally dilated, often tomentose, sometimes glabrous. It is an uncommon plant found at the edges of montane forest, altitude range 2700–3050m (9000–10,000ft). High Aberdares (Kenya); not known elsewhere.

R. keniensis   Plate 743
A stout, scrambling shrub with reddish-green stems covered, especially thickly above, with loosely-spreading yellowish hairs interspersed with small, hooked or deflexed prickles scarcely 3mm ($\frac{1}{8}$in) in length. Leaves trifoliolate, leaflets broadly ovate to ovate-oblong, 8–11.5cm (3–$4\frac{1}{2}$in)×4–7.5cm ($1\frac{1}{2}$–3in), obtuse or acute, scarcely acuminate, basally rounded to cordate, terminal leaflet often larger and

broader than the lateral ones, all serrate or obscurely biserrate, dark green and softly hairy above with yellowish appressed hairs, more densely hairy beneath with fulvous or whitish, somewhat shining hairs. Inflorescence a rather stout pyramidal panicle up to 26×18cm (10×7in), the branchlets widely ascending, the axis, peduncles and pedicels densely and softly ochreous-villous. Flowers large and showy c. 2.5cm (1in) diameter, calyx ochreous or whitish-tomentose, deeply divided into ovate or ovate-oblong, caudate-acuminate lobes 7–10mm ($\frac{1}{4}$–$\frac{2}{3}$in) long, spreading at anthesis. Petals white or pale pink, 11×10mm ($\frac{2}{3}$in) long, rounded but abruptly narrowed at the base; margin waxy especially at the apex. Found at the edges of upland rain forest and river banks; altitude range 1950–2670m (5750–8000ft). Aberdares, Mt Kenya, Kinangop, Kiambu and Limuru (Kenya); not known elsewhere.

R. pinnatus   Plate 744
A variable, sometimes scrambling, widely spreading shrub up to 6m (20ft) tall. Flowering shoots with rather slender, greenish-red or red, subglabrous or tomentose stalks; prickles straight or hooked, glabrous up to 6mm ($\frac{1}{4}$in) long (often less), sometimes congestedly numerous. Leaves imparipinnate, the uppermost trifoliolate; leaflets small, ovate to ovate-lanceolate (the terminal one the longest), acute or acuminate, base rounded to cordate, sharply or deeply serrate, green but paler beneath. Inflorescence up to 35cm (14in) long, a rather lax panicle of pink or white flowers, petals 4×2.5mm ($\frac{1}{8}$×$\frac{1}{10}$in), shorter than sepals; drupes black when ripe, pubescent. Locally common in upland rain-forest and montane forest clearings and edges; altitude range 2400–2500m (7875–8200ft). Throughout Kenya in this ecological zone, also in Tanzania. Widespread through tropical and subtropical Africa. The var. *pinnatus* is recorded as above; in Uganda the var. *afrotropicus* is recorded in the Ruwenzori Mts and Buganda, and also in Kenya and Tanzania.

R. steudneri   Plate 745
A densely-haired scrambler with trifoliolate leaves and pink to purple flowers with large petals. It is allied to the Blackberry of northern Europe. The glabrous fruit is deep orange to plum-coloured. Flower c. 18mm ($\frac{2}{3}$in) across. Locally common in undergrowth in forest clearings and edges at 1500–3150m (5000–10,500ft) in nearly all the moist montane areas of East Africa; also in Ethiopia and Zaire.

48–50. Leguminosae (Fabaceae)

An enormous group of trees, shrubs, lianes and herbs found throughout the world. They are sometimes treated as an order containing three families but it is now more usual to consider them as a family with three subfamilies, Caesalpinioideae, Papilionoideae and Mimosoideae. Their leaves are almost always alternate and stipulate and usually compound. Flowers are perigynous as in the Rosaceae and the fruit in the form of one, or very rarely more than one, free carpel which usually splits lengthwise into two valves, occasionally splitting transversely or indehiscent. Bipinnate leaves fairly common, simple leaves very rare. 1220 species in 168 genera in East Africa.

48. Caesalpinioideae

Mainly tropical trees or shrubs or rarely herbs. Leaves pinnate, bipinnate or rarely simple. Flowers zygomorphic; the upper petal inside the two lateral petals; stamens usually free, often fewer or more than ten. One hundred and fifty species in forty-four genera in East Africa. In the Miombo woodlands of southern Tanzania, most of the dominant trees belong to this subfamily.

BAUHINIA

Characterized by their camel's foot leaves. Shrubs, small trees (rarely climbers); leaves simple, conspicuously bi-lobed, rarely divided as far as the base; flowers large and showy, in short usually few-flowered racemes or solitary; calyx spathaceous; five petals; one to ten fertile stamens; stigma capitate or small, sometimes ± unilateral. Pods oblong to linear, few- to many-seeded. Five species in East Africa.

Bauhinia taitensis   Plate 58

A shrub which grows to a height of 1.7m (5ft) with many stems and branches. Its rough bark is grey-brown and its small leaves are covered with down. Yellowish, creamy-white flowers are produced in great numbers; petals 13–24mm ($\frac{1}{2}$–1in) long. One of five species in East Africa. Found at 300–1070m (1000–3500ft). Machakos, Taita Hills and Northern Province (Kenya); Tanzania and Uganda, no record; not known elsewhere.

   NB Closely related to *B. tomentosa* but has normally much smaller (1–2.6cm ($\frac{2}{5}$–1in) long, 1.5–3.3cm ($\frac{3}{5}$–1$\frac{3}{5}$in) broad) and more deeply divided leaves, and can be recognized by the much smaller flowers and especially by the cuneate-based white petals. *B. tomentosa* has leaves up to 7cm (*c*. 3in) long, occasionally to 9cm (3$\frac{3}{5}$in) and 1.2–6.5cm (occasionally 11cm (4$\frac{2}{5}$in)) ($\frac{1}{2}$–2$\frac{3}{5}$in) broad.

B. tomentosa   Plate 308

An erect shrub growing up to 7.5m (25ft) in height. Its leaves are bilobed up to 6.5cm (2$\frac{1}{2}$in) wide, hairless or with minute soft hairs beneath, rounded at the apex with three main nerves in each lobe. The flowers are large, 3–4cm (1$\frac{3}{5}$–1$\frac{3}{5}$in) across, solitary or in axillary pairs, or sometimes in inflorescences of a few flowers together with a corolla of five petals up to 5cm (2in) long, all yellow in colour but sometimes with the upper petal having a maroon or purple spot at the base. Altitude range 20–1600m (65–5200ft). Coastal, central and northern districts (Kenya); Moshi, Dodoma, Uzaramo (Tanzania); Uganda, no record; also in Somalia, Ethiopia, Zaire and south to Zambia and Zimbabwe, and tropical Asia.

CAESALPINIA

Shrubs or trees, erect or more often scrambling or climbing; armed with spines or prickles or sometimes unarmed. Leaves always bipinnate in East Africa; stipules various, minute to conspicuously leafy; leaflets opposite, rarely alternate, glandular or sometimes eglandular. Inflorescences of terminal sometimes falsely lateral, or terminal and axillary racemes or panicles; bracts usually quickly falling. Five sepals, imbricate, sometimes very narrowly so or valvate; the lower sepal often cucullate and clasping the others; five petals, subequal except for the modified upper one; ten stamens, fertile; filaments alternately longer or shorter, all pubescent or villous but glabrous below; anthers dorsifixed; ovary free, subsessile or stipitate; style glabrous; stigma truncate or oblique; pods very variable, usually flat or ± compressed, not winged, bi-valved, hard and woody or thick and pulpy. Ten species in East Africa.

Caesalpinia bonduc   Plate 309
A bush or shrubby tree, spreading or half climbing to 5m (16ft) high. Stems pubescent and more or less densely armed with spreading, straight (or the larger ones slightly deflexed) prickles of various lengths. Stipules conspicuous, leafy of two to three unequal-sized lobes resembling leaflets up to 2.5cm (1in) long, mucronate and rounded to emarginate at apex. Leaves, petiole with rhachis armed on lower side with recurved prickles. Pinnae three to nine pairs, leaflets six to nine pairs per pinna, ovate-oblong or elliptic-oblong, sometimes subacute, not or scarcely acuminate, pubescent to glabrous except for midrib and margins. Racemes axillary, pedunculate, simple or with one to two branches below. Petals yellow or greenish-yellow, 12–13mm ($\frac{1}{2}$in) long, 3–4mm ($\frac{1}{8}$–$\frac{1}{6}$in) wide. Found on or near sea-shores; altitude range 0–15m (0–50ft). Kilifi, Lamu (Kenya); Tanga, Rufiji (Tanzania); Zanzibar; Uganda, no record; also widespread in tropics.

NB The hard-shelled seeds float well on the sea and remain viable after as much as two and a half years afloat. This characteristic largely dictates its habitat.

C. decapetala   Plate 310
A climbing or struggling bushy shrub or tree up to 10m (33ft) high with scattered prickles. Leaves bi-pinnate with rhachis armed with downwardly hooked prickles; pinnae four to ten pairs; leaflets eight to twelve pairs per pinna, elliptic-oblong or slightly ovate and rounded at apex. Inflorescence a raceme, to 30cm (12in) long, at the end of main or lateral branches. Petals yellow to yellowish-white, 10–15mm ($\frac{2}{5}$–$\frac{3}{5}$in) long, 8–15mm ($\frac{1}{3}$–$\frac{3}{5}$in) wide. Not a true native but originally from tropical and subtropical Asia, naturalized and also in gardens in Kenya. Found in lowland rain-forest, scattered-tree grassland and bushland; altitude range 410–2040m (1380–6800ft). Throughout Kenya including Lodwar; Usambara Mts (Tanzania); Bunyoro (Uganda); also in Ethiopia southwards to South Africa.

C. trothae   Plates 660 & 746
A shrub from 0.3–3m (1–10ft) in height (occasionally to 5m (16$\frac{1}{2}$ft)), erect but sometimes somewhat climbing. Young stems glabrous to pubescent, armed with scattered, straight or spreading, or sometimes more or less curved prickles, varying in length up to 9mm ($\frac{1}{3}$in). Leaves, petiole often more or less prickly, pinnae three to seventeen pairs, leaflets four to thirty-three pairs per pinna, narrowly oblong or oblong-elliptic, or the uppermost slightly obovate, 4–10mm ($\frac{1}{6}$–$\frac{2}{5}$in) long, though they can be slightly less and slightly longer than this, and from 1mm to 4mm ($\frac{1}{6}$in) wide, rounded at apex and usually mucronate, more or less pubescent or puberulous on midrib and margins or becoming quite glabrous, usually minutely crenulate. Racemes terminal and lateral, 2.5–15cm (1–6in) long (occasionally 24cm (10in)), simple. Bracts ovate or elliptic-acuminate, usually falling off while flower buds are still young. Flowers mauve-pink, sepals 8–12mm ($\frac{1}{3}$–$\frac{1}{2}$in) long; petals obovate, 9–20mm ($\frac{1}{3}$–$\frac{4}{5}$in) long, 4.5–15mm ($\frac{1}{6}$–$\frac{3}{5}$in) wide. Upper petal smaller than the others with a transverse usually bidentate, wing-like projection on inner side at apex of claw. Pods boat-shaped or anvil shaped, 1.5–5cm ($\frac{3}{5}$–2in) long, 1.5–2.2cm ($\frac{3}{5}$–1in) wide. Found in dry scrub with trees and deciduous bushland; altitude range 150–1070m (500–3500ft). Machakos, Tsavo West and East, Taita district, Tsavo bridge and Kwale district (Kenya); Dodoma, Morogoro, Iringa (Tanzania); Uganda and elsewhere, no record.

NB There are two subspecies: C. trothae ssp. trothae confined to East Africa, and ssp. erlangeri with fewer leaflets recorded in the Northern Frontier districts of

Kenya and in Ethiopia and Somalia at 100–800m (328–2800ft).

CASSIA

Leaves parapinnate, often with glands and stipules on the rhachis; pods cylindrical. Forty-eight species in East Africa. *Cassia* in Africa is now being divided into three groups which are very easily recognized.

Cassia abbreviata **Plate 311**

A small, many-branched tree which grows to 7.5m (25ft) in height. Leaves up to 25cm (10in) long, consisting of five to thirteen pairs of leaflets, each up to 4cm ($1\frac{1}{2}$in) long, elliptic or elliptic-oblong, apex rounded or emarginate. Fragrant golden-yellow flowers form terminal and axillary corymbs with persistent and conspicuous bracts. Pedicels are 63mm ($2\frac{1}{2}$in) long, petals 13mm ($\frac{1}{2}$in) and the filaments of the three larger stamens are dilated at the base. Pods cylindrical. Found in Kenya in some coastal areas and in dry bushland from 50–1500m (160–4900ft); Mpwapwa, Rungwe, Lindi, Handeni, Mpanda, Morogoro, Lushoto (Tanzania); Uganda, no record; also south to Zimbabwe, Zambia, Mozambique.

C. afrofistula **Plate 312**

A shrub or small tree from 1.2–6m (*c.* $3\frac{1}{2}$–20ft) high. Young branchlets minutely puberulous in East Africa, soon glabrous. Leaves with petiole and rhachis eglandular. Leaflets in four to nine pairs, petiolate, ovate to ovate-elliptic 2–10cm ($\frac{3}{4}$–4in) long, obtuse or subacute at apex. Inflorescence usually an erect, large, pyramidal terminal panicle composed of terminal and lateral racemes. Panicle 75–100cm (30–40in) or more long; racemes 15–38cm (6–15in) long. Bracts all falling while flower buds are young. Petals bright yellow, to 3cm ($1\frac{1}{5}$in) long, 1–2cm ($\frac{1}{5}$–$\frac{3}{4}$in) wide, three filaments, each with an S-bend near base and an abrupt, conspicuous swelling little more than half way along their length. Pods cylindrical. Found in coastal evergreen bushland and common in dry coral areas of Zanzibar; altitude range 1–90m (3–300ft). Kilifi, Tiwi, Malindi, Tana River District and Mombasa (Kenya); Tanga, Mafia Island, Lindi, Zanzibar (Tanzania); Uganda, no record; also in Mozambique.

NB This species must not be confused with *C. fistula*, which is a native of Asia and has been introduced into East African gardens. *C. fistula* has pendulous racemes, one to three together, and leaflets almost equal at base, with more numerous lateral nerves and minutely appressed-puberulous beneath. The pods have hard woody walls, while those of *C. afrofistula* can be cracked between thumb and finger.

C. bicapsularis **Plate 313**

A shrub, often spreading, scrambling or climbing up to 1.5–9m ($4\frac{1}{2}$–30ft) high. Stems in East Africa glabrous. Leaves; petiole eglandular; rhachis with a prominent clavate or subglobose gland between the lowest pair of leaflets. Leaflets in three pairs (sometimes two) obovate-elliptic to suborbicular 1–3cm ($\frac{2}{5}$–$1\frac{2}{5}$in) long; rounded at apex, glabrous in East Africa, 0.7–2.4cm (*c.* $\frac{3}{10}$–1in) broad. Racemes three to fifteen flowered, the peduncle usually well-developed and obvious. Petals yellow or orange, obovate, 1–1.3cm ($\frac{2}{5}$–$\frac{1}{2}$in) long. Pods, oblong-linear, straight, cylindrical, rounded at apex, 8–15cm (*c.* 3–6in) long, 1–1.5cm ($\frac{1}{5}$–$\frac{3}{5}$in) broad. Found in grassland, bushland, old cultivations, roadsides; altitude range 0–2130m (0–7000ft). This species is not a true native of East Africa, but from the West Indies and western South America. It may be found within its altitude zone throughout Kenya where escapes from cultivation have occurred; Mwanza, Maasai, Morogoro (Tanzania); Ankole, Teso, Entebbe (Uganda); no record elsewhere in Africa but probably an escape.

C. didymobotrya **Plate 314**
A poisonous shrub or small tree which grows to 6.5m (20ft) in height. The bright yellow flowers, *c*. 3cm (1⅖in) across, appear to have a dark blob on the top where the still unfolded buds show brown; pods flat. The roots provide an antidote to the poison produced by the stem and leaves. The Maasai use an infusion of the leaves as a purgative and the hard stems can be used to produce fire by rotating them between the hands against a softer wood in Boy Scout fashion. The spark can be encouraged with the breath and used to ignite dry kindling such as the soft lining of a weaver bird's nest. It is common everywhere in East Africa except very dry areas from 600–2100m (2000–7000ft) and often seen, especially along or just beyond the ditches and depressions at the sides of roads. Also in Ethiopia, Sudan, Zambia, Zimbabwe, Malawi, Mozambique.

C. fallacina **Plate 315**
A perennial herb or shrublet with a woody rootstock and spreading or prostrate stems up to 35cm (13¾in) long which are shortly crisped-pubescent or puberulous without spreading hairs. Leaves oblong-lanceolate up to 5cm (2in) long, gland above middle of petiole, peltate and flattened, raised on a distinct slender yellowish stalk 1–2.25mm (*c*. ⅒in) long. Leaflets sessile, usually nine to twenty-seven pairs, oblong, asymmetric, straight or slightly curved, mostly 3–10mm (⅛–⅖in) long, glabrous, except for short hairs on margins and sometimes midrib, sometimes with some appressed pubescence on lower surface. Midrib very strongly eccentric running along one margin of leaflet for its whole length. Inflorescence one to two-flowered. Petals yellow, 5–8mm (⅕–⅓in) long, 3–6.5mm (⅛–¼in) wide; pods flat. Found in grassland and open grassland; altitude range 100–1160m (300–3800ft). Machakos, Tsavo, Magadi, Kwale – near Lunga Lunga (Kenya); Maasai, Mpwapwa (Tanzania); Uganda, no record; also in Somalia.

C. floribunda Similar to *C. occidentalis* but with fewer leaflets and cylindrical pods which do not open spontaneously but remain closed when ripe. The flowers are yellow *c*. 20mm (⅘in) across, pods subterete. It is locally common in Kenya in cultivation in cleared forest at higher altitudes than *C. occidentalis* from 910–3200m (3000–10,500ft); Arusha, Lushoto (Amani), Njombe (Tanzania); Toro, Ankole (Uganda); also widespread in tropical Africa but an alien, probably from America.

C. grantii **Plate 451**
A prostrate perennial which produces annual branches from woody roots. Oblong leaves bear six to eleven pairs of large, oblong, blunt leaflets. The yellow flowers, *c*. 12mm (½in) long, often have a tinge of red or a red stripe on the outside of the unopened or semi-open bud. Pods flat. Found in Kenya in dry bushland at 1200–1800m (4000–6000ft), though on Mt Kenya it has also been recorded at 2100m (7000ft) and higher; Musoma, Morogoro, Songea, Tanga, Kondoa (Tanzania); Karamoja, Mt Moroto (Uganda).

C. hildebrandtii **Plate 316**
Similar to *C. grantii* but usually much more hairy with rather more, smaller, leaflets. Petals yellow 4–12mm (⅙–½in) long, 3.5–10mm (⅐–⅖in) broad; pods flat. Locally common in stony grassland at medium altitudes, 760–2130m (2500–7000ft) (*C. grantii* prefers dry bushland). Aberdares, Narok, Rift Valley, Machakos and Nairobi (Kenya); Bukoba, Maasai, Moshi (Tanzania); Ankole, Masaka, Mengo (Uganda); also Ethiopia, Eritrea, Somalia and Zaire.

C. kirkii An erect, pubescent annual with long, linear tapering leaves having twenty to forty narrowly oblong leaflets and clustered yellow flowers at the upper nodes. Pods flat; petals 8–15mm ($\frac{1}{3}$–$\frac{2}{3}$in) long, 5–11mm ($\frac{1}{5}$–$\frac{2}{5}$in) wide. Common in tall grassland, especially where seasonally flooded; altitude range 900–2300m (2290–7500ft). Elgon, Mau, Aberdares, Kitale, western region, Kisii, Narok, Machakos and Nairobi (Kenya); Buha, Morogoro, Songea (Tanzania); Toro, Mengo, Entebbe, Kampala (Uganda); also in Zaire, Malawi, Zambia, Zimbabwe.

C. mimosoides   Plate 317
An exceedingly variable prostrate to erect herb up to 1.5m (c. 4$\frac{1}{2}$ft) high, usually an annual, sometimes with the stems becoming woody above ground and enabling the plant to become perennial. Stems variable in indumentum, usually puberulous with short curved hairs, sometimes densely clothed with longer spreading hairs. Leaves linear to linear oblong, more or less parallel-sided, gland usually at or near top of petiole, sessile, normally orbicular or nearly so and dish-shaped when dry, leaflets sessile in sixteen to seventy-six pairs, obliquely oblong to oblong-elliptic or linear-oblong, 2.5–8mm ($\frac{1}{10}$–$\frac{1}{3}$in) long and very narrow, acute or subacute and shortly mucronate, glabrous or nearly so. Inflorescence supra-axillary, sometimes axillary, one to three flowered, pedicels shortly puberulous, sometimes spreading-hairy. Flowers yellow, obovate, usually appressed-hairy; petals 4–13mm ($\frac{1}{6}$–$\frac{1}{2}$in) long, 2–9mm ($\frac{1}{12}$–$\frac{1}{3}$in) wide. Pods flat. Found in clearings in forest, forest margins, wooded grassland, grassland, cultivated and waste ground, sandy river-beds, lakes and sea shores; altitude range 0–2740m (0–8900ft). Cheranganis, Kitale, Kisii, Rift Valley, Machakos, Magadi, Nairobi, Kajiado and coastal areas (Kenya); all regions of Tanzania; and Zanzibar; all regions of Uganda; also Sudan, Eritrea, Zaire, Malawi, Zambia, Zimbabwe, Mozambique and widespread in tropical Africa.
    NB The range of varieties in *C. mimosoides* is large, and they have been classified into seven groups which are best identified by using *FTEA*.

C. occidentalis   Plate 318
An erect herb, sometimes slightly woody, up to 2m (6ft) high. Stems subglabrous. Leaves to 25cm (10in) long, leaflets in three to six pairs (usually four to five) in East Africa, ovate to ovate-elliptic or sometimes lanceolate, 5–12cm (2–4$\frac{3}{4}$in) long, acute or acuminate at apex, glabrous except for ciliolate margins. Flower 1–1.5cm ($\frac{2}{5}$–$\frac{3}{5}$in) long. Racemes from upper axils, very short, almost umbellate. Petals yellow, obovate. Pods, narrow, semi-flattened. An introduction, possibly from tropical America. The plant, sometimes called 'Stinking Weed', has a most unpleasant smell. Usually a weed of cultivation, roadsides and waste ground near villages and buildings but also found in grassland and lake-shores; altitude range 0–1740m (0–5600ft). Kiambu, Taita, Tana River (Kenya); Shinyanga, Mafia Island, Songea (Tanzania); Pemba, Zanzibar; West Nile, Teso, Entebbe (Uganda).

C. singueana   Plate 319
A tree which grows up to 6m (20ft) with scaly and fissured grey or brown bark. Masses of glorious golden-yellow flowers, c. 36mm (1$\frac{3}{8}$in) across, are produced on short corymbose racemes which are clustered at the end of the branches. Found from sea level to 1980m (6500ft) all over the warmer, medium rainfall savannah areas of Kenya and often seen in both East and West Tsavo; Shinyanga, Rungwe, Tanga (Tanzania); Acholi, Karamoja, Teso (Uganda); widespread in tropical Africa, also Comoro Isles.

C. usambarensis A prostrate, pubescent perennial with annual branches from a thickened rootstock and ovate leaves, with five to eleven pairs of leaflets. The flowers are yellow-orange, 12mm (½in) across, solitary and long-pedicillate. Altitude range 1750–2600m (5750–8500ft). Locally common over a wide range within upland forest areas (Kenya); Maasai, Shinyanga, Tanga (Tanzania); Uganda and elsewhere, no record.

DELONIX

A small group of three species, two native to Eastern Africa, and one, the magnificent *D. regia*, a native of Madagascar, widely planted in coastal areas as an ornamental tree.

Delonix elata   **Plate 59**
A tree of the dry bushland, usually 4.5–6m (15–20ft) high, although sometimes up to 12m (40ft), with a spreading crown and drooping branches. The shining, grey-buff bark is smooth. The bi-pinnate leaves are 7.5–15cm (3–6in) long, the pinnae usually in four to six pairs and the leaflets in ten to fourteen pairs, oblong to oblanceolate-oblong and 6–12mm (¼–½in) long. The corymb is terminal, or comes from the upper axils with only one flower in an inflorescence open at a time. The white corolla fades to a creamy yellow and the staminal filaments, 6–11mm (¼–⅜in) long, are pale brown to reddish, and hairy at the base. Altitude range 100–1000m (330–3300ft). Common in Kenya; Lushoto, Kondoa, Iringa (Tanzania); Karamoja (Uganda); also northwards to Egypt and eastern Zaire.

Parkinsonia aculeata   **Plate 320**
A small tree up to 6m (20ft) tall not truly native to East Africa but an exotic species which may become naturalized from tropical and subtropical America, with smooth green bark. The branchlets are armed with spines, the leaves bi-pinnate with one to three pairs of pinnae, composed of elongate flattened green rhacides up to 30cm (12in) or more long, bearing very small obovate-elliptic to obovate-oblong or oblong leaflets along the margins. Flowers yellow in elongate racemes. Altitude range to 1800m (6000ft). Cultivated in Kenya, Tanzania, Uganda. Two other species, which are native to East Africa.

Pterolobium stellatum   **Plate 201**
A large, trailing shrub with pegged prickles on the woody stems, recurved prickles on the leaves and petioles; pinnae five to thirteen pairs, leaflets seven to fifteen pairs, narrowly oblong or elliptic-oblong with the terminal ones more or less obovate, and masses of creamy-yellow flowers or bright red, winged fruits. Raceme 5–13cm (2–5in) long, 2–5cm (⅘–2in) wide; raceme aggregated into panicle up to 35cm (*c.* 14in) long, up to 22cm (8½in) wide. A common and annoying wait-a-bit type of thorn in drier forest and bushland edges but not found with *Combretum* or *Commiphora*, altitude range 850–2290m (2800–7400ft). Elgon, Tinderet, Aberdares, Mt Kenya, Kisii, Baringo, Rift Valley, Nairobi and Kajiado (Kenya); all regions of Tanzania except Songea; all regions of Uganda; also widespread from Sudan, Eritrea south to Zimbabwe, Mozambique. The only species in the genus.

Tamarindus indica   **Plate 452**
An evergreen unarmed savannah tree up to 16m (52ft) high with a stout bole and compact rounded crown with drooping branches which reach to within two metres (6ft) or so of the ground. Bark pale grey, with scales about 2.5cm (1in) in diameter. Leaves pinnate, up to 15cm (6in) long, leaflets usually ten to fifteen pairs, opposite, oblong, 1.25–2.5cm (½–1in) long, base unequally rounded, apex rounded or emarginate. Flower *c.* 2.5cm (1in) across. Racemes small, slender, drooping, usually about 7.5cm (3in) long; four sepals, yellow inside, reddish outside; three petals,

yellow streaked with red or orange. Pods, thick and indehiscent. The mature bark contains seven per cent tannin, and the fruit pulp yields a pleasant cooling drink, valuable in fevers and as a laxative. Chutney and a jam, like damson cheese, can also be made from the fruit. A recipe for the cooling drink is 'to 50gms (2oz) of fruit pulp, add two pints of milk or water, boil, strain and allow to cool, sweeten to taste'. The over-ripe fruits can be used to clean copper or brass. Found in drier savannah areas, frequently growing on or alongside anthills; altitude range 1–1350m (3–4500ft). Coastal, southern and northern districts, and Nyanza (Kenya); all regions of Tanzania; all regions of Uganda except Buganda; also widespread in the tropics of the Old World. The only species in the genus.

Tylosema fassoglense (*Bauhinia fassoglensis*)   **Plate 321**
A large trailing climber with tendrils and cordate notched leaves. Flowers conspicuous, 55mm (2¼in) across, ranging from yellow to pink; pods flat, one to two seeded. Locally common in hot country with medium rainfall throughout East Africa; altitude range 90–1800m (300–6000ft). Also southern Sudan, to Zimbabwe, Zambia, Malawi.

49. Papilionoideae (Faboideae)
THE PEA FAMILY

Tropical and temperate herbs, shrublets, shrubs and trees. Their leaves are most commonly tri-foliolate but are also often pinnate and sometimes simple or palmate. Flowers are zygomorphic, the upper (adaxial) petal or 'standard' outside the two lateral petals ('wings') which in turn enclose the two lower petals, which are more or less united to form the 'keel'. There are ten stamens, variously united or, less often, free. 945 species in 105 genera in East Africa. The chief tribe in most tropical countries is centred around *Phaseolus* – which includes the Scarlet Runner and other beans. Members of this tribe are often twiners and nearly always have pinnately trifoliolate leaves, often with stipels.

Adenocarpus mannii   **Plate 322**
A shrub with erect habit up to 4.5cm (*c.* 15ft) high. Stems much branched, leafy, densely pilose; cortex ultimately flakes off longitudinally. Leaves trifoliolate, densely arranged on short shoots; leaflets subequal, oblanceolate-elliptic up to 12mm (½in) long, acute, densely pilose beneath, sparsely so above, or glabrescent with the edges often incurved. Inflorescence dense, six to twenty flowered. Petals yellow; standard orbicular, 8mm (⅓in) in diameter, with a short claw, shortly pilose on back, wings and keel about equal in length to the standard; keel obtuse at apex; stamens 9mm (⅓in) long. Found in margins of upland rain-forest, upland grassland, moor and on rocky mountain summits; altitude range 1500–4000m (4900–13,100ft). Only species in East Africa. Rift Valley, Tinderet, Mt Kenya (Kenya); Mbulu, Morogoro, Uluguru Mts, and Mbeya (Tanzania); Karamoja, Kigezi, Elgon (Uganda); also in Rwanda, Zaire, southern Sudan, Ethiopia, Malawi, Zambia.

AESCHYNOMENE
Erect or prostrate shrubs, subshrubs, annual or perennial herbs, rarely climbers, mostly covered with tubercular-based hairs. Leaves alternate, or subfasciculate on short lateral branches, paripinnately two to many foliolate; stipules truncate or

produced below point of attachment. Stipels absent. Inflorescence axillary or less often terminal or leaf opposed, falsely racemose or paniculate (rarely umbellate), sometimes flowers solitary to ternate or in fascicles. Calyx either two-lipped, lips practically free (measured from base of calyx), the upper lip entire or bifid, the lower entire or trifid or campanulate with unequal lobes. Flowers small to fairly large, mostly yellow, lined with purple. Standard usually rounded or pandurate, often emarginate, clawed, with tiny appendages at base of claw; wings straight or falcate; stamens sometimes in two joined groups of five or the vexillary filaments free in a few species; anthers uniform; ovary linear, usually stipitate, two to twenty-eight ovuled; style inflexed, mostly glabrous; stigma terminal; pods linear or elliptic, slightly curved, one to twenty-eight jointed. Forty-four species in East Africa; especially common in southern Tanzania.

Aeschynomene cristata var. pubescens   Plate 323

A herb or shrub with immersed, procumbent rooting stems covered with prominent lenticels and erect branches, forming dense, coppice-like growths, 1–3m (1–10ft) tall. Stems thick and soft at the base, glabrous to densely covered, with sticky tubercular-based golden-brown hairs. Leaves forty to eighty-six foliolate; leaflets linear to oblong 0.6–2.2cm (c. $\frac{1}{5}$–$\frac{7}{8}$in) long, rounded to emarginate and mucronate at apex, obliquely emarginate at base, entire or finely serrate, glabrous. Venation sometimes obvious and purplish beneath. Petiole and rhachis long-hairy. Inflorescences axillary, two to eight flowered (sometimes single). Standard deep yellow to orange-yellow or sometimes brownish-purple, 1.8–3.3cm (c. $\frac{3}{4}$–1$\frac{2}{3}$in) long and wide, round, pubescent above on outside; wings deep yellow to orange-yellow, keel petals yellow or brownish, hairy. Pods jointed. Found in permanent and seasonal swamps, edges of dams, lakes and rivers; altitude range 0–1200m (0–3900ft). Kwale, Lamu, Baringo (Kenya); Rungwe, Songea, Lindi, Zanzibar (Tanzania); Teso, Busoga, Mbale (Uganda); also widespread in tropical Africa and from Sudan to Zimbabwe.

NB This is the species which provides 'Ambatch', for the extremely light fibre raft-boats of the Tugen and Njemusi people on Lake Baringo. It has sometimes been said that 'Ambatch' comes from A. elaphroxylon on Lake Baringo, but exhaustive search has never revealed the latter on this lake. It can be distinguished from A. cristata which has straight pods; as distinct from those of A. elaphyloxylon which are spirally contorted. A. pfundii, a third species, is also alleged to provide 'Ambatch' but it has never been recorded on or near Lake Baringo. All three species, however, provide 'Ambatch' in their own environments. A. elaphroxylon is common around Lake Victoria and on the Nile.

A. elaphroxylon A spiny shrub or tree from 2–9mm (6–30ft) tall, with eight to fifteen pairs of broad-oblong retuse leaflets to each spiny leaf. The stem is often swollen, pithy and acts as a float. The leaves twenty to forty foliolate. Leaflets truncate or slightly emarginate at the apex, rounded at the base, entire, somewhat glaucous beneath, glabrescent above, pubescent on the margins and midnerve beneath. Venation dark beneath. Inflorescences axillary one to four flowered. Calyx densely pubescent with long sticky bristly hairs, two-lipped, the lips entire or two to three toothed at the apex. Standard, yellow to orange, 3–4.7cm (1$\frac{1}{2}$–2in) long, rounded puberulous above on outer surface, wings and keel yellow. Found in lake-sides and in pools and swamps bordering lakes, usually actually standing in several feet of water; altitude range 520–1350m (1650–4400ft). Near Lake Victoria in Kenya, Tanzania and Uganda; also Sudan, Ethiopia to Zambia, Malawi, Mozambique.

A. schimperi **Plate 324**

A shrubby, aromatic herb or small shrub up to 3m (10ft) tall (though sometimes only 0.6m (1½ft)) usually erect but occasionally straggling, stems soft at the base, pubescent to hispid with yellow often sticky tubercular-based hairs, often reddish and sometimes glabrous. Leaves sometimes sensitive, eighteen to sixty-eight-foliolate, leaflets linear to linear-oblong, rounded to slightly emarginate, rounded at the base, subentire or very finely serrulate. Inflorescence axillary, single-flowered (rarely two to four). The standard orange-yellow to orange, sometimes streaked with crimson, 0.8–3.3cm (⅓–1⅗in) long and wide, the wings and keel greenish, speckled or lined with purple; the petals of the wings bristly and laciniate. Found in swampy places, stream banks, lakeside and rock pools in grassland or wooded places, often actually in water; altitude range 60–2340m (200–7700ft). Recorded widely throughout the Eastern African region and tropical Africa.

Amphicarpa africana **Plate 661**

A perennial climbing herb from 0.6–3.6m (1¾–12ft) long. Stems slender, covered with reflexed reddish hairs. Leaflets three, elliptic or obovate, acute or rounded and apiculate at apex, sparsely to very densely covered with appressed greyish or reddish hairs beneath. Racemes lax, numerous, many-flowered: rhachis 2.5–15cm (1–6in) long. Calyx often purple, appressed pubescent. The standard mauve or violet, duller outside, white towards the base, obovate-oblong, 1–1.6cm (⅖–⅗in) long, 5–7mm (⅕–¼in) wide, wings pale; keel white tinged purple or blue. The cleistogamous flowers in many, very short, few-flowered axillary racemes. Found in upland rain forest, forest edges, bamboo forest and grassland derived from forest; altitude range 1680–2700m (5500–8850ft). Only species in East Africa. Aberdares, Nairobi, Taita Hills (Kenya); Mbulu, Arusha, Mpande (Tanzania); Toro (Ruwenzori Mts), Kigezi, Mbale (Uganda); also Zaire, Burundi, Sudan, Ethiopia, Malawi and Zambia.

Argyrolobium fischeri **Plate 453**

A bushy woody herb or subshrub, up to 2m (6½ft) tall. Stems rather stout at the base, densely covered with subappressed or spreading silvery or golden-brown hairs. Leaflets three, elliptic to elliptic-oblong, occasionally lanceolate, up to 20–60mm (⅘–2⅖in) long and 9–26mm (⅓–1in) wide, thinly to very densely covered with appressed or more or less spreading hairs on both surfaces, usually more densely so underneath. Racemes subumbelliform or sometimes elongate, with a 1–12cm (⅖–4¾in) peduncle, six to forty flowered. Lower bracts usually lanceolate, upper ones often smaller and narrower. Calyx, 10–12mm (⅖–½in) long, densely covered with fine subappressed (less commonly spreading) hairs. Upper lobes oblong-lanceolate. Standard obovate-orbicular to suborbicular, bright yellow, becoming orange or reddish flushed with age, densely silky pubescent outside, 10–13mm (⅖–½in) long, wings with rows of folds between the upper veins, keel petals with a crest on the lateral surface towards the base and a claw shorter than the blade-width, generally glabrous along the margins. Petals 8–10mm (⅓–⅖in) long. Found in evergreen bushland and grassland and streamsides; altitude range 1350–2400m (4425–7875ft). One of eight species in East Africa. Northern Frontier, Mt Kulal, Maralal, Machakos, Elgon and western Kenya (Kenya); western Usambara Mts, Iringa, Songea (Tanzania); Karamoja, Kigezi, Mbale (Uganda); also in southern Sudan, Ethiopia, eastern Zaire, Rwanda, Malawi, Zambia.

Cadia purpurea **Plate 662**

A graceful, unarmed obconical shrub, 1–5m (3–16ft) tall, the branches diverging from near the base and curving slightly upwards. Bark brown with narrow longitudinal cracks and elliptic-oblong transverse lenticels. Twigs brown, shortly appressed pubescent. Leaflets opposite, subopposite or alternate on 1mm long petiolules; often inrolled in dry conditions, twenty to thirty in number, narrowly oblong, 23mm (1in) long and 5mm ($\frac{1}{8}$in) wide, entire, emarginate, dark green and glabrous above, pale green and puberulous on midrib and margins beneath. Flowers on axillary short shoots, hanging singly in one or more of the two to four bracts. Receptacle obconical, greenish-yellow, glandular within. Calyx persistent, campanulate, valvate in bud, purplish-green and sparsely appressed pubescent outside. Petals, c. 30mm (1$\frac{1}{8}$in) long, 14mm ($\frac{1}{2}$in) wide, cuneate-obovate with about seven forking nerves from base, cream at first, later wine-red, variously imbricate. Filaments crimson borne on rim of receptacle; ovary pale green, glabrous, style tapering. Pod, brown, straight or slightly curved. Found on slopes just outside 'cedar' (*Juniperus procera*) forest, with rainfall c. 800mm (c. 31in) per annum; altitude range 1500–1800m (4900–6850ft). Northern Frontier areas (Kenya); Tanzania and Uganda, no record; also in Ethiopia, Eritrea, Somalia and Arabia.

Calpurnia aurea (*C. subdecandra*) A small tree with imparipinnate leaves about 25cm (10in) long with six to fourteen pairs of elliptic to long leaflets rounded at the apex. Flower yellow, c. 25mm (1in) across. The fruits, carried in membraneous pods 15cm (6in) long, remain on the tree for a long time. The only species in East Africa. Common in forests on the Mau, the Laikipia Escarpment and in the Rift Valley from 2100–2500m (7000–8000ft) though along streams it descends to lower altitudes, e.g. 1500m (4900ft) at Hippo Pool in the Nairobi National Park (Kenya). Mbulu, Moshi, Ufipa (Tanzania); Karamoja (Uganda); also Eritrea, Ethiopia, Zimbabwe, Zambia, Malawi.

Canavalia cathartica   **Plate 663**
A herb, or more often a climber, with pinnately trifoliolate stipellate leaves and axillary racemes of pinkish-purple, scented flowers, c. 3mm ($\frac{1}{8}$in) long, 2.4mm ($\frac{1}{10}$in) across, with a white mark in the middle of the standard; the calyx is five-lobed, two-lipped, the two upper lobes broad and rounded, the three lower, small and acute; corolla keel incurved, often twisted; stamens ten (rarely nine + one), anthers all similar, ovary many-ovuled, the style glabrous; the pods linear or oblong and seven to nine seeded, The pod often winged along the top. It is found in coastal bushland on raised coral in Kenya and is also widespread in coastal areas of Asia from 1–30m (3–100ft), in altitude. Lushoto (Usambara Mts), Tanga, Pangani, Zanzibar (Tanzania); Uganda, no record. Widespread in old world tropics.

C. rosea   **Plate 664**
A perennial climber or trailer up to 10m (33ft) long. Stems silken hairy when young, glabrous when old. Leaflets elliptic to oblong-elliptic to almost round 2.5–9.5cm (1–4in) long, 1.5–9cm ($\frac{3}{4}$–3$\frac{1}{2}$in) wide, obtuse or emarginate (but sometimes minutely apiculate at the apex), broadly cuneate, rounded or truncate at the base (very rarely subcordate). Glabrous to sparsely pubescent on both surfaces though sometimes densely so beneath, margins often ciliate. The inflorescence, 4–18cm (1$\frac{3}{4}$–7in) long, hanging or upright. Standard pink to purple or bluish mauve with a white or yellow area near the base, rounded or elliptic, keel pale magenta; 2.5–3cm (1–1$\frac{1}{4}$in) long, 1.5–2cm ($\frac{3}{4}$–$\frac{3}{4}$in) wide. Mainly a plant of coastal beaches and bushland bordering high-water mark and usually associated with *Ipomoea pes-caprae*; altitude range 0–30m (0–100ft). Rarely found inland (Kenya); Tanga, Uzaramo, Zanzibar (Tanzania); Uganda, no record; also throughout the coastal parts of tropical Africa.

C. virosa   Plate 665

A perennial climber or trailer, 3–15m (10–50ft) tall, reaching the tops of quite tall trees. Stems mostly adpressed, ferruginous pubescent when young, later glabrous. Leaflets ovate, to 16cm (6¼in) long, occasionally to 23cm (9in); acuminate to a short, blunt tip or rounded, rounded at the base, very sparsely to densely pubescent on both surfaces, often densely silky when young. Inflorescence, 6–21cm (2¼–8in) long, carried on a peduncle 12–28cm (4¾–11in) long. Calyx densely pubescent. Standard mauve with white veins, and green towards the base, 2.7–3cm (1–1⅛in) long, 1.7cm (c. ¾in) wide; wings and keel mauve, white towards base. Found in grassland, grassland with scattered trees, thickets and sometimes by lake shores; altitude range 280–1800m (900–5900ft). Western Kenya, Kisumu, Chyulu Hills, coastal regions (Kenya); Mbulu, Singida, Ulanga districts (Tanzania); Kigezi, Teso, Masaka (Uganda).

Craibia laurentii A tree up to 18m (c. 60ft) tall, buds, leaves and twigs almost glabrous or the twigs shortly pubescent when young. Leaflets five to seven, elliptic-lanceolate, acuminate, up to 17cm (c. 6¾in) long and c. 5cm (2in) broad. Five to six principal nerves on each side. Inflorescence a many-flowered terminal panicle, densely covered with short brown hairs. Calyx campanulate, also covered with short appressed brown hairs, tube c. 3.5cm (1⅜in) long, lobes broadly ovate c. 1.5cm (c. ¾in) long. Corolla white, 12–15mm (½–¾in) long. Found in dry forest, along creeks and gullies on hillsides; altitude range 600–1350m (1950–4400ft). One of six species in East Africa. Mathews Range, West Suk and northern districts (Kenya); Tanzania, no record; West Nile, Teso, Mbale (Uganda); also in southern Sudan.

Clitoria ternatea   Plate 827

A very beautiful climber with pale to bright blue flowers which grow singly or in pairs from the axils of the leaves which are pinnate with five to seven leaflets. Flower 15–35mm (⅜–1⅜in) across. It may be covered in blossoms, which produce flat green seed pods. One of two species in East Africa. Thrives in warm, dry bushland conditions and is widespread at altitudes below 1500m (c. 5000ft); also in Zanzibar, Somalia and south to Zimbabwe, Zambia, Malawi.

CROTALARIA

Herbs or shrubs, very varied in habit. Leaves simple, single-foliolate or digitately three (to seven) foliolate; leaflets entire. Flowers usually in terminal leaf-opposed or, less commonly, axillary racemes, sometimes modified as heads, occasionally solitary or in axillary clusters; calyx (four) five-lobed (sometimes effectively three-lobed); corolla longer than calyx, usually yellow or yellow green, less commonly white or blue; standard almost always with two callus-like appendages at base inside, keel generally with a prominent beak, twisted or not, stamens all joined; anthers dimorphic, five large, alternating with five small; ovary stipitate; style curved; pods inflated, subsessile to long-stipitate, single to many seeded. Sometimes seen as in Meru National Park (Kenya) in great drifts or clumps, and in some districts baskets are woven from the fibres of the branches and stems. 200 species in East Africa.

Crotalaria agatiflora   Plate 325

Handsome, softly woody shrub or small tree 1.5–10m (5–33ft) tall, with attractive greenish-yellow flowers (often visited by sunbirds), whose keels are up to 45 or 55mm (1¾ or 2⅛in) long. Found in upland grassland, open bushland, and especially at the edge of montane and riverine forest between 1140 and 3150m (3800 and

10,500ft), in nearly all the moist uplands of East Africa. Also in Ethiopia and eastern Zaire.

NB This is a very variable plant; four subspecies are recognized in *FTEA*, and in addition, several local variants are recognizable though not named. Three of the subspecies are under 5m (16ft) tall, and not found above 2550m (8500ft), but ssp. *engleri* is a small tree up to 10m (33ft) tall, and occurs from 1650–3150m (5500–10,500ft). It is readily grown from seed and in Nairobi gardens, with more handsome flowers, but a shorter lifespan. It replaces the *Laburnum* in England.

C. axillaris **Plate 454**

A shrub or woody herb of upland areas. It is coarsely hairy with elliptic leaflets and clusters of yellow flowers in the axils. The keel, 15–18mm ($\frac{3}{5}$–$\frac{3}{4}$in) long, which conceals the stamens and styles, is as long as the wings (the two side petals), and rounded with a twisted beak. The seed pod is oblong to club-shaped, 45mm (1$\frac{4}{5}$in) long, 6–12mm ($\frac{1}{4}$–$\frac{1}{2}$in) across. This plant is found at 1300–2300m (4400–7500ft) in dry evergreen forest and derived communities, persisting in disturbed places. Aberdares, Mt Kenya, Rift Valley, Embu, Machakos, Nairobi and Kajiado districts (Kenya); Kilimanjaro, Kigoma, Uzaramo, Zanzibar (Tanzania); Toro (Uganda); also Ethiopia, eastern Zaire, Malawi, Zambia and Mozambique.

C. barkae **Plate 202**

Annual or short-lived perennial with a leading shoot, generally up to 100cm (3$\frac{1}{2}$ft) tall, much-branched with the lower branches long and decumbent, or prostrate. Stem pilose with appressed or spreading hairs. Leaves tri-foliolate, leaflets lanceolate, elliptic-lanceolate or elliptic from 15–70mm ($\frac{3}{5}$–2$\frac{4}{5}$in) long, glabrous to sparsely pilose above, sparsely pilose beneath. Racemes lax, 2.5–14cm (1–5$\frac{1}{5}$in) long, two to six flowered, standard obovate or suborbicular, longer than the calyx (10–20mm ($\frac{2}{5}$–$\frac{4}{5}$in) long), white to greenish-white or bright yellow and sometimes marked reddish-purple, pubescent apically outside. Wings shorter to nearly as long as keel; keel, 10–17mm long ($\frac{2}{5}$–$\frac{3}{5}$in) across, bent at right angles in the lower half with a long, slightly incurved untwisted beak, conspicuously lanate along the upper margin proximal to the beak. Found in deciduous bushland and grassland, persisting on roadsides, gravel pits and cultivated ground, altitude range 900–1400m (3000–4500ft). Kajiado, Machakos, Chyulu Hills, Taita Hills, Tsavo West (Merka), Kilifi, Lamu (Kenya); lake areas, Maasai, Tabora, Mpwapwa, Kondoa, Mbeya, Iringa (Tanzania); Uganda, no record; also Ethiopia, Sudan, Eritrea, south to Mozambique, Zimbabwe.

NB There are five subspecies classified in Kenya which appear to be found in separate areas, ranging from Lamu and Kilifi at the coast to Machakos and the Tsavo West National Park. They are described in *Upland Kenya Wild Flowers* and are best identified by botanists. The five subspecies tend to be selective in their habitat.

C. brevidens **Plate 326**

An erect to spreading annual or short-lived perennial, with variously-shaped but mostly narrow leaflets and sublax racemes of cream, or usually clear yellow flowers with reddish-brown veins; calyx basally truncate, pubescent; keel shallow, shortly rounded with a projecting beak 1.2–2.4cm ($\frac{1}{2}$–1in) long, conspicuously lined. The pods are subsessile, narrowly cylindrical, often a little curved at ends, 35–40mm (1$\frac{2}{5}$–1$\frac{3}{5}$in) long and up to eighty-seeded. Altitude range var. *intermedia* 600–2700m (2000–8850ft); var. *parviflora* 1450–2100m (4750–6900ft). The photograph shows *C. brevidens* var. *parviflora*, which is the smaller-flowered variety of this species (the keel being only 12–14mm ($\frac{1}{2}$in) long and occurring around Nairobi, east to

Embu, also on high ground north to Laikipia and west to the Mau (Kenya). The common, large-flowered form *C. brevidens* var. *intermedia* is found almost everywhere in Kenya in its altitude range; lake areas, Maasai, Mbeya, Iringa (Tanzania); all regions of Uganda; also in Sudan, Ethiopia, Rwanda, Zaire.

NB *C. dewildemaniana* is very similar to *C. brevidens* var. *parviflora* but the keel (smaller than in *C. brevidens* var. *parviflora*) is strongly rounded with slightly incurved beak, and the flowers give the appearance of being more closely grouped up the peduncle. The pods are also generally smaller. Only the ssp. *oxyrhyncha* is recorded in Kenya in Elgon, Tinderet, Mau, Kitale, Rift Valley, Machakos, Nairobi and Kajiado. Size of flower: beak 5–7mm ($\frac{1}{5}$–$\frac{1}{4}$in). Altitude range 900–2160m (3000–7200ft) but mainly 1500–2160m (5000–7200ft).

C. cephalotes **Plate 455**

A small, erect, coarsely hairy annual, branched from the base with narrow leaflets, and small yellow-red marked flowers in dense terminal heads surrounded by longer spreading linear leaves, bearing leaflets 3–5cm (1$\frac{1}{5}$–2in) long. The raceme is contracted to a short, dense, sessile head which is surrounded by the leaves described above; the inflorescence sunk within the leaves which surround it like a nest; the keel 4–5mm ($\frac{1}{6}$–$\frac{1}{5}$in) long, is angled with a narrow twisted beak; the pods globose-ellipsoid, two-seeded. It is found in open and woodland grassland often in disturbed rocky places; altitude range 900–2100m (3000–7000ft). Elgon, Kitale, western Kenya, Narok, Rift Valley, Machakos and Kajiado (Kenya); all regions of Tanzania except Tanga; all regions of Uganda; also in Ethiopia, south to Transvaal.

C. cleomifolia **Plate 327**

A striking shrubby perennial which grows to 1–4.5m (3–14$\frac{1}{2}$ft) tall. Generally recognized by its predominately five-foliolate leaves. It has three- to five-foliolate leaves, elliptic leaflets and long racemes of bright yellow flowers faintly lined with red. Flower *c*. 16mm ($\frac{3}{5}$in) long. The calyx has long bracteoles from its blunt base. The standard, upper petal is elliptic; the keel is rounded with a narrow, slightly incurved beak and much larger than the wings. Locally common by streams and swamps or in grassland and bushland near forest at 1150–2500m (3500–8500ft). Recorded in all parts of East Africa except arid areas, widespread in tropical Africa.

C. deflersii **Plate 456**

A bushy herb with tomentellous branches, long, tri-foliolate leaves, elliptic to obovate leaflets and long racemes; standard broad, bright yellow usually with a wine-coloured basal zone, turning reddish over-all; keel very short (much shorter than the broad wings) 6–8mm ($\frac{1}{4}$–$\frac{1}{3}$in) long and little exceeding the subsequently reflexed calyx-lobes, rounded with a rather short, ultimately twisted beak, 1–1.4cm ($\frac{2}{5}$–$\frac{3}{5}$in) long. Standard 12–16mm ($\frac{1}{2}$–$\frac{3}{5}$in). The pod is oblong, club-shaped, tomentellous sixteen to twenty seeded. Found in deciduous bushland often in rocky places at 1200–1500m (4000–5000ft), but can be as low as 600m (2000ft). Rift Valley, Magadi and South Horr (northern Kenya) (Kenya); Maasai, Mbulu (Tanzania); Uganda, no record; also in Somalia. It is very similar to *C. verdcourtii* which is often more hairy with a longer keel and pod with twenty-four to thirty-six rough seeds and found in wooded grassland at 600–1700m (2000–5450ft) in Nanyuki, Embu, Machakos and Kajiado (Kenya).

C. goodiiformis (*C. saxatilis*) **Plate 328**

A slender-stemmed, much-branched shrub with membranaceous, elliptic to obovate leaflets; the yellow flowers in a thread-like rachis, developing thin-valved oblong club-shaped pods, attenuate at both ends. This *Crotalaria* can be up to 3.3m

(12ft) high, with solitary, paired, or few and racemose eight to eighteen flowers. Flower: 1–1.2cm ($\frac{2}{5}$–$\frac{1}{2}$in) long; keel 8mm ($\frac{1}{3}$in) long; pod up to 3.75cm (1$\frac{1}{2}$in) long. The bracteoles are curved up like two horns from just below the calyx. Altitude range 70–2100m (230–6900ft). Found in Eastern Highlands, Ukambani, and coastal districts and is well known by its Kikuyu name of *Muchingiri* (Kenya); all regions of Tanzania; Uganda, no record; also in eastern Zaire, Mozambique.

C. laburnifolia **Plate 457**

A robust, semi-soft plant with yellow flowers, the standard often speckled reddish-brown and hanging loosely in racemes, the keel 20–30mm long. Widespread in bushland and wooded grassland from sea level to 1830m (6000ft) in all parts of East Africa except Zanzibar; elsewhere from the Sudan and Somalia to eastern Zaire and the Transvaal; also in southern Asia and north-east Australia.

NB Three subspecies occur in East Africa, among which ssp. *eldomae*, found at high altitudes in central Kenya and northern Tanzania, is remarkable for its long petioles and small leaflets. Ssp. *tenuicarpa*, found below 1500m (5000ft) in northern, central and coastal Kenya, especially near Voi, and in the Tanga province of Tanzania, is remarkable for the long (up to 9cm (3$\frac{3}{5}$in)) stipe (stalk) of the pod.

C. lachnocarpoides **Plate 458**

A perennial woody herb or shrub up to 2m (6$\frac{1}{2}$ft) (sometimes to 2.7m (9ft)) tall, usually much branched and bushy above. Stem terete, silky tomentose. Leaves shortly petiolate, tri-foliolate; leaflets oblanceolate-oblong, or narrowly oblong-elliptic, rarely elliptic up to 35–75mm (1$\frac{2}{3}$–3in) long and 12–25mm ($\frac{1}{2}$–1in) wide, densely grey silky pilose on both surfaces. Racemes lax or dense, six to twelve flowered. Calyx 10–15mm ($\frac{2}{5}$–$\frac{3}{5}$in) long, pod up to 30mm (1$\frac{1}{5}$in) long. Standard suborbicular, yellow, tinged yellowish-brown outside, fading orange-red. Wings longer than the semi-orbicular keel (11–18mm ($\frac{2}{5}$–$\frac{3}{4}$in) long), with a short, slightly incurved or straight, blunt, untwisted beak. Found in grassland, often with scattered trees or shrubs or at forest margins and in upland evergreen bushland; altitude range 1200–2650m (3850–8700ft). Certain plants from the Mau range in Kenya have exceptionally large flowers with the keel up to 18mm ($\frac{3}{4}$in) long. Northern Frontier and western districts, Kitui (Kenya); all regions of Tanzania; all regions of Uganda except Buganda; also in Sudan, Ethiopia, Rwanda, Zaire, Malawi, Zambia, Zimbabwe, Mozambique.

C. lanceolata An erect annual, laxly branched; stem ribbed, appressed puberulous or rarely shortly spreading pubescent. Leaves tri-foliolate, rarely some upper ones single; leaflets mostly linear to lanceolate, (lower ones sometimes elliptic), generally up to 105mm (4in) long, glabrous, thinly covered with appressed hairs beneath. Racemes, 8–38cm (3$\frac{1}{6}$–15in) long, with many, fairly closely-arranged flowers, bracts subulate or filiform, expanded at the base. Standard broadly elliptic or suborbicular, yellow-veined, reddish-purple and glabrous outside. Wings shorter or longer than keel; keel 6.5–11mm ($\frac{1}{4}$–$\frac{2}{5}$in) long, rounded about the middle with an incurved or projecting untwisted beak. Found in grasslands of valleys, deciduous woodland, forest margins and along roadsides; altitude range 1–2150m (3–7200ft). Aberdares, Machakos and Nairobi (Kenya); Rufiji, Songea, Tunduru (Tanzania); Toro, Busoga, Masaka (Uganda); also southern Ethiopia to Zimbabwe, Mozambique.

C. lebrunii **Plate 329**

This *Crotalaria* has flowers similar to *C. laburnifolia*, 25–30mm (1–1$\frac{1}{5}$in) long, but the seed pods are pointed and elliptic and it is mainly confined to forest edges at

2130–2350m (7000–7700ft). Aberdares, Mt Kenya and Nyambeni Hills; it can be seen near the forest lodge, the Ark (Kenya); Tanzania, no record; Karamoja (Mt Moroto), Kigezi (Uganda); elsewhere, eastern Zaire.

C. massaiensis   Plate 330
A decumbent or spreading perennial, much-branched from the base, sometimes with underground runners, and slender, pubescent branches, minute stipules and mostly rather small or narrow leaflets, elliptic-obovate to obovate up to 10–15mm ($\frac{2}{5}$–$\frac{3}{5}$in) long and 7–8mm (c. $\frac{1}{3}$in) wide, glabrous above, appressed pubescent below with rather long hairs beneath. The inflorescence, a raceme, 4–11cm (1$\frac{3}{4}$–4$\frac{1}{3}$in) long, twelve to twenty-four flowered, pedunculate, lax; standard suborbicular-obovate, yellow, finely brownish veined, glabrous outside; calyx 4–5mm ($\frac{1}{6}$–$\frac{1}{5}$in) long. Wings, c. 6–8mm ($\frac{1}{4}$–$\frac{1}{3}$in) long; shorter than the keel 4–6mm ($\frac{1}{6}$–$\frac{1}{4}$in)); keel angled in the lower half with a rather short (4–6mm ($\frac{1}{6}$–$\frac{1}{4}$in)) almost straight untwisted beak. Found in deciduous bushland, often in rocky places, seasonal stream beds, on clay soils and persisting on cultivated ground and roadsides; altitude range 600–1800m (1950–2625ft). Baringo, Magadi, Nanyuki, Mt Kulal and Voi (Kenya); Tanzania, no record; northern region – Karamoja (Uganda); also in southern Ethiopia and Somalia.

C. mauensis   Plate 331
A robust, bushy herb or shrub growing to 1.8m (6ft) in height, covered with short brown hairs and with elliptic leaflets. Yellow flowers form rather dense racemes with a broadly-lobed calyx the same length as the chubby corolla, 12–15mm ($\frac{1}{2}$–$\frac{3}{5}$in); standard 12–15mm ($\frac{1}{2}$–$\frac{3}{5}$in) long. Found at altitudes of 1680–2300m (5400–7500ft). From Machakos in the east to Mumias in the west (Kenya); Maasai, Mbulu (Ngorongoro), Kilimanjaro (Tanzania); Uganda and elsewhere, not known.

C. natalitia   Plate 459
A woody herb or small shrub up to 2.6m (c. 5ft) tall, with one to several thin stems, and rather strictly ascending branches mostly towards the top, occasionally some-what procumbent in burnt or heavily grazed areas. Branches ribbed, usually rather densely appressed (or slightly spreading) pubescent. Leaves usually mostly crowded on abbreviated lateral shoots, tri-foliolate; leaflets linear-oblanceolate, oblanceolate to oblanceolate-elliptic up to 42mm (1$\frac{3}{5}$in) long, glabrous above, appressed pubescent beneath. Racemes, up to 22cm (8$\frac{3}{5}$in) long, with few to many laxly or rather densely arranged flowers towards the top. Standard suborbicular, yellow, sometimes tinged red-brown or sepia outside, fading to reddish-orange, glabrous outside; wings broadly oblong, longer than the keel; keel, 11–14mm ($\frac{2}{5}$–$\frac{3}{5}$in) long, abruptly rounded in the middle, beak slightly incurved and untwisted, conspicuously white lanate-pubescent on the lateral surface towards the margin. Calyx glabrous or appressed pubescent, 6–9mm ($\frac{1}{4}$–$\frac{1}{3}$in) long. Found in deciduous woodland and bushland, riverine forest and margins of upland rain-forest, upland grassland and evergreen bushland, also persisting on roadsides and cultivated ground; altitude range 0–3000m (0–9850ft). Western Kenya, Mau, Northern Frontier (Ndoto Mts), Chyulu Hills and Aberdares (Kenya); Tanga district, Iringa, Songea (Tanzania); Kigezi, Mbale, Masaka districts (Uganda); also in Zanzibar, eastern Zaire, Malawi, Zambia, Zimbabwe and Natal.

   NB There are two varieties of this species: var. *natalitia*, with calyx and upper part of the pedicel glabrous; and var. *rutshuruensis*, with calyx and upper part of the pedicel appressed pubescent. The latter is the most common in East Africa, and the immediate neighbouring areas.

C. polysperma   Plate 828

An erect, well-branched hairy annual with elliptic leaflets and twelve to twenty flowered racemes of large blue flowers, the pilose calyx nearly the same length as the angular keel, 1.6–1.8cm ($\frac{3}{5}$–$\frac{3}{4}$in) long. The pod is broadly oblong to club-shaped, 3.5 to 4.5cm (1$\frac{2}{5}$–1$\frac{4}{5}$in) long with from seventy to one hundred seeds. Found in deciduous bushland and grassland; altitude range 900–2000m (1000–6200ft). Northern Frontier, Turkana, Rift Valley and Central Province (Kenya); all regions of Tanzania except Songea; northern and eastern regions of Uganda; also Sudan, Eritrea, southern Ethiopia, south to Zimbabwe, Mozambique.

C. pycnostachya   Plate 332

An annual, much-branched, either erect and bushy or with radiating decumbent branches. Stem conspicuously ribbed, shortly appressed pubescent. Leaves tri-foliolate; leaflets wedge-shaped, oblanceolate or oblong-oblanceolate up to 44mm (1$\frac{3}{4}$in) long, long-cuneate and glabrous above, thinly appressed puberulous beneath. Racemes, up to 9cm (3$\frac{1}{2}$in) long, subsessile or short pedunculate, dense, many-flowered. Standard obovate, pale yellow, glabrous outside, wings longer than the keel; keel 4–5mm ($\frac{1}{6}$–$\frac{1}{5}$in) long, abruptly rounded with a short untwisted beak. Found in grassland and deciduous bushland, stony hillsides and dry river beds, becoming a weed in cultivated or old waste land mainly in low rainfall areas; altitude range 750–1680m (2450–5500ft). Northern Frontier areas, Kisii, Kajiado and Maralal (Kenya); Seronera, Great Ardai Plain (Tanzania); Karamoja, Kangole and Moroto (Uganda); also in southern Sudan, Ethiopia and Somalia.

C. recta   Plate 333

A robust erect perennial 1–2.7m (3–9ft) tall, with ribbed, densely appressed pubescent stems, short stout petioles, linear-lanceolate stipules, generally elliptic to obovate leaflets and long subdense racemes of yellow flowers marked reddish-purple at the base of the broad standard and the wings inside, veined outside; calyx glabrous, keel, 12–15mm ($\frac{1}{2}$–$\frac{3}{5}$in) long, rounded with a short twisted beak enveloped by the wings. The pod is broadly oblong-club-shaped, 5–6cm (2–2$\frac{2}{5}$in) long, glabrous. It is found in grassland or at lower altitudes in swamp margins, also persisting on cultivated ground; altitude range 850–2550m (2800–8200ft). Elgon, Tinderet, Mau, Aberdares, Kitale, western areas, Embu, Machakos and Kajiado (Kenya); lake areas, Maasai, Tabora, Morogoro, Mbeya, Iringa, Songea (Tanzania); all regions of Uganda; also southern Sudan, Eritrea and south to Transvaal.

C. retusa   Plate 334

An erect annual or short-lived perennial up to 1.3m (4ft) tall, usually well-branched. Stems obscurely-ribbed, densely appressed to spreading pubescent. Leaves simple, blade oblanceolate to oblong-obovate from 33–105mm (1$\frac{1}{3}$–4in) long, rounded or emarginate at apex, glabrous above, finely appressed pubescent below. Raceme up to 30cm (c. 12in) long, often considerably less, laxly or densely many-flowered. Standard obovate-orbicular, pale yellow often finely purple-veined inside and reddish-diffused outside with darker veins; wings oblong-obovate, longer than keel, and bright yellow; keel rounded with a short, slightly incurved, twisted beak 13–15mm ($\frac{1}{2}$–$\frac{3}{5}$in) long. Found in coastal grassland, waste places, old cultivations and around dwellings; altitude range 0–240m (0–800ft) occasionally to 1100m (3500ft). Kwale, Vipingo (Kenya); Tanga township, Morogoro, Rufiji, Zanzibar, Pemba (Tanzania); Kampala (Uganda); widespread in tropical Africa.

C. uguenensis   Plate 460

A straggling, conspicuously pilose short-lived perennial with well-developed stipules, variably shaped leaflets and long racemes of pale yellow flowers lined or flushed reddish-purple. Similar to *C. ukambensis*, but less robust, with shorter hairs and bracts, smaller flowers (keel 7–8mm ($\frac{1}{3}$in) long, not much exceeding the wings) and pubescent pods only 1.2–1.8cm ($\frac{1}{2}$–$\frac{3}{4}$in) long. The keel is strongly rounded with a narrow incurved beak 4–6mm ($\frac{1}{6}$–$\frac{1}{4}$in) long. Standard ± size of keel. It is found in deciduous bushland, often around rocky outcrops or on clay soils with *Acacia* wooded grassland from 600–1800m (2000–6000ft). Rift Valley, Magadi, Nanyuki, Machakos and Kajiado (Kenya); lake areas, Maasai, Tanga (Tanzania); all regions of Uganda except Buganda; also in Ethiopia.

C. vatkeana **Plate 335**

A straggling and ascending annual, sometimes with procumbent lower branches, generally well-branched. Stem thinly covered with appressed hairs, more dense on younger parts. Leaves tri-foliolate; leaflets variable, linear-lanceolate or lanceolate to elliptic or obovate-elliptic up to 70mm (2$\frac{3}{4}$in) long. Racemes long-pedunculate, 13–17cm (6$\frac{2}{3}$–9in) long, with many, rather crowded flowers towards the top. Standard obovate-oblong, yellow-veined, purple and glabrous outside; wings shorter than the keel; keel 8–10mm ($\frac{1}{3}$–$\frac{2}{5}$in) long, shortly rounded about the middle with an almost straight rather projecting untwisted keel. Found in margins and clearings of upland rain-forest, upland evergreen bushland, grassland also persisting on roadsides and cultivated ground; altitude range 1300–3000m (4250–9850ft). Nairobi, Nyambeni Hills, western Kenya, Elgon and Mau (Kenya); Ngorongoro, Moshi (Tanzania); Imatong Mts (southern Sudan).

C. verdcourtii A bushy herb with tomentose branches, long-petiolate stipulate leaves; elliptic to obovate leaflets and long racemes; the standard broad, bright yellow, usually with a wine-coloured basal zone, turning reddish over-all. Calyx of mature flowers 10–12mm ($\frac{2}{5}$–$\frac{1}{2}$in) long. Keel 11–13mm (*c.* $\frac{1}{2}$in) long, much shorter than the broad wings and little exceeding the subsequently reflexed calyx lobes; rounded with a rather short, ultimately twisted beak (11–14cm (*c.* $\frac{1}{2}$in) long). The pod is oblong club-shaped, tomentellous with twenty-four to thirty-six rough seeds. Found in wooded grassland; altitude range *c.* 600–1700m (2000–5600ft). Nanyuki, Embu, Machakos, Kajiado, Chyulu Hills (Kenya); Tanzania and Uganda, no record; also in southern Sudan, southern Ethiopia.

C. zanzibarica **Plate 461**

An erect annual or short-lived perennial. Stem ribbed, appressed puberulous. Leaves tri-foliolate; leaflets lanceolate to elliptic-oblong, 60–105mm (2$\frac{2}{5}$–4in) long, glabrous or rarely puberulous above, appressed puberulous beneath. Stipules absent. Raceme to 30–40cm (12–15$\frac{3}{4}$in) long, with many closely arranged flowers. Standard obovate-elliptic, or suborbicular, yellow-veined, reddish-purple and glabrous outside; wings a little shorter to a little longer than the keel with a dark mark at base; keel shortly rounded about the middle with a slightly incurved, sharp, untwisted beak (12–13mm ($\frac{1}{2}$in) long). Found in clearings in rain-forest and bushland, *Brachystegia* woodland, uplands, swamps and valley grasslands, also on roadsides and cultivated ground; altitude range 0–1800m (0–5900ft). Shimba Hills (Kenya); Tanga, Morogoro, Songea, Zanzibar (Tanzania); Uganda, no record; also Mozambique and locally widespread as an escape from cultivation.

Desmodium repandum **Plate 419**

A loosely-branched herb with tri-foliolate leaves bearing ovate to rhomboid leaflets; the reddish-pink flowers, 18mm ($\frac{3}{4}$in) across, are borne in terminal panicles or pseudo-racemes. Common in shade or forest, particularly along streams and pathways, where its sticky fruits easily attach themselves to clothing. In all *Desmodium* species, the pods break transversely into one-seeded portions. Recorded throughout tropical and subtropical East Africa; altitude range 1000–3300m (3280–10,000ft).

D. salicifolium var. salicifolium   Plate 747
A woody perennial herb or shrub with flexuous stem erect to 2.6m (*c*. 4½ft) or creeping with ascending to erect inflorescences; stems reddish to pale brown, terete below, to angular, striate. Leaves tri-foliolate, leaflets lanceolate or lanceolate to nearly elliptic. Inflorescence racemose paniculate, the racemes lax to very dense. Flowers from yellow or pinkish green to vermilion or cream or white with bluish-mauve keel. Standard orbicular, 4–7mm (⅛–¼in) long; wings oblong, 3–6mm (⅛–¼in) long; keel petals equalling standard in length, 1–2mm (1/12in) wide. Found in wet places at the edge of rain-forest, river margins, swamps and wet grassland; altitude range 550–2100m (1800–6900ft). Recorded throughout East Africa.

NB Var. *densiflorum* has dense, congested inflorescences.

Dolichos kilimandscharica An erect, rarely decumbent perennial herb 0.25–1.2m (8–40in) tall, from a massive woody rootstock, 14–45cm (5½–18in) long and 7–30cm (2¾–12in) diameter, usually but not always flowering when leaves are undeveloped or absent. Stems few, simple or sparsely branched, usually densely pubescent with more or less appressed silvery, greyish or ferruginous hairs; some stems developing twining tips. Leaflets, three (to four) ovate to elliptic-lanceolate, the laterals oblique, acute or rather blunt at apex, cuneate to very slightly cordate at base, densely pubescent to silvery-velvety, often with ferruginous hairs on the nerves contrasting with the silvery parts. One to four flowers in fascicles in the axils of bracts which become leafy in the lower parts of the inflorescence. Standard purple, sometimes greenish-brown or yellow outside, or entirely white, 1.3–2.9cm (½–1⅛in) long, 1.3–2cm (½–⅝in) wide, round or rounded-oblong, emarginate; the base of the style is thickened, tapering and yellowish, a characteristic of *Dolichos*. Wings dark, keel cream, shaded purple. Found in grassland and *Combretum*-wooded grassland; altitude range 900–2700m (2950–8850ft). Especially in Central Province, also Aberdares, Embu, Machakos, Kajiado and Nairobi (Kenya); all regions of Tanzania; northern region of Uganda; also in Sudan, Ethiopia, Malawi, Zambia, Zimbabwe, Mozambique.

D. luticola   Plate 560
A small pubescent perennial herb, suberect or decumbent, 10–25cm (4–10in) tall, from a rather slender woody rootstock. Stems with very long, white, fine hairs. Three leaflets, elliptic to oblong-elliptic, subacute to broadly rounded at the apex, rounded or truncate at base. Racemes axillary, condensed umbel-like. Calyx frequently flushed very dark blackish-purple. Standard 9mm (⅓in) long and wide, basically green, yellow at the base, lilac-mauve at apex, dusky outside and with deeper purple lines inside at junction of purple and yellow parts, round or oblate; wings greenish-yellow, magenta at apex, lilac-mauve at base, keel greenish-yellow. Altitude range 1500–1800m (5000–6000ft) rarely to 2100m (7000ft). Locally common in black cotton soil and recorded around Nairobi and in Machakos and Kajiado (Kenya); Maasai, Moshi (Tanzania); Uganda and elsewhere, no record.

D. oliveri   Plate 561
A perennial plant of varying habit, generally an erect or scrambling shrub, the shoots becoming scandent at their tips, or a woody climber; less often a woody herb from 0.3–2.4m (1–7½ft) tall, often flowering when quite leafless. Rootstock thick

and woody, usually a large tuber, but sometimes a collection of oblong-ellipsoid tubers. Stems rather angular, sparsely pubescent to velvety with silvery to rust-red hairs. Leaflets, three, usually paler beneath, ovate, subacute to emarginate and mucronate at the apex, rounded to cuneate at the base, densely covered with appressed hairs usually velvety-silvery beneath, three-nerved for up to half their length. Flowers 1.5cm (⅝in) long, 1.5–1.8cm (⅝–¾in) broad, scented, one to five in axillary fascicles, sometimes appearing to be in false terminal inflorescences or in larger axillary inflorescences when leaves on the slender side branches are not developed. Standard purplish-red flushed red-brown or green outside, mostly lilac at base and flushed crimson at apex. Wings pink to reddish, or bluish-purple, keel sometimes slightly twisted at the apex, mostly white with a purple tip. Found in grassland, thicket, scrub bushland and woodland often on rocky or disturbed ground; altitude range 950–1950m (3100–6400ft). Recorded over most of Kenya from Kitale to Kajiado, and western areas to Machakos (Kenya); lake areas, Maasai, Tanga, Mpwapwa, Kondoa (Tanzania); northern and eastern regions of Uganda; also Ethiopia.

NB In some areas, the stems of the climbing form are noticeably thinner than those of the more shrubby forms.

D. sericeus A pubescent twiner with ovate leaflets and large and many mauve or purple flowers. The whole plant is similar to *D. trilobus* which is smaller in most of its parts and has solitary pedunculate mauve flowers. Standard 1–1.6cm (⅜–⅝in) long, 1–2cm (⅜–⅝in) wide. *D. sericeus* is a very variable species with at least four subspecies recorded in East Africa, the variations occurring in the hairiness and size of all parts and in the pods. Common in evergreen and montane forest edges and clearings. Altitude range 1170–2550m (3800–8364ft). Widespread throughout East Africa; also in Sudan, southern Ethiopia, Zaire to Zimbabwe and Mozambique.

ERIOSEMA
With forty-four species in East Africa, is closely related to *Rhynchosia*: both have short, two-seeded pods. It is never found in really dry areas. The flowers of all species are yellow or yellow and brown with the exception of *E. cordifolium*.

Eriosema montanum   Plate 336
A perennial herb, often subshrubby, 0.2–1.5m (6–50in) tall, branched. Branches mostly erect sometimes straggling or trailing, pubescent to densely shaggy with ferruginous hairs. Leaflets three, ovate, obovate-elliptic or elliptic to oblong-lanceolate, 3–11cm (1½–4⅓in) long, usually acute, but sometimes rounded or acuminate at the apex, rounded at the base, softly pubescent to velvety with orange glands on both surfaces, venation sometimes raised beneath. Raceme ferruginous and hairy; raceme with flowers: 2–7cm (¾–2¾in) long. Standard 5–6.5mm (*c.* ¼in) wide, yellow, flushed or veined with red or purple-brown, obovate, sparsely pubescent along the middle or glabrescent with orange-yellow glands. Wings yellow; keel greenish-yellow or white sometimes tinged with brown, glandular. Found in grassland, scrub, bushland and forest edges; altitude range 900–2520m (2950–8250ft). Kitale, Cheranganis, Rift Valley, Mau, Western Kenya and Kisii (Kenya); Moshi, Mbeya, Njombe (Tanzania); Karamoja (Mt Debasien), Kigezi, Mbale (Uganda); also in Ethiopia, Zaire, Malawi, Zambia, Zimbabwe.

NB Var. *brevipedunculatum* with short racemes, aggregated at the apices of the branches, (looking falsely paniculate), is found in Kigoma and Mpanda in Tanzania and in Zambia at 1170–1710m (3800–5575ft).

E. psoraleoides   Plate 337
A downy, erect, woody shrub with rounded oblanceolate to cuneate leaflets and long axillary racemes of yellow flowers. Locally common in disturbed rocky bushland from sea level to 2000m (6500ft) throughout East Africa. Also in Sudan, south to Mozambique, Zimbabwe.

E. cordifolium   Pink and yellow flowers 5–6mm (c. ¼in) long. It is found in short upland grassland above 2290m (7500ft) on Tinderet and Elgon (Kenya); Tanzania, no record; Ankole (Uganda); elsewhere Sudan, Ethiopia.

E. glomeratum   Yellow flowers 6–8.5mm (¼–⅓in) long, on short stalks and leaves mostly elliptical. It is a spreading, hairy herb and common in its altitude range of 1–1500m (3–5000ft) but rare up-country (Kenya); Tanga, Mafia Island, Zanzibar (Tanzania); West Nile, Teso, northern Mengo (Uganda); also south to Zambia, eastern Zaire.

E. jurionianum   A hairy species with elliptic leaves and ovoid spikes which have brown and yellow flowers, 5–8mm (⅕–⅓in) long. It is locally common in Kenya at upland forest edges, from 2000–2800m (6550–9200ft); Maasai/Mbulu (Tanzania); Acholi, Karamoja, Mbale – Elgon (Uganda); also in Ethiopia, Zaire.

E. nutans   Lanceolate to elliptic leaflets. Its dense, cylindrical racemes of yellow flowers look a little like a delicate column of lupin flowers, corolla 7mm (c. ¼in) long. Common in wooded grassland and forest edges; altitude range 1200–2400m (3900–7900ft). Aberdares, Tinderet, Kitale, Rift Valley and Machakos districts (Kenya); Mbulu, Ufipa, Mbeya (Tanzania); Ankole, Mbale – Sebei (Uganda); elsewhere Sudan, Ethiopia, Eritrea, south to Zimbabwe, Mozambique, etc.

E. robustum   Very hairy yellow flowers c. 13mm (c. ½in) long, 9mm (c. ⅓in) wide. Common in wooded grassland around Kitale and also found in the Aberdares, Rift Valley and Kisii (Kenya) at altitudes of 1500–2200m (4900–7200ft); Ngura (Tanzania); Mbale – Bugishu (Uganda); elsewhere Ethiopia, Rwanda, Burundi.

Erythrina abyssinica   Plates 509 & 510
A deciduous tree growing up to 12m (40ft) in savannah or scrub land and partial to laterite or rocky subsoils. The leaves are tri-foliolate with their stalks covered with grey hairs when young, becoming hairless, or nearly so, as they grow older. The leaflets are generally sparingly downed above and densely covered with grey hair below. They are broadly ovate to rhomboid or rounded with the terminal leaflet up to 20cm (8in) broad, usually broader than long, blunt at the apex and broadly rounded to cordate at the base. The branches are stout, armed with strongly recurved thorns and densely haired when young. The flowers appear before the leaves open and are a bright coral red to scarlet in colour. They form dense, erect, poker-like inflorescences 5–15cm (2–6in) long. Seeds are bright red and black. This plant can be found in most parts of East Africa with annual rainfall of 75mm (35in) or more, at altitudes 200–2100m (600–6800ft), but not in dense forest. Also widespread from Sudan and Ethiopia to Zimbabwe and Mozambique. One of seventeen species in East Africa.

E. burttii   Plate 420
A flat-topped tree 3.5–15m (11–50ft) tall, with raised corky bosses bearing curved prickles on the old, deeply-fissured, very rough, corky bark; flowering when leaves are not developed. Stems grey, wrinkled, roughened by leaf and peduncle scars,

soon glabrous, prickly. Leaves often borne on abbreviated side shoots; leaflets elliptic to broadly obovate or round 1.2–5cm (½–2in) long and wide, rounded to deeply emarginate at apex, cuneate to rounded at base, soon glabrous or with scattered hairs on the main veins beneath; midrib without prickles. Inflorescence covered with deciduous, ferruginous, stellate hairs. Standard 2.5–4.5cm (1–1⅘in) long, 2–3.5cm (¾–1⅖in) wide; scarlet, short-clawed, recurved, obovate, rounded; keel and wings usually blood-red or crimson, with margins and veins almost black, shiny, more or less equal, a third to half the length of the standard. Found in *Acacia-Combretum, Acacia-Commiphora* bushland or derived grassland; altitude range 800–1650m (2600–5500ft). Machakos, Kajiado (Kenya); Maasai, Moshi, Kilosa (Tanzania); Uganda, no record; not known elsewhere.

E. melanacantha (*E. rotundato-obovata*) A tree with a much-branched spreading crown 6–20m (20–65ft) tall with large corky bosses bearing curved prickles on old branches. Leaflets glabrous or subglabrous above, stellate pubescent beneath, terminal leaflets rounded-obovate or transversely-elliptic up to 6.75cm (2½in) long and 7.5cm (3in) broad. Flowers bright brick-red. Inflorescence covered with a deciduous, velvety, ferruginous, stellate tomentum. Standard 5–7.5cm (2–3in) long, 1.8–3.3cm (⅗–1⅗in) wide; very short-clawed, elliptic, narrowly rounded; keel and wings brownish-salmon, more or less equal and a quarter to a third the length of the standard. Seeds a dull brownish colour with a small black patch at one end of hilum. Found in *Acacia–Commiphora* bushland and semi-desert grassland; altitude range 300–1500m (1000–4920ft). Northern Frontier districts, Mathews Range, Meru and Kitui (Kenya); Maasai, Moshi, Tanga (Tanzania); Uganda, no record; also in Ethiopia, southern Somalia.

Galactia argentifolia **Plate 666**

An erect, or sometimes rather straggling herb or subshrub up to 1.5m (4½ft) tall. Stems densely velvety with silvery or greyish hairs above, pubescent below; extreme tips sometimes showing climbing tendencies. Three leaflets, paler beneath, elliptic or elliptic-oblong, 2.5–5.5cm (*c*. 1–2in) long, rounded or slightly emarginate at the apex, rounded at the base, finely appressed pubescent above, very densely appressed silvery velvety beneath. Racemes few-flowered, dense, bracts small, lanceolate, 3–4mm (⅛–⅙in) long. Calyx appressed silvery pilose. Standard mauve or violet, obovate, glabrous, 1.4cm (⅗in) long, *c*. 8mm (*c*. ⅓in) wide. This is an interesting plant, as it is undoubtedly a native of East Africa, though most *Galactia* species are in America. Found in grassland, and open savannah; altitude range 0–450m (0–1475ft). Shimba Hills, Lunga Lunga area, Kilifi district (Kenya); Uzaramo, Dar-es-Salaam (Tanzania); Uganda and elsewhere, not known.

INDIGOFERA

147 species in East Africa. Generally small, red flowers, leaves usually imparipinnate, pods usually cylindrical, most hairs medifixed.

Indigofera arrecta A stout rather woody herb 1–2m (3¼–6½ft) tall though occasionally it can be 3m (nearly 10ft) in height. The leaves are up to 6cm (2⅖in) long with seven to seventeen leaflets, each of which is up to 20mm (*c*. ⅘in) long. The inflorescence is a many-flowered raceme up to 5cm (2in) long but usually shorter than this; the flowers are red inside when open, but the outside is covered with short stiff brown hairs; corolla *c*. 5mm (⅕in) long. Seed pod deflexed and straight and brown in colour, 12–17mm (*c*. ½–⅔in) long with four to eight seeds. The flowers at higher altitudes are rather larger in size with a greater proportion of brown or black hairs than those at lower altitudes. It is found in grassland, bushland and forest margins up to 2500m (8100ft) throughout East and tropical Africa.

I. atriceps A coarse branching sub-erect herb up to 2m (6½ft) tall, covered with short bristles often dark or black in colour except for those on the leaflets. The seed pods always have pale or reddish glandular hairs on them and are up to 10mm ($\frac{2}{8}$in) long. The leaf rachis is 1–6cm ($\frac{2}{8}$–2$\frac{2}{8}$in) long with leaflets nine to thirteen in number. The inflorescence is a dense, many-flowered, pedunculate raceme on a peduncle, and the corolla is a dull red in colour, *c.* 7mm (*c.* $\frac{1}{4}$–$\frac{5}{16}$in) long. This is a very variable species and is found in moist grassland, in bracken and at the edges of montane forest from 1100–2500m (3600–8100ft) almost everywhere within its zone in East Africa; also Ethiopia, eastern Zaire, Mozambique, Malawi.

I. brevicalyx A spreading, sparsely appressed-strigulose perennial with five to thirteen leaflets, each with three translucent blisters, one beneath each side and one at the tip. The inflorescence is a two- to three-flowered raceme up to 5cm (2in) long, brick-red in colour; corolla 8mm ($\frac{1}{3}$in) long. Each lobe of the calyx which can be up to 1.5mm ($\frac{1}{16}$in) long has a blister. It is found in short grassland from 900–2300m (3000–7700ft) almost everywhere in this altitude zone though it is not recorded in western Kenya; Mbulu, Moshi, Lushoto (Tanzania); Ankole, Kigezi, Bufindi (Uganda); also in eastern Zaire, Rwanda, Burundi, Ethiopia and Eritrea.

I. nairobiensis   **Plate 748**
A perennial herb with a woody rootstock, the branches usually procumbent, sometimes more or less erect, up to 50cm (20in) long, more or less strigose, the hairs appressed or spreading at the tips. Leaflets five to eleven, narrowly cuneate-oblong or oblanceolate, 15×5mm ($\frac{3}{8}$×$\frac{1}{4}$in), appressed, strigose on both surfaces, red-black processes often present in axils. Racemes three- to fifteen-flowered, 1.2–6cm ($\frac{1}{2}$–2$\frac{2}{8}$in) long, bracts linear up to 4mm ($\frac{1}{8}$in) long. Corolla puberulous outside, pink-red. Stamens 6–7mm ($\frac{1}{4}$in) long. Found in grassy places with rainfall 700–1000mm (*c.* 27–40in), altitude range 1600–2400m (5250–7875ft). Rift Valley, Nyahururu, Machakos, Nairobi, Magadi and north-eastern areas (Kenya); Maasai (Tanzania); elsewhere, not known.

I. schimperi   **Plate 749**
A perennial with dense, appressed, silvery indumentum, 1m up to rarely 3m (3–9ft) tall; leaf rachis up to 6cm (1$\frac{3}{8}$in) long including a petiole of 3mm ($\frac{1}{8}$in) long. Leaflets five to ten, alternate up to 25mm (1in) long and 20mm ($\frac{4}{8}$in) broad; raceme many-flowered up to 20cm (7$\frac{3}{8}$in) long including a peduncle of 1–2cm ($\frac{2}{8}$–$\frac{4}{8}$in) long. The calyx much less than half as long as the corolla; standard densely covered and glistening with appressed silver or yellowish indumentum. (In var. *schimperi*, the stamens are only 5–7mm ($\frac{1}{5}$–$\frac{1}{4}$in) long – in var. *baukeana*, they are 7–10mm ($\frac{1}{4}$–$\frac{2}{8}$in) long. Found in grassland and bushland, often in areas with impeded drainage; altitude range up to 1900m (6300ft); rainfall tolerance: ±600mm (24in). Mau, Aberdares, Narok, Embu, Machakos, Nairobi and Kajiado (Kenya); lake areas, Maasai, Mpwapwa, Kondoa, Morogoro, Songea (Tanzania); northern, eastern regions of Uganda; also Zambia, Malawi, Zimbabwe, Mozambique.

I. spicata A prostrate or ascending perennial with ridges but more or less flattened stems. The leaves are up to 4 or 5cm (*c.* 2in) long with five to eleven alternate leaflets which are usually about 1cm ($\frac{3}{8}$in) long. The inflorescence is a many-flowered dense raceme, a pinkish-red in colour on a peduncle from 1–4cm ($\frac{2}{8}$–1$\frac{1}{2}$in) long. Widespread throughout East Africa in disturbed grassland up to 2300m

(7500ft); also Sudan, Ethiopia, Zaire, southern tropical Africa.

I. tanganyikensis A stiff erect herb up to 1m ($3\frac{1}{4}$ft) tall, covered in short spreading hairs with leaves up to 5cm (2in) long with seven to fifteen leaflets which are channelled and sticky at the margins. The inflorescence is two- to three-flowered, the calyx lobes are usually gland-tipped and the corolla is pale red in colour, 7mm (*c*. $\frac{1}{4}$in) long. It is found in grassland and bushland on rocky or sandy soils mainly from 1000–2000m (3300–6600ft). Mau, Mumias, Kisii, Narok, Rift Valley, Machakos and Nairobi (Kenya); Mwanza, Tabora (Tanzania); Kigezi, Busoga, Mengo - Entebbe (Uganda); also eastern Zaire, Rwanda, Burundi, Ethiopia (Harar).

I. volkensii **Plate 750**
A branching herb up to 40cm (15–16in) tall from a perennial rootstock, with a white, rather dense, somewhat spreading hairy indumentum; the leaf rachis up to 25mm (1in) long, leaflets three to seven, the terminal usually much larger than the lateral ones; alternate, lanceolate-oblong, strigose on both surfaces; the flower a many-flowered raceme, deep pink to red. Raceme up to 7cm ($2\frac{4}{5}$in) long; calyx 4–6mm ($\frac{1}{6}$–$\frac{1}{4}$in) long; stamens 4–5mm ($\frac{1}{5}$in) long. Found in *Acacia-Commiphora* woodland, open wooded grassland and as a weed in cultivated land in areas with rainfall from 250–1000mm (10–40in); altitude range 200–2200m (650–7200ft). Narok, Baringo, Rift Valley, Magadi, Kajiado, Machakos, Nairobi, Nanyuki and Chyulu Hills (Kenya); lake areas, Maasai, Tanga, Mpwapwa, Kondoa, Morogoro (Tanzania); northern region of Uganda; also Sudan, southern Ethiopia.

Lablab purpurea (*Dolichos lablab*) **Plate 667**
A climbing perennial (rarely an annual) herb 1–5m (3–16ft) long; outside the uplands of Kenya sometimes erect perennial. Stems pubescent or glabrous. Leaflets ovate-triangular, 2.5–15cm (1–7in) long, 1.5–14cm ($\frac{3}{5}$–$5\frac{1}{2}$in) wide, acuminate, cuneate to truncate at base, glabrous or pubescent. Inflorescence axillary, bracts deciduous, ovate-lanceolate, 4mm ($\frac{1}{6}$in) long. Calyx glabrous or pubescent; tube 3–4mm ($\frac{1}{8}$–$\frac{1}{6}$in) long, lower lobes triangular or linear oblong, 2–4mm ($\frac{1}{12}$–$\frac{1}{6}$) long, the upper pair joined to form an entire or marginate lip. Standard 1.2–1.5cm ($\frac{1}{2}$–$\frac{3}{5}$in) long, 1.2–1.5cm ($\frac{1}{2}$–$\frac{3}{5}$in) wide; entirely crimson or purple, or cream tinged with mauve outside and purple inside, or entirely white; oblate or round, glabrous, wings purple, keel pale, tinged mauve at the apex. Pods oblong, falcate, two to five seeded. Seeds white or red to black. Altitude range 0–2400m (0–7900ft). Only species in East Africa. Found in bushland, grassland and cultivation and recorded throughout East Africa, tropical Africa and south to eastern Cape Province.

NB The herb is cultivated in East Africa and was formerly known as *Dolichos lablab* or *Njahi* in the Kikuyu language. At one time it was a major source of protein for African peoples and was widely used as a green manure in plantation crops. It is natural that in a plant so widely cultivated there are a number of subspecies and forms.

Lupinus princei **Plate 829**
An erect annual or short-lived perennial, the stem covered with a soft tomentum of fine, only slightly spreading hairs. Seven to eleven (occasionally thirteen) leaflets oblanceolate-cuneate to narrowly oblong-elliptic, appressed pilose on both surfaces. The inflorescence is a raceme with irregular verticillate flowers; the standard blue with a white and yellow median zone, and glabrous; wings blue as long as the keel which is narrow and curved up to a short blunt beak. Found in upland grassland, often associated with old pastoral encampments extending down to savan-

nah woodland; altitude range 1500–2800m (4900–8150ft). Tinderet, Mt Kenya, Rift Valley – Menengai and Kajiado (Kenya); Maasai, Mbeya, Iringa, Songea (Tanzania); Uganda, no record; also in Ethiopia – a white form has been recorded in southern Ethiopia.

NB Various other species are cultivated for ornament or green manure e.g. *L. albus*, *L. angustifolius*, and *L. luteus*. They may become locally naturalized in some areas in due course.

MACROTYLOMA

Pinnately tri-foliolate herbs, usually twining. Flowers yellow on short pedicels, single or in small clusters in the leaf axils. Pods flat. Formerly placed in *Dolichos*, but without the hard, swollen, glistening style-base of that genus. Fourteen species in East Africa.

Macrotyloma axillare(*Dolichos axillaris*) **Plate 338**
A more or less pubescent twiner with elliptic leaflets and flowers 12–24mm (½–1in) long. Found in three varieties in grassland, bushland and the margins of forest and cultivation between 1–2520m (3–8400ft), in all parts of East Africa except the western provinces of Kenya; also from southern Arabia and Nigeria to Angola, Natal, Madagascar and Ceylon.

MILLETTIA

Twenty-four species in East Africa, all trees or shrubs with imparipinnate leaves and blue or purple flowers.

Millettia dura A shrub or tree up to 10.5m (35ft) with ash-grey longitudinally striate bark. Lilac flowers in clusters, three or four together on pendent panicles, 10–20cm (4–8in) long. Altitude range 1200–1650m (4000–5500ft). Often seen around Mt Kenya at forest edges and in secondary scrub in the Embu and Meru districts on the wetter side of the mountain (Kenya); Bukoba, Buha (Tanzania); Ankole, Kigezi, Kagera River (Uganda); also eastern Zaire, Rwanda, Burundi.

M. usaramensis **Plate 562**
A shrub or small tree up to 3–7m (10–23ft) – sometimes 10m (33ft) tall; bark grey; buds small, rounded. Leaf rachis up to 16cm (6⅓in) long, including a petiole 2–3cm (*c.* ⅘–1⅕in) long prolonged about 1cm (⅖in) beyond lateral leaflets. Seven to seventeen leaflets, from broadly ovate at the base to lanceolate at the tip of the leaf up to 7cm (2¾in) long, more or less asymmetric, somewhat acuminate, apex rounded, truncate or emarginate, main nerves five to seven on each side. Pseudoracemes axillary, nearly always under 14cm (5½in) long, the floriferous branchlets 1–15mm (up to ⅗in) long; blade of standard 11×13mm (⅖×½in), claw 2–3mm (*c.* ⅛in) long. Corolla purplish-blue, blade of standard thinly white-silky outside, cordate but not thickened or folded at the base. Found in wooded grassland and margins of lowland forest in rainfall areas of 900–1800mm (35–70in) pa; altitude range 10–1200m (33–4000ft). Nyika country (*c.f.* Taru Desert), Kwale (Kenya); Mwanza, Tanga, Morogoro, Zanzibar (Tanzania); Uganda, no record; also Mozambique.

Mucuna gigantea var. **quadrialata** **Plate 11**
A large woody liane attaining 8–15m (26–50ft) in length. Stems at first covered with stiff orange-brown hairs, later glabrescent. Leaflets elliptic or ovate, the laterals oblique, 4–11.5cm (1⅘–4⅗in) long, acuminate and markedly apiculate at apex, rounded at the base, glabrous. Inflorescences mostly from the thick lower stems. Calyx covered with fine grey pubescence and also long deciduous orange-brown

bristles, tube 7–11mm ($\frac{1}{3}$–$\frac{2}{3}$in) long. Standard 2.5–3.5cm (1–1$\frac{2}{5}$in) long, *c.* 2.5cm (1in) wide, pale creamy-green, white or pale lilac, eventually turning black, round, with very sparse orange bristly hairs particularly outside on top of claw; wings and keel similarly coloured. Ssp. *quadrialata* has predominantly large flowers. Found in bushland, forest edges, usually by water and often right to the coastal foreshore. Altitude range 0–1140m (0–3700ft). Six other species in East Africa. Meru, western Kenya, Kwale, Kilifi, South Horr (Kenya); Musoma, Pare district, Ulanga (Tanzania); Ankole, Busoga, Mengo (Uganda); Zanzibar and Pemba (Tanzania); also in Zaire, Mozambique.

Mundulea sericea   Plate 668
A bush, shrub or tree up to 7.6m (25ft) high, usually with straight stems and bushy rounded crown. Bark greenish-brown and smooth at first, becoming yellow, corky and fissured in age. Branchlets softly tomentellous. Leaves up to 15cm (6in) long, twelve to twenty leaflets, glabrous above, appressed-pubescent below, oblong to oblong lanceolate, up to 5cm (2in) long and 6mm ($\frac{1}{4}$in) broad. The flowers are crowded in terminal and leaf-opposed racemes up to 15cm (6in) long, the corolla purple-pink and the standard pubescent, about 2cm ($\frac{4}{5}$in) long. Blade of standard 18mm ($\frac{7}{10}$in) long, 15mm ($\frac{3}{5}$in) wide; wings (including claw of 2mm) 17mm (*c.* $\frac{3}{4}$in) long; keel (including claw of 4mm) 18mm ($\frac{3}{4}$in) long. The pod is flat, pale brown to yellow, and finely tomentose, 5–7.5cm (2–3in) long, only 6mm ($\frac{1}{4}$in) broad. This plant is used to stupefy fish so that they may be caught, and on account of this its natural range has probably been extended. Insects attack the seeds, which accounts for its rarity in areas apparently well suited to it. Rainfall tolerance 300–1100mm (12–43in) pa. One species only in mainland East Africa. Found in coastal and dry savannah areas from 10–1950m (33–6400ft) (Kenya); all regions of Tanzania except Songea; northern region of Uganda; also in Sudan, Somalia, south to Zimbabwe, Mozambique.

Ophrestia hedysaroides   Plate 61
A perennial climber up to 2m (6$\frac{1}{2}$ft) long, or, more rarely, a suberect and woody herb 0.3–0.9m (1–3ft) tall. Stems covered with yellowish-brown, spreading pubescence. Leaves pinnately tri-foliolate (rarely five-); leaflets elliptic up to 8cm (3$\frac{1}{8}$in) long and up to 3.9cm (1$\frac{1}{2}$–in) broad, rounded or emarginate and mucronate at the apex, rounded or cuneate at the base, pubescent on both surfaces, but especially on the raised venation beneath; sometimes velvety. The flowers in subsessile axillary (rarely pseudo-terminal) clusters. Calyx densely covered with spreading ferruginous hairs. The standard is white, greenish at the base, elliptic or rounded-oblong, emarginate and silky outside (very rarely coral red at the base). The lobes are joined at the base. Flower cluster 1.5–2.5cm ($\frac{3}{5}$–1in) long; standard 11mm ($\frac{2}{5}$in) long, 6mm ($\frac{1}{4}$in) wide; lobes 4–5mm ($\frac{1}{5}$in) long. Found in bushland, forest edges, grassland and cultivations; altitude range 0–1270m (0–4150ft). Coastal districts in East Africa, and also in Zaire.

Ormocarpum kirkii   Plate 669
A shrub or small tree 2–9m (6$\frac{1}{2}$–29ft) tall, twigs whitish, sparsely white pubescent when young, occasionally also with swollen-based hairs. Leaves imparipinnate, at first spaced out on long shoots, later in fascicles on short shoots; stipules up to 6mm ($\frac{1}{4}$in) long; leaflets subalternate, seven to thirteen, elliptic-oblong, the terminal one, obovate, usually 7–12mm ($\frac{1}{4}$–$\frac{1}{2}$in) long and 4–7mm ($\frac{1}{6}$–$\frac{1}{4}$in) broad, sometimes, however, up to 24mm (1in) long and 10mm ($\frac{2}{5}$in) broad, the margin revolute, darker above than beneath. The racemes white pubescent, one- to three-flowered. Flowers, 16mm ($\frac{2}{3}$in) in diameter, purple or mauve fasciculate-cymose; the withered

corolla persists, calyx glabrous and broadly-toothed. Seed smooth, straw-coloured, c. 4mm (⅙in) long. Pod transversely jointed coiled within the persistent corolla; one-seeded. Found in *Acacia-Commiphora* and coastal bushland and grassland in rainfall areas from 250–900mm (10–35in); altitude range 20–1700m (65–5600ft). Machakos, Kajiado and coastal districts (Kenya); Maasai, Tanga, Mpwapwa, Kondoa, Mbeya, Iringa, Songea (Tanzania); Uganda, no record; also in Somalia, Zaire (Katanga), Malawi, Zambia, Zimbabwe, Mozambique.

Parochetus species   Plate 830

Closely related to *P. communis*. Until recently it was considered that there was only one species of this genus, but it is now thought that the African plant is distinct from the true *P. communis* which grows in the Himalayas. A prostrate, glabrous or sparsely pilose herb, rooting at the nodes; leaves digitately tri-foliolate on long petioles; stipules ovate, acute, scarious, leaflets cuneate-obovate, entire, crenate or 'coarsely-toothed'. Inflorescence an umbel up to four-flowered but generally two-flowered; bracts brown, 2–4mm (¹⁄₁₂–⅙in) long; calyx, c. 6–7mm (c. ¼in) long, divided in the middle into ovate acute unequal teeth, the upper pair united almost at the tip. Corolla glabrous, bright blue, up to 17mm (⅔in) long. Found in forests, especially in moist places and forest clearings, usually on soils of volcanic origin; altitude range 1500–3450m (4900–11,600ft); generally in areas with over 1100mm (44in) of rain pa; Aberdares, Mt Kenya, Nyambeni Hills, Chyulu Hills, Limuru (Kenya); Maasai, Morogoro, Mpwapwa, Kondoa (Tanzania); western, eastern Uganda; also in Ethiopia, Rwanda, eastern Zaire, Malawi, Mozambique.

Platycelyphium voënse (*P. cyananthum*)   Plate 563

A small deciduous tree from 3–7.5m (10–22ft) tall with a short trunk, sometimes several stemmed and ascending branches; bark pale grey, brown or yellowish-brown, peeling when old in papery strips like a *Commiphora*. Young branches glabrous to pubescent, the leaves and flowers mostly borne on lateral spur-shoots. Racemes produced before the leaves, laxly eight to sixteen (to thirty), flowered. Calyx, 5–7mm (⅕–¼in) long, purplish-green to black, sparsely hairy except for fringe of hairs at mouth, sticky; corolla, violet to deep blue, with a creamish-green patch which darkens with age at base of standard, sweetly scented. Stamens free. Fruit flat, papery, indehiscent, single-seeded. Found in deciduous bushland and *Acacia-Commiphora* semi-arid areas. Altitude range 80–1000m (250–3300ft). Only species in genus. Northern areas, Taita, Voi-Tsavo, Kwale (Kenya); Tanga, Mbeya, Iringa (Tanzania); Uganda, no record; also Ethiopia (Ogaden), Somalia.

Pseudarthria confertiflora   Plate 751

An erect, woody herb or subshrub from 0.5–1.5m (1½–5½ft) tall; stems strongly ribbed, pubescent to velvety. Leaflets lanceolate, elliptic or obovate-elliptic, 4–14cm (1½–5½in) long, acute to rounded and mucronulate at apex, cuneate to rounded at base, subentire but usually broadly crenulate, rough above, pubescent to velvety beneath. Inflorescence 5–27cm (2–10⅘in) long, a narrow panicle composed of short (1–10cm (⅖–4in) long), false racemes, the flowers mostly crowded in the upper parts; pedicels at first erect, later reflexed, corolla reddish-purple, standard rounded, 6–8mm (¼–⅓in) long, 5mm (⅕in) wide. Pods slightly curved, densely pilose. Closely resembles *Desmodium salicifolium*, but differs in the pods which split lengthwise and not transversely. Found in grassland, grassland with scattered trees, thicket and bracken areas in forest glades; altitude range 900–2300m (2950–7550ft). Elgon, Nanyuki, Rift Valley (Kenya); Maasai, Tanga, Mpwapwa, Kondoa, Morogoro, Mbeya, Iringa (Tanzania); all regions of Uganda; also Sudan, Ethiopia, Zaire.

Pseudarthria hookeri An erect plant with panicles of pink flowers at the leaf axils and pinnately tri-foliolate leaves. Flower c. 7mm (¼in) long. Common in wooded grassland at altitudes up to 2290m (7500ft) throughout East Africa. Also in Ethiopia, Sudan, Zaire to Zimbabwe, Mozambique.

Psoralea foliosa   **Plate 831**
A much-branched aromatic shrub 0.3–3.3m (1–4ft) tall. Stems densely pubescent, digitately tri-foliolate, dotted with translucent glands about 3mm (⅛in) in diameter. Leaflets oblanceolate, apiculate up to 4cm (1⅜in) long and 1.7cm (⁷⁄₁₀in) wide, undulate at the margin. Flowers, crowded in dense terminal subcapitate racemes, half hidden among the leaves or sometimes two or three together in the axils of the upper leaves. Calyx pubescent with many black hairs. Inside of standard dark purplish blue, rest of corolla paler or white, standard clawed, 9mm (⅓in) long, 7mm (¼in) wide. Only species in East Africa. Found in upland grassland, bushland and forest margins. Altitude range 1600–3100m (5250–10,150ft). Mt Njiru, Northern Frontier areas, Mt Kenya and the Cheranganis (Kenya); Maasai, Mbeya, Iringa (Tanzania); Uganda, no record; also in northern Malawi, eastern Zambia, Zimbabwe.

RHYNCHOSIA
Pinnately tri-foliolate, glands on lower surface. Some species very hairy; corolla yellow and red except R. albissima and R. hirta; pods short, two-seeded. Thirty-five species in East Africa.

Rhynchosia elegans   **Plate 462**
A perennial climbing herb, 1–2.5m (3–c. 8ft) long from a woody rootstock. Stems glabrescent and mostly rather densely covered with appressed white hairs, particularly on the ridges, and with numerous reddish gland-dots. Three leaflets, ovate or rhomboid, the laterals oblique, 1.2–8cm (½–3¼in) long, subacute to acuminate, rounded, truncate, cuneate or slightly subcordate at base, pubescent or glabrescent and gland-dotted above, pubescent to densely velvety below with dense yellow to red gland-dots beneath; ventilation prominent below. Inflorescences axillary, lax, the flowers mostly paired along the rhachis which is glandular-hairy. Flower 1.25–2.1cm (½–⅞in) long, to 1.25cm (½in) wide. Standard yellow, densely veined with dark purple or crimson outside; wings yellow, keel white or yellowish with purple veins inside at the tip, which coalesce to give a purple flush. Found in bushland, dry evergreen forest, rocky outcrops and edges of swamps; altitude range 1080–2100m (3250–6900ft). Rift Valley, Nairobi, Kajiado, Narok (Kenya); Longido Mt (Tanzania); Teso district (Uganda).

R. holstii   **Plate 463**
A trailing plant with ovate to rhomboid leaves and long racemes of yellow flowers, c. 15mm (⅜in) long, streaked with red (rather like widely-spaced sweet pea flowers). Found in rocky grassland, from 900–2200m (2000–7100ft). Particularly around Nairobi, Embu and Machakos (Kenya); Mpwapwa, Morogoro, Ulanda (Tanzania); Mengo, Mubende, Kampala (Uganda); also in eastern Zaire and Zimbabwe.

R. nyasica   **Plate 464**
A perennial, somewhat sticky, erect, rarely prostrate herb or subshrub with several stems up to 1m (3ft) tall from a woody rootstock. Stems pubescent and glandular. Three leaflets, oblate, ovate or rarely kidney-shaped, the laterals usually oblique, rounded to shortly acuminate at the apex, rounded or shortly cordate at base, glabrescent to pubescent and glandular on both surfaces. Inflorescences short,

axillary, often subsessile; bracts deciduous, linear-lanceolate; calyx pubescent and glandular. Standard 1–1.3cm (c. ½in) long, 8–9mm (⅓in) wide; yellow, often with purple veins, broadly elliptic-ovate, wings yellow, keel greenish-yellow. Found in grassland with scattered trees, woodland, semi-arid *Acacia* thicket; altitude range 400–1500m (1300–4900ft). Not common. Aberdares, Embu and Fort Hall (Kenya); Lushoto district, Mpanda (Tanzania); Karamoja, Busoga and Mengo (Uganda).

R. usambarensis   Plate 465
A glandular and spreading, hairy, twining herb with ovate, acute leaves which have paler areas near the veins, and long pedunculate racemes of orange-yellow flowers, c. 1cm (⅜in) long. Locally common in upland grassland and forest edges from 1200–2400m (4000–8000ft) in East Africa; also in Ethiopia.

R. albissima   Yellow and purple flowers, c. 12mm (½in) long, 8mm (⅓in) wide. Common at the coast (Kenya) but rarely found elsewhere; Tanga, Pangani, Morogoro (Tanzania); Karamoja, Bokora (Uganda); also Mozambique, Zimbabwe.

R. densiflora   Yellow flowers, 7–14mm (¼–½in) long, and a low, prostrate habit. Found in stony grassland from 1000–2100m (3300–6900ft). Mumias to Machakos (Kenya); Musoma (Seronera), Shinyanga, Mbulu (Lake Manyara National Park), Pare, Arusha, Njombe (Tanzania); Ankole, Karamoja, Oropoi Escarpment, Busoga, Mengo (Uganda); also Ethiopia, Sudan, Zaire, Mozambique, Zimbabwe, Zambia, Malawi.

R. hirta   Dull, white-green flowers, 2cm (¾in) long, in racemes. Its blue seeds open in the pod when ripe. It is widespread in dry woodland edges and *Combretum* bushland, from 1–1800m (3–5900ft) (Kenya); Mwanza, Korogwe, Kondoa, Zanzibar (Tanzania); Kigezi, Teso, Masaka (Uganda); widespread throughout tropical Africa and south to Zimbabwe, Mozambique.

R. orthobotrya   A glandular-hairy woody herb with ovate leaves and long spikes of small yellow and red subsessile flowers, c. 10mm (⅜in) long. Found in wooded grassland from 1000–2100m (3300–6900ft). Baringo and westwards (Kenya); Ngara, Mbulu, Moshi (Tanzania); West Nile, Bunyoro, Mengo (Uganda).

SESBANIA
Tall, stiff herbs or shrubs; leaves abruptly pinnate with many leaflets; flowers yellow, standard usually flecked with purple, in axillary racemes; pods long, narrow, many-seeded; always in wet or damp areas. Eighteen species in East Africa.

Sesbania goetzei   Plate 466
A shrub up to 3m (10ft) high with twigs and leaflets densely and softly pubescent. Leaflets in five to ten pairs up to 1.25cm (½in) long, 0.5cm (⅓in) broad. Flowers solitary or in pairs, yellow with purple-spotted standard and with a free appendage near base. Blade of standard 18–24mm (¾–1in) long, 6mm (¼in) wide at base. Pod thicker at the centre than at the margin. Seeds green, not mottled. Altitude range 1100–2000m (3600–6560ft). Found in land liable to flooding, beside alkaline or marginally alkaline lakes, sometimes forming pure stands, and recorded at Lakes Nakuru, Naivasha, Amboseli (Kenya); also in Tanzania, Zambia and Ethiopia.

S. sesban   Plate 467
A shrub or small tree up to 6m (20ft) in height with hairy or downy branchlets. The leaves are up to 10cm (4in) long with leaflets up to 7.5cm (3in) long and in nine to

twenty-seven pairs in number, covered with short, soft hairs. The flowers are 1.25cm (½in) long, *c.* 2cm (⅘in) across, yellow in colour with a plain or mottled standard. The seed pods are up to 11cm (4⅓in) long. Widespread in most districts from 100–2200m (300–7200ft) but not common below 1000m (3280ft) and usually found near water throughout East Africa; also southern Sudan, Ethiopia, southern Somalia, south to Zimbabwe, Mozambique.

SOPHORA

Trees, shrubs or herbs. Leaves imparipinnate, eight to thirty-six foliolate; stipels setaceous or often absent; flowers in terminal, or axillary, few to many, racemes; bracts often fairly large; calyx campanulate to tubular, with very shallow to prominent and acute lobes; petals yellow, white, blue or purple; stamens free or shortly joined at base; anthers dorsifixed; ovary shortly stipitate; style incurved with a small terminal stigma; fruit moniliform, often winged, one- to fourteen-seeded. Two species in East Africa.

Sophora inhambanensis **Plate 339**
A shrub, 1–2m (3–6ft) high, young branches, leaves, inflorescences and calyces densely whitish to silvery or golden pubescent, the calyces and both surfaces of the leaflets strongly sericeous (silky). Leaves with petiole and rhachis together 7–12cm (2¾–4¾in) long – sometimes 15cm (6in) – with five to seven pairs or leaflets; lateral leaflets elliptic to obovate or oblanceolate, cuneate and slightly asymmetrical at base, obtuse to subacute at apex. Terminal leaflet up to twice as long as the lateral ones, cuneate and equal-sided at base. Flowers many in terminal racemes up to 25cm (10in) long; calyx campanulate with five shallow teeth. Petals yellow, the limb suborbicular, cordate, the claw more or less distinct, wings and keel slightly shorter than standard, 17–22mm (⅔–9/10in) long, 15–18mm (⅗–¾in) wide. Stamens free. Found on sandy foreshores. Kilifi, Malindi, Lamu (Kenya); Pangani, Bagamoyo (Tanzania); Uganda, no record; also in Mozambique.

S. tomentosa A shrub 1–3m (3–10ft) high; young branches, petioles, leaf-rhacides and undersurface of leaflets puberulous or pubescent when young, but glabrescent later. Leaves with five to seven pairs of leaflets (sometimes four or up to nine); lateral leaflets broadly elliptic to suborbicular up to 4cm (1⅗in) long and 3cm (1⅕in) broad; asymmetrical at the base with the distal side rounded and the proximal side more or less cuneate, rounded at the apex. Terminal leaflets slightly larger than the lateral ones, equal-sided and cuneate at the base. Flowers, many, in terminal racemes up to 25cm (10in) long, bracts linear, 3–5mm (⅛–⅕in) long. Calyx campanulate with five shallow teeth (very small). Petals yellow, standard, 14–20mm (½–⅘in) long, 11–14mm (⅖–½in) wide, with the limb cuneate and gradually narrowed below to a short broad claw. Stamens free. Wings and keel about equal to the standard or slightly shorter. The sap may be used as a fish poison. Found on coastal foreshores, 0–50m (0–160ft), in Kenya, Tanzania, Mozambique.

TEPHROSIA

Fifty-seven species in East Africa. Standards silky, never glabrous; inflorescence a pseudo-raceme; pods flat, usually several-seeded; leaves usually imparipinnate, occasionally one or three foliolate.

Tephrosia emeroides **Plate 564**
A softly woody, stiffly erect perennial with appressed hairs; leaves with five to thirteen leaflets; calyx golden brown; flowers pink or rose in lax terminal pseudo-racemes and also in many of the upper leaf axils. Standard, *c.* 13mm (½in) long, with

appressed golden hairs outside. Claw of keel 3mm ($\frac{1}{8}$in) long. Found in semi-evergreen bushland in rainfall areas of 800–1000mm (40–50in); altitude range 1200–2200m (3800–7200ft); and recorded in Aberdares, western Kenya, Narok, Rift Valley, Nanyuki and Nairobi (Kenya); Tanzania, no record; northern region of Uganda; also in Ethiopia, northern Somalia.

T. holstii **Plate 421**

An annual or perennial, yellowish hairy herb with unifoliolate leaves. The flowers are orange or brick red, usually in short, dense terminal pseudo-racemes, but also often in the axil of the uppermost leaf. The standard, upper petal is hairy, the outside about 12mm ($\frac{1}{2}$in) long and the style is hairless and curved into a semi-circle. It is found in upland grassland and forest margins from 1200–2400m (4000–8000ft) in the Mau, Tinderet, Kitui, Mumias, Embu, Machakos and Kajiado districts and around Nairobi (Kenya); Moshi, Kondoa, Morogoro (Tanzania); no record in Uganda; also in southern Ethiopia.

T. interrupta **Plate 670**

A robust, bushy, woody herb with leaves formed of nine to twenty-one leaflets. Its purple flowers are grouped in darkly-haired terminal pseudo-racemes with several flowers at each node and short lateral branches sometimes developed with the lower nodes well separated. The standard, 14–20mm (*c.* $\frac{5}{8}$–$\frac{4}{5}$in) long, upper petal, is covered with brown hairs. It is common in mountain areas in scrub margins, the edges of bush patches and on rocky outcrops at altitude range 1575–2800m (5250–9250ft), chiefly where cloud or mist is frequent in Kenya; Maasai, Tanga, Morogoro, Mbeya, Iringa (Tanzania); all regions of Uganda except Buganda; also Sudan – Imatong Mts, Ethiopia, Eritrea.

T. villosa **Plate 671**

An annual or short-lived perennial, 0.3–1.3m (1–4ft) tall, leaflets eleven to fifteen; flowers purple in rather dense terminal pseudo-racemes and also often in the upper leaf axils; the standard densely fulvous-tomentose, 11–13mm ($\frac{2}{5}$–$\frac{1}{2}$in) long, 9–10mm ($\frac{1}{3}$–$\frac{2}{5}$in) wide; the calyx also densely tomentose with hairs up to 2mm (*c.* $\frac{1}{12}$in) long. Found in *Acacia-Commiphora* bushland, altitude range 0–1300m (0–4250ft) – in drier areas occasionally up to 2200m (7300ft); rainfall zone 400–1100mm (16–44in). Recorded in Northern Frontier, western Kenya, Rift Valley, Magadi, Mombasa and Machakos (Kenya); all regions of Tanzania; northern region (Uganda); also from Somalia south to Mozambique.

TRIFOLIUM

Twenty-two species in East Africa. Herbs, leaves tri-foliolate, flowers white or purple, pods short, often two-seeded, included in the persistent corolla. As it needs phosphorus, usually confined to volcanic soils in East Africa.

Trifolium burchellianum ssp. **johnstonii** **Plate 672**

A perennial with a tap-root, its stems, hairless (or nearly so), creeping or rooting at the nodes or, less often, ascending. Its leaflets are hairless (or nearly so), mostly cuneate-obovate, cuneate-oblong or cuneate-elliptic, emarginate or, less often, truncate or rounded at the tip. Inflorescences are many-flowered and more or less round with stout pedicels. Flower head 2–3cm ($\frac{4}{5}$–1$\frac{1}{5}$in) across. The corolla is purple. It is found in moist upland grassland, moist forest edges and glades or moorland openings at 1650–3500m (5500–11,500ft) all over Kenya, rare in the alpine zone; Maasai, Ngorongoro, Arusha (Tanzania); Elgon (Uganda); also southern Ethiopia.

T. cryptopodium A perennial with creeping stems which root at the nodes. It is very much dwarfed and compact at higher altitudes. There is no free leaf stalk between the stipules and the cuneate-obovate toothed leaflets. The mauve flowers, *c.* 9mm (⅖in) long, are arranged in compact hemispherical heads of twenty to thirty blossoms. The seed pods are tiny and hidden in the calyx and bear only one or two seeds. It is common at 1800–4100m (5900–13,500ft) in moist open places in the upland forest zone and in all sorts of grassy, rocky or moist localities in the moorland and alpine zones of the wetter mountains of Kenya; Maasai, Kilimanjaro – Marangu (Tanzania); Elgon (Uganda); also Ethiopia.

T. rueppellianum **Plate 673**
An annual with hairless, erect, or sometimes prostrate stems, not rooting at the nodes. Its hairless leaflets are oval, oblong or obovate, rarely broadly lanceolate, and less then three times as long as they are wide, rounded and usually blunt-ended. The inflorescence is usually fifteen- to thirty-flowered, *c.* 37mm (1½in) across, and more or less round, and the corolla usually purple, although on rare occasions it may be white. It is found in upland grassland, moorland tracks in forest or as a weed in cultivated land, usually in rather wet places at 1000–3600m (3300–12,000ft) in central and western Kenya; Maasai, Arusha, Iringa, Moshi (Tanzania); Karamoja – Mt Debasian, Elgon (Uganda); also Sudan – Imatong Mts, Eritrea, Ethiopia, eastern Zaire.

T. semipilosum **Plate 752**
'Kenya white clover', and a perennial with a strong taproot and prostrate stems covered in long, soft hairs which often root at the nodes. Leaves pinnately trifoliolate. The leaflets are orbicular, elliptic, oblong-elliptic, ovate or cuneate-obovate; rounded, truncate, or emarginate at the tip but with soft, silky hairs underneath, though these can be few in number, at the margins, on the midribs and the two lateral leaflets beneath. These silky hairs are on one half of the leaflet only, hence the name *semipilosum*. Pods flat, falcate. The head-like inflorescence is white or pale pink in colour, *c.* 2cm (⅘in) across; the standard 8–9mm (*c.* ⅓in) long. The pedicels are reflexed in fruit which distinguishes it from most other East African clovers. Found in Kenya; Maasai, Ngorongoro, Moshi, Mbeya, Biharamulo, Musoma, Iringa (Tanzania); Kampala, Karamoja (Uganda); also Eritrea, Ethiopia, Malawi.

Vatovaea pseudolablab **Plate 674**
A woody climber up to 1.5m (4½ft) tall from an enormous woody tuber. Stems branched, often pale reddish-brown, glabrous to sparsely pubescent. Leaflets ovate to narrowly-ovate-rhomboid, sometimes tri-lobed, oblique, glabrous or with sparse hairs along the margin. Inflorescence two- to three- to many-flowered on a peduncle 6–21cm (2⅓–8⅕in) long which is appressed puberulous to densely silvery pubescent. Standard, 1–1.8cm (⅖–¾in) long, 1.3–2.1cm (½–⅘in) broad, a dull purplish or brownish claret with green base and green veins inside, greenish outside; wings magenta-purple, green below; keel greenish, flushed purple or magenta-purple with apex greenish; pod flat, falcate. Only species in East Africa. Locally common in dry grassland, especially on soils with impeded drainage; altitude range 270–1350m (900–4400ft). Recorded in Magadi, Machakos, Kajiado, Northern Frontier areas (Kenya); Maasai, Tanga, Mpwapwa, Kondoa (Tanzania); northern region (Uganda); also in Sudan, Ethiopia, Somalia.

VIGNA

Thirty-five species in East Africa. Leaves nearly always pinnately tri-foliolate, rarely single-foliolate. Flowers usually in pedunculate pseudo-umbels. Pods sub-cylindrical, several-seeded. At first glance the flowers of *Vigna* species remind one of sweet peas. All *Vigna* species are climbing or trailing plants and many prefer damp or moist ground from 1–2450m (3–8100ft), either near or alongside swamps or forest edges. Some also grow in cultivated land, in grassland or montane grassland, and forest glades, while others are found in rocky places, dry grassland, bushland and dry forest areas. The genus is fairly catholic in its habitat. The flowers range from pinkish-violet to blue-purple or an unusual shade of yellowish-green, although *V. monophylla* has yellow and mauve flowers.

Vigna frutescens   Plate 566

A perennial, prostrate or climbing herb, 0.5–1.5m (1½–4½ft) long or erect at first and only 7–20cm (c. 3–8in) tall when appearing in burnt grass or bush; sometimes flowering before the leaves appear. Rootstock a woody tuber often 5cm (2in) wide; stems densely ferruginous pubescent, usually velvety, sometimes glabrous. Three leaflets, ovate, oblong-ovate or rhomboid (rarely hastate) in outline, entire to deeply tri-lobed, acute to slightly emarginate and mucronulate at apex, broadly cuneate or rounded at base, sparsely to densely velvety pubescent (rarely glabres-cent). Inflorescence axillary or terminal, subumbellate, several-flowered, flowers scented. Standard 1.5–2.5cm (⅝–1in) long, 1.5–2.8cm (⅝–1⅛in) wide, mauve-lilac or whitish, often greyish outside, usually tinged yellow inside basal area surrounded by a dark deep purple zone, emarginate, glabrous or velvety outside. Wings pale mauve-lilac with very pale tips, the beak short, slightly incurved. A rather variable species. Found in dry grassland subject to seasonal burning; altitude range 500–2100m (1640–6900ft). Northern Frontier areas, Samburu, Kitale, Tinderet and Magadi (Kenya); Bukoba, Moshi, Mpanda (Tanzania); Acholi, Karamoja (Mt Debasian), Masaka (Uganda); also Sudan, Ethiopia, Mozambique and throughout tropical Africa.

V. macrorhyncha   A perennial trailing or twining herb up to 1.2m (3½ft) long from a

very thick rootstock, 18cm (7in) long × c. 2.5cm (1in) wide. Stems numerous, glabrous or sparsely pubescent. Three leaflets, linear-lanceolate to ovate-lanceolate, ovate, oblong or rhombic, acute, acuminate or rounded at apex, cune-ate to rounded at base, glabrous or very sparsely hairy (on margins), venation transparent, often drying a dark colour. Raceme lax, bracts deciduous; standard 1–1.3cm (⅜–½in) long, 1–1.5cm (⅜–⅝in) wide, usually pinkish-mauve inside, green-ish at the base and outside, emarginate at apex, wings vinaceous, keel white at base, beak mauve incurved through almost a circle. Seeds dark crimson-brown or orange-brown, speckled black. Found in grassland subjected to annual burning, bushland, woodland and forest margins, often on black volcanic soils; altitude range 0–2100m (0–6900ft). Recorded throughout East Africa; also Sudan, Ethiopia, Rwanda, Zaire, Zambia, Zimbabwe.

V. membranacea ssp. membranacea   Plate 567

An annual or perennial twiner, rarely suberect; stems ridged at first, spreading-pilose with tubercle-based hairs, later glabrescent; leaflets often marked with a pale blotch, ovate or ovate-triangular in outline, rounded, truncate, or subhastate at the base, often three-lobed. Calyx glabrous or pilose with tubercle-based hairs; tube 2–3mm (¹⁄₁₂–⅛in) long. Corolla glabrous, 10–23mm (⅜–1in) long, pink, blue or mauve, the keel sometimes twisted, but the beak not incurved. Found in grassland, bushland and dry evergreen forest; altitude range 1000–2400m (3280–7900ft).

Recorded in Elgon, Aberdares, Kitale, Rift Valley, Machakos, Nairobi and Kajiado (Kenya); Ulanga (Tanzania); Karamoja, Mengo (Uganda); also in Sudan (Red Sea Hills), Ethiopia.

Three other subspecies occur in Kenya:

a) *V. membranacea* ssp. *caesia* Recorded in Machakos, Tsavo area, Taita district, Voi, Kilifi and Malindi (Kenya), in *Commiphora* bushland and coastal mixed bushland, from 0–900m (0–2950ft).

b) *V. membranacea* ssp. *hapalantha* Recorded in Mombasa district, Kilifi and Malindi in coastal grassland and thicket from 0–15m (0–50ft).

c) *V. membranacea* ssp. *macrodon* A rather more robust climber than the other ssp. Recorded in Kiambu and Nairobi – Karura Forest (Kenya) in evergreen forest and shrubland from 1275–2100m (4200–6900ft).

V. monophylla An erect, tufted herb from a tuberous or rhizomatous rootstock with hairless lanceolate to ovate leaves. The yellow and mauve flowers, 10–14mm ($\frac{2}{5}$–$\frac{1}{2}$in) long, are carried on long peduncles which stand above or exceed the leaves. It is common in the Kitale and western Kenya districts (Kenya), from 1000–2100m (3300–6900ft); Bukoba, Ufipa, Songea (Tanzania); Ankole, Kigezi, Busoga (Uganda); also Zaire, Ethiopia, Malawi, Zambia, Zimbabwe.

V. praecox A perennial climber up to 3m (10ft) long, flowering in the dry season when quite leafless. Stems sparsely appressed, pubescent when young, later glabrous. Three leaflets, ovate, elliptic or rhomboid, the laterals oblique, very shortly bluntly acuminate or obtuse and mucronate at apex; more or less rounded at the base, appressed pilose on both surfaces, fairly prominently three-nerved from the base. Flowers more or less sessile, to shortly-stalked, tight, close brittle clusters, the rhachis somewhat thickened and conspicuously scarred. Calyx glabrous, tube 2.5mm ($\frac{1}{10}$in) long, lobes deltoid, the upper part joined to form a low rounded lip. Standard 9mm ($\frac{1}{3}$in) long, 1.3cm ($\frac{1}{2}$in) wide, green outside, mauve and white inside or veined with dull purple, transversely oblong, emarginate; claw very short, wings bright rich mauve, greenish yellow at base, keel white or greenish tinged purple with the beak markedly incurved (through 270°). Found in dry *Acacia*, *Terminalia* and *Commiphora* bushland and semi-arid areas; altitude range 375–1000m (1200–3280ft). Recorded in Machakos, Tsavo West and East, Kibwezi and Taru desert (Kenya); Tanga (Tanzania); elsewhere not known.

V. schimperi A twining plant with a large rootstock; the stems are velvety with closely pressed rust-coloured hairs which later tend to become hairless and the leaflets entire, covered in soft hairs on both sides. The inflorescence is so much condensed that it almost appears to be an umbel, with the corolla, 18–25mm ($\frac{3}{4}$–1in) long, hairless and greenish yellow-orange or brown in colour, and like a rather thin half-open sweet pea flower. The seed pods are carried erect, velvety in appearance with a covering of closely pressed rusty hairs and range from 4–9cm ($1\frac{3}{5}$–$3\frac{1}{2}$in) long. This is a widespread plant in upland grassland and forest edges from 1350–2800m (4500–9300ft) in Kenya; Maasai, Ufipa, Ngorongoro (Tanzania); Acholi, Toro, Kigezi (Uganda); also Sudan, Ethiopia, Zaire.

V. unguiculata (*Dolichos unguiculatus*)   **Plate 832**
The Cowpea – an annual or perennial erect, trailing or climbing herb 1–3m (3–10ft) long. Stems striate, glabrous or slightly hairy, particularly over the petiole-bases, sometimes with minute stiff hook-like hairs. Three leaflets, ovate, rhomboid or

lanceolate, the laterals oblique 1.5–16.3cm ($\frac{3}{4}$–6in) long and 1–12.5cm ($\frac{2}{5}$–5in) wide, all entire or terminal leaflets subhastate to three-lobed, mucronate, acute to rounded at the base, glabrous or sparsely pubescent on both surfaces. Inflorescence axillary, few to several flowered, bracts deciduous and lanceolate; corolla 12–33mm ($\frac{1}{2}$–1$\frac{1}{3}$in) long, tubes 3–5.5mm ($\frac{1}{8}$–$\frac{1}{4}$in) long. Lobes triangular-lanceolate, acuminate and ciliolate, 2.5–14mm ($\frac{1}{10}$–$\frac{3}{5}$in) long, upper pair joined for about half their length or only at the base. Standard white, greenish, yellow or lilac-purple, paler outside, round, rounded or emarginate, glabrous, wings blue to purple, keel usually white or pale, not twisted. Found in bushland; altitude range mostly under 1500m (4900ft). Recorded in Kisii, Rift Valley and Kajiado, Tsavo National Park and Taita Hills (Kenya); all regions except Mpwapwa, Kondoa (Tanzania); Buganda (Uganda); also throughout tropical Africa. Widely cultivated.

NB There are several wild subspecies to be found in East Africa, e.g. *V. unguiculata* ssp. *dekindtiana* and ssp. *mensensis* as well as three cultivated forms.

V. vexillata   Plate 568
A perennial climber or trailer with a narrow woody rootstock. Its leaflets, down-covered on both sides, are rarely somewhat lobed with the stipules subcordate. The two- to six-flowered inflorescence is mauve and subumbellate, the pedicels 1–2mm ($\frac{1}{12}$in) long, the calyx with long bristly hairs which are often brownish, but there are also short white hairs; flower 3cm (1$\frac{1}{8}$in) across. It is found from 1–2200m (3–7200ft) in grassland, bushland and forest edges but not in dry areas and is especially widespread in central and western districts throughout East Africa; widespread in tropical Africa.

ZORNIA
Ten species in East Africa. Leaves digitately two- or four-foliolate, pods transversely jointed. Stipules well developed and leafy.

Zornia setosa A trailing, perennial herb with prostrate stems radiating from a woody vertical root, up to 64cm (2ft) in length, leaves four-foliolate, very variable in size, leaflets of upper leaves obovate, rarely oblanceolate, rounded at the apex. Calyx c. 3.5mm ($\frac{1}{8}$in) long. Flowers longer than the bracts, petals yellow, pink, blood red or mauve, variously marked with deeper colours, standard up to 9mm ($\frac{1}{3}$in) long. Found in grassland and cultivated land and areas of impeded drainage; altitude range 1100–2400m (3600–7900ft). Recorded throughout Kenya; lake areas, Maasai, Tanga, Tabora, Mpwapwa, Kondoa (Tanzania); all regions of Uganda; also in Ethiopia, Rwanda, Burundi, eastern Zaire, Zambia.

Z. setosa ssp. obovata   Plate 468
This subspecies is very similar to *Z.setosa*, described above.

50. Mimosoideae
THE ACACIA FAMILY

These plants are tropical or subtropical trees and shrubs or, less often, herbs with bi-pinnate or, rarely, pinnate leaves. Their flowers are small and regular, grouped in dense inflorescences. Petals are valvate in the bud and often united below to form a tube. The stamens have short anthers. There are 124 species in East Africa belonging to twenty-one genera, more than half of them in *Acacia*.

Acacia brevispica   Plate 203
A shrub or small tree from 1–7m (3–23ft) high, often semi-scandent and forming coppice. Young branchlets densely pubescent or puberulous with many minute reddish glands. Prickles scattered, recurved or spreading arising from longitudinal bands along the stem which are usually paler than the intervening lenticellate bands. Leaves, pinnate, six to eighteen pairs, 1–4cm ($\frac{2}{3}$–1$\frac{3}{8}$in) long, straight or slightly curved; leaflets numerous, linear or linear-oblong. Flowers white or yellowish white, heads 10–15mm ($\frac{2}{3}$–$\frac{3}{8}$in) diameter, racemosely arranged or aggregated into a rather irregular terminal panicle, 15–30cm (6–12in) long. Calyx eglandular outside, puberulous or glabrous. Found in bushland, thickets and scrub; altitude range 170–1830m (550–6000ft). Recorded in its habitat throughout East Africa; also from Ethiopia south to Mozambique.

A. drepanolobium   Plate 204
Commonly known as the 'Whistling Thorn', this plant not only carries long and extremely spiky thorns, its branches also bear small galls, like oak apples, in which small ants live which sally forth to bite the lips of rhinoceros, giraffe and other browsers, providing an additional defence. Small creamy-white flowers, *c.* 12mm ($\frac{1}{2}$in) across, with a mimosa-like scent, seasonally cover the plant, which is abundant in certain types of grassland, often on black cotton soils at altitudes of 600–2650m (2000–8700ft), such as in Nairobi National Park (Kenya); Shinyanga, Moshi, Dodoma (Tanzania); Karamoja, Moroto, Mbale (Uganda); also Zaire, Sudan, Ethiopia, Eritrea.

A. kirkii   Plate 422
A flat-crowned tree with a stout bole, radiating branches and greenish peeling bark and slender straight spines up to 25mm (1in) long. There are six to fourteen pairs of pinnae with a sessile gland between the lowest and between one or two of the upper – sometimes between all pairs. Leaflets are numerous, linear and pointed. The pink flowers, *c.* 1cm ($\frac{3}{8}$in) in diameter, form round heads, with peduncles solitary or clustered in the axils. It is generally found at altitudes 1200–1950m (4000–6500ft) in the Southern Province, Kiambu and Nairobi districts (Kenya); Mbulu, Nzega, Dodoma, Bukoba (Tanzania); Acholi, Kigezi, Masaka, Mengo (Uganda); also Zaire, Rwanda, Burundi, Zambia.

A. mellifera ssp. mellifera   Plates 205 & 206
A glabrous tree up to 8m (25ft) high, only found in the very driest savannah areas. Branchlets ash grey to pale brown. Thorns paired, sharply recurved about 6mm ($\frac{1}{4}$in) long and grey with black tips. Pinnae two to three pairs; leaflets one to two pairs, obovate 6–13mm ($\frac{1}{4}$–$\frac{1}{2}$in) long, about 13mm ($\frac{1}{2}$in) broad. Flowers white with pinkish core, in spikes 25–38mm (1–1$\frac{1}{2}$in) long. Pod reticulate, flat and oblong, broad with two to four seeds. Though this *Acacia* is found in very dry areas, there are indications that where erosion causes severe rainfall run-off it colonizes these areas and competes with *A. senegal*. It is often gregarious; altitude range generally below 1100m (3600ft), unusually up to 1680m (5500ft). Found in Northern Frontier areas – Moyale, Kajiado, Magadi, Kilifi –Sokokwe forest and Nairobi National Park (Kenya); Maasai, Pare, Handeni (Tanzania); Karamoja, Mbale (Uganda); also Sudan, Eritrea, Somalia, Ethiopia.

NB Ssp. *detinens*, which has two to four pairs of pinnae, occurs in southern Tanzania and southwards to Cape Province.

A. nilotica   Plate 340

A savannah tree usually 3–4.25m (10–15ft) high, occasionally up to 9m (30ft). Bark dark brown to almost black, cracking on the branches to show an underlying rust-red layer. Young parts ash-grey, tomentose, spines slender, sharp, straight, directed slightly downwards, brownish-white with darker tips, up to 6.25cm (2½in) long. Leaves glabrous, pinnae two to eleven pairs; leaflets seven to twenty-five pairs. Flowers, 7mm (c. ¼in) across, in bright yellow balls. Pod jointed, straight or slightly curved, rounded at both ends, purplish-brown with a whitish hairy bloom; soft-skinned, wrinkled and exuding a gum when squeezed. Altitude range 30–2300m (100–7600ft). Found in coast, Rift Valley, southern and northern districts (Kenya), two ssp.: *A. nilotica* ssp. *leiocarpa*, found in Kilifi and Lamu districts (Kenya); Morogoro, Kilwa (Tanzania); Uganda, no record; also in Somalia. *A. nilotica* ssp. *subalata* has pubescent or subtomentose fruits and twigs and is found in Baringo, Machakos, Narok (Kenya); Shinyanga, Mbulu, Mpwapwa (Tanzania); Acholi, Karamoja, Mbale (Uganda); also doubtfully in Sudan.

A. senegal   Plate 207

A tree or bush which grows in dry bushland and usually less than 5m (16ft) high, although it will occasionally reach twice that height. It frequently forms dense thicket. The stem is short and low-branching, and the crown of mature trees is flattened. Short thorns are grouped in threes at the swollen nodes, the centre one is sharply recurved, the other two more or less straight and pointing forward. The flowers, red in bud and creamy-white when open, are sweetly scented and usually appear before the leaves open. The dense racemes, 5–10cm (2–4in) long, may be solitary or two or three together. Found at altitudes of 120–1680 (400–5500ft) in Kenya; Musoma, Moshi, Mpwapwa (Tanzania); Acholi, Mbale, Bunyoro (Uganda); widespread in tropical Africa and south to Natal.

A. seyal   Plate 341

A tree of the savannah growing to 9m (30ft) in height, found in colonies on flats of black cotton soil and on stony ground at the base of hills. Its crown is flat-topped and its stem smooth. At times, new growth is covered with a mealy, creamy-yellow or rust-red powder which comes off when rubbed to expose the very thin bark below. The bark is shed annually, scaling off very regularly in rectangles. On the lower part of the twigs are white thorns with grey flecks and red tips which are up to 6.25cm (2½in) long. There are two variations of this species: var. *fistula* with white bark, on which some of the thorns are always galled with greatly swollen bases, and var. *seyal* with red bark which rarely has galls. The yellow flowers, which appear before the leaves open, are highly scented and borne in great profusion in round heads *c.* 12mm (½in) in diameter. A colony when in flower is an arresting sight. The tree is widespread throughout East Africa at altitudes of 550–1800m (1800–6000ft); widespread in northern tropical Africa and var. *fistula* to Zimbabwe, Malawi and Mozambique.

ALBIZIA

No thorns; filaments of stamens united to form a tube. Twenty-one species in East Africa.

Albizia anthelmintica   Plates 208 & 209

A smooth-barked, deciduous, large bush or tree growing to 8m (25ft) in height. Its leaves have one to four pairs of pinnae leaflets in one to five pairs. The flowers appear before the leaves. Both calyx and corolla are a pale green, the stamens are white. The whole gives the appearance of many compact, tiny powder puffs grouped close together on solitary or clustered peduncles. Flower head *c.* 2cm ($\frac{4}{5}$in) across. Widespread in dry savannah country from 80–1500m (250–5000ft) except in Rift Valley and western Kenya in the lake area (Kenya); Shinyanga, Moshi, Mpwapwa, Morogoro (Tanzania); Acholi, Karamoja (Uganda); also Sudan, Eritrea, Somalia, south to Zimbabwe, Mozambique.

A. grandibracteata   Plate 210
A very graceful tree, now widely planted as an ornamental tree, up to 30m (100ft) high, deciduous; crown rounded or flat, bark smooth or pock-marked at base; lenticels frequently coalescing in vertical columns, heart-wood pinkish with red streaks. Young branchlets at first with short, dense, spreading pubescence, brownish when dry, slowly glabrescent. Leaves: pinnae two to three pairs, each pinna broadening towards base; leaflets of two distal pairs of pinnae three to six pairs, obliquely rhombic to obovate with the distal pair largest, 29–72mm ($1\frac{1}{8}$–*c.* 3in) long and 16–32mm ($\frac{5}{8}$–$1\frac{1}{4}$in) wide; lower pairs down to 12×8mm ($\frac{1}{2}$–$\frac{1}{3}$in), apex acute, surface beneath more or less pubescent between midrib and margins. Flowers subsessile; corolla 7–10mm ($\frac{1}{4}$–$\frac{2}{5}$in) long, pink to white, densely pubescent, and minutely so outside; staminal tube pink or red, exserted 1.2–2.2cm ($\frac{1}{2}$–1in) beyond the corolla. Found in lowland and upland rain forest, riverine forest, a first-stage colonizer, sometimes in grassland possibly relict from forest; altitude range 1160–2130m (3800–7000ft). Recorded Elgon, western Kenya, Rift Valley (Kenya); lake areas (Tanzania); all regions of Uganda.

Dichrostachys cinerea ssp. cinerea   Plate 753
An *Acacia*-like shrub or tree which grows to 5m (16ft) or occasionally as high as 12m (40ft). Its branchlets are armed with sharp woody spines at the end of the lateral twigs. There are two flower types. Those nearest to the point of attachment are neuter and have ten long pink or mauve stamenoids, while those towards the end of the branch are functional and are composed of a pistil and ten short yellow stamens. The flowers are dense and, since they hang down, the pink part is always above the yellow part. Inflorescence 35–75mm ($1\frac{2}{5}$–3in). Pods spirally coiled. Found at altitudes up to 1700m (5000ft) at forest edges, in woodland or savannah; where overgrazing has taken place it will form thickets. Only species in East Africa. Coastal, southern and northern districts of Kenya; Shinyanga, Tabora, Mpwapwa, Zanzibar, Pemba (Tanzania); Karamoja, Teso, Toro (Uganda); widespread in tropical Africa and Sudan, south to Zimbabwe, Mozambique.

Mimosa pudica var. unijuga   Plate 754
An annual or perennial herb, up to 1m (3ft) high, often prostrate or straggling and sometimes woody below. Stems sparsely armed with prickles, about 2.5–5mm ($\frac{1}{10}$–$\frac{1}{5}$in) long, in addition varying from densely hispid to subglabrous. Leaves sensitive, collapsing when touched, unarmed; leaflets ten to twenty-six pairs, linear-oblong, venation diverging from and not parallel with midrib. Flowers lilac or pink, *c.* 1.25cm ($\frac{1}{2}$in) long, *c.* to 1cm ($\frac{2}{5}$in) wide, in ovoid pedunculate heads. The corolla in var. *unijuga*, even in bud, is glabrous or almost entirely so outside, with no projecting setiform hairs in bud. In var. *hispida* the corolla at least in bud is densely grey, puberulous outside in the upper part, and the heads in bud appear densely bristly owing to setiform hairs projecting beyond the corolla up to 1.5mm ($\frac{1}{16}$in). Var. *tetrandra* has heads in bud with few and short or no projecting setiform hairs. The species probably originated in South America. Known as 'The Sensitive Plant'. Generally found on banks of drainage canals in irrigation areas and on margins of rain-forest, probably not a native plant but an escape and more records are needed on its habitat; altitude range 30–1200m (100–4000ft). Four other species in East

Africa. Var. *unijuga* recorded in Nairobi, Kilifi, Rabai Hills (Kenya); Lushoto (Tanzania); var. *hispida* recorded in Uganda, Tanzania but not Kenya; var. *tetrandra* only in Tanzania.

51. Hamamelidaceae

Only one genus with three species represented in East Africa. Leaves simple, stipulate, alternate and with a stellate indumentum. Flowers in heads.

Trichocladus ellipticus ssp. **malosanus**   **Plate 342**
A scandent shrub or thicket-forming tree up to 10m (33ft) high. Leaves simple, alternate, elliptic to oblanceolate, 5–20cm (2–8in) long, lower surface silver buff with darker dots of rust-coloured, stellate tomentum, upper surface glabrous; apex acute, base cuneate. Flowers yellow in axillary and terminal heads, sweetly scented, pentamerous with very narrow petals. Flower head 1.25cm ($\frac{1}{2}$in) diameter. Five stamens alternating with the petals. Found in montane forest, often in dense thickets; altitude range 1200–2700m (4000–9000ft). Widespread throughout Kenya; lake areas, Maasai, Tanga, Morogoro, Mbeya, Iringa (Tanzania); all regions of Uganda; also in Ethiopia, Zaire, Malawi, Zambia, Mozambique. Ssp. *ellipticus* in South Africa.

52. Celastraceae

Trees, shrubs or climbers without tendrils, with or without latex, leaves alternate or opposite, simple; stipules inconspicuous; inflorescence cymose or clustered; flowers bisexual, regular; calyx four- to five-lobed, imbricate or rarely valvate; stamens three to five, inserted on or below the disc margin; anthers one- to two-celled; ovary superior, mostly trilocular; style short, lobed; seeds one or two in each cell of the fruit with aril. Fifty-three species in nine genera in East Africa.

Maytenus arbutifolia   **Plate 211**
A shrub or small tree up to 1.8m (*c.* 6ft) high, usually with spines, sometimes terminating short shoots and up to 6.2cm (2in) long. Stems brown and puberulous when young, becoming glabrous later. Leaves elliptic to nearly ovate, apex obtuse to rounded with margins crenulate-serrulate and base cuneate to truncate, 8cm ($3\frac{1}{2}$in) long, 4.2cm ($1\frac{3}{4}$in) wide. Cymes up to 2.5cm (1in) long, axillary or one to three on short axillary shoots. Flowers two to fifteen in each cyme, white to cream or greenish-white, *c.* 4mm ($\frac{1}{4}$in) across. Found in riverine forest margins and thicket; altitude range 1470–2340m (4900–8100ft). Cheranganis, Tinderet, Embu, Machakos, western Kenya, Kitale, Kisii, Kajiado, Magadi, Narok (Kenya); lake areas (Tanzania); all regions of Uganda except northern; also in Ethiopia, Eritrea, Somalia, Rwanda, Burundi, Zaire.

M. senegalensis   **Plate 212**
A savannah shrub up to 7.5m (25ft) tall. Branchlets armed or unarmed. Spines

(when present) very variable, short and slender or long and stout, frequently bearing leaves and flowers. Leaves serrulate, pale green or glaucous, variable in shape and size, usually obovate-elliptic, about 8cm (3½in) long and 3.25cm (1¼in) broad, apex rounded or emarginate, base cuneate (apex occasionally subacute). Cymes axillary on long peduncle, flowers white more or less sessile, c. 4mm (⅛in) across. Sepals five united, petals five, stamens five. Found in savannah from the coast to 2100m (7000ft) throughout East Africa; also in Sudan, Ethiopia, Somalia south to Mozambique.

53. Icacinaceae

Trees or shrubs, sometimes climbers; leaves simple, alternate, rarely opposite, stipules absent; inflorescence axillary or terminal; flowers bisexual or unisexual by abortion; regular; calyx small, four- to five-lobed, valvate or imbricate, petals four to five; stamens same number and alternate with petals; anthers two-celled; ovary superior, single-celled; fruit a drupe. Twelve species in six genera in East Africa.

Pyrenacantha malvifolia   **Plate 213**
A straggling or climbing, more or less pubescent perennial shrub with a massive, white, tuberous stem rhizome from which the shoots spring; stem with papery thin, light green bark; leaves suborbicular, cordate, crenate. Inflorescence a woolly catkin; male flower spike to 6cm (1⅞in) long; each flower c. 2mm (1/12in) across. Fruit pubescent and ovally compressed. Occasionally found on sandy or rocky soils in Acacia-Commiphora scrub; altitude range 0–1680m (0–5600ft). Rift Valley, Magadi, Northern Frontier (Kenya); Tanga (Tanzania); Uganda, not known; also Ethiopia, Somalia.

54. Viscaceae
THE MISTLETOE FAMILY

The members of this family (formerly grouped with the Loranthaceae) are parasitic on trees. Flowers small, dullish yellow-green. Eighteen species in three genera in East Africa.

Viscum fischeri A hairless, pendulous plant with broad or narrow oblanceolate to obovate leaves with smooth edges; the peduncle is 5–7mm (c. ¼in) long and bears four to seven flowers, dull greenish-yellow in colour, 2–4mm (c. ⅛in). Found only in Kenya from 1600–2300m (5900–7500ft); Tanzania, Uganda and elsewhere, not known.

V. nervosum Similar to V. fischeri but its elliptic leaves have crisped edges and the one to three flowers, 2–4mm (c. ⅛in), are grouped together on a short peduncle. Altitude range 0–2300m (0–7500ft) (Kenya); Tanga, Mbeya, Iringa (Tanzania); all regions of Uganda; also Ethiopia, Zaire.

V. schimperi (V. hildebrandtii) A hairless plant, pendulous or erect, with almost sessile (stalkless) flowers and fruit, the fruit smooth or slightly warty and the leaves reduced to scales. The flowers are yellow-green, 2–4mm (c. ⅛in). Found among *Acacia* species, especially in dry country, and most plants are female. It has been recorded in Mau, Mt Kenya, Mumias, Machakos and Nairobi (Kenya) from 600–1800m (2000–5900ft); elsewhere, not known.

NB There are three other species closely related to *V. schimperi* which are widespread in East Africa and also occur in Ethiopia and northern Somalia. It is not easy to tell them apart.

V. tuberculatum The most widespread mistletoe in Kenya. The plant is hairless, erect or pendulous, with usually yellowish, obovate to oblanceolate leaves. Flowers, 2–4mm (c. ⅛in), dull greenish-yellow in colour in more or less sessile clusters. It is found in all upland dry woodland from 1500–2500m (5000–8200ft) over most of upland Kenya; all regions of Tanzania except lake areas, Songea; all regions of Uganda; also Ethiopia, northern Somalia, Rwanda, Zambia.

55. Loranthaceae

Nearly all members of this family are parasitic on trees. They depend on birds for pollination and have rather firm, often red or orange, flowers. The calyx is short, sometimes reduced to a rim, the petals are free or united and the stamens the same number as the petals and attached to them. The ovary is inferior, and the fruit a berry. About ninety-eight species in twelve genera in East Africa. The true *Loranthus* does not occur in East Africa and some species formerly placed in Loranthaceae are now in Viscaceae. As the Loranthaceae are not pollinated by insects, they need not flower after rain, when insects are on the wing. In dry areas during the dry season they, with the Aloes (also bird-pollinated), may be the only plants in bloom. To aid identification, a list is given here of the trees and shrubs which act as host plants to certain species of Loranthaceae.

Emelianthe panganensis	*Commiphora*
	Adansonia
	Sterculia
	Euphorbia
	Lannea
	Boswellia
Englerina heckmanniana	*Grewia*
	Combretum
	Acacia
	Cordia
	Commiphora
Englerina woodfordioides	Montane and riverine forest
Phragmanthera dschallensis	*Acacia*
Phragmanthera regularis	*Ficus*
	Croton
	Bersama

Oncocalyx fischeri	*Acacia*
	Grewia
	Maytenus
	Cordia
Oncocalyx sulphureus	*Rhus*
	Pittosporum
	Grewia
	Euclea
	Dovyalis
Oncocalyx ugogensis	*Acacia*
	Grewia
	Capparaceae
	Ziziphus
	Terminalia
	Commiphora
	Balanites
Plicosepalus curviflorus	*Acacia* always
	Albizia rarely
Plicosepalus meridianus	*Commiphora* usually
Tapinanthus zizyphifolium	*Acacia*
	Commiphora

Emelianthe panganensis Plate 511

A hairless plant, with alternate, very fleshy, crisped leaves. The almost stalkless flowers, *c.* 8mm (⅓in) long, are pink, grey, green or dark red and have five prominent ridges below the curved lobes and stamens. This uncommon plant is parasitic mostly on *Commiphora* in dry bushland at 350–1700m (1150–5600ft) (Kenya); all regions of Tanzania except Mpwapwa, Kondoa, Songea; northern region (Gulu) of Uganda; also in Somalia. Genus now divided and placed as *Emilianthe*.

Englerina heckmanniana Plate 469

A tomentose plant with mostly opposite, ovate leaves; flowers fasciculate, 35–40mm (1⅜–1⅝in) long, yellow-green and orange, very hairy outside; filaments toothed at apex. An uncommon plant found in evergreen dry woodland and *Combretum* savannah; altitude range 1100–1800m (3600–5900ft). Narok, Rift Valley, Machakos (Kenya); lake areas, Maasai, Mpwapwa, Kondoa, Mbeya, Iringa (Tanzania); Uganda and elsewhere, not known.

E. woodfordioides Plate 512

A glabrous plant with alternate or opposite penni-nerved, linear to broad-lanceolate leaves; flowers in dense pedicellate fascicles, grey below, red at tip and with black interior. Flower *c.* 25mm (1in) long. Petals four to five not reflexed, toothed at apex. Common in montane rain-forest on a wide variety of hosts including many introduced trees. Altitude range 1600–3000m (5250–10,150ft). Recorded in almost all rain-forest areas in its altitude range (Kenya); lake areas, Maasai, Shinyanga, Tanga (Tanzania); all regions of Uganda except northern (Gulu); also in Ethiopia, eastern Zaire, Rwanda, Burundi.

Oncocalyx fischeri Plate 343

A finely pubescent plant when young, with small attenuate elliptic to oblanceolate

leaves. Flower, with pubescent bract and yellow, much-contorted petals and stamens, 20–27mm (⅜–1in) long. Common in dry upland grassland and evergreen
bushland; altitude range 950–1900m (3100–6200ft). Cheranganis, Tinderet,
Aberdares, Narok, Baringo, Rift Valley, Embu, Machakos, Nairobi, Kajiado
(Kenya); also Ethiopia, Somalia to central Tanzania.

O. sulphureus (*Tieghemia sulphurus*. *Loranthus sulphurea*)   A glabrous plant with
elliptic to obovate three-nerved leaves; flowers three to five in each fascicled
group, red with yellow tip; five petals, remaining erect, not contorted at anthesis.
Flower corolla 25–40mm (1–1⅝in) long. An uncommon plant found in dry upland
forest; altitude range 1700–2600m (5575–7525ft). Mau, Aberdares, Narok, Rift
Valley, Nairobi and Mt Ol Lolokwe (Samburu) (Kenya); Mt Kilimanjaro (Tanzania);
Uganda and elsewhere, no record.

O. ugogensis (*Odontella ugogensis*)   **Plate 344**
A woody hemi-parasite. The branches are usually terete, greyish and slender.
Leaves alternate with those of the previous year falling off at the time of flowering,
elliptic-oblong, rounded at apex, obtuse or cuneate at base, up to 5.2cm (2in) long
and 2.9cm (1⅛in) wide, glabrous or puberulous, very glaucous, almost succulent
and distinctly three-nerved. Flowers in fascicles on axillary leafy cushion-like short
shoots almost sessile; corolla 3cm (1⅛in) long, yellow at the middle and greenish-
yellow at both ends. Lobes reflexed below the middle and free. Altitude range
15–1500m (50–4900ft). Very widespread in the arid areas of Kenya in *Acacia-
Commiphora* bushland; also in the Maasai areas of Tanzania; no record Uganda
and elsewhere.

Phragmanthera dschallensis (*Loranthus dschallensis*)   **Plate 513**
Very similar to *L. rubescens* but with oblong to linear leaves tapering gradually at
the base (cuneate). Flower *c.* 5cm (2in) long. It is, however, found in *Combretum*
country and drier bushland; altitude range 750–1900m (2500–6300ft). Baringo,
Nanyuki, Machakos (Kenya); lake areas, Maasai, Shinyanga, Tabora, Mpwapwa,
Kondoa, Mbeya, Iringa (Tanzania); northern region (Gulu) of Uganda; also in
eastern Ethiopia, Somalia and north Zambia.

P. regularis var. **usuriensis**   **Plate 470**
A large hemi-parasitic shrub forming a grey mass with branches up to 2m (6½ft)
long; stems and leaves deep dull green, younger branchlets fulvous-tomentose.
Leaves ovate-oblong or oblong, to 18cm (*c.* 7in) long and 11cm (*c.* 4in) wide, obtuse
or rounded at apex, rather fleshy. Flowers in fascicles, many-flowered, tomentellous, orange outside. tube deep orange inside, lobes orange turning orange-red;
filaments and style deep crimson. Flower *c.* 4cm (1⅜in) long. Found in montane
forest and woodland margins; altitude range 900–2640m (3000–8800ft). Widespread in Kenya; all regions of Tanzania except Tabora; all regions of Uganda
except eastern; also in Rwanda, Mozambique.

P. regularis (*L. rufescens: UKWF L. rubescens*)   A stellate-tomentose plant especially on the young parts, with large ovate-elliptic, penni-nerved (with pinnate-
nervatim) leaves. Flowers, *c.* 4cm (1⅜in) long, covered with reddish hairs, the
corolla lobes only free at apex; anthers chambered transversely. Common in
highland savannah; altitude range 1200–2400m (4000–8000ft). Cheranganis,
Tinderet, Mau, Aberdares, Kitale, western regions, Narok and Machakos (Kenya);
Maasai, Shinyanga (Tanzania); Uganda, no record; also in Ethiopia and Yemen.

Plicosepalus curviflorus   **Plate 514**
Plant glabrous, creeping over the surface of its host by means of root-like rhizomes;
leaves variable, suborbicular to oblong, cuneate to sagittate, rarely both on the
same plant; flowers in umbels, petals red and yellow, 25–35mm (1–1⅜in) long,
curved from the base, free. Common in *Acacia* trees in dry bushland, grassland,
high savannah; altitude range 60–2100m (200–6900ft). Tinderet, Baringo, Rift
Valley, Magadi, Ngong Hills, Nanyuki, Machakos and Kajiado (Kenya); lake areas,
Maasai, Shinyanga, Mpwapwa, Kondoa, Mbeya, Iringa (Tanzania); northern
(Gulu) and eastern regions (Jinja, Lake Kioga) of Uganda; also in southern Sudan,
Ethiopia and eastern Zaire.

P. meridianus (*Loranthus meridianus. Tapinostemma meridianum*)   **Plate 755**
A glabrous parasite growing on trees and shrubs with suborbicular leaves; flowers
shortly pedicillate, red with a green tip, buds acute, petals variously contorted and
reflexed. Flower 4cm (1⅜in) long. It is named as *Loranthus meridianum* in *UKWF* but
has recently been reclassified as *Plicosepalus*. In the latter, the roots spread out
over the host plant as long, thin, rooted or attached tentacles, as in the Orchid
genus, *Polystachya* or *Aerangis*, whereas in the former the roots tend to form a
thick, lumpy attachment to the host. An uncommon plant found in dry bushland with
Acacia mellifera in Kenya; altitude range 100–1400m (300–4600ft). Maasai,
Shinyanga, Mpwapwa, Kondoa, Mbeya, Iringa (Tanzania); northern region (Gulu)
of Uganda; also Somalia.

Tapinanthus pennatulus (*Loranthus brunneus* of *UKWF*)   **Plate 471**
Plant glabrous, with broad-elliptic, three-nerved subopposite leaves; flowers in
sessile clusters, yellow-orange with a green band and a red tip, corolla 50mm (2in)
long, with a basal bulb and erect lobes at apex, filaments entire. A rare plant found
in upland forest; altitude range 600–1500m (1950–5900ft)1 Aberdares and Mt
Kenya (Kenya); Tanzania, no record; all regions of Uganda except eastern (Jinja,
Lake Kioga); also in Zaire.

T. oehleri (*Loranthus oehleri*)   **Plate 515**
A glabrous plant with alternate, oblanceolate to obovate leaves; cuneate at base;
flowers in sessile clusters, red and orange; corolla with a basal bulge, and erect
lobes; the filaments toothed. Flower 25mm (1in) long. An uncommon plant found in
dry country on *Commiphora*; altitude range 900–1500m (2950–4900ft). Magadi
and Machakos (Kenya); Maasai (Tanzania); Uganda and elsewhere, not known.

T. ziziphifolius (*L. ziziphifolius*)   **Plate 547**
This plant is fairly common in moister areas than *Emilianthe panganensis* and
parasitic on *Rhus* species and other evergreen shrubs. It is covered with down or
short hairs, except on the flower and old leaves. Its leaves are oblanceolate and
three-nerved. The flowers, *c.* 35mm (1⅜in), form almost stalkless clusters of pink or
crimson with bands of green. The corolla has a bulb at the base and erect lobes; the
filaments are entire. Altitude range 1400–2250m (4600–7400ft). Nairobi area and
in the Aberdares, Rift Valley, Embu and Machakos districts (Kenya); Maasai,
Shinyanga (Tanzania); Uganda and elsewhere, no record.

56. Rhamnaceae

Mostly trees or shrubs often climbing by hooks, tendrils or twining; leaves always simple, usually stipulate, alternate or opposite. Inflorescence cymose, flowers small hermaphrodite, calyx tubular, four- to five-lobed, lobes valvate, four to five petals opposite to and half enclosing the stamens; intrastaminal disc usually present; ovary superior or perygynous, two to four carpels, fruit various, occasionally with wings. Twenty-four species in eleven genera in East Africa.

Helinus integrifolius   Plate 12
A woody perennial climbing by means of tendrils, up to 6m (20ft). Leaves ovate to broadly obovate, base subcordate, upper surface glabrous, lower one puberulous, pedicel and fruit glabrous. Inflorescence single- to several-flowered, pedunculate axillary umbel; petals small, 1.8mm ($\frac{1}{14}$in) long, white, at end of long corolla tube. Found in disturbed dry bushland and in *Commiphora* woodland; altitude range 0–1700m (0–5500ft). Aberdares, Mt Kenya, Rift Valley, Magadi, Tsavo West, Machakos and Kajiado (Kenya); Mbulu, Dodoma, Morogoro (Tanzania); Uganda, no record; also in Somalia, Zaire, Malawi, Zimbabwe, Mozambique.

H. mystacinus   Similar to *H. integrifolius* but the pedicels and fruit are hairy. Petal *c.* 1.4–1.8mm (*c.* $\frac{1}{16}$–$\frac{1}{14}$in) long. It is found in scrub, grassland and evergreen woodland and has a far wider range than *H. integrifolius*; altitude range 100–2300m (340–7500ft). From east to west in Kenya; Ngara, Arusha, Mbeya (Tanzania); Ankole, Mbale, Bugishu, Masaka (Uganda); also in northern Ethiopia, Somalia, Rwanda, Burundi, Zaire, Zambia, Zimbabwe, Mozambique.

57. Vitaceae (Ampelidaceae)
THE VINE FAMILY

Most of this family are plants which climb by means of tendrils but, less often, are also erect herbs, shrubs or rarely, trees. Their leaves are alternate, often with stipules simple or palmate or pinnatifid, three- to five- (or even up to seven-) foliolate. The small flowers are yellowish or reddish. The calyx is entire or toothed, the petals free valvate and the stamens opposite to the petals and of the same number. The ovary is superior and the fruit a berry. About 127 species in six genera in East Africa. Most of the species belong to *Cyphostemma*, which has a wide range of habitat, rainfall and altitude, some preferring dry or rocky bushland, others widespread in bush grassland and still others found in upland or montane forest areas.

Cyphostemma adenocaule   Plate 13
A five-foliolate climber with a twice-branched axis to the leaf with suborbicular, usually glabrous leaflets; glands entirely absent. Flowers cream; bud 0.4cm ($\frac{1}{8}$in) long. This is a common *Cyphostemma* in dry bushland and recorded throughout East Africa; altitude range 0–1500m (0–5000ft).

VITACEAE

C. nieriense
A climber with tendrils and five-foliolate leaves, leaflets orbicular to obovate, finely pubescent to glabrescent, with widely spaced venation, sparsely glandular on pedicels and stem, without glands on the white to cream flowers and fruit; bud 4mm (⅛in) long. A common climber in forest and bushland edges with a wide ecological range from dry *Acacia* bushland to dry upland forest areas; altitude range 470–1900m (1550–6250ft). Widespread in Kenya; lake areas, Tabora (Tanzania); Buganda (Uganda); elsewhere, no record.

Plate 14

C. nodiglandulosum
A climber with three- to five-foliolate leaves, the leaflets elliptic, grey to white tomentose below; glands present only at the nodes (hence the name). Inflorescence a corymbose cyme, flower buds cylindrical, about 4mm (⅛in) long; petioles with no long glandular hairs, flowers creamy white. A common plant of dry upland areas; altitude range 12–3000m (40–9850ft). North-eastern areas, Rift Valley, Cheranganis, Magadi, coast hinterland (Kenya); Tanzania, Uganda and elsewhere, not known.

Plate 214

C. orondo
A climbing, often trailing, rarely erect herb which grows from a swollen tuberous taproot with or without tendrils. It has three to seven leaflets which are linear and elliptical and densely covered with down underneath. Its pale, greenish-yellow flowers form inflorescences 22–28cm (9–11in) across; bud *c.* 4mm (⅛in) long. Common in bushed grassland at 1200–2250m (4000–7500ft) over most of Kenya; lake areas, Maasai, Shinyanga, Mpwapwa, Kondoa (Tanzania); northern (Gulu) and western regions of Uganda; also Ethiopia.

Plate 345

NB In *Cyphostemma* the flowers almost never spread open, but remain with upright parallel sepals, giving a bud-like appearance.

58. Rutaceae
THE ORANGE FAMILY

A small to medium-sized tropical and warm temperate family of trees, shrubs, shrublets and, less often, herbs, of which only trees and shrubs are present in East Africa. Their leaves are dotted with translucent oil glands. Flowers are usually rather small, regular, free and four to five in number. Stamens are equal in number to the petals or twice as many. Their ovaries consist of four or five more or less free carpels, with styles distinct or connate. The fruit is usually indehiscent. Forty-six native species in thirteen genera in East Africa.

Calodendrum capense
A magnificent flowering tree, popularly known as the Cape Chestnut. Its flowers, carried in large terminal panicles all over the head and sides of the tree, are almost a cyclamen-lilac in colour. Petals *c.* 3cm (1¼in). It has two flowering seasons: February to early May and late August to early December, and grows throughout the central forest areas of Kenya, including the Taita Hills and Mt Kulal at 1200–2200m (4000–7300ft); Maasai, Mpwapwa, Kondoa, Morogoro (Tanzania); western region, Buganda (Uganda); also Malawi, Zimbabwe and the Cape.

Plate 756

NB The only other species, *C. eickii*, is confined to the Usambara Mts.

Clausena anisata   **Plate 62**
An unarmed shrub or tree usually 2–3m (6–10ft) high, occasionally 9m (30ft). Bark grey-green. Leaves strongly aromatic, up to 5cm (c. 2in) long; eleven to thirty-seven leaflets, alternate, entire or crenulate, glandular-punctuate, more or less pubescent below, especially on the nerves, obliquely ovate-lanceolate, very variable in size, 2.5–10cm (1–4in) long, 0.8–3.75cm (⅓–1½in) broad, apex obtusely acuminate, petioles very short. Flowers creamy-white, in axillary panicles, 7.5–36cm (3–14in) long. Altitude range 0–2400m (0–8000ft). Common in semi-arid or dryish localities, savannah bush and at forest edges throughout East Africa and from Ethiopia south to Mozambique.

59. Balanitaceae

A small tropical family of trees or shrubs consisting of the single genus *Balanites*, with six species in East Africa. The leaves are always two-foliolate; the flowers four- or five-merous; the stamens twice as many as the petals; the fruit a drupe.

Balanites glabra   **Plate 15**
A very spiny tree up to 12m (40ft) high with flexuous, glabrous, often leafless branches. Spines 7.5cm (3in) or more long. Leaves sessile or subsessile, consisting of leaflets obovate spathulate up to 5cm (2in) long and 2cm (1⅜in) wide but usually smaller, glabrous coriaceous, the apex rounded; base somewhat acute. Flowers clustered, especially on the long spines, sepals ovate-elliptic, petals glabrous and narrowly oblong, white. Flower 1cm (⅜in) across. Drupes shaped like a gooseberry, green-striped, turning pink, and edible. Found chiefly in river beds; altitude range 900–1500m (3000–5000ft). Nairobi, Kajiado, Magadi and Northern Frontier areas (Kenya); lake areas, Maasai, Shinyanga, Tanga (Tanzania); Uganda, no record; also Ethiopia, Somalia.

60. Burseraceae

A family of trees and shrubs, often with resinous bark. Leaves alternate, exstipulate, pinnate, trifoliolate or occasionally unifoliolate. Flowers small, regular, in panicles. Stamens twice as many as the petals. Disc present. Ovary superior with two ovules usually in each cell. Fruit a drupe or capsule.
Flowers tetramerous, fruit a dehiscent drupe, leaves unifoliolate, trifoliolate or pinnate = *Commiphora*.
Flowers pentamerous, fruit a capsule, leaves pinnate = *Boswellia*.
About seventy species in three genera in East Africa, sixty-four of which are in *Commiphora*, and conspicuous in dry bushland below 1700m (5600ft).

Boswellia neglecta (*B. hildebrandtii*, *B. elegans*)   **Plate 215**
A tree of the savannah growing up to 6m (20ft) high but usually much smaller. Leaves imparipinnate to 6.25cm (2½in) long of eight to twenty pairs of small, sessile,

pubescent, ovate-oblong entire leaflets 3–13mm ($\frac{1}{10}$–$\frac{1}{2}$in) long and 2–5mm ($\frac{1}{12}$–$\frac{1}{5}$in) wide, subtruncate at base. Flowers, 4–5mm ($\frac{1}{6}$–$\frac{1}{5}$) across, creamy-yellow in colour, five-merous, in small clustered panicles up to 2.54cm (1in) long which appear before the leaves. Fruit, red, triangular pear-shaped, 2cm ($\frac{4}{5}$in) long, three-celled and three-seeded. The stem provides a gum which is used in commerce and a kind of incense locally in East Africa. Altitude range 200–1400m (650–4600ft). Northern and southern areas and coastal districts in dry bush (Kenya); Maasai, Shinyanga, Tanga (Tanzania); northern region (Gulu) of Uganda; also in eastern Ethiopia and Somalia.

61. Meliaceae

Trees or shrubs. Leaves alternate, exstipulate, pinnate with the exception of *Turrea*, which has simple leaves. Flowers regular, normally in panicles, four- to five-merous. Petals usually free. Stamens as many as or twice the number of petals, united into a tube. Ovary superior, two- or more-celled. Fruit a capsule, berry or drupe. Seeds often winged. Forty species in eleven genera in East Africa.

NB The Persian Lilac (*Melia azederach*) belongs to this family.

Trichilia emetica (*T. roka*)   **Plate 216**
A tree growing from 4$\frac{1}{2}$–12m (15–40ft) in height, though occasionally it can attain 27m (90ft). Two distinct forms occur: one a small, erect tree in savannah grass-lands subject to grass fires and away from water, the other a much larger spreading tree mainly found in moister areas less subject to grass fire hazard. The bark of the former is grey to pale brown, corky, coarsely fissured and flaking; the cork layer shows prominently beneath the fissures and in the flaking. The bark of the latter is smooth or only minutely scaling, red-brown in colour but with a greenish layer easily exposed by removing the brown scales. Leaves up to 45cm (18in) long, in terminal clusters, leaflets seven to eleven in number, subsessile, pubescent or subglabrous below, 3.75–15cm (1$\frac{1}{2}$–7in) long and 1.8–7cm ($\frac{3}{4}$–2$\frac{4}{5}$in) broad, elliptic to oblong elliptic, the basal pair sometimes nearly rounded, and the terminal leaflet often obovate. The leaflets increase in size from below upwards. The flowers are yellow-white, on stout racemes up to 10cm (4in) long, pedicillate, calyx four, partite, five petals, strap-shaped with incurved tips, 13–19mm ($\frac{1}{2}$–$\frac{3}{4}$in) long; capsule four-valved, globose and crimson when ripe; seeds brown with a scarlet or orange aril. The powdered bark may be used as an emetic. Widespread from 1–1825m (3–6000ft) (Kenya); all regions of Tanzania; all regions of Uganda except Buganda; also in Sudan, Ethiopia south to Zimbabwe, Mozambique.

Turraea fischeri (*T.*sp. 2 in *KTS*)   **Plate 63**
A tree up to 6m (20ft) in height; leaves papillose on both surfaces, intermixed with longer hairs, the base cordate up to 3.75cm (1$\frac{1}{2}$in) long and 2.5cm (1in) wide, apex acuminate. Flowers creamy-white with a robust, often curved, trumpet-shaped staminal tube up to 2.5cm (1in) long; petals *c*. 3cm (1$\frac{1}{5}$in) long. Altitude range *c*. 1750m (5750ft) and below. Ngong Hills down to Magadi, and also in Northern Frontier areas where a district variety (*T.* sp. *B*.) occurs (Kenya); lake and central areas (Tanzania); northern region of Uganda; elsewhere, no record.

T. mombassana   Plate 64
A much-branched shrub up to 3m (10ft) in height. Leaves obovate to obovate-lanceolate up to 2.5cm (1in) long, glabrous when mature except for tufts of hair beneath the nerve axils, rounded emarginate to subacuminate at apex, cuneate at base. The flowers are white, usually solitary in the leaf axils, the calyx teeth linear-lanceolate, and the staminal tube up to 5cm (2in) long. Altitude range 1–1800m (3–6000ft). Coastal regions, common near Nairobi (Kenya); all regions of Tanzania except Tabora and Songea; Uganda, no record; also in Malawi.

T. parvifolia   Plate 65
A small-stemmed shrub, 2–4m (6½–13ft) high. Stems smooth, cylindrical and dark grey; branches slender, whippy and drooping. Leaves 4.2cm (1¾in) long, 2cm (⅘in) wide, fasciculate, oblanceolate, apex retuse to mucronate, base cuneate. Inflorescence one- to four-flowered. Flowers pedunculate, fascicled with the leaves; corolla, c. 10mm (⅜in) long, split to the base to expose staminal tube, greenish-cream, fading yellow. Found in open *Acacia-Commiphora* bushland and especially around rock outcrops; altitude range 260–1250m (900–4100ft). Northern Frontier areas, Cheranganis, Embu, Machakos, coast hinterland (Kenya); Tanzania and Uganda, no record; also in Somalia.

62. Sapindaceae

A medium-sized family of tropical and subtropical trees, shrubs or climbers. Their alternate leaves are usually compound and without stipules. The flowers are usually small, regular, with sepals and petals free and five in number. There are usually five to twelve free stamens, and the superior ovary is usually trilocular. Fifty-five species in twenty-five genera in East Africa.

Dodonaea angustifolia *(D. viscosa)*   Plate 472
A shrub or tree which will usually reach a height of 2–4m (6–12ft). It has red-brown, viscous and hairless branchlets; thin, hairless and almost stalkless oblanceolate leaves, 5–10cm (2–4in) long and 12–24mm (½–1in) broad with apex obtusely apiculate and base long attenuate. Flowers yellow-green or deep creamy-white, 5mm (⅛in) across, grouped in short terminal panicles or subracemous. The pale reddish-brown fruit is flat, 15mm (⅝in) across, rounded to deeply emarginate and broadly two- or more-winged including membraneous wings and c. 2cm (⅘in) across (the illustration shows these characteristic fruits). The fruits are blown by the wind and *Dodonaea* is, therefore, a pioneer species when forest is invading grassland. The wood makes good walking sticks; in dry regions the plant is sometimes used as a hedge. Widespread up to 2740m (9000ft). In *UKWF*, *D. angustifolia* has been named *D. viscosa*, but the latter has mostly bisexual flowers and subspherical seeds and is a purely coastal plant. Most of the East African material is *D. angustifolia*, which has bisexual flowers and compressed seeds with a dorsal ridge and usually narrower leaves and is widespread in higher-altitude forest areas than the coastal *D. viscosa* – with an altitude range of 1–30m (3–100ft) only. Northern Frontier areas, Rift Valley, Nairobi, Machakos, Nanyuki, western Kenya, Kajiado (Kenya); all regions of Tanzania and Uganda; also in Ethiopia and south to Mozambique, Zimbabwe.
    NB Although *D. angustifolia* is an upland tree or shrub, some specimens have been recorded from Zanzibar at or on sea level.

Haplocoelum foliolosum
Plate 346

A deciduous shrub or tree up to 6m (20ft) in height. Bark grey; young foliage yellow or pink; leaves paripinnate, 2.5–6.75cm (1–2½in) long. Leaflets in four to eleven but usually eight pairs, sessile or subsessile, obliquely rhombic obovate or ovate, apex emarginate or rounded, base unequal-cuneate, 1–2.5cm (⅜–1in) long, 0.6–1.25cm (¼–½in) broad. Flowers, 0.2cm (₁₂in) across, usually precocious, fragrant, yellow, pedicellate, without corollas, very numerous in dense axillary clusters. Found in savannah woodland, often forming thickets, on rocky outcrops, dry *vleis* and stream washouts at 540–1800m (1800–6000ft). Western areas, Northern Frontier, Kajaido, Magadi (Kenya); local, unpredictable, Tanzania; throughout Uganda; also Ethiopia, southern Somalia, Sudan, Rwanda to Zimbabwe, Mozambique.

Lepisanthes senegalensis (*Aphania senegalensis*)
Plate 217

An understorey tree usually 9–12m (30–40ft) high but occasionally up to 21m (70ft). Bark smooth, pale brown or grey. Leaflets two to six (usually four) entire, coriaceous, opposite (rarely subopposite), broadly oblanceolate to elliptic or obovate-elliptic, 7.5–18cm (3–7in) long, 2.5–6.25cm (1–2½in) broad, apex very obtusely pointed or emarginate, base cuneate. Flowers, 3mm (⅛in) across, creamy-white with a strong unpleasant smell, in rather lax terminal panicles, bracts, sepals and petals ciliate. Panicle up to 10cm (4in) long. Stamens seven to eight. The drupe is glabrous, red, fleshy, edible and sweet to the taste; the seed, however, is bitter and maybe poisonous if eaten in quantity. Found in semi-arid areas, often riparian; altitude range 300–1500m (1000–5000ft). Nyanza, Taita Hills, Machakos, Northern Frontier areas and Karasuk (Kenya); lake areas, Maasai, Shinyanga, Tanga, eastern and southern (Songea) regions (Tanzania); all regions of Uganda; also in Ethiopia west to Senegal and south to Mozambique.

Pappea capensis
Plate 347

A tree up to 15m (50ft) high, with an oak-like appearance. Branchlets dark grey, pubescent or puberulous. Leaves crowded at the end of the twigs, simple, entire or slightly undulate, glabrous above, usually pubescent on the midrib and nerves below, oblong 5–12cm (2–5in) long, apex rounded to emarginate, base unequal rounded to subcordate, lateral nerves ten to eighteen on each side of midrib. Inflorescence racemose, axillary, spike-like with the small yellow flowers clustered on condensed side-branches, male flowers with eight stamens, female flowers with a three-celled hairy ovary. Inflorescence 3.75–12cm (1½–5in) long. Found on rocky sites on hills; altitude range 1200–2100m (4000–7000ft). Kajaido, western Kenya, Nyanza and Northern Frontier areas (Kenya); all regions of Tanzania except Tabora and eastern region; all regions of Uganda except eastern (Jinja, Lake Kioga); also Ethiopia, Somalia south to Mozambique, Zimbabwe and the Cape.

63. Anacardiaceae

A family of trees and shrubs, often with resinous bark. The exstipulate leaves which are not gland-dotted (cf. *Rutaceae*, in which the leaves are gland-dotted) are nearly always alternate and in indigenous species are nearly always compound. Flowers smallish in panicles and usually five-merous with reduction in the central parts, polygamous. Ovary superior, five-celled. Fruit a drupe. Forty-two species in nine genera in East Africa.

LANNEA

Trees or bushes, fire-resistant, and coppiced with ease. Bark tough, stringy, hairs usually stellate. Leaves one- or three-foliolate or imparipinnate with opposite leaflets; inflorescences racemes or spikes; flowers polygamous; calyx four- or five-fid or -partite; petals as many, imbricate, disc small; stamens eight or ten; ovary sessile, single-celled; styles four, fruit oblong or ellipsoid, compressed. Seventeen species in East Africa.

Lannea floccosa (*L. rivae*)   A small tree up to 6m (20ft) in height, with dark grey bark. Leaves always all unifoliolate, more or less densely stellate-hairy, below and above. Flowers, *c.* 5mm (⅕in) across, fragrant with deep yellow petals tinted with red at the tips. Altitude range 350–2030m (1160–6760ft). Found in the semi-arid areas of northern districts, Kitui and Machakos (Kenya); Maasai, Shinyanga, Tanga (Tanzania); Uganda, no record; also in southern Ethiopia.

L. alata   **Plate 218**
A bush or much-branched tree up to 6m (20ft) high. Leaves up to 2.5cm (1in) long, glabrous except on rachis and midrib below; rachis narrowly and interruptedly winged, leaves four to seven pairs of obovate, incised leaflets. Flower spikes whitish, *c.* 4mm (⅕in) across. Fruit rounded, 1.25cm (⅕in) diameter, green with a red bloom and edible. The roots, as in *L. stuhlmannii*, but more so, produce a wool which protects against excessive heat and was used in February 1941 to float the East African forces over the Juba River in the Abyssinian Campaign. A tree of the *Nyika* or thicket, dry bush country; altitude range 15–1200m (50–4000ft). Coastal areas, Machakos, Kitui and northern districts (Kenya); Maasai, Mkomazi (Tanzania); Uganda, no record; also southern Somalia.

L. humilis   A deciduous savannah tree or shrub up to 6m (20ft) high, but usually smaller. Bark almost black on larger trees. Leaves tufted at the ends of the branchlets; leaflets thirteen to nineteen, oblong, 6–36mm (¼–1½in) long, rounded at both ends, white or fulvous-tomentose below. Flowers unbranched, sepals tomentose, petals glabrous and in well-developed specimens flat-topped; flower spike 1.25–3.75cm (½–1½in) long. Altitude range 1200–1380m (4000–4600ft). It is very like *L. floccosa* and common in the savannah areas of north-eastern region, Karamoja and Suk (Kenya); lake areas, Maasai, Tabora, Mpwapwa, Kondoa, Mbeya, Iringa (Tanzania); northern region of Uganda; also Sudan, Rwanda, Zambia, Zimbabwe.

L. schimperi   A savannah tree from 4–11m, rarely 15m (13–35ft) in height. Bark rough, dark grey or black, not spirally grooved. Leaflets five to nine, subsessile, elliptic to ovate-lanceolate, 6.25cm (2½in) long and *c.* 5cm (2in) broad, apex more or less acuminate, indumentum of leaflets floccose, pinkish, salmon-coloured or reddish-ferruginous, composed of long-armed, weak, curly, star-shaped hairs only, densely matted beneath and concealing the undersurface. Racemes simple, clustered at the ends of twigs, appearing when the tree is leafless. Flowers yellow; raceme 5–12cm (2–5in) long. Found in medium to high rainfall savannah; altitude range 1250–1800m (4000–6000ft). Kitale, western and Uasin Guishu regions (Kenya); all regions of Tanzania and Uganda.

L. stuhlmannii   A savannah shrub or tree up to 12m (40ft) in height. Bark grey, flaking off in fragments 10cm (4in) long. Crown rounded and spreading, with drooping branchlets. Leaves two- to five-foliolate (occasionally seven-foliolate), crowded at the ends of the twigs; leaflets usually three to five, rarely one or seven, elliptic, *c.* 2.5–7.5cm (1–3in) long, 1.25–6.25cm ($\frac{1}{2}$–2$\frac{1}{2}$in) broad, acuminate. Racemes up to 15cm (6in) long, axillary, erect, slender, simple or once-branched. Flowers fugitive, creamy and strongly scented. A deep red and a brown dye are said to be obtainable from the bark, and a brown wool or kapok is obtainable from the roots in warmer districts. Altitude range 0–1400m (0–4600ft). Widespread in savannah from the coast to about 1400m (4600ft) (Kenya); all regions of Tanzania including Zanzibar and Pemba, but no record Morogoro; all regions of Uganda except eastern; also Sudan, Ethiopia, Somalia, Rwanda, Malawi, Zambia, Zimbabwe, Mozambique.

Rhus natalensis   Plate 473
A bush (occasionally a small tree to 6m (20ft)) in savannah or scrub, stream banks and forest edges. Branchlets grey-brown; leaves pale green, trifoliolate. Leaflets sessile, obovate to oblanceolate or oblong-lanceolate, glabrous beneath, sometimes slightly pubescent on midrib, apex obtuse, base cuneate or attenuate-cuneate, margin entire or crenulate, central leaflet *c.* 3.75–6.25cm (1$\frac{1}{2}$–2$\frac{1}{2}$in) long (occasionally to 10cm (4in)), mostly attenuate-cuneate to the base. Panicles slender, 15cm (6in) long; flowers greenish-yellow, very small; petal 1–1.5mm long. Widespread except in very dry areas throughout our region and tropical Africa; altitude range 1–3000m (3–9850ft). Ten other species in East Africa.

64. Umbelliferae
THE PARSLEY FAMILY

Annual or perennial herbs or shrubs with alternate, mostly exstipulate, mostly divided leaves with a sheathing base; all parts of the plant with a resinous smell when crushed, owing to the presence of oil in oil ducts. Flowers bisexual or unisexual in umbels which are often compound, the primary rays subtended by bracts or bracts absent, and the pedicels subtended by bracteoles, or bracteoles absent. Calyx present as five teeth or petaloid lobes or obscure; five petals, free, often inflexed, pointed or notched; stamens five inserted at the edge of the nectar-bearing disc; ovary inferior with two uni-ovulate carpels and two styles. Fruit a dry schizocarp, variously ridged and ornamented. About eighty-five species in thirty-four genera in East Africa. The *Umbelliferae* are overwhelmingly adapted to temperate climates and conditions, and in tropical Africa, with a few exceptions they are rarely found below *c.* 1000m (3280ft). There are many poisonous plants in the family, e.g. Hemlock, and one (not poisonous) in East Africa, *Steganotaenia araliacea*, achieves the stature of a small tree up to 5m (16ft) high; *Heteromorpha trifoliata*, reaches 6m (20ft).

Alepidea longifolia   Plate 66
A glabrous perennial herb with a rosette of lanceolate ciliate leaves and an erect stem bearing heads of irregular umbels; involucre white, turning pink, persistent. Flower 1cm ($\frac{3}{8}$in) across. Locally abundant in montane grassland, especially on shallow soils and where burnt; altitude range 1530–3600m (5000–11,800ft). Elgon, Cheranganis, Tinderet, Mau, Aberdares, Mt Kenya and western regions (Kenya); Maasai, Tabora, Mpwapwa, Kondoa, common in Mbeya, Iringa (Tanzania); Imatong Mts and Elgon (Uganda); also Ethiopia, eastern Zaire south to Mozambique.

Caucalis incognita (*Agrocharis incognita*)   A weak-stemmed annual herb densely covered with short hairs (tomentose) often subscandent with three times pinnatisect leaves, ovate to deltoid in outline, with ovate to oblong dentate segments. The dense, head-like umbel is 1–2cm (⅖–⅘in) across, more or less sessile in a head, and the flowers have white petals, though in rare instances these can be purple. It is abundant in all upland areas in forest edges and grassland, and the fruits can be a nuisance sticking to clothing. Altitude range 1600–3300m (5900–10,800ft). Widespread in altitude range (Kenya); lake areas, Maasai, Shinyanga, Tanga, eastern region, Mbeya, Iringa, Usambara Mts and Uluguru Mts below 1400m (4500ft) (Tanzania); all regions of Uganda except Buganda; also in Sudan, Ethiopia, south to Zimbabwe and Mozambique.

Diplolophium africanum   **Plate 219**
An erect perennial with long capillary leaf segments, glabrous except for inflorescence bracts and bracteoles pubescent, ovate as long as the umbel rays and pedicels respectively, cream-yellowish; umbels 5–8cm (2–3in) across, umbel rays pubescent, curved inward in fruit, holding the loose pubescent mericarps in a cup. Locally abundant in upland wooded grassland; altitude range 1100–2600m (3600–7525ft). Cheranganis, Mau, Aberdares, Kitale, western region, Rift Valley, Kajiado, Chyulu Hills (Kenya); lake areas, Maasai, Mpwapwa, Kondoa (Tanzania); all regions of Uganda; also in Ethiopia, Zaire.

Haplosciadium abyssinicum   **Plate 220**
A perennial rosette herb with pinnate leaves. Its white flowers spring out from the rosette of leaves and are always close to the ground. Flower *c.*4mm (⅙in) across. It is a plant of alpine and high grassland areas in Kenya at 2150–4550m (7000–13,100ft). Kilimanjaro (Tanzania); Ruwenzoris and Mbale – Mt Elgon (Uganda); also Ethiopia.

Oenanthe palustris   A creeping perennial, rooting at the nodes, robust in growth, with three times pinnate or ternate leaves, the leaf segments are acute in outline with short bracteoles. The flowers are greenish-white; the umbels are compound; the main umbel *c.* 4cm (1½in) across composed of about fifteen small umbels each *c.* 8mm (⅓in) across. Locally common around open water and by streamsides from 1800–2700m (6000–8850ft). It is poisonous to stock. Tinderet, Mau and Aberdares (Kenya); Maasai, Shinyanga, western regions (Tanzania); western region, Buganda (Uganda); also Ethiopia.

O. procumbens   Similar to *O. palustris* but smaller and less robust and the leaf segments are triangular in outline with the leaf segments serrate. Flowers greenish-white. It is a fairly common plant on the shady floor of bamboo forest from 2100–3200m (7000–10,500ft). Cheranganis, Mau escarpment, Aberdares and Mt Kenya (Kenya); Morogoro (Tanzania); western region of Uganda; elsewhere, no record.

65. Ericaceae
THE HEATHER FAMILY

A medium-sized family of shrublets, shrubs or small trees, rare in the tropics but very well represented in South Africa and South-East Asia. Their simple leaves are often small and linear, without stipules. Stamens usually number twice as many as their corolla tubes and fruit is usually in capsule form. There are twenty-three species in East Africa belonging to four genera and all are found above 1400m (4600ft), with the exception of *Philippia mafiensis*, which is locally dominant on Mafia Island, probably because the humid maritime environment has something in common with the normal montane environment.

Blaeria filago   Plate 757
A low, hairy shrub with numerous erect, unbranched stems bearing racemes of pink flowers, 2–4mm (⅛in) long. It is found in disturbed, often burnt, alpine moorland at 2000–4250m (9500–13,950ft). Elgon, Aberdares, Mt Kenya (Kenya); Mt Kilimanjaro, Mt Meru (Tanzania); Mbale – Mt Elgon (Uganda); elsewhere, no record.

66. Oleaceae
THE OLIVE FAMILY

Trees, shrubs or climbers; leaves opposite, or rarely alternate or whorled, simple or compound, exstipulate; inflorescence terminal or axillary, racemose or cymose, bracteolate. Flowers bisexual, regular, calyx tube four- to six-lobed, corolla tube four- to six-lobed; stamens, two only, more or less epipetalous, disc absent, ovary superior two-celled, stigma capitate and lobed, fruit capsular with two to four axile seeds. Thirty-seven species in five genera in East Africa.

Jasminum floribundum   Plate 67
A branched, glabrous, low shrub or scrambler with slender, twig-like branches. Leaves imparipinnate, typically with five leaflets (sometimes up to nine or reduced to three) opposite; leaflet blades ovate to elongate-ovate, the lateral sometimes asymmetrical especially at the base; the terminal the larger, ranging considerably in size even on the same leaf. Inflorescence very lax, terminal or axillary, the final cymes generally three- to seven-flowered, appearing red or crimson on the outside, scented. Corolla tube 1.5–2cm (⅜–⅝in) long. Altitude range *c.* 2100m (6900ft). Found in open hillsides and savannah bush, and recorded throughout Kenya; Tanzania, no record; eastern region, Uganda; also Sudan, Ethiopia, Eritrea.

Schrebera alata   Plate 474
A deciduous tree up to 27m (90ft) tall. The bole is fluted, the bark dark grey, smooth. Leaves imparipinnate, petiole narrowly winged at the base. Leaflets five, ovate-elliptic to lanceolate-oblong; terminal leaflets 6.25–12cm (2½–4¾in) long and 2.5–3.73cm (1–1½in) broad, acute at the apex, narrowed very gradually at the base. Flowers small, white and purple, very fragrant, borne on lax terminal much-branched cymes; individual flower 8mm (⅓in). The corolla has a group of brownish swollen hairs at the base. Found in bushland and drier forests; altitude range 1500–2100m (5000–7000ft). Common in Nairobi area and old Kiambu forest (Kenya); Maasai, Tanga, Mbeya, Iringa (Tanzania); northern, eastern regions of Uganda; also in Ethiopia, Malawi.

67. Apocynaceae

THE PERIWINKLE or DESERT ROSE FAMILY

A large family of trees, shrubs, lianes or, rarely, herbs almost confined to the tropics and subtropics, often poisonous or producing important medicinal drugs, nearly always with a clear or milky latex which may contain rubber. Their leaves are entire, nearly always opposite, without stipules and pinnativeined. The flowers are regular, the calyx of five free or almost free sepals. The tubular corolla is five-lobed and there are five stamens, their anthers free or slightly touching. The ovary is superior and often separates into two follicles in fruit. The seeds often have tufts of long hair at one or both ends. Eighty-five species in twenty-nine genera in East Africa.

Adenium obesum   **Plate 516**
The 'Desert Rose' – a widespread succulent shrub, sometimes a small tree, from 0.3–5m (1–16ft) high. Flowers vary from pink to deep rose, tubular in form with petals turned out at the end of the tube and the base of the stem swollen. Flower c. 5cm (2in) long, 2.5cm (1in) across. This is a plant of arid areas, found in rocky, sandy and low-altitude districts from 50–1230m (160–4000ft). Throughout Kenya; all regions of Tanzania except lake areas and Tabora; northern region (Gulu) of Uganda; also Ethiopia, Somalia south to Mozambique, Zimbabwe.

Acokanthera schimperi (*A. friesiorum*)   **Plate 68**
A heavily foliaged evergreen tree which grows to 5–7.5m (15–25ft) in height and occasionally reaches 12m (40ft) or more. Its leaves are opposite, elliptic or broadly elliptic or, sometimes, obovate, mostly 25–55mm (1–2½in) long and about 25mm (1in) broad, acute or obtuse at the apex, mucronate, shining above and dull beneath. The flower clusters are axillary, stalkless or nearly so, the tubular flowers white or white flushed with pink, and fragrant. Corolla c. 6mm (¼in) across; tube 8mm (⅜in) long. Berry purple-black when ripe. A decoction from the leaves and bark produces the deadly arrow poison used by the Akamba and by poachers. Found at the edges of dry forest or in evergreen bushland at 1100–2300m (3600–7500ft) in Kenya; lake areas, Maasai, Shinyanga (Tanzania); northern (Gulu) and eastern (Jinja, Lake Kioga) regions of Uganda; also Ethiopia, Somalia south to Mozambique, Zimbabwe.

Carissa edulis   **Plate 69**
A scrambling bush with many branches, growing to 3m (10ft) in height, with simple or bifurcated spines. The leaves are ovate to ovate-lanceolate or elliptical and about 5cm (2in) long. The flowers, c. 12mm (½in) across, are white inside and red outside and are carried in terminal corymbose racemes. Found in most districts with a reasonable rainfall from sea level to 2000m (6500ft) in bush country or at forest edges. It is sometimes seen scrambling on ant heaps, and one example near the Hippo Pool in Nairobi National Park climbs to 18m (60ft) high. All regions of Kenya; Tanzania except Mpwapwa, Kondoa, Songea; all regions of Uganda; also Ethiopia, Somalia south to Mozambique, Zimbabwe.

Catharanthus roseus (*Vinca rosea*)   **Plate 675**
An annual or perennial, much-branched undershrub or herb; leaves elliptic-oblong, obtuse, fleshy: flowers pink or white, axillary, solitary or paired; three sepals, subulate. Corolla salver-shaped, lobes overlapping to the left. An escape from cultivated gardens; altitude range 1–1800m (3–5900ft). Usually found in disturbed places near habitation in drier districts in Kenya, Tanzania and Uganda. It came

originally from Madagascar and has medicinal qualities producing an anti-cancer drug.

Saba comorensis (*S. florida*)   **Plate 70**
A climbing or scrambling bush, the stem with numerous whitish lenticels, leaves glabrous, leathery, opposite, ovoid-oblong, obtuse, rarely acuminate; flowers clustered, salver-shaped, corolla lobes as long as the tube, 3.5cm (1⅜in) across, or just shorter, oblong; the fruit a berry up to 6cm (2in) in diameter. The flowers are white, 3.5cm (1⅜in) across, sweet-scented, in corymbs of cymes. Recorded on stony ground in riverine forests; altitude range 30–1850m (100–6050ft). Aberdares to western regions, Kisii and Machakos (Kenya); all regions of Tanzania except Kondoa, Mpwapwa; all regions of Uganda; also Zaire, Rwanda, Burundi, Sudan, Ethiopia, southern Somalia, Mozambique.

68. Asclepiadaceae

A large tropical and warm temperate family of herbs, twiners, lianes or stem-succulents, more rarely shrublets or shrubs, and never true trees. Closely related to the *Apocynaceae*, differing in that the stamens unite to form a solid mass around the style, and the pollen unites into waxy masses (pollinia) as in the *Orchidaceae*. A corona is often present inside the corolla. The united part of the corolla is often very short. Fruit consists of two follicles (or one by abortion) and contains numerous feathered, winged or flattened seeds. 311 species in 54 genera in East Africa.

Key

Plants erect: *Calotropis, Gomphocarpus, Kanahia, Stathmostelma*

Plants twining: *Ceropegia, Oxystelma, Glossonema, Pergularia* (and many others not illustrated)

Plants succulent: *Caralluma, Stapelia, Huernia, Edithcolea*
(not twining)

Calotropis procera   **Plate 569**
A tall plant with soft woody stems. The leaves spring from the widely-spaced branches at intervals up the stem and are ovate and markedly veined. The closely-massed flowers are purple, violet or white, 20–24mm (*c.* ⅞in) across. It is common in ground which has been disturbed, such as old fields, and especially where seasonally flooded in arid country. It is fairly widespread in Kenya from Mumias to Kajiado at altitudes of 300–1200m (1000–3900ft); all regions of Tanzania; northern (Gulu) and western regions of Uganda; also widespread in tropical Africa.

CARALLUMA

The *Caralluma* species, of which seventeen have been recorded in Kenya, are generally found in dry, rocky or stony areas. One or two tolerate dry, sandy, alkaline soils, e.g. *C. speciosa* and *C. socotrana*. They are erect or creeping fleshy plants with four to six angles on each stem, though occasionally there may be only three. The flowers in most species are purple black to intense dark black in colour. Solitary or in lateral or terminal heads. Often they look like stiff, dark, mop heads standing up out of the fleshy, succulent stems. Many of them grow at lower altitudes from 274–1200m (900–4000ft) in semi-arid areas in the north, north-east and east of Kenya.

Caralluma dummeri **Plate 16**
A decumbent fleshy perennial with ascending often variegated stems bearing lines of conical projections. The greenish or cream flowers are more or less terminal, pedicillate, with or without hairs inside. The flower is often five-petalled with an open throat, 30–40mm (1⅕–1⅗in) across. Found in *Combretum* woodland and adjacent grassland in rocky places with a sandy soil; altitude range 1200–1650m (3700–5400ft). Throughout Kenya; Maasai, Tanga (Tanzania); all regions of Uganda; elsewhere, no record.

C. russelliana (*C. foetida*) **Plate 570**
A massive erect succulent with four-angled stems up to 5cm(2in) thick and with a large head of smallish, black-purple or dark violet flowers. The corolla lobes are without hairs along the margins but minutely pubescent within; corona hairy on the back. Flower: 1.5cm (⅗in) across; head 8.5cm (3⅖in) across. Uncommon, found in dry country; altitude range 100–1680m (330–5600ft). Baringo and Nanyuki (Kenya); Tanzania, no record; northern region of Uganda; also Ethiopia, Somalia.

C. speciosa **Plate 548**
A massive erect succulent, with four-angled stems and few, but large, black-purple or dark violet flowers (similar to *C. russelliana* but shorter stems and larger, less numerous, flowers). Size of flower 20–25mm (⅘–1in) across; inflorescence 60mm (2⅖in) across. Uncommon and found in dry alkaline country; altitude range 450–1200m (1475–3950ft). Magadi (Kenya); Maasai, Tanga (Tanzania); northern region of Uganda; also Ethiopia, Somalia.

C. socotrana An erect caespitose fleshy perennial with cylindrical or obscurely angled stems bearing terminal groups of two to three black purple flowers, 20–30mm (⅘–1⅕in) across. Altitude range 850–1200m (2800–3750ft). It has only been recorded in alkaline alluvial soil or stony ground at Magadi (Kenya); Tanzania and Uganda, no record; also Somalia and Socotra.

C. subterranea **Plate 549**
A rhizomatous perennial plant, with subterranean, then ascending stems bearing linear leaf-scales. Corolla velvety-pubescent above, the hairs without swollen persistent bases, outer coronal lobes erect and denticulate. Purple flowers (rarely green), 10mm (⅖in) across, scattered along the stem. This is a rare plant, similar to *C. vibratilis*, which can be distinguished by its darker flowers in terminal groups, the sometimes superficial rather than subterranean stems, and the club-shaped, delicate, loosely attached (vibratile) hairs on the basal edges of the pubescent lobes; corona lobes apparently in one whorl. Found in dry stony grassland; altitude range 1200–1800m (4000–5900ft). Western regions and Rift Valley (Kenya); lake areas, Maasai (Tanzania); Uganda, elsewhere, no record.

C. tubiformis **Plate 475**
A leafless stem succulent with erect fleshy stems 12–15cm (5–6in) tall, 12–14mm (½in) in diameter, grey-green mottled with purple with fleshy opposite conical spines *c.* 15mm (⅗in) long. Flowers shortly pedicellate, two to three together at the apex of the stem, bell-shaped; 24mm (1in) long including lobes, 10mm (⅖in) in diameter. Found in open rocky places in dry country; altitude range 700–1200m

ASCLEPIADACEAE

(2300–3850ft). North-east Frontier, Rift Valley, Machakos, Voi, Kitui in Kenya only.

C. turneri
Plate 550

A tufted succulent shrub growing in clump-like cushions. Stems are ascending, rooting and bunching at the base, quadrangular and variegated with soft, toothed margins, up to 20cm (7¾in) high. Flowers are borne on long, slender rachis, arching up to 40cm (c.16in). Corolla pendulous, c. 1.2cm (½in) long, lobes oblanceolate, pale green at base, increasingly spotted with maroon towards the lip. Found in residual limestone outcrop or scree in *Acacia-Commiphora* bushland and in shallow soil crevices on steep hillsides; altitude range 820–2000m (2700–6560ft). Samburu (Ndoto Mts), Kajiado, Baringo, Turkana and Kisumu area (Kenya); Mbulu (Tanzania); Karamoja (Uganda); also Ethiopia, Somalia.

Ceropegia ballyana
Plate 476

A hairless, succulent climber with broad oblong or elliptic leaves and large solitary flowers, c. 65mm (2⅝in) long, of most unusual appearance. The corolla is greenish to yellow with purple spots and long lobes ending acutely. A plant of dry bushland, it often entwines itself high up in the branches of medium-sized trees and high bush, from 1200–1400m (3950–4600ft). Rare. Baringo and Embu (Kenya); Maasai (Tanzania); Uganda and elsewhere, no record. Forty-four other species in East Africa.

C. denticulata
An erect or climbing herb, roots hardly swollen; stem succulent, sometimes somewhat angular; green with occasional longitudinal white spots; leaves succulent, ovate to 3cm (1⅛in) long, sometimes serrate. Flower c. 4.5cm (1¾in) long. Corolla yellow-green with varying amounts of brown-maroon streaks and spots especially towards the top of the tube, lobes banded green, white, blackish with vibratile clavate hairs at tips. Found in bushland; altitude range 980–2040m (3250–6800ft). Aberdares, Kisii, Narok, Rift Valley, Embu, Machakos, Nairobi and Kajiado (Kenya); Tanga (Tanzania); Uganda and elsewhere, no record.

C. racemosa
Plate 477

A slender twiner with lanceolate leaves. Flowers in lax slender inflorescences. Corolla with a deep purple tube with narrow yellow lobes connivent at the tip; corolla tube and lobes 20–25mm (⅘–1in) long, lobe 6–7mm (¼in). Found in open, usually evergreen, bushland; altitude range 1000–1850m (3280–6050ft), sometimes to 2000m (6500ft). Turkana, Rift Valley, Embu, Machakos, Nanyuki, coast (Kenya); Maasai, Tabora, Mbeya, Iringa (Tanzania); northern region of Uganda.

C. seticorona
Plate 478

Fibrous roots, stems succulent, blue-grey in colour, leaves ovate, fleshy; corolla yellow with varying amounts of maroon spots and streaks, or sometimes nearly all maroon, occasional ciliate hairs on lobes; corolla tube 3.3cm (1⅜in) across. Found in thorny bushland; altitude range 15–1680m (50–5600ft). Kisii, Baringo, Magadi, Nanyuki, Embu, Machakos, Nairobi and Kajiado (Kenya); lake areas, Maasai (Tanzania); Uganda and elsewhere, no record.

C. succulenta
Plate 479

Climbing or, less frequently, erect herb with thick, succulent stem. Leaf nodules prominent or depressed; leaves large oval-elliptic with white veins. Flowers, c. 55mm (2⅛in) long, on a peduncle 5–10cm (2–4in) long. Yellow-green corolla with maroon spots, and whitish lobes with green tips and short ciliate hairs on the edges.

145

ASCLEPIADACEAE

Found in dry forest; altitude range 1400–2800m (4600–9000ft). Aberdares, Nairobi, Narok and Rift Valley districts (Kenya); western region of Uganda; Tanzania and elsewhere, no record.

Edithcolea grandis   Plate 551
A low, succulent, leafless plant with quite short, half erect, half prostrate stems which have horny, conical, yellow knobs upon them. The very conspicuous flowers, up to 12cm (4¾in) across, are purple and yellow, edged with vibratile, club-shaped hairs. It is in danger of extermination and should *not* be collected. Districts such as Nairobi are too wet and cool for this and similar succulents, which will not grow there even if transplanted. A rare plant, it is found in dry rocky country in Kenya at 900–1830m (3000–6000ft). Tanga (Tanzania); northern region of Uganda; also Somalia and southern Ethiopia.

Glossonema revoilii   Plate 480
An erect, pubescent, much-branched perennial herb from a thin woody rootstock, with oblong-elliptic leaves, cymes sessile, flowers cream-yellow with maroon centre, fading to bronze, 0.8cm (⅓in) across. An uncommon plant found in dry, rocky bushland; altitude range 600–1500m (2000–5000ft). Magadi, Nanyuki, Machakos, Loitokitok and Kajiado (Kenya); lake areas, Maasai (Tanzania); Uganda, no record; also in Ethiopia, Somalia.

Gomphocarpus fruticosus   Plate 221
A branched, erect shrub with needle-shaped to linear-oblong leaves and white and maroon flowers, 14mm (⅝in) across. The fruits are ovate in outline like sharply pointed pears and covered in almost hairless purple bristles. The leaves are usually up to 8cm (3in) in length. It is the commonest *Gomphocarpus* in Kenya and is found in dry montane grassland and along watercourses in warmer lowland country at 950–2700m (3100–8900ft). Throughout Kenya in its altitude range; all regions of Tanzania except Mpwapwa Kondoa, Songea; all regions of Uganda; also Ethiopia, Rwanda, Zaire south to Zimbabwe. One of thirteen species in East Africa.

G. integer   Plate 222
A delicate, erect, sparsely-branched perennial with white woolly hairs on young plants and needle-shaped leaves. The flowers are yellow, green and pink, *c.* 18mm (*c.* ¾in) across. Fruits ovate-acuminate in outline with a few hairless bristles on one side or entirely smooth. Altitude range 900–2150m (2950–7050ft). Locally common in the Aberdares, Kisii, Narok, Baringo, Rift Valley, Nanyuki, Machakos and Nairobi (Kenya); lake areas, Maasai, Tabora, Mpwapwa, Kondoa (Tanzania); northern region (Gulu) of Uganda; also Ethiopia, Somalia.

G. kaessneri   Plate 348
A branching, bushy perennial about 1m (3¼ft) tall with a milky juice and a yellowish-green corolla with a conspicuous dark chocolate corona. Corolla *c.* 15mm (⅝in) across. As in all species of *Gomphocarpus* the fruit is inflated and conspicuous, like a small bladder. Locally common in grassy, stony places at 900–1830m (3000–6000ft). Rift Valley, Magadi, Machakos, Nairobi and Kajiado districts; generally replaced in western regions by *G. semilunatus*, though *G. kaessneri* has been recorded in the Mumias area (Kenya); lake areas, Maasai, Kondoa, Mpwapwa, Tabora (Tanzania); Uganda and elsewhere, no record.

G. physocarpus
Plate 758

A sparsely-branched, erect shrub with lanceolate leaves and green and white flowers, occasionally tinged with purple; flower 13–18mm ($\frac{1}{2}$–$\frac{3}{4}$in) across. Fruit broadly ovate in outline, rather abruptly constricted into a short more or less hooked apex, covered with scattered minutely pubescent bristles. An uncommon plant found in dry upland grassland; altitude range 750–2550m (2450–8350ft). Tinderet, Mau, Aberdares, Narok (Kenya); lake areas, Maasai, Tanga, Tabora (Tanzania); all regions of Uganda; also in southern Sudan, Ethiopia.

G. semilunatus
Plate 223

A large erect perennial with crowded lanceolate leaves and purple-pink flower; corona mostly with an erect tooth within the central hollow. Flower 16mm ($\frac{3}{8}$in) across. The fruit is covered with slightly rough bristles and is reminiscent of a small bladder covered in prickles. A common species, especially in western Kenya, and is found growing in disturbed places and on flooded grassland or roadsides in medium-altitude grasslands from 1300–2550m (4300–8400ft). Elgon, Tinderet, Mau, Aberdares, Kitale, Mumias, Kisii, Narok and Rift Valley (Kenya); lake areas, Maasai, Tanga, Tabora, Kondoa, Mpwapwa, Mbeya (Tanzania); eastern region (Jinja, Lake Kioga) of Uganda; also Zaire.

G. stenophyllus
Plate 224

Similar to *G. integer*, but with yellowish or reddish flowers and a much narrower, smooth fruit, pointed at the top. Flower 12mm ($\frac{1}{2}$in) across. Locally common in dry grassland or often on disturbed ground or rocky soils at medium altitude from 1400–2700m (4600–8900ft). Elgon, Tinderet, Mau, Aberdares, Kitale, Nanyuki, Machakos, Nairobi and Kajiado (Kenya); Maasai, Tabora, Mpwapwa, Kondoa, Mbeya (Tanzania); Uganda no record; also, south Ethiopia.

Huernia aspera (*H. keniensis*)
Plate 552

A fleshy, trailing herb with four to six rows of conical fleshy projections on the stem, and lateral more or less pendulous dark purple-black flowers. Corolla up to 15mm ($\frac{3}{8}$in) long. *H. keniensis* (in *UKWF*) is a form of this very variable species with longer flowers, the corolla being more than 15mm ($\frac{3}{8}$in) long; stems are four- to six-ridged and sometimes reach 1m (3ft) in length when hanging over rocks. The flowers have an evil smell. Found in rocky places from 500–1600m (1650–5250ft) throughout Kenya and Tanzania. Elgon, Tinderet, Aberdares, Kitale, Rift Valley, Nanyuki and Machakos (Kenya); lake areas, Maasai, Tanga (Tanzania); Uganda and elsewhere, no record.

Kanahia laniflora
Plates 71 & 72

A glabrous shrub with many erect stems and linear leaves. Flowers large, pure white, in lateral pedunculate cymes; corolla deeply five-lobed; flower *c.* 11mm ($\frac{3}{8}$in) across. A characteristic plant and abundant along watercourses in dry country; altitude range 100–1200m (328–4000ft). Baringo, Nanyuki and Machakos (Kenya); lake areas, Tanga, Morogoro, Mbeya, Iringa (Tanzania); northern region of Uganda; also in Sudan, Ethiopia, Somalia. The only species in East Africa.

Oxystelma bornouense
Plate 553

A glabrescent climber with cordate leaves and big maroon and white flowers, up to 3cm (1$\frac{1}{8}$in) across. A rare plant found in riverine forest, altitude range 105–900m (350–3000ft), and only recorded in the Athi River and at Tsavo East (Kenya); Tanzania and Uganda, no record; also from Senegal to Somalia. The only species in East Africa.

Pachycarpus eximius Similar to *P. grantii* but has broader leaves and shorter inner corona teeth. Flower 2cm (⅘in) across. An uncommon plant, altitude range 900–2150m (2950–7050ft), found in western Kenya from Kitale area to Kisii (Kenya); lake areas, Morogoro, Mbeya, Iringa (Tanzania); all regions of Uganda; also Sudan, Rwanda, Zaire. One of thirteen species in East Africa.

P. fulvus Leaves ovate to oblong, more or less cordate, and arresting umbels of cream, orange and brown flowers *c.* 2.5cm (1in) across. A rare plant, altitude range 1500–1800m (5000–6000ft), found in wooded grassland in western Kenya and recorded on Elgon and in Kitale (Kenya); Mbeya, Iringa (Tanzania); western region (Uganda); elsewhere, not known.

P. grantii An erect, pubescent perennial with ovate to lanceolate or oblong leaves which are scabrid along the margin and with conspicuous umbels of white and maroon or purple flowers *c.* 1.7cm (⅔in) across. An uncommon plant found in dry upland grassland, altitude range 2100–2700m (7000–9000ft), and recorded in Cheranganis, Tinderet, Aberdares and Mt Kenya (Kenya); lake areas, Maasai, Mpwapwa, Kondoa (Tanzania); Buganda (Uganda); elsewhere, not known.

P. lineolatus **Plate 571**
An erect, pubescent perennial from a tuberous root system with lanceolate-oblong leaves with a scabrid edge. The corona tubes are overtopped by the staminal column and inserted on the stalk of that column which is as long as the anthers. Flowers, *c.* 1.8cm (¾in) across, greenish with purplish corona. It is a rare plant, altitude range 300–2100m (1000–7000ft), found in grassland and recorded in western Kenya and the coast (Kenya); all regions of Tanzania; all regions of Uganda; also Ethiopia south to Zimbabwe and Mozambique.

P. rhinophyllus **Plate 481**
An erect, pubescent perennial from a tuberous root system, with lanceolate-linear leaves which are truncate at base; flowers in yellow and brown umbels, sometimes sessile, 2cm (⅘in) across. Locally common, altitude range 1500–2100m (5000–7000ft), and found in Aberdares, Mt Kenya, Narok, Machakos, Nairobi and Kajiado (Kenya); lake areas, Maasai, Shinyanga, Tanga (Tanzania); Uganda and elsewhere, no record.

P. schweinfurthii Similar in every way to *P. lineolatus* except for oblong-ovate leaves, the corona lobes equalling the staminal column and the stalk of the staminal column rather more or less than half as long as the anthers. Flower 1.5cm (⅗in) across. It is locally common in dry wooded grassland, altitude range 1200–2400m (4000–8000ft), and recorded in Elgon, Cheranganis, Kitale, western Kenya, Kisii Embu and Kajiado (Kenya); all regions of Tanzania; all regions except northern (Gulu) of Uganda; also in Zaire.

Pergularia daemia **Plate 17**
A climbing or trailing herb or soft shrub with tomentum of mixed stout and subulate hairs on nearly all parts; racemes very long-pedunculate, often exceeding the leaves; petals green, sometimes with purple tinges; corona pure white, follicles conical, often covered with soft, fleshy processes. Flower *c.* 10mm (⅖in) across. The fruit is variable, some being very woolly and others, principally in drier areas, almost glabrous. This is probably the commonest climbing *Asclepiad* in East Africa and is found in disturbed places in dry country; altitude range, at and below 1800m (6000ft). One of two species in East Africa. Widespread in Kenya; all regions of

Tanzania; western region, Buganda (Uganda); also in Sudan, Ethiopia, Somalia, Malawi.

Sarcostemma andongense   Plate 225
A scandent, almost leafless and succulent shrub growing in clumps. Stems are thick and stouter than those of *S. viminale*, *c.* 9mm (3⅜in) in diameter, whitish and arching to *c.* 2m (6½ft) high, sprawling over other plants. With copious white latex. Flowers in terminal clusters 7cm (*c.* 3in) across on the arching stems, greenish-yellow, sulphur-coloured or whitish; lobes with strongly reflexed margins, fragrant. One of five species in East Africa. Widespread in semi-arid and arid areas, altitude range 230–1800m (770–5900ft), in Kenya, Maasai (Tanzania); Karamoja (Uganda); also Ethiopia, Eritrea, Somalia, south to Zimbabwe, Mozambique.

Stapelia semota   Plate 349
An uncommon short stem-succulent, the only East African member of a large genus that is almost confined to southern Africa. Many botanists consider that the genus should be subdivided and would probably rename this *Orbea semota*. The leaves are very much reduced, being the tips of succulent spine-like processes. The flowers are usually chocolate-coloured *c.* 55mm (2⅛in) across. The yellow variety illustrated used to occur in Nairobi but is now thought to be extinct as a wild plant. Altitude range 1500–1800m (4900–*c.* 6000ft) in Kenya; Mpwapwa, Kondoa (Tanzania); Uganda, no record; also Rwanda.

Stathmostelma rhacodes   Plate 517
An erect, sparsely-branched herb with linear glabrous leaves from a fusiform tuber and usually only one terminal umbel, with some pedicels less than 4cm (1⅜in) long and red and orange flowers *c.* 2cm (⅝in) across when open. Ten species in East Africa. Common in seasonally wet or waterlogged grassland especially on shallow soil, altitude range 1440–2400m (4800–8000ft) and recorded in Tinderet, Mau, Aberdares, Kitale, Kisii, Narok, Baringo, Rift Valley, Machakos and Nairobi (Kenya); Maasai (Tanzania); Uganda, no record; also in Sudan.

Tenaris rubella (*T. rostrata*)   Plate 759
An erect, loosely branched herb with linear leaves and paired flowers on long-pedunculate terminal inflorescences: flowers pink to maroon; corolla star shaped, each lobe 1.5cm (⅝in) long. A rare plant in dry grassland, altitude range 1500–2115m (5000–7050ft). Only species in East Africa, recorded in Chyulu Hills and Narok (Kenya); lake areas, Maasai, Tanga (Tanzania); western region, Buganda (Uganda); also in Rwanda, Burundi (and South Africa).

69. Rubiaceae
THE COFFEE or MADDER FAMILY

A very large family of trees, shrubs, climbers and herbs, mainly tropical but with some herbaceous genera in temperate regions. Their leaves are entire, opposite or, less often, whorled, with interpetiolar stipules. The flowers are regular with the corolla usually tubular, the stamens of the same number as the corolla lobes and the ovary inferior. 631 species in 102 genera in East Africa.

Agathisanthemum bojeri **Plate 18**

A perennial branched herb or shrub from 0.3–1.5m (1–4½ft) tall; young stems densely pubescent, becoming glabrescent with age and often with the brown bark peeling off. Leaves subsessile, pale; blade narrowly lanceolate to lanceolate, narrowly elliptic or ovate-oblong up to 5.8cm (2⅓in) long, subacute to acute and sometimes apiculate at the apex, cuneate at the base, glabrous above, pubescent on the nerves beneath. Leaves often appear whorled owing to presence of short undeveloped leafy shoots at almost every node. Inflorescence laxly corymbose or sometimes dense subcapitulate clusters 1–7cm (⅖–2¾in) across. Corolla tube 1–2.5mm (up to ⅒in) long, white, cream or greenish white. Found in grassland, forest edges, bushland, open woodland and also as a weed in cultivation, particularly in coastal areas, altitude range 0–1200m (0–3900ft). One of three species in East Africa. Kwale, Mombasa, Kilifi, Malindi (Kenya); Lushoto, Bagamoyo, Uzaramo, Dar-es-Salaam, Zanzibar (Tanzania); also in Somalia, Zimbabwe, Mozambique.

Carphalea glaucescens (*Dirichletia glaucescens*) **Plate 73**

An erect or scrambling shrub 60–350cm (2–10ft) tall. The corolla is tubular, *c.* 2cm (⅘in) long, white or pale pink and has four or five short spreading lobes. The pinkish-green calyx limb is asymmetric, more or less heart-shaped. It grows and persists until the fruiting stage and is usually the most conspicuous part of the flower. This plant is found in dry bushland at altitudes of 200–900m (650–3000ft). In Kenya; Moshi, Lake Chala and Kilimanjaro, Pare, Mpwapwa, Iringa – Ruaha National Park (Tanzania); Uganda, no record; also Somalia and Ethiopia.

Chassalia umbraticola **Plate 74**

A common forest undershrub up to 3.6m (12ft) high with glabrous elliptic leaves to 10cm (4in) long, apex acute, cuneate at the base, stipules apiculate. Flowers, sweet-scented, in terminal branched inflorescences, the ultimate components, three to several flowered clusters; inflorescence components white, tinged purple; calyx tube 1.2–2mm (*c.* $\frac{1}{12}$in) long; cream with purple upper margin, corolla tube 1.5–2cm (⅗–⅘in) long; cream or white, often tinged purple sometimes at the base of the tube and tips of the lobes, glabrous or finely puberulous. Style up to 1.7cm (⅔in) long. The lobes conspicuously winged. Found in coast bushland and woodland, altitude range 0–450m (0–1476ft) occasionally up to 800m (2624ft) and recorded in Kwale, Shimba Hills, Kilifi (Kenya); Tanga District, Morogoro, Uzaramo, Zanzibar and Pemba (Tanzania).

NB This species is generally characterized by the elliptic-acute (not long-acuminate) leaf blades and short petioles.

Conostomium keniense (*C. floribundum*) **Plate 75**

A perennial herb or shrub to 0.15–1.5m (5–50in) tall, with much-branched four-ribbed stems, usually woody at the base, at first scabridulous or shortly scabrid-pubescent, soon glabrescent, or entirely glabrous. Leaf blades narrowly-linear to linear-lanceolate up to 6cm (2⅖in) long, acute at apex, narrowed at base, glabrous to scabrid-pubescent, the margins often inrolled. Flowers axillary, pedicellate forming terminal raceme-like inflorescences at the apices of the branchlets which bear smaller and less conspicuous leaves. Pedicels straight or slightly or distinctly curved. Corolla tube 2–5cm (⅘–2in) long, lobe 0.8–1.5cm (⅓–⅗in) wide, white or cream often tinged blue, purple or green outside, sweetly scented. Lobes oblong-lanceolate, both tube and lobe glabrous outside. One of two species in East Africa. Found in deciduous bushland, dry grassland, rocky hillsides, rock crevices, altitude range 600–1800m (1950–5900ft) possibly to 150m (500ft), and recorded in

Mathews Range, Muranga, Kitui, Meru, Baringo (Kenya); Tanzania and Uganda, no record; also in southern Ethiopia.

C. quadrangulare   Plate 76
Usually a perennial herb from 30–60cm (12–24in) tall, with one to several unbranched or sparsely branched glabrous four-ribbed stems from a woody root. Leaves linear-lanceolate to lanceolate, narrowly tapering, acute at apex, narrowed to subcordate at base, glabrous but a few hairs above near the base. Flowers, axillary, sessile forming a leafy-spike-like inflorescence, 10–25cm (4–10in) long (sometimes up to 40cm (16in) long). Corolla white or pinkish, the tube, 9–15cm (3½–6in) long, and lobes often greenish outside. The buds very distinctly apiculate; seeds chestnut brown. Found in deciduous bushland, grassland with scattered trees, always in dry places and mostly in sandy areas by dry rivers, rocky ledges and stony overgrazed land, altitude range 60–1800m (200–5900ft). Northern Frontier areas, Samburu, West Suk, Meru, Isiolo and lower Timau (Kenya); Tanzania, no record; Karamoja, Jinja, Lake Kioga (Uganda); also in Sudan, Ethiopia.

Diodia aulacosperma   Plate 833
An annual, erect, decumbent or prostrate, unbranched or much branched, usually semi-succulent herb, up to 35cm (14in) tall, sometimes to 90cm (3ft). Stems angular, usually glabrous, leaves subsucculent, blades oblong, elliptic to elliptic-lanceolate to almost rounded, 5cm (2in) long and 2.2cm (c. 1in) wide, acute to rounded at apex, base narrowed, scabrid on both surfaces and on margin. Flowers c. 7mm (¼in) long, white, pink, mauve or blue, one to several in dense axillary clusters up to 1.6cm (⅝in) wide. Corolla funnel-shaped. Found on coastal strand and low coastal areas and in grassland near high tide marks, on sandy soil on coral cliffs, dune bushland in open Acacia woodland, on waste ground and as a weed in cultivated land, altitude range below 50m (164ft). Recorded in its habitat in Kenya, Tanzania, Zanzibar, Somalia and Zambia.

Feretia apodanthera ssp. keniensis   Plate 77
A well-branched, deciduous shrub up to 3m (10ft) tall, the twigs being at right angles to the stem. Leaves papery, oval, 2.5cm (1in) long, narrowed at both ends. Flowers white, very fragrant up to 2.5cm (1in) in diameter and shortly stalked, appearing before the leaves in axillary subfascicles. Corolla funnel-shaped 1.25cm (½in) long, anthers inserted at mouth of corolla. Found at the coast usually in bush or coral rag, altitude range 1–50m (3–165ft) in Kenya; Tanzania and Uganda, no record; also in southern Somalia.

   NB Ssp. keniensis only occurs in Kenya and Somalia. Ssp. apodanthera occurs in Uganda and Tanzania, Sudan, Ethiopia and southern Somalia. Ssp. tanzaniensis occurs in lake areas, Tabora, Mpwapwa, Kondoa, Mbeya and Iringa in Tanzania. Neither occur in Kenya.

Galium aparinoides
A 'sticky' climber or scrambler with oblanceolate, rounded leaves, ending abruptly in a sharp point (apiculate). The brownish-yellow flowers, 4mm (c. ⅛in) across, are arranged in lateral cymes. One of seven species in East Africa, always above 900m (c. 3000ft). Locally common on montane forest edges and recorded in the Cheranganis, Mau, Aberdares, Mt Kenya, Kitale and Kajiado from 1700–3700m (5600–12,100ft) (Kenya); Arusha, Mt Meru, Kilimanjaro, western Usambara Mts (Tanzania); Mt Moroto, Elgon (Uganda); also Malawi and possibly Ethiopia.

GARDENIA

Small trees or shrubs with long tubular or funnel-shaped six to nine-merous corollas and large hard many-seeded indehiscent fruits (which may be eaten by elephants and other large mammals). Eleven species in East Africa.

Gardenia ternifolia var. jovis-tonantis   Plate 78

A savannah shrub or tree which grows to 5m (14ft) in height, but usually stunted and twisted with pale bark. The fragrant, creamy-white flowers have a conspicuous corolla 45–100mm (1¾–4in) across the lobes of which are sometimes slightly twisted in the bud. The woody fruit is the size and shape of a chicken's egg. It is found in coastal areas and at altitudes up to 2100m (6900ft) in western Kenya, Kitale, the Cheranganis, Kajiado and Machakos districts (Kenya); Shinyanga, Bukoba, Mwanza, Maasai, Tanga, Tabora, eastern Region, Songea, Mbeya (Tanzania); all regions of Uganda; also Ethiopia to Zambia and Mozambique.

G. volkensii   Plate 226

A small branching deciduous tree with light grey bark. Its hairless leaves are arranged in pairs from the ends of three whorled branches. Broadly spoon-shaped and emarginate with a blunt apex, they are 25mm (1in) long and broad. The flowers are white and fragrant 10–11cm (c. 4in) long. It is widespread in Kenya from sea level up to 1830m (6000ft) and is often found in bush in areas of medium rainfall, and recorded in Shinyanga, Bukoba, Mwanza, Maasai, Tanga, Tabora, eastern region (Tanzania); northern region – Gulu (Uganda); also southern Ethiopia, Mozambique, Zimbabwe.

Heinsia crinita ssp. parviflora   Plate 79

A shrub or small tree up to 5m (16ft) in height; leaves elliptic to lanceolate up to 7.6cm (3in) long and 1.25cm (½in) wide, apex acuminate, base acute, petiole short: stipules 5mm (⅛in) long, falling early. The flowers are white, fragrant, solitary or in lax terminal racemes, pedicels up to 3.75cm (1½in) long, the corolla tube is jasmine like and the tube appressed pubescent up to 20mm (⅜in) long with the limb 22–35mm (1–1⅜in) across; berry 1.25cm (½in) in diameter. Two other species in East Africa. Altitude range 15–660m (50–2150ft). Common in coastal regions (Kenya); Tanga, Morogoro, Songea – Lindi (Tanzania); Uganda, no record; also in southern Somalia, Malawi, Zimbabwe, Mozambique.

NB *H. crinita* is divided into two subspecies: *H. crinita* ssp. *crinita* in West and Central Africa and ssp. *parviflora* in coastal areas from southern Somalia to Mozambique. The corolla of the former is markedly wider, up to 62mm (2½in) across than that of the coastal subspecies.

H. densiflora   A scandent shrub up to 4½m (15ft) in height covered with tawny hispid hairs. Leaves elliptic to oblong-elliptic up to 12½cm (5in) long and 3.75cm (1½in) broad, apex acute, base rounded; petiole 6mm (¼in) long. Flowers white 2.54cm (1in) long, sessile in short dense cymes and corolla tube slender 20mm (⅜in) long, limb 40–50mm (1¾–2in) across, densely pubescent outside. Found in coastal areas from 1–500m (3–1500ft) in Kenya and Tanzania; Uganda, no record; also in southern Somalia, Malawi, Zimbabwe, Mozambique.

Kohautia caespitosa   Plate 760

Sparsely pubescent perennial or annual herb, usually branched below with linear to elliptic leaves. Flowers scented; corolla white, buff, grey, yellowish, pink or lilac, the tube c. 1.4cm (⅜in) long, often purplish and the lobes 4–10mm (⅛–⅜in) long, ochraceous, nearly always pale inside. Ten other species in East Africa. Found in

open *Acacia-Commiphora* woodland; recorded in Northern Frontier areas – Wajir, Kitale (Kenya); Arusha, Lushoto, Kondoa, Iringa (Tanzania); Karamoja – Mt Debasien (Uganda); also in Sudan, Somalia, Eritrea, Zimbabwe.
NB There are four variants to the species: *K. caespitosa* var. *caespitosa*; *K. caespitosa* var. *delagoensis*, *K. caespitosa* var. *amaniensis* and var. *kitaliensis*. Var. *amaniensis* is almost unknown in Kenya highlands. *K. caespitosa* var. *caespitosa* is a low altitude species – 200m (650ft): the other variants are at higher altitudes in grasslands and scrub.

Oldenlandia corymbosa An erect, sparsely-branched annual herb with linear leaves and one or two white flowers on pedicels and peduncles which together often equal the leaves and tend to nod when in fruit. When the flowers are solitary this species resembles *O. herbacea* but it does not become black when dry. Corolla tube *c.* 0.8mm long; limb 2.5mm ($\frac{1}{10}$in) across. Thirty-six other species in East Africa. Found on shallow soils and sand in dry areas. Altitude range 1–2300m (3–7550ft). Recorded in Elgon, Aberdares, Kitale, Baringo, Rift Valley, Embu and Western Kenya (Kenya); Tabora, Mpwapwa, Kondoa, Morogoro (Tanzania); Uganda, no record; also widespread in tropical Africa.
NB Var. *linearis* with mostly erect plants and leaves more erect than in other species with often longer linear blades is recorded in all regions of Tanzania and northern Karamoja and eastern – Teso regions (Uganda); also in Ethiopia, Somalia south to Zimbabwe. Two other varieties are recorded: var. *nana*, var. *caespitosa* in *FTEA*.

O. friesiorum Plate 572

A perennial, procumbent, carpet-forming herb with stems 15–30cm (6–12in) long, sometimes rooting at the nodes, glabrous. Leaf blades ovate or oblong ovate, acute or very slightly acuminate at the apex up to 3.8cm (1$\frac{1}{2}$in) long, rounded at the base with short dense adpressed hairs on the margins and in a narrow belt parallel to the margin on the upper surface, otherwise glabrous. Flowers in few-flowered terminal or axillary cymes, the cymes solitary or in threes. Corolla tube 2mm ($\frac{1}{12}$in) long, white, pale lilac, blue or pink, the throat densely hairy, lobes oblong 2–3mm ($\frac{1}{12}$–$\frac{1}{8}$in) long, 1–1.2mm wide, hairy at the base; style 1–2mm or 3–4.5mm ($\frac{1}{8}$–$\frac{1}{6}$in) long. Found in upland evergreen forest, clearings and forest edges, bushland, grassland, roadsides and gravel tips, altitude range 1800–2550m (5900–8000ft). Recorded in Muranga, Meru, North West Mt Kenya (Kenya); Mbeya, Iringa (Tanzania); Uganda and elsewhere not known.

O. herbacea

An erect, much branched, glabrescent (nearly hairless) annual with linear leaves and solitary white flowers on slightly ascending pedicels; corolla tube 6mm ($\frac{1}{4}$in) long; limb *c.* 5mm ($\frac{1}{4}$in) across. It is found in stony open soil in dry grassland country from 1–2190m (3–7200ft). The plant dries black and is easily recognisable in this condition. Widespread in western, central and eastern Kenya; all regions except Mpwapwa, Kondoa (Tanzania); all regions of Uganda; also widespread in tropical and Southern Africa.

O. johnstonii Plate 80

A low trailing plant, sometimes shrubby at base, with ascending stems and ovate to elliptic leaves, acute at the apex, rounded or cuneate at base. The flowers are pedicillate, white, three to five together with a long peduncle. Corolla tube *c.* 1.25–1.4mm long, limb *c.* 2mm across. It is locally common in dry forest areas, wooded grassland and grassland near water. Altitude range 350–2000m (1150–6500ft). Especially near Nairobi National Park, and Ngong (Kenya);

Maasai, Tanga, Mbeya, Iringa, Songea (Tanzania); Uganda, no record. Elsewhere, not known.

O. monanthos A creeping, mat-forming herb rooting at the nodes with lanceolate to oblong leaves and solitary or paired pink-purple flowers on long pedicels; corolla tube 1–3mm (*c.* $\frac{1}{8}$in) long; 4mm ($\frac{1}{6}$in) across, white, bluish, pink or violet, with a densely hairy throat. Locally common and widespread in montane grassland, especially along path sides and often on shallow soil, altitude range 1350–3500m (4400–11,800ft). Found on Elgon, the Cheranganis, Tinderet, Aberdares and Mt Kenya, also recorded in Kajiado and Nairobi (Kenya); Maasai (Ngorongoro Crater), Arusha (Ngurdoto Crater), Moshi (Tanzania); Karamoja – Mt Debasien, Mbale – Mt Elgon (Uganda); also Ethiopia.

O. scopulorum An erect, much branched, glabrescent, shrubby, short-lived perennial or annual, with linear leaves and small cymes of white, lilac or bluish-pink flowers, corolla tube 2.5mm ($\frac{1}{10}$in) long; limb *c.* 2.5mm ($\frac{1}{10}$in) across. It is widespread and common in grassland at medium altitudes from 900–2520m (2950–8250ft). Recorded in Tinderet, Mau, Loita, Nanyuki, Nandi Hills, Aberdares, Kitale, Rift Valley and Narok (Kenya); lake areas, Maasai, Tabora, Mpwapwa, Kondea; Uganda, no record; also Rwanda.

O. wiedemannii An erect much branched pubescent annual or weak perennial herb or wiry shrub with linear leaves and pale pink or purple flowers in terminal clusters; corolla tube 2.5mm ($\frac{1}{10}$in) long. One of the commonest *Oldenlandia* species and found in dry bushland on shallow rocky soil. Altitude range from 340–2400m (1100–7900ft). Rift Valley, Machakos, Magadi and Kajiado (Kenya); lake areas, Maasai, Tanga, Mpwapwa, Kondoa, Mbeya, Iringa (Tanzania); Uganda and elsewhere, not known.

Otomeria elatior **Plate 761**

Uncommon, with scarlet flowers 17–27mm ($\frac{5}{8}$–1in) long, (the flowers being more scarlet than shown in the illustration). Altitude range 1000–1600m (3280–5250ft). Found in swampy places in wooded grassland in western Kenya; lake areas, Tabora, Mbeya, Iringa, Songea (Tanzania); all regions (Uganda); also in Sudan to Zimbabwe, Mozambique.

O. oculata **Plate 762**

A herb with many erect, unbranched stems and ovate, lanceolate leaves. The pink, or sometimes white, corolla, 18–32mm ($\frac{3}{4}$–1$\frac{1}{4}$in) long, has a dark centre; the tube is narrow and cylindrical and the spreading lobes 5–10mm ($\frac{1}{5}$–$\frac{2}{5}$in) long. It is uncommon and found in dry rocky grassland in such districts as Baringo, Nanyuki, Embu and Machakos (Kenya) at altitudes 530–1650m (1750–5400ft); Tanzania, no record; Karamoja (Uganda); also Ethiopia.

Pavetta abyssinica **Plate 81**

A forest undershrub up to 2.5m (8ft) high. Leaves glossy, elliptic, 8.75cm (3$\frac{1}{2}$in) long and 5cm (2in) wide, hispidulous-pubescent beneath. Flowers in corymbose inflorescences on flowering shoots longer than the leaves. Corolla tube mauve outside, white within 8–22mm (*c.* $\frac{1}{3}$–1in) long; lobe 4–10mm ($\frac{1}{6}$–$\frac{2}{5}$in) long, style 2.5cm (1in) long. Found in Highland forests, altitude range 1050–2500m (3450–8200ft), throughout Kenya; Northern Province, Tanga, Central Province, Morogoro, Mbeya (Tanzania); Northern Province, Fort Portal, Eastern Province (Uganda). One of seventy species in East Africa.

NB i) There are four recorded synonyms: *P. kenyensis, P. maitlandtii, P. silvicola, P. trichotropis.*

ii) The leaves are usually black-spotted, the corolla usually four-merous, white or cream, with a long slender tube in *Pavetta*.

P. stenosepala   Plate 82

An upright straggling or creeping shrub with a red peeling bark. Leaves crowded at the ends of branches with bacterial nodules scattered along the veins. Flowers in terminal corymbs, white. The corolla tube 1–2cm ($\frac{2}{3}$–$\frac{4}{5}$in) long tapering from base to throat 0.5–1.5mm; lobes 3–5.5mm ($\frac{1}{8}$–$\frac{1}{5}$in) long. Found in coastal regions and coastal hinterland, altitude range 1–1300m (3–4250ft) (occasionally to 1800m (5900ft)). Kenya, Tanzania and Zanzibar; not known elsewhere.

Pentanisia ouranogyne   Plate 834

A rhizomatous low-growing herbaceous plant with linear to lanceolate leaves. The flowers are bright blue on terminal corymbs and, at first sight, remind one of a brilliant blue *Verbena*. Corolla tube *c.* 7mm ($\frac{1}{4}$in). It is often seen along roadsides and in other areas of disturbed ground such as the surrounds of hut sites. It thrives in dry country, especially where a small amount of rainfall run off can augment the normal water supply. Widespread in Kenya favouring altitudes 550–2400m (1800–7875ft); Shinyanga, Arusha, Iringa (Tanzania); Acholi, Karamoja, Mbale (Uganda); also Sudan and Ethiopia.

PENTAS

Tall herbs or softly woody shrubs, corolla tubular, fruit a capsule. Twenty-three species in East Africa.

Pentas lanceolata   Plate 763

An erect branched woody shrub with ovate-lanceolate leaves and mauve to white flowers 3mm ($\frac{1}{8}$in) long; corolla *c.* 15mm ($\frac{3}{8}$in) across, corolla tube 2–4cm ($\frac{4}{5}$–1$\frac{1}{2}$in) long. It grows at forest edges at 1520–3000m (5000–10,000ft). The flower head is usually wider, flatter and more densely packed than in our photograph. A very variable species found in all moist upland parts of Kenya. Maasai, Arusha – Mt Meru, Kilimanjaro – Marangu (Tanzania); Acholi, Karamoja – Mt Moroto (Uganda); also Yemen, Sudan, Ethiopia, and eastern Zaire.

P. lanceolata var. nemorosa   Plate 764

A variety of *P. lanceolata* with smaller leaves, six to eleven lateral nerves on each side, and corolla lobes 6.5–8mm ($\frac{1}{4}$–$\frac{1}{3}$in) long; usually an erect or straggling herb to 1.5m (50in) tall, stems sparsely to fairly densely hairy. Leaves ovate or ovate-lanceolate to elliptic-lanceolate, glabrescent to hairy. Flowers in few many-flowered heads, deep pink. Found in edges of paths and glades in secondary evergreen forest and in grassy places; altitude range 1380–2300m (4525–7550ft). Mathews Range, Ngong Hills, Muranga, Nairobi – Kiambu Road (Kenya); Moshi (Tanzania); Uganda, no record; also in Ethiopia.

P. longiflora   Plate 83

It has leaves paired or in whorls; leaf blades lanceolate or rarely ovate-lanceolate, acute at apex, narrowed at base, glabrous to velvety or pubescent, often ferruginous. Flower white to cream; corolla tube 25–40mm (1–1$\frac{3}{8}$in) long. It has a loose inflorescence of several separate corymbs. Locally common throughout Kenya in dry wooded grassland often with *Combretum* from 1000–2400m (3000–7900ft) (Kenya); Maasai, Tanga, Tabora, Mbeya, Iringa (Tanzania); all regions except northern (Uganda); also in Rwanda, Burundi, Zaire, Malawi.

P. parvifolia
Plate 518

An erect shrub with elliptic lanceolate leaves and usually with dense (though sometimes loose) corymbs of bright red flowers c. 5cm (2in) across with long thin corolla tubes 8–14mm ($\frac{1}{3}$–$\frac{5}{8}$in) long. It is common in dry bushland and wooded grassland at 1–2400m (3–c. 8000ft) and can be seen growing in the garden around Ngulia Lodge in Tsavo West, transplanted from the wild, and also in mass on the edges of the lava belts in that Park (Kenya); Pare, Uzaramo, Lindi, Zanzibar (Tanzania); Karamoja – Mt Moroto (Uganda); also southern Ethiopia.

P. zanzibarica
Plate 765

A herb or shrubby herb, or rarely a shrub, 0.3–2.6m (1–8ft) tall with one to two stems (sometimes up to six) from a somewhat woody rootstock; stems greenish or purple tinged, mostly strict and unbranched, often densely hairy above. Leaf blades lanceolate to ovate or elliptic, acute at the apex, cuneate at the base, hairy on both surfaces; 4–14.5cm (1$\frac{3}{4}$–6in) long, 1.4–6cm ($\frac{1}{2}$–2$\frac{3}{8}$in) wide. Inflorescence 2–6.5cm ($\frac{4}{5}$–2$\frac{3}{8}$in) across lax or somewhat globose, terminal and axillary. Flowers white, pink or generally lilac, bluish mauve or in one form bright crimson red 5–9mm ($\frac{1}{5}$–$\frac{3}{8}$in) long. Calyx tube hairy. Found in dry grassland, forest glades and edges, open woodland especially in the Rift Valley. Altitude range 0–2600m (0–8500ft) and recorded in Tinderet Mau, Loita Hills, Aberdares, Kitale, Narok, Rift Valley, Nairobi and Kajiado (Kenya); all regions except Tabora (Tanzania); western region, Buganda (Uganda); also in eastern Zaire.

NB There are five distinct varieties of *P. zanzibarica* identified in Uganda, Elgon and Tanzania. More detail is available in *FTEA*, Vol. *Rubiaceae*.

PYSCHOTRIA (including **Grumilea**)

This is a large genus of shrubs or small trees with eighty-one species in East Africa. Flowers small, white or cream; fruit a drupe containing one or two one-seeded pips.

Psychotria amboniana
Plate 84

A shrub 1–3m (3–10ft) tall; young stems mostly pale, greyish white, often chestnut when older with grooved, slightly peeling epidermis, glabrous (see note). Leaf blades oblong-elliptic, narrowly to broadly elliptic, narrowly obovate and even more or less linear-lanceolate up to 8cm (3$\frac{1}{4}$in) long, acute to shortly acuminate at apex, very narrowly cuneate at base, glabrous on both surfaces. Flowers five-merous in many-flowered, rather congested, glabrous panicles or rarely subumbellate. Corolla white or cream glabrous outside, lobes narrowly oblong, 3–4mm ($\frac{1}{8}$–$\frac{1}{6}$in) long; tube 4–6mm ($\frac{1}{6}$–$\frac{1}{4}$in) long. Altitude range 0–300m (0–c. 1000ft). Found in coastal forest and derived thickets and scrub, grassland with scattered trees in the coastal areas of Kenya and Tanzania from Lamu to Pangani and Uzaramo.

NB There are two varieties of the species: var. *amboniana* young stems and twigs glabrous and var. *velutina* in which they are pubescent. The latter appears to have an upper altitude limit of c. 100m (328ft).

70. Caprifoliaceae

Shrubs or small trees, rarely herbs; leaves opposite, simple or compound; stipules absent or interpetiolar; inflorescence cymose; flowers bisexual, regular or irregular, four- to five-merous; calyx imbricate or open; corolla imbricate with a short or long tube; stamens epipetalous, alternating with petals; ovary inferior with one-numerous ovules per loculus; fruit a fleshy berry, drupe or achene. Only one native species in East Africa (*Sambucus*).

Lonicera japonica   Plate 85
This is a garden honeysuckle, which has escaped and grows in the wild. The photograph was taken on the South Kinangop (Kenya). Both the Herbarium, at Nairobi and Kew would appreciate specimens, as no records of it in the wild exist.

Sambucus africana   Plate 227
A fleshy herb which grows to 5m (16ft) which is allied to the Elder of European hedgerows although its closest relative grows in the Himalayas. Its leaflets are obovate, large, sharply serrate, acute, acuminate, asymmetric or irregularly adhering to the petiole and covered with very fine down. The petals of the flower *c.* 1cm (⅜in) across are white, often a bright creamy white, the calyx minutely lobed. The fruit is black and edible. It is found at 1830–3140m (6000–10,300ft) in the bamboo and montane forest zone, especially where bamboo has died. Elgon, Mau escarpment, Aberdares and Mt Kenya (Kenya); Embazai Crater in Maasai (Tanzania); Elgon (Uganda); elsewhere, no record.

71. Dipsacaceae

Annual or perennial herbs, leaves opposite or verticillate, exstipulate. Inflorescence a head, flowers bisexual, zygomorphic, protandreous; epicalyx often present, corolla tube four to five lobed, stamens usually four, epipetalous, anthers two-celled, ovary more or less inferior single-loculed, sessile with one solitary pendulous ovule. Fruit, an achene, often enclosed in epicalyx. Eight species in four genera in East Africa; occurring only above 900m (*c.* 3000ft).

Dipsacus pinnatifidus   Plate 86
Erect herb to 3m (10ft), leaves connate at base, ovate to lanceolate, serrate toothed or pinnatipartite; involucral bracts linear-lanceolate, stiff and spiny. Flowers white 2.5–4cm (1–1⅝in) across; 6–15mm (¼–⅜in) long. Found in the upper forest and lower alpine zones, commonly by streamsides in the heath (*Erica*) woodland; altitude range 2000–3950m (6560–13,100ft). Northern Frontier areas, Elgon, Mt Kenya, Kajiado, Mau and Aberdares (Kenya); Maasai (Tanzania); northern, western regions (Uganda); also in Sudan, Ethiopia, Zaire.

Pterocephalus frutescens   Plate 766
A trailing shrub, leaves linear-lanceolate, entire or variously dentate, or divided; involucral bracts ovate, acute and pubescent. Flowers pinkish-red, pubescent outside. Corolla tube five-lobed with marginal flowers 20mm (⅜in) long. Calyx with

long plumose bristles about as long as the corolla. Flower head flat or globose 2.5–4.5cm (1–1¾in) across. Found amongst grasses on eroded ground and on stony soils, on dry exposed hillsides; altitude range 1500–2800m (4950–9200ft). Aberdares, Mau, Narok, Rift Valley, Kajiado and Chyulu Hills (Kenya); Maasai (Tanzania); Uganda, not known. Only species in East Africa. Also in Ethiopia, Somalia.

Scabiosa austro-africana   Plate 87
A perennial herb, from 0.15–1.2m (½–3½ft) high, with erect, pubescent or glabrous stems. Leaves markedly heterophyllous, glabrous or pubescent, the radical ones sessile, toothed or lobed in the lower part, lanceolate often narrowing to the midrib. Lower stem leaves more deeply lobed, with the lobes narrowly linear, rarely toothed or entire. Upper stem leaves smaller, deeply dissected with linear segments. Inflorescence of one to several heads 2–4cm (¾–1¾in) across. Calyx small, pilose with bristles 5–10mm (¼–⅜in) long. Corolla 0.5–2cm (¼–¾in) long, white, rarely pinkish or tinged with mauve, larger and unequally lobed in the marginal flowers, smaller and more equally lobed in the inner flowers. Found in upland grassland and open bushland; altitude range 1200–1900m, possibly to 2500m (3800–6250ft, 8200ft) in Machakos, Kajiado and Chyulu Hills (Kenya); all regions (Tanzania); Uganda, no record; also in Rwanda, Zaire, south to Zimbabwe, Mozambique and southern Africa.

S. columbaria   Plate 767
An erect or ascending annual or perennial herb; stem puberulous or glabrous; leaves entire or various divided (in the Kenya sp.); heads terminal, flat or globose, receptacle hairy; calyx of five bristles in fruit 3–6mm (⅛–¼in) long; epicalyx present, eight-grooved, winged in fruit. The rootstock is thick, with a rosette of spathulate, entire or divided leaves involucral bracts linear-lanceolate, pubescent. The corolla pinkish-mauve, tube five-lobed 5–20mm (¼–¾in) long. Altitude range 2100–4100m (6900–13,450ft). Found in Erica shrub on rocky slopes and streamsides, in Tarchonanthus – Leleshwa and Philippia bushland and forest clearings; Elgon, Cheranganis, Mau, Mt Kenya, the Aberdares and in Kitale, Rift Valley and Nanyuki (Kenya); Maasai (Tanzania); all regions except Buganda (Uganda); also Ethiopia, southern Africa.

NB The above two species are the only Scabious recorded in East Africa.

72. Compositae (Asteraceae)
THE DAISY FAMILY

The daisies form one of the largest families, found throughout the world. It consists mainly of herbs or shrublets but includes a few real trees, among them Brachylaena huillensis, found in the forests around Nairobi, the wood from which is used by the Akamba wood carvers. The flowers are small (florets) and are grouped together (hence Compositae) in heads surrounded by involucral bracts. These flower heads may easily be mistaken for flowers, especially when the outer florets are flattened, forming rays, the involucral bracts resembling a calyx and the rays the petals. The true calyx may be absent or reduced to scales, or turned into bristles or hairs – the 'pappus'. The corolla may be tubular or split down one side and flattened – 'ligulate'. The anthers are united into a tube, up through which the style grows, pushing out the pollen. The ovary is inferior and produces a dry, single-seeded fruit called an achene. There are nearly 877 species of Compositae in East Africa, belonging to some 125 genera. In so large a family it helps to be able to recognize the tribes. Four of the most important of these are:

a) *Vernonieae* in which florets are all tubular – so that there are no rays – are nearly always purple, and their involucral bracts are in many rows, including *Vernonia, Bothriocline, Ethulia, Gutenbergia*.

b) *Heliantheae* in which the leaves are opposite and the involucral bracts in several rows, have yellow flowers. Ray florets are usually present and the pappus formed of bristles, including *Aspilia, Bidens, Guizotia, Tagetes*.

c) *Senecioneae* which have the involucral bracts in one row with only a few very much reduced bracts outside it, including *Senecio, Crassocephalum, Emilia, Gynura, Euryops, Kleinia, Notonia, Cinetaria*.

d) *Lactuceae* have strap-shaped florets, usually yellow or blue. A milky latex is present, including *Lactuca, Launea, Taraxacum, Reichardia, Sonebus*.

Thirty-nine of the species in twenty genera are alien to East Africa.

Acanthospermum hispidum
Plate 19

An erect, much-branched, tomentose and minutely glandular annual with rhomboid-elliptic leaves and subsessile heads of small yellow flowers 3mm (⅛in) across, disseminules (enlarged bracts enclosing the achenes) boldly spiny with two apical diverging spines larger than the rest. A common weed of cultivation; altitude range 190–1890m (630–6300ft) in the warmer parts of upland Kenya and recorded in western Kenya, Kisii, Machakos and Kajiado (Kenya); all regions except lake areas (Tanzania); northern region (Uganda); elsewhere, not as yet known. NB First recorded in Kenya in 1945 and spreading. One of two species in East Africa; both alien. Not indigenous but introduced from America.

Anisoppapus africanus
Plate 350

A perennial rhizomatous plant with ascending stems and broadly ovate crenate leaves. The yellow, star-like flowers *c*. 1cm (⅜in) across, are slightly cupped and borne at the end of long flexible stalks. One of eleven species in East Africa. Common in dry upland areas at 1520–2139m (5000–7000ft). Recorded in Elgon, Mau, Kitale, Kisii, Nairobi and Kajiado districts (Kenya); lake areas, Maasai, Tabora, Mbeya, Iringa (Tanzania); western region, Buganda (Uganda); southern Sudan, Ethiopia, Rwanda, Zaire, Zambia, Malawi, Mozambique.

Anthemis tigrensis
Plate 88

An annual or short-lived perennial with spreading branches. Its downy, twice-pinnatisect leaves are oblong in outline with the ultimate segments white. The rays of florets are also white. Flower head, including rays, *c*. 3cm (1⅛in) in diameter. It is fairly common along roadsides and in disturbed places at the upper forest limits and in the lower alpine zone from 1750–4200m (5800–13,800ft) but is rather rare below 2400m (7900ft). The only species in East Africa. Recorded in Elgon, Mau, Kitale, Kisu, Nairobi, Kajiado (Kenya); Maasai – northern volcanoes (Tanzania); eastern region (Uganda); also Ethiopia.

Aspilia mossambicensis
Plate 351

A much-branched herb or shrub with rough, elliptic-lanceolate, to ovate, opposite leaves. Its yellow flower heads *c*. 2cm (⅝in) across, are solitary or grouped in loose terminal cymes. It is common all over East Africa at 5–2130m (15–7000ft) except in the driest areas. If not controlled by burning it grows to a large size and may scramble over neighbouring bushes. One of thirteen species in East Africa. Found throughout Kenya; all regions except western (Tanzania); all regions of Uganda; also Sudan, Ethiopia, Somalia south to Zimbabwe, Mozambique.

A. pluriseta Differs from *A. mossambicensis* in obscure details of the inflorescence. It is less common but widespread at altitudes 1050–2250m (3500–7250ft) in Kenya; lake areas, Maasai, Tanga, Tabora, Mbeya, Iringa (Tanzania); all regions except western (Uganda); also Sudan, Ethiopia, Somalia south to Zimbabwe, Mozambique.

Athroisma gracile Similar to *A. psyllioides* but distinguished by a tendency to produce thread-like leaves and with the involucral bracts hardly fringed at margin; the achenes smooth and less than 1mm ($\frac{1}{25}$in). Flower heads 10–13mm ($\frac{2}{5}$–$\frac{1}{2}$in) across. It is found in almost the same habitat but often in rocky soils and in more northern localities; altitude range 750–2000m (2460–6560ft). One of five species in East Africa. Narok, Rift Valley, Magadi, Nanyuki, Machakos and Nairobi (Kenya); lake areas, Maasai, Tabora, Mbeya, Iringa (Tanzania); western and eastern regions (Uganda); also in southern Ethiopia.

A. psyllioides   **Plate 89**
An annual or perennial herb with short, linear to lanceolate, entire or toothed, leaves. Inflorescence of crowded, sessile, many-flowered corymbose heads 10–13mm ($\frac{2}{5}$–$\frac{1}{2}$in) across, with short peduncles and long tubercular achenes. The inflorescence is pink or white and the involucral bracts conspicuously fringed at apex. It is the commonest species of *Athroisma* occurring in grassland, particularly along roadsides through black cotton soils; altitude range 750–2000m (2460–6560ft). Recorded in Narok, Rift Valley, Magadi, Nanyuki, Machakos and Nairobi (Kenya); lake areas, Maasai, Tabora, Mbeya, Iringa (Tanzania); western and eastern regions (Uganda); also in southern Ethiopia.

Berkheya spekeana   **Plate 352**
An erect annual plant with bright yellow flowers c. 4cm (1$\frac{1}{2}$in) across, borne singly or in loose clusters. The leaves are oblong, pinnate and spiny and white-woolly below. One of four species in East Africa. A common plant at altitudes 1800–3000m (6000–10,000ft) in most districts but especially in western Kenya; lake areas, Maasai, Tabora (Tanzania); all regions of Uganda; also Sudan, Ethiopia, Rwanda, Zaire.

BIDENS

This genus has sixty-eight species recorded in East Africa: they are woody herbs rather than shrubs, always with very soft wood. The genus has a wide habitat range from coastal areas to the higher altitudes. The flowers are yellow or rarely white; the pappus consists of a few stiff spines often becoming barbed.

Bidens biternata Tends to take the place of *B. pilosa* in western Kenya. It is more hairy and tends to have more yellow in the flowers, but it is still the detestable Black Jack. Flower head: c. 2cm ($\frac{4}{5}$in) across. 5–2300m (16–7550ft). It is recorded in North-east Frontier, Central Province, Kajiado, Machakos, Coast (Kenya); lake areas, Maasai, Mbeya, Iringa, Songea (Tanzania); northern and eastern regions (Uganda); also in Sudan, Ethiopia, Somalia, south to Zimbabwe, Mozambique.

B. cinerea (B. lineata) A near relative of *B. schimperi*. It also has solitary yellow-rayed flower heads *c.* 20mm (⅘in) across and is found in the same districts. Leaf segments are linear to oblong-ovate and the heads nearly always solitary. In *B. schimperi* the leaf segments are usually oblong, obtuse. Altitude range 1–2000m (3–6560ft). Nairobi, Machakos, Kajiado and Magadi (Kenya); Maasai (Tanzania); Uganda and elsewhere, no record.

B. grantii
Plate 353

An erect annual or short-lived perennial with twice pinnatisect leaves terminating in lanceolate to oblong segments. Flower heads 4cm (1⅜in) across yellow in loose terminal dichasia. Pappus bristles may be present and long or virtually absent. Found in highland grasslands; altitude range 1950–2430m (6500–8100ft) and only recorded rarely in Molo, Ngong and Chyulu Hills (Kenya); lake areas, Maasai, Tabora (Tanzania); northern and eastern regions (Uganda); also in Zaire.

B. kilimandscharica
Plate 354

An erect short-lived perennial shrub, glabrous or hairy, much-branched above; leaves once or twice pinnatisect, rarely more or less simple, with ovate, serrate lobes. Heads in loose terminal dichasia. Flower heads yellow 40mm (1⅜in) across including rays. A very variable species which can flower in its first year. It may be mistaken for *B. coriacea* but the latter has glabrescent, simple, serrate leaves with sparsely-branched erect stems. Found in upland forest edges, especially in drier districts and on stony soils; altitude range 1100–2700m (3600–8850ft). Cheranganis, Tinderet, Mau, Mt Kenya, Aberdares, Rift Valley and Machakos (Kenya); Maasai, Tabora (Tanzania); northern region (Uganda); also in Malawi.

B. kirkii var. flagellata
Plate 355

An erect glabrescent perennial from a woody rootstock, bearing leaves divided into linear or filamentous segments and loose terminal corymbs of yellow heads 2cm (⅘in) across. Common in higher altitude grasslands, 1500–3000m (5000–10,000ft); especially on thin soils and recorded in Cheranganis, Tinderet, Mau, Aberdares, Mt Kenya, Kitale, Rift Valley and Machakos (Kenya); Tanzania, no record; northern region (Uganda); also in southern Ethiopia, Zaire.

B. pilosa
Plate 90

An erect annual, often branching above, with pinnate mostly trifoliolate leaves and white-rayed or rayless flowers 1cm (⅜in) across. The common 'Black Jack' weed of gardens and the most common species of *Bidens*, it nearly always grows on poor or exhausted soils from 400–2400m (1300–7900ft) and is widespread in Kenya, Tanzania and Uganda; also throughout tropical Africa.

B. schimperi
A straggling annual (though sometimes found erect) with pinnatifid leaves. Solitary yellow-rayed flower heads 3–4cm (1⅛–1⅜in) across. Often found in the Nairobi, Machakos, Magadi and Kajiado districts in Kenya, from 300–2400m (1000–7900ft). All regions (Tanzania); Uganda, no record; also Sudan, Ethiopia, south to Zimbabwe, Mozambique.

B. taitensis
Plate 356

An erect, perennial shrub to 3m (10ft) high, stems usually semi-woody at the base. Two to three leaves, pinnatisect or tripartite with deeply trifid segments, ovate in outline, *c.* 14cm (5½in) long, including petiole, lobes oval, the terminal ones lanceolate, incise-dentate. Involucre green, ray florets golden yellow 2.5cm (1in) long, disc florets yellow. Found in montane heavily grazed grassland and at the edge of clearings; altitude range 1080–2700m (3600–9000ft) from Taita Hills and along the Rongai route to Kilimanjaro (Kenya and Tanzania).

Bothriocline calycina (*Erlangea calycina*)   **Plate 676**
A rhizomatous tomentose perennial herb with sessile oblong to lanceolate leaves and solitary purple heads over 15mm (⅝in) across. All the florets are tubular and the pappus of two to twenty very caducous stiff bristles. Locally common in disturbed grassland; altitude range 1350–2400m (4500–8000ft) in Tinderet, Magadi, Machakos, Nairobi and Kajiado (Kenya); Maasai (Tanzania); Uganda and elsewhere, not known. Thirty-five species in East Africa, closely related to Vernonia.

B. fusca   **Plate 573**
Very similar to *B. tomentosa* but has rather more purple flowers c. 5mm (c. ⅛in) across. It is common on roadsides and in disturbed places in the higher forest zones, almost always above 2590m (8500ft). Widespread except coast (Kenya); Maasai (Tanzania); northern region (Uganda); elsewhere, not known.

B. tomentosa (*Erlangea tomentosa: B. longipes*)   **Plate 574**
An erect shrub with lanceolate-elliptic serrate leaves and terminal corymbs of violet-coloured heads c. 6mm (¼in) across. It is common on the edges of forest over most of Kenya from Kisii and Mumias in the west to Kajiado and Nyambeni in the east in the altitude range 1300–3000m (4250–9850ft) although seldom found above 2440m (8000ft), (Kenya); Tanzania, no record; all regions except Buganda (Uganda); also Rwanda, Burundi, Zaire.

CARDUUS
Herbs with prickly leaves and involucral bracts. Florets purple or white, all tubular; the pappus is mainly white and falls off whole as one piece. Nine species in East Africa, all above 1500m (c. 5000ft).

Carduus chamaecephalus   **Plate 575**
A prostrate spiny rosette plant with thick fleshy roots and pinnatifid leaves which are tightly pressed to the ground. Purple flower heads c. 3mm (⅛in) across appear in the centre of the rosette. It is common in short alpine and subalpine grassland at 3050–3500m (10,000–11,500ft). All regions except Northern Frontier and coast (Kenya); Mts Kilimanjaro, Meru (Tanzania); Mt Elgon (Uganda); also Sudan, Ethiopia, Zaire.

C. keniensis   **Plate 576**
A spiny rosette plant with large pinnate oblong leaves which grows to a height of 1m (3ft). The flowers are borne on a single central stem as a spiny apical panicle, pinkish in colour c. 10cm (4in) across. This is a conspicuous plant in tussocky grassland in the moorland areas of Elgon, the Aberdares, and Mt Kenya at 3050–4050m (10,000–13,300ft) (Kenya); Mts Kilimanjaro, Meru (Tanzania); eastern region (Mt Elgon) (Uganda); elsewhere not known.

C. kikuyorum   **Plate 577**
An erect, tall, pubescent herb with leaves more or less oblong, parallel-sided, pappus over 15mm (⅝in) long, with clusters of sessile terminal spiny heads with white to pale purple flowers c. 15mm (⅝in) across. Very similar to *C. nyassanus* which has elliptic to oblong, pinnatifid leaves. *C. kikuyorum* has outer phyllaries less than half as long as innermost, and not obscuring the bases of the median series, inner phyllaries mostly with a lanceolate or linear but not oblong apex, and

all others with a short apical spine less than 5mm (¼in) long. *C. nyassanus* is almost the exact opposite – outer phyllaries longer than innermost and obscuring the median series; innermost with a long, more than 5mm (¼in), apical spine. *C. nyassanus* occasionally grades into *C. kikuyorum*. Altitude range 3000–3800m (9850–12,450ft). Elgon, Cheranganis, Mau, Aberdares, Mt Kenya, Kajiado (Kenya); Maasai, Morogoro, Mbeya, Iringa (Tanzania); western region (Uganda); also Rwanda, Burundi, Zaire.

C. millefolius Very similar to *C. keniensis* but has much narrower linear leaves. The spines are shorter and finer than in *C. keniensis* and purplish in colour. It is also found in similar districts and habitats but usually in wet soil by streamsides. Each flower head *c.* 12mm (*c.* ½in) across. Elgon, Mt Kenya, Aberdares (Kenya); Tanzania, Uganda and elsewhere not known.

Cineraria deltoides (*C. grandiflora*)   **Plate 357**
A pubescent erect or sometimes supported herb with petiolate, auriculate, sub-orbicular to triangular, serrate leaves and a terminal corymb of rayed yellow heads 14–18mm (⅜–¾in) across including rays. A common species of roadsides, forest edges and cliffs; altitude range 2000–3400m (6500–11,000ft). The higher the altitude in which it grows the larger the head and the broader and blacker the achenes. Recorded in Elgon, Cheranganis, Kitale, Mau, Aberdares, Mt Kenya, Tinderet and Kajiado (Kenya); all regions except lake areas and Songea (Tanzania); all regions except Buganda (Uganda); also Sudan, Ethiopia, Rwanda, Zaire, Zambia, Zimbabwe, Mozambique. Probably Malawi.

Cirsium vulgare   **Plate 677**
An erect, often robust, annual with stalkless, oblong to elliptical, deeply pinnatifid leaves. Its large solitary purple heads *c.* 3cm (1½in) across have spreading bracts. It is a weed in arable land, especially in wheatfields, and is not a true native but was introduced from Europe. It is found at altitudes of 1830–2440m (6000–8000ft) in Kenya. Tanzania and Uganda, no record; also Ethiopia. Two other species in East Africa (one alien).

CONYZA

Has alternate leaves and dull yellowish flowers; pappus a single row of bristles. Twenty-two species in East Africa.

Conyza hypoleuca   **Plate 358**
An erect shrub often white-woolly on stems and under leaves with oblanceolate cob-webby leaves and small terminal groups of yellow heads 6mm (¼in) across; whole inflorescence 60–90mm (2⅖–3⅗in). Locally common in dry montane bush; altitude range 2000–2700m (6560–8850ft). Tinderet, Mau, Aberdares and Narok (Kenya); Tanzania, no record; northern region (Uganda); also in Ethiopia.

C. newii   **Plate 359**
A branched shrub (sometimes annual) sparsely tomentose on the stem and glabrous on the elliptic sharply serrate leaves which seldom clasp the stem at base. The heads, often three to four in number, are bright yellow 8mm (⅓in) across. Common in rocky shallow soils within the montane forest areas; altitude range 1800–3000m (5900–9500ft), especially on escarpment slopes in Cheranganis, Tinderet, Mau, Aberdares, Kisii, Rift Valley, Machakos and Kajiado (Kenya); Maasai, Tanga, Mpwapwa, Kondoa, Morogoro (Tanzania); western, eastern regions (Uganda); elsewhere, not known.

COMPOSITAE

NB It can be distinguished from *C. pallidiflora*, which is similar to *C. newii*, in that the leaves of *C. pallidiflora* clasp the stem at the base and the bisexual (central) florets number less than ten (more than twenty in *C. newii*). The heads in *C. newii* are also a much brighter yellow.

C. pyrrhopappa var. oblongifolia
Plate 228

An erect, woody herb or shrub with oblanceolate, usually remotely dentate leaves, narrowing gradually to the base, and dense terminal corymbs 4cm (1¾in) across of pale whitish heads 6mm (¼in) across. This variety is a large shrub of dry, rocky hills; altitude range 1200–2400m (4000–8000ft) but the more common form is to be found in disturbed upland bushland. Found in Cheranganis, Tinderet, western Kenya, Narok, Baringo, Machakos, Nairobi, Kajiado (Kenya); lake areas, Maasai, Tanga, Mpwapwa, Kondoa, Mbeya, Iringa (Tanzania); all regions of Uganda; also Ethiopia, Zaire, Malawi, northern Nigeria, Angola.

C. stricta
Plate 229

An erect pubescent annual with linear to oblanceolate, entire to pinnatifid leaves and a terminal corymb of many-flowered small pale yellow heads 4mm (⅛in) across. Common in disturbed places in dry grassland; altitude range 900–2300m (2950–7550ft); rare above 2000m (6560ft). Widespread throughout Kenya; all regions except Mpwapwa, Kondoa, Songea (Tanzania); all regions except Buganda (Uganda); also recorded in Sudan, Ethiopia, Zaire, Malawi, Mozambique.

CRASSOCEPHALUM

Closely related to Senecio, but ray florets absent and there is an abruptly narrowed pubescent apex to the stigmas. Thirteen species in East Africa.

Crassocephalum mannii (*Solanecio mannii*)
Plate 360

A much-branched, soft wooded shrub or tree which grows to 7.6m (25ft) high. Its stem is green throughout its length and its leaves are serrate, oblong-elliptic, up to 10cm (4in) wide and 45cm (18in) long with the apex acuminate and the base cuneate. The small, yellow, unpleasantly-scented flowers are all of one kind forming a head of dense panicled cymes, in a terminal inflorescence up to 60cm (2ft) long. It is widespread throughout Kenya in scrub in wetter areas at altitudes 1220–2440m (4000–8000ft) and is often used to demarcate small holdings and even to support banana trees which are heavy with fruit; all regions of Tanzania and Uganda; also Ethiopia, Rwanda, Burundi, Zaire, Zambia, Malawi, Zimbabwe.

C. montuosum
Plate 361

An erect, woody annual or weak perennial with ovate to elliptic, simple to basally pinnatifid, hairless leaves. The flowers are in tight terminal clusters of pale yellow heads c. 6mm (c. ¼in) across. It is common in clearings in montane forest over most of Kenya at altitudes of 2130–2900m (7000–9500ft); all regions except Mpwapwa, Kondoa, Songea (Tanzania); all regions of Uganda; also Sudan, Ethiopia south to Zimbabwe, Mozambique.

C.×picridifolium
Plate 362

This name has been given to a confusing group of plants found in upland areas of East Africa between 1050 and 2550m (2500–8500ft). The group probably arose through hybridization between *C. vitellinum* and another species, *C. paludum* (which grows in swamps, when the habitat was disturbed by forest clearance for agriculture.

164

C. sarcobasis   Plate 678
A pubescent to glabrescent annual with ovate to elliptic, entire or pinnatifid leaves and long pedunculate purple or red heads. It is rather variable and may have solitary to corymbose heads. Size of flower head c. 10mm (⅜in) across. Found in disturbed often cultivated ground; altitude range 1100–2100m (3600–6900ft) and is most common in the west of Kenya at higher altitudes. Recorded in Elgon, Cheranganis, Tinderet, Mau, Aberdares, Mt Kenya, Kitale, western Kenya and Kisii (Kenya); all regions (Tanzania); eastern region (Uganda); also in Sudan, Ethiopia, Burundi, Zambia, Mozambique, probably Zimbabwe.

C. vitellinum   Plate 423
A trailing perennial herb with ovate, often auriculate leaves and solitary long pedunculate, orange-yellow flower heads 1.8cm (c. ⅜in) across. It is common in grassy clearings in upland forest and woodland; altitude range 1050–2550m (3500–8500ft) throughout Kenya; lake areas, Tabora, Mbeya, Iringa (Tanzania); all regions of Uganda; also Rwanda, Burundi, Zaire, Zambia.

NB Certain *Crassocephalum* have now been reclassified in *Solanecio*. Also closely related to *Senecio* and *Kleinia*, they differ in minute technical details. Thirteen species in East Africa. *C. mannii* (Plate 360) becomes *Solanecio mannii*.

ECHINOPS
Easily recognized stiff plants with spiny leaves and bracts and numerous small single-flowered heads (capitula) which are densely crowded into globose 'heads of heads'. Twelve species in East Africa, all above 1000m (3300ft).

Echinops amplexicaulis   Plate 519
A robust, erect herb with usually stalkless leaves which are shallowly lobed and ovate-elliptical. Its red florets are arranged in coarse, spherical inflorescences c. 6cm (2⅜in) across. It is common and conspicuous in wooded grassland and at the edges of cultivation in north-western Kenya and parts of the eastern wall of the Rift Valley at 1700–2400 (5600–7900ft). It is recorded in Elgon, Cheranganis, Mau, Aberdares, Tinderet, Kitale, Mumias, Baringo and Rift Valley districts, and, in high rainfall grassland is found, on rare occasions, at altitudes down to 1400m (4600ft) (Kenya); lake areas, Maasai, Tabora (Tanzania); all regions of Uganda; also Sudan, Ethiopia, Zaire.

E. angustilobus   Plate 91
A robust, erect herb with petiolate, much pinnatifid leaves and a few medium to large, round inflorescences with whitish-grey florets c. 5cm (2in) across. Stem and upper sides of leaves are glandular-hairy and cob-webby, phyllaries ciliate above but not appendaged. It is found in grassland in high altitude zones 2010–2850m (6600–9350ft). Western Kenya and Cheranganis, Tinderet, Mau, Aberdares (Kenya); Maasai (Tanzania); Uganda, no record; also Ethiopia.

E. hispidus   Plate 92
A robust, erect herb with petiolate pinnatifid leaves and a few large globose inflorescences with white flowers c. 60–90mm (2⅜–3⅜in) across. Stem and upper side of leaves with stiff bristles, phyllaries narrowed below the terminal (often small) bristly appendage. Altitude range 1200–2200m (3900–7200ft) and locally common in upland grasslands in western Kenya. Recorded in Cheranganis, Elgon, Tinderet, Mau and also Aberdares (Kenya); Maasai (Tanzania); Uganda, no record; also in Ethiopia. (It is generally found at slightly lower altitudes than *E. angustilobus*).

E. hoehnelii **Plate 230**

An erect, branched herb with pinnatifid oblong leaves and a few smallish spherical inflorescences *c.* 30mm (1⅕in) across, with white, pale blue or purple-pink flowers. This species is common in forest edges and open high altitude woodland and heathland; altitude range 2300–3100m (7650–10,250ft). The Aberdares and Mt Kenya (Kenya); Maasai – Mts Kilimanjaro, Meru (Tanzania); western and eastern regions – Ruwenzori and Elgon (Uganda); also southern Ethiopia, Rwanda, Zaire.

Emilia coccinea (*E. javanica*) **Plate 424**

An erect, glabrescent annual with oblong or lanceolate amplexicaul leaves and loosely arranged terminal bright orange heads 6–8mm (¼–⅓in) across: florets almost twice as long as the involucres: achenes minutely pubescent. A conspicuous annual weed of roadsides and waste places, often in dry country and at low altitudes 5–1700m (16–5575ft). Widespread throughout Kenya, Tanzania and Uganda and in tropical Africa. Thirty-eight species in East Africa related to *Senecio*.

Erythrocephalum minus **Plate 520**

A rhizomatous or tuberous rooted perennial herb, often white-woolly with alternate, simple often entire leaves and solitary heads of red or dark pink flowers 3.5cm (1⅜in) across. The outer florets are bisexual with a two-lipped corolla. One of ten species in East Africa. This is a rare plant; altitude range 0–390m (0–1300ft), found in dry districts such as the Taru desert (Kenya); Tanga, Tabora, Morogoro, Mbeya, Iringa (Tanzania); Uganda and elsewhere, no record.

Erigeron karvinskianus **Plate 768**

A decumbent, branching perennial herb, *c.* 45cm (18in) high. Stems slender and slightly angled. Leaves subsessile, 3×2cm (1⅕×⅘in), the upper ones entire and the lower ones three-lobed, narrowly ovate with lobes obtuse and mucronate at apex, the base narrowly cuneate. Flower heads terminal on branches, hemispheric 10mm (⅖in) across. Ray florets white or pink. A weed found in roadsides, lawns and forest edges; altitude range 1100–2400m (3600–8000ft), probably indigenous to Central America. Only species (alien) in East Africa. Recorded in Kitale, Cheranganis, Tinderet, Kitui, Embu, Machakos, coast hinterland (Kenya); Maasai, Tanga, Morogoro, Mbeya, Iringa (Tanzania); eastern region (Uganda). Also Rwanda, Malawi, Zambia.

Eupatorium adenophorum **Plate 93**

An erect, pubescent herb or shrub with opposite ovate-elliptic leaves and a terminal corymb of pale yellow or cream heads 0.5cm (⅕in) across. A rare plant found in forest edges in western Kenya and Kitale; altitude range 1960–2300m (6530–7600ft) and also recorded once in Aberdares (Kenya); not known elsewhere. An American species which has only recently appeared in western Kenya. Two species in East Africa.

E. africanum An erect, sparsely pubescent herb from a woody rootstock with lanceolate-elliptic, dentate or entire leaves and a terminal lobed corymb of white heads. An uncommon plant found in wooded grassland in western Kenya; altitude range 1530–1950m (5100–6500ft) and recorded in Cheranganis, Aberdares, Kitale and Mumias (Kenya); not known elsewhere.

Ethulia sp. **A** **Plate 769**

An erect, woody herb, generally an annual, pubescent or tomentose, with oblanceolate, linear, serrate leaves and linear phyllaries to the crowded heads. The inner achenes are often two-winged. This is a plant which grows in the central districts of Kenya; the Aberdares, Rift Valley, Machakos, Kajiado and Nairobi, it is often found in swamp grassland. Altitude range 1500–2400m (5000–8000ft). The inflorescences are corymbs of purple heads *c.* 5mm (*c.* $\frac{1}{5}$in) across with the bracts in several rows and the florets tubular. Maasai, Mpwapwa, Kondoa (Tanzania); Uganda and elsewhere, not known. One of eleven species in East Africa closely resembling *Vernonia* but without pappus.

E. scheffleri **Plate 679**
An erect, woody, hair-covered herb with oblanceolate, linear, serrate leaves which is generally an annual. The inflorescences are corymbs of purple heads *c.* 5mm ($\frac{1}{5}$in) across made up of tubular florets with blunt bracts in several rows. The achenes are three- to four-winged. It is found at 1600–2200m (5200–7250ft) in Narok and the Rift Valley and is common in swampy grasslands near Nairobi (Kenya); Maasai (Tanzania); Uganda, not known; also Malawi.

E. vernonioides (*Hoehnelia vernonioides*) **Plate 770**
An erect, weak, hairless and sparsely-branched shrub with oblong to narrow-elliptic, serrate leaves. The inflorescence is a terminal corymb of purple heads *c.* 1cm ($\frac{2}{5}$in) across. It is locally abundant at 1650–2750m (5350–9000ft). Recorded in Tinderet, Elgon, Cheranganis, Mau, Aberdares, Mt Kenya, Kitale (Kenya); Maasai, Mbeya, Iringa (Tanzania); Uganda, no record; also found in Malawi.

EURYOPS

Shrubby plants with small crowded leaves, related to Senecio; five species in East Africa.

Euryops brownei **Plate 363**
An erect shrub with many branches and short leaves with dense masses of yellow, star-like flower heads *c.* 18mm ($\frac{3}{4}$in) across at apices of branches. It is common at the upper limits of forest areas and in lower moorland heath zones on the drier sides of the Aberdares and Mt Kenya (Kenya) at altitudes above 2600m (8500ft); Maasai – Mt Meru (Tanzania); Uganda and elsewhere, no record.

E. elgonensis Similar to *E. brownei* but wider leaves. Flower head 2cm ($\frac{4}{5}$in) across. It is confined to Mt Elgon (Kenya). Tanzania and elsewhere, not known.

E. jacksonii A low, trailing species or an erect shrub with yellow heads 17mm (*c.* $\frac{5}{8}$in) across. Similar to *E. brownei*. Found in rocky places in dry upland areas, especially Rift Valley and western Aberdares (Kenya); Tanzania, Uganda and elsewhere, not known.

Felicia muricata **Plate 578**
A low, erect or trailing, weakly-woody shrub, sometimes rhizomatous, which has linear leaves. It has solitary heads *c.* 75mm (3in) across of spreading blue rays with a yellow centre, the rays frequently of a deeper blue than those illustrated. It is found in dry grassland on clay soils at 1600–2800m (5250–9200ft) in Mau, Aberdares, Narok and Nairobi districts and is common in the Rift Valley (Kenya); Maasai (Tanzania); Uganda, no record; also Zimbabwe. One of five species in East Africa.

F. abyssinica ssp. **neghellensis** Flower head *c.* 75mm (3in) across. Closely related to *F. muricata* and is widespread in the highlands of Kenya; lake areas, Maasai, Tabora, Mbeya, Iringa (Tanzania); Uganda, no record; also found in

Ethiopia. The two species are difficult to distinguish from each other.

Gerbera viridifolia A tomentose rosette herb with petiolate oblong-elliptic leaves and solitary heads of pinkish-white flowers 3cm (1¼in) across. It is locally common in wooded grassland in Elgon, Tinderet, Kitale, Mau, Loita Hills, Mt Kenya; altitude range *c.* 1500–2200m (4900–7200ft) and also recorded at Maralal at 2400m (8000ft) (Kenya). One of two species in East Africa.

NB *Piloselloides hirsuta* (Plate 771) is very similar to *G. viridifolia* above, but has expanded scapes below the heads *c.* 3cm (1¼in) across, staminodes are not present in the ray florets and achene-hairs inflated: it is common in upland and highland grassland; altitude range *c.* 1800–2400m (5900–7900ft) in Elgon, Cheranganis, Tinderet, Mau, Aberdares, Mt Kenya, Machakos and Kajiado (Kenya); all regions except Tanga (Tanzania); all regions of Uganda; also in southern Sudan, Ethiopia, south to Malawi, Zimbabwe, southern Africa (probably Mozambique).

GUIZOTIA

Closely related to Aspilia; pappus absent. Five species in East Africa.

Guizotia reptans (*G. jacksonii*)   **Plate 364**
A creeping herb with elliptic, obscurely dentate, opposite leaves and shortly pedunculate, solitary flower heads 3cm (1¼in) across. Found in disturbed ground and short grass in the bamboo and heath zones; altitude range 2400–3300m (8000–11,000ft), and recorded in Elgon, Mau, Aberdares and Mt Kenya (Kenya); Tanzania, Uganda, elsewhere, not known.

G. scabra   **Plate 365**
An erect, usually rough herb with a wiry, perennial rootstalk which bears oblong, dentate or entire leaves. Its many yellow heads *c.* 3cm (1¼in) across each form a loose terminal corymb. It sometimes grows as an annual. It is common in upland grassland in Kenya, especially around Nairobi, but is widespread in East Africa at altitudes 1520–2780m (5000–9000ft). All regions except Tanga, Morogoro (Tanzania); all regions of Uganda; also Sudan, Ethiopia, Somalia south to Zimbabwe, Mozambique.

GUTENBERGIA

Related to Vernonia but with a more hairy corolla, eight to ten ribbed achenes and no pappus. Thirteen species in East Africa.

Gutenbergia cordifolia   **Plate 680**
A small to medium, erect herb with opposite or alternate, simple leaves, usually with white hairs below. The flower heads are solitary, *c.* 14mm (*c.* ⅝in) across, or in terminal corymbs with purple florets which are tubular and bisexual. It is found in rocky, eroded or poor grassland over most of Kenya, except in the north west, at 1200–2400m (3900–8000ft); all regions except Tabora, Songea (Tanzania); all regions of Uganda; also southern Sudan, Ethiopia.

G. fischeri   **Plate 681**
A small, erect herb, normally perennial, with undulate leaves, white and felty below. Purple flower heads, *c.* 6mm (¼in) across, form small terminal corymbs. It is found in rocky eroded grassland south of a line from Mt Kenya to Tinderet at altitudes 1200–2200m (4000–7200ft) (Kenya); Maasai (Tanzania); Uganda and elsewhere, not known.

G. ruepellii Similar to *G. fischeri*, except that the leaves are oblong-linear and sessile and the involucres smaller. Flower head: 4–5mm (*c.* ⅕in) across. It is found at the same altitudes north of the line from Mt Kenya to Tinderet (Kenya); all regions except Tanga, Songea (Tanzania); northern and eastern regions (Uganda); also Sudan, Ethiopia, Nigeria.

GYNURA

Similar to Senecio but with a long pubescent tip to the stigma, twice as long as the normal portion of the stigma. All the species in this genus have yellow to orange flowers of a similar type. Six species in East Africa.

Gynura pseudochina (*G. miniata*) **Plate 366**
An erect, perennial herb with oblanceolate pinnatifid leaves. Three to seven orange-yellow flower heads, *c.* 15mm (⅗in) across, are carried on a terminal corymb. Altitude range 400–1700m (1300–5575ft). It is locally common in grassland on black cotton soil in the Nairobi and Kajiado districts (Kenya); Maasai, Tanga, Morogoro (Tanzania); Uganda, no record; also in Ethiopia, southern Somalia, Sudan, Zambia, Malawi.

G. amplexicaulis Grows erect from a creeping rootstalk. It has oblanceolate leaves and bears a few orange flower heads 12mm (*c.* ½in) across in a long terminal corymb. It is locally common in disturbed ground in western Kenya, Elgon, Kitale and Kisii (Kenya); lake areas (Tanzania); all except northern region (Uganda); also Sudan, Rwanda, Burundi, Zaire.

G. scandens **Plate 425**
A weak climber or scrambler with auriculate, ovate, fleshy, serrated leaves. Its orange-yellow flower heads, 11mm (⅜in) across, grouped more closely on terminal corymb than in the two preceding species. It is found in the wetter situations of normally drier areas at altitudes up to 2100m (7000ft) in the Elgon, Tinderet, Mau, Aberdares, Mt Kenya, Kitale, Narok and Rift Valley districts (Kenya); all regions except Mpwapwa, Kondoa (Tanzania); all except northern regions (Uganda); also Rwanda, Burundi, Zaire, Malawi, Zambia.

G. valeriana A weak, juicy herb with oblanceolate, pinnatifid leaves and a loose terminal corymb or yellow-orange flower heads 7mm (¼in) across. So far it has been found only on the Chyulu Hills (Kenya); in the wetter forest areas of Maasai, Tanga, Morogoro (Tanzania); Uganda, no record; also in Malawi.

Haplocarpha rueppellii **Plate 367**
An alpine plant with generally glossy leaves, although in western Kenya they may be dull in appearance. Flower heads are a rich yellow, *c.* 2–3cm (⅘–1⅖in) across. Two other species in East Africa. Grows in Kenya in areas subject to frost where soil is loose and unstable at altitudes 2400–4000m (7800–13,000ft). Maasai – Mt Kilimanjaro (Tanzania); Elgon (Uganda); Ethiopia.

H. schimperi A flat, rosette-leaved plant with the leaves close to the ground and small, pale yellow flowers 9mm (*c.* ⅓in) across in the centre of the rosette. It is uncommon but found in short grassy clearings in dryer mountain forest areas of Kenya at 2440–3040m (8000–10,000ft). Tanzania, Uganda, not known; also Ethiopia.

HELICHRYSUM

Contains the well-known 'Everlasting Flowers' which grow mostly above 1500m (c. 5000ft) with two species at sea level. The involucral bracts are enlarged, highly coloured, shiny and persistent; the flower inside them inconspicuous. Eighty species in East Africa.

Helichrysum brownei   Plate 231

A low, bushy shrub with short, linear leaves with solitary white flower heads, c. 16mm (⅝in) across, or clustered small heads at the stem apex. The plant itself is grey-silver in colour. It is locally common in high altitude shrubby vegetation above the heath zone on the Aberdares, and Mt Kenya above 3350m (11,000ft) (Kenya); Tanzania, Uganda, and elsewhere, not known.

H. cymosum ssp. fruticosum

One of the so-called 'everlasting flowers', this is a weak or wiry, straggling plant, although it can also be low and erect with yellowish, woolly, linear, oblong or lanceolate leaves, erect or reflexed in some cases. The yellowish-brown flower heads c. 3mm (⅛in) across form dense terminal balls or corymbs, 12–18mm (½–¾in) across. A very variable plant found in a wide range of habitats in Kenya in stony grassland at 1200–4700m (3600–15,000ft); all regions except Mpwapwa, Kondoa (Tanzania); all regions of Uganda; also southern Sudan, Ethiopia, Rwanda, Burundi, Zaire, Malawi, Zimbabwe, probably Mozambique.

H. foetidum   Plate 368

An erect, glandular, hairy annual branching above into the diffusely corymbose golden yellow heads; leaves lanceolate to oblong. It is similar to H. setosum but has smaller heads, 10mm (⅜in) across, saucer-shaped with the inner phyllaries exceeding the florets by only one quarter of their length. It is locally common in disturbed places in dry upland forest areas and recorded in Cheranganis, Kitale, Tinderet, Mau, Aberdares, Mt Kenya, Nairobi and Kisii (Kenya); Maasai, Tanga, Morogoro, Mbeya, Iringa (Tanzania); all regions except Buganda (Uganda); also in Sudan, Ethiopia, eastern Zaire, Rwanda (probably south to southern Africa). H. setosum is found in grassy clearings in montane rain forest; altitude range 1500–3240m (5000–10,800ft) and has been recorded in Elgon, Mau, Aberdares, western Kenya, Machakos and Kajiado (Kenya). Widespread in Tanzania; western and eastern regions (Uganda); south to Zimbabwe, Mozambique.

H. formosissimum   Plate 482

A similar shrub to H. nandense but grows up to 3m (10ft) in height. Its dense corymbs of flower heads usually white, but sometimes pink. Common and found in open, tussocky and burnt grassland and along roadsides in the bamboo zone at 2700–4100m (8850–13,500ft) (Kenya); Maasai (Tanzania); western and eastern regions (Uganda); also southern Sudan, Ethiopia, Rwanda, eastern Zaire.

H. glumaceum   Plate 94

A shrubby, low-growing, grey, hairy perennial with linear acute leaves. The white or pink flower heads, c. 2mm (1/12in) across, 5mm (⅕in) long, form tight clusters in racemes on naked peduncles. A low altitude species, common in dry, and wooded grassland over most of east and central Kenya at altitudes up to 2250m (7400ft) and in northern areas; lake areas, Maasai, Tanga, Mpwapwa, Kondoa (Tanzania); all regions except Buganda (Uganda); Sudan, Ethiopia, Somalia.

H. kilimanjari
Plate 369

A small, wiry, erect annual with oblanceolate or oblinear, pale-backed leaves and reddish stems. The yellow to brownish-yellow flower heads *c.* 8mm (*c.* ⅓in) across are carried in a terminal corymb. An uncommon species, it is found in disturbed, burnt places at the lower end of the alpine zone on Mt Elgon, Mt Kenya, the Cheranganis and the Aberdares at 1200–3950m (4000–13,000ft) (Kenya); Maasai, Tanga, Tabora, Mbeya, Iringa (Tanzania); eastern region (Uganda); elsewhere, not known.

H. meyeri-johannis
Plate 483

A rhizomatous perennial, white-woolly (especially on the stems and undersides of the leaves) with erect stems from a leaf-rosette; stems with appressed leaves and bearing a dense terminal corymb of pink or white heads 3cm (1⅛in) across. Fairly common in damp alpine grasslands; altitude range 2800–4100m (6500–13,650ft). Elgon, Cheranganis and Mt Kenya (Kenya); Maasai – Mt Kilimanjaro (Tanzania); Elgon (Uganda); elsewhere, unknown.

H. nandense
Plate 484

A large, loose shrub growing to 2.7m (9ft) in height. Its white flower heads, *c.* 15mm (⅝in) across, may be tinged with pink. It is generally found in the lower alpine areas, on the edges of forests and along roadside banks but is common from 2100–3000m (6900–9800ft) throughout Kenya; Maasai (Tanzania); all regions except Buganda (Uganda); Rwanda.

H. odoratissimum
Plate 370

A rather straggling plant covered with silvery hairs, its leaves incline downwards and are linear-lanceolate. Despite its generally weak habit, it has reasonably strong, erect, smooth or naked stems which support dense corymbs of yellow flower heads, *c.* 6mm (¼in) long, which have an aromatic smell. It is very common throughout Kenya, except in the driest localities, at altitudes of 910–2100m (3000–7000ft) and occasionally found at lower altitudes down to 760m (2500ft); all regions of Tanzania; western and eastern regions (Uganda); southern Sudan, Ethiopia, Rwanda, eastern Zaire.

H. setosum
Plate 371

An erect, glandular-hairy annual, branching above into the diffuse corymbose golden-yellow heads 2cm (⅜in) across; leaves lanceolate to oblong, clasping at base, without a cob-webby hairy covering, glandular on both surfaces. Locally common in grassy clearings in montane rain forest; altitude range 1350–3000m (4500–10,000ft) and recorded in Elgon, Mau, Aberdares, western Kenya, Machakos and Kajiado (Kenya); Maasai, Tanga, Tabora (Tanzania); western, eastern regions (Uganda); south to Zimbabwe, Mozambique.

Hirpicium diffusum
Plate 372

A spreading-bristly annual with oblong to linear or oblanceolate, entire to pinnatilobed leaves and solitary yellow flowers *c.* 14mm (⅜in) across. Two other species in East Africa. A common plant in disturbed places in dry grassland; altitude range 500–1900m (1650–6250ft) – occasionally to 2700m (8875ft), and recorded in Tinderet, Mau, Aberdares, Narok, Baringo, Rift Valley, Nanyuki, Machakos, Nairobi and Kajiado (Kenya); all regions except Morogoro, Songea (Tanzania); northern region (Uganda); also Ethiopia.

KLEINIA

Twenty-one species in East Africa, of which seven were always in *Kleinia* and fourteen were formerly in *Notonia*. The latter are less stiff and usually have better developed leaves.

Kleinia squarrosa Plate 772

A fleshy, sprawling stem-succulent up to 3m (10ft) tall, with elliptic leaves on the very young shoots which are soon shed. Stems about 4mm ($\frac{1}{6}$in) in diameter. Flower heads cylindrical, *c.* 15mm ($\frac{5}{8}$in) long, borne two to eight together in umbels at the end of the branches, each head containing about ten flowers. The plant tends to scramble and climb when growing among bushes but can be erect up to 1m (3ft) tall. Found in dry bushland; altitude range 100–2000m (300–6560ft). Northern, central and eastern Kenya; northern and eastern Tanzania; northern Uganda; also Ethiopia and Somalia.

K. abyssinica var. **abyssinica** (*Notonia abyssinica*) Plate 521

A hairless herb with ascending stems and oblanceolate to obovate leaves which are usually entire, acute and fleshy. One to seven bright red flower heads *c.* 15mm ($\frac{5}{8}$in) across form loose terminal cymes. It is found in rocky soils and along bushed stream banks at 760–2440m (2500–8000ft) in western areas of Kenya; lake areas, Maasai, Tanga, Mpwapwa, Kondoa, Mbeya, Iringa (Tanzania); all regions (Uganda); also Sudan, Ethiopia, Rwanda, Burundi, Zaire, Malawi, Zambia.

K. gregorii (*Notonia gregorii*) Plate 522

A glabrous, rhizomatous herb with erect, cylindrical, mottled, leafless stems and solitary terminal red heads; phyllaries ridged towards the base. Leaves represented by short deciduous scales less than 1cm ($\frac{3}{8}$in) long. The plant can be distinguished from both *N. abyssinica* and *N. hildebrandtii* by its solitary terminal head. Locally common in dry rocky grassland, especially where disturbed; altitude range 1200–2100m (4000–7100ft). Recorded in Kisii, Narok, Rift Valley and Machakos (Kenya); lake areas, Maasai (Tanzania); Uganda and elsewhere, not known.

K. abyssinica var. **hildebrantii** (*Notonia hildebrandtii*) Plate 523

Slightly smaller than, and now considered to be a form of *N. abyssinica*. Carrying the same red flower heads *c.* 2cm ($\frac{4}{5}$in) across, it is found in rocky soils and along bushed stream banks at the same height throughout eastern, northern and central Kenya and especially around Nairobi.

K. implexa (*Notonia implexa*) Similar to *N. petraea* but is pubescent with elliptic and constantly solitary heads. Florets orange, 20mm ($\frac{4}{5}$in) long, 15mm ($\frac{5}{8}$in) across. Altitude range 660–1710m (2200–5700ft). A rare plant, only recorded in Kajiado (Kenya).

K. petraea (*Notonia petraea*) Plate 426

A glabrous trailing succulent herb with obovate to suborbicular glabrous leaves and one to four yellow-orange heads, 3.5cm ($1\frac{3}{8}$in) across, on erect naked peduncles, pappus exceeding the florets. Locally common in dry bushed grassland; altitude range 780–2190m (2600–7300ft). Tinderet, Aberdares, Narok, Rift Valley, Nanyuki, Machakos and Nairobi (Kenya); lake areas, Maasai, Mpwapwa, Kondoa, Morogoro (Tanzania); Uganda and elsewhere, not known.

LACTUCA
Leaves alternate, a milky latex present; florets all ligulate, usually yellow, less often blue; closely related to Launea. Fourteen species in East Africa.

Lactuca glandulifera A scrambling, downy herb with pinnate or pinnatifid leaves with three to five pinnae, the lowermost with a narrowed leaf stalk. The ligules (strap-like shaped florets) are yellow inside and dull purple outside. The flower heads themselves are c. 1cm (⅜in) long, plum-purple when closed and yellow when open. It is locally common in the montane rain forest on Mt Elgon, the Cheranganis, Tinderet, Mau, the Aberdares, Mt Kenya and the Nyambeni Hills from 1900–2400m (6200–7900ft) (Kenya); Maasai, Tabora, Mbeya, Iringa, Songea (Tanzania); all except northern region (Uganda); southern Ethiopia, Rwanda, Zaire, Malawi, Mozambique.

L. inermis (*L. capensis*) An erect herb, usually branched, only above, with pin-natifid entire leaves and a diffuse mass of terminal blue flower heads 16mm (⅝in) across. It is common everywhere in disturbed ground in the medium altitude grasslands especially along roadsides and widespread throughout Kenya; all regions (Tanzania and Uganda); and in Sudan, Ethiopia, south to Zimbabwe, Mozambique.

Launaea cornuta   **Plate 373**
A rhizomatous, perennial with erect stems from a rosette of leaves at ground level, stems branching above into the diffuse inflorescence; leaves linear-lanceolate or elliptic in outline, entire or pinnatifid into linear segments. Flower heads yellow, c. 1cm (⅜in) across, and the heads held at various levels, close to and distant from the centre of the plant. The commonest species of *Launea*, especially around Nairobi, growing along roadsides and in disturbed grassland; altitude range 1–2250m (3–7500ft); Mau, Narok, Rift Valley, Nanyuki, Machakos and Nairobi (Kenya); all regions (Tanzania and Uganda); and in Somalia, Rwanda, Malawi, Zambia, Zimbabwe. One of nine species in East Africa.

L. hafunensis   **Plate 374**
An erect, many stemmed, divaricately branched (no single stem being dominant), bushy herb from a woody rootstock; leaves linear-lanceolate in outline, pinnatifid. Flower heads 17mm (⅜in) long, 7mm (¼in) across, terminal to each branchlet, often corymbose and held at periphery of the bush-shaped plant. Common in some areas of dry alluvial soils; altitude range 600–1700m (1950–5575ft) and recorded in Kajiado and Machakos (Kenya); Maasai (Tanzania); Uganda, no record; and Ethiopia, Somalia.

Microglossa pyrifolia (*Conyza pyrifolia*)   **Plate 375**
A scrambling though sometimes erect shrub with narrow-ovate, acuminate, petiol-ate leaves, some leaves are abruptly narrowed into the petiole, ligules cream and spreading; often hanging corymbs of yellow heads 4mm (⅛in) long; 4mm (⅛in) wide; outer florets in ± one row, four to six bisexual florets. Abundant in disturbed dry forest almost everywhere; altitude range 450–2600m (1475–8525ft) (Kenya); all regions except lake areas, Mpwapwa, Kondoa (Tanzania); western, eastern reg-ions (Uganda); also throughout tropical Africa. One of five species in East Africa.

M. sp. A Very similar to *Microglossa pyrifolia* but is more erect in habit (rarely scrambling): the leaves are broad-ovate, acuminate and petiolate and abruptly narrowed into the petiole. The corymbs are terminal and erect, with pale cream heads, (not yellow as in *M. pyrifolia*), 4mm (⅛in) long; 4mm (⅛in) wide, outer florets in many rows, bisexual florets nought to three. Common in disturbed forest country altitude range 450–2600m (1475–8525ft) but less widespread than *M. pyrifolia* being recorded in Tinderet, Mau, western Kenya, Kisii, Baringo, Embu, Machakos and Magadi (Kenya); all regions except lake areas, Mpwapwa, Kondoa (Tanzania) western, eastern regions (Uganda); also throughout tropical Africa.

Psiadia punctulata (*P. arabica*)   **Plate 376**
An erect, round-topped shrub with entire, lanceolate-elliptic, glossy leaves which produce a gum-like secretion when young. The bright yellow flower heads, c. 5mm (c. ⅛in) across, form terminal racemes. An abundant plant on the edges of disturbed bushland, in evergreen woodland and in dry .forest areas at 1200–2300m (4000–7500ft). Nairobi area westwards (Kenya); lake areas, Maasai, Tanga, Mbeya, Iringa (Tanzania); northern regions of Uganda; also Sudan, Ethiopia, Somalia, Zimbabwe, Mozambique.

Reichardia tingitana   **Plate 377**
An erect, glabrous annual with oblanceolate dentate leaves and terminal axillary heads borne on swollen peduncles which become hardy and corny in fruit. Flower, yellow, florets many, 16mm (⅝in) long, 18mm (⅝in) across. An uncommon weed of disturbed and rocky places; altitude range 1050–2100m (2450–6900ft). Rift Valley, Nairobi, Baringo, Mt Kulal (Kenya); Maasai (Tanzania); Uganda, no record; also in Sudan, Ethiopia, northern Somalia.
    NB *Reichardia*, of which there are about ten species, mainly in the Mediterranean areas, has only *R. tingitana* in Africa where it may be native.

SENECIO
A huge genus of some 1000 species growing all over the world including the common groundsel of European gardens; seventy-one species in East Africa. Leaves alternate, the involucral bracts are arranged in a more or less coherent single row with (or without) a few much smaller bracts outside it. The outer florets are female and usually though not always ligulate; the inner florets tubular and bisexual; the pappus of many rows of simple hairs. It is convenient to treat the tree (Dendro) senecios separately from the rest.

TREE SENECIOS
The tree senecios or giant groundsels are either trees or shrubs growing up to 9m (30ft) in height. Their stems are branched, ending in a rosette or cabbage of large leaves which often hang on after drying. The dwarf species have a sparse and flattened branching system. The taller species have deeply furrowed corky bark; almost all species have magnificent panicles of yellow flowers. There are now considered to be only three species of this group in Kenya, each with its own subspecies and distribution.

Senecio keniensis ssp. **brassica**   **Plate 378**
A dwarf form belonging to the giant groundsel family which reaches a height of 1.8m (6ft) when its yellow flowers are in bloom. It is confined to open moorland at altitudes from 3300–3900m (10,800–12,750ft) on Mt Kenya only (Kenya).

S. keniensis ssp. **brassiciformis**   Inflorescence up to 2m (6½ft) tall. Found only in the Aberdares mountains (Kenya) at 3000–3500m (9850–11,500ft).

S. johnstonii ssp. **battiscombei**   **Plate 379**
A tree growing to 6m (20ft) high with ovate-lanceolate leaves which are up to 45cm
(18in) long and 15cm (6in) wide. They have a broadly acuminate apex and shortly
dentate margin. The flower head contains yellow ray florets and the petiole may be
covered with long white hairs above; panicle up to 1.3m (4ft) tall. This striking plant
grows only in Kenya, on Mt Kenya and the Aberdares at 3350–3810m
(11,000–12,500ft).

S.j. ssp. **barbatipes**   Flower panicle c. 1m (3¼ft) tall. Found only in Kenya on Mt
Elgon at 360–4300m (12,000–14,100ft).

S. johnstonii ssp. **cheranganiensis**   **Plate 380**
A tree up to 10m (30ft) in height with branching at acute angles. Leaves lanceolate
to 40cm (16in) long and 10cm (4in) wide; apex acute, margin dentate, alternate and
decurrent to the winged petiole, lamina glabrous above, glabrous or pilose below.
Capitula with yellow ray florets in panicles 1m (3¼ft) high. Found only in the
Cherangani Hills from 2550–3200m (8500–10,500ft).

S.j. ssp. **dalei**   Flower panicle c. 75cm (30in) tall. Found only in Kenya on the
Cheranganis at 3050–3400m (10,000–11,150ft).

S.j. ssp. **elgonensis**   Flower panicle c. 1m (3¼ft) tall. Also found only in Kenya on Mt
Elgon at altitudes 2900–4200m (9400–13,755ft).

S. johnstonii ssp. **johnstonii** is found only on Mts Kilimanjaro and Meru in Tanzania. Ssp. *cottonii* only on Mt Kilimanjaro. There are also other ssp. in Ruwenzori
Mts, Zaire, and Rwanda.

S. keniodendron   Flower inflorescence up to 1.3m (4ft) tall. Found on Mt Kenya at
altitudes of 3500–4650m (11,500–15,250ft), though it has been recorded on the
Aberdares (Kenya)..

The following do not belong to the tree senecio group:
S. jacksonii   A creeping perennial, white-tomentose below and often above with
entire, often linear leaves, (rarely with a few distant acute teeth), glabrescent, and
long peduncles to the solitary yellow heads, achenes hairy; flower head 1.5cm (⅝in)
across. Found in rocky streamsides and wet solifluction soils in the alpine zone;
altitude range 2950–4200m (9800–14,000ft), and recorded in Elgon, Aberdares
and Mt Kenya (Kenya); Tanzania, no record; Mt Elgon (Uganda); elsewhere, not
known.

S. keniophytum   A creeping perennial, white-tomentose below and often above
the more or less crowded oblanceolate serrate leaves with one to five terminal
yellow-rayed heads, 18mm (c. ¾in), on short peduncles; achenes glabrous. It is
often white-woolly on all parts and is confined to the alpine zone of Mt Kenya;
altitude range 3550–4700m (11,650–15,400ft), where it is one of the first to colon-
ise stony disturbed soils beside glaciers and streamsides. It is similar to *S. jacksonii*
but the leaves and achenes distinguish them as well as the length of the peduncle.
S. jacksonii has a wider distribution, and entire, often linear leaves, long peduncles
and hairy achenes.

S. moorei   **Plate 381**
An erect shrub or woody herb, cobwebby, hairy to glabrescent, with oblanceolate,

minutely dentate leaves, which are auriculate at the gradually narrowed base; heads, 18mm (¾in) across, campanulate, conspicuously yellow-rayed in large corymbs. Common in grassland at higher altitudes in forest clearings above 2400m (8000ft). Recorded in Tinderet, Mau, Aberdares, Mt Kenya, Kitale, Rift Valley (Kenya); Tanzania, no record; eastern region (Uganda); elsewhere, not known.

S. hadiensis (S. petitianus) Plate 382
A robust, glabrous, semi-succulent, trailing climber with elliptic, more or less entire, or minutely toothed, leaves and large terminal corymbs of yellow, rayed or unrayed heads c. 6mm (¼in) across. It is common in all upland drier forest edges; altitude range 800–2700m (2660–9000ft) sometimes flowering in masses over large tracts of country. Recorded in Tinderet, Mau, Aberdares, Narok, Rift Valley, Nanyuki and Machakos (Kenya). There is a local belief that the leaves of this plant cause liver fluke in cattle. Also recorded in lake areas, Maasai, Tanga (Tanzania); all except eastern region (Uganda); also in Ethiopia, Somalia, Rwanda, Zaire.

S. roseiflorus Plate 682
An erect herb or weak shrub with purple flowers which are open and daisy-like c. 2cm (⅘in) across. It is locally common in the dryer alpine areas of Mr Kenya and the Aberdares at altitudes 2900–4000m (9500–13,100ft) (Kenya); Tanzania, Uganda and elsewhere, not known.

S. schweinfurthii Plate 383
A glandular-pubescent to pubescent perennial with trailing woody stems and terminal rosettes of sessile, linear-oblong leaves; inflorescence axillary or separate from terminal leaf rosette, erect with a loose corymb of rayless yellow heads c. 11mm (⅘in) across. Locally common in disturbed places in montane and alpine grassland; altitude range 2400–4900m (7575–16,100ft), especially at higher altitudes. Recorded in Cheranganis, Tinderet, Mau, Aberdares, Mt Kenya, Kitale, Kajiado (Kenya); Mts Kilimanjaro, Meru and craters (Tanzania); Uganda and elsewhere, no record.
   NB There is no record of this species on Mt Elgon (Kenya).

S. syringifolius Plate 232
A dull grey-green, semi-succulent climber with twining stems and ovate or triangular leaves which often have lateral lobes at their base. Its flowers form a loose corymb without rays, cream, pale yellow, yellow or orange in colour. Flower head: c. 7mm (¼in) across. It is common in montane rain forest and the bamboo zone in Elgon, Mau, Aberdares, Mt Kenya, Kajiado, Machakos and the Chyulu Hills at 2100–3000m (6700–9850ft) and in the Chyulus extending down to 1600m (5250ft) (Kenya). Maasai, Tanga, Morogoro, Mbeya, Iringa (Tanzania); western region (Uganda); also Malawi.

Sonchus oleraceus Plate 384
An erect branched annual with glaucous sharply toothed and often pinnatifid leaves; flowers yellow, 1.5cm (⅗in) long, 1.2cm (½in) across head, in a terminal umbel-like cyme. It is very similar to S. asper but has the auricles at leaf base pointed and more or less triangular in outline, achenes minutely roughened on the outside. In S. asper, the auricles are rounded and the achenes smooth. Both common weeds of cultivation and gardens during the rains at medium altitudes, range 75–2700m (250–8850ft). Widespread and cosmopolitan.

SPHAERANTHUS

Stems more or less winged; leaves alternate, often decurrent into the wings of the stem; heads small, crowded together into spherical or oblong 'heads of heads'; florets tubular, purple. Twenty-eight species in East Africa.

Sphaeranthus cyathuloides   Plate 773

An erect, hairless, woody herb with narrow lanceolate-linear minutely serrate leaves and unwinged stems. Its pink inflorescence c. 15mm (⅜in) long, is conical and pointed at the apex. It is fairly common in wet places within grassland around Nairobi, in Machakos, and in Tsavo National Park at altitudes 500–1800m (1650–5900ft) (Kenya); lake areas, Maasai, Mbeya, Iringa (Tanzania); Uganda and elsewhere, no record.

S. napierae   Plate 774

A down-covered, trailing herb with ascending stems bearing elliptic, serrate leaves and subentire, continuous wings, with hairy, gradually-narrowing bracts. The rounded inflorescence is purple with flower heads c. 15mm (⅜in) across. It is a common endemic in fresh water in central and western Kenya at altitudes 1450–2000m (4900–6550ft). Tanga, Mpwapwa, Kondoa, Morogoro (Tanzania); Uganda and elsewhere, no record.

S. suaveolens   Plate 775

A hairless, trailing herb with ascending stems bearing elliptic, serrate leaves and subentire, continuous wings. Its terminal inflorescence is round and purple c. 14mm (⅝in) across. The smell of the leaves resembles apples. This is the commonest form of *Sphaeranthus*, found in or alongside fresh water all over Kenya at altitudes 1220–2500m (4000–8200ft); all regions except lake area (Tanzania); eastern region, Buganda (Uganda); also Ethiopia, Zaire, Zambia, Malawi, Mozambique.

S. gomphrenoides   A weaker ascending herb with lanceolate leaves and interrupted stem wings. Its inflorescences are smaller than in *S. suaveolens* or *S. napierae*, paler in colour and more rounded at the apex. It is locally common in water courses and ephemeral pools in hotter country than either of the above, at altitudes of 760–1200m (2500–4000ft) (Kenya); lake areas, Maasai, Mbeya, Iringa (Tanzania); eastern region (Uganda); also southern Ethiopia, Zaire, Rwanda, Zambia.

S. ukambensis   Plate 776

An erect, scabrid-pubescent herb with narrow lanceolate-linear, minutely serrate leaves and unwinged stems; inflorescence pink and conical, spike 3cm (1⅛in) long. Fairly common in wet places around Nairobi; altitude range 10–2100m (30–7000ft), and recorded in Machakos, Kajiado and Nairobi district (Kenya); lake areas, Maasai, Mpwapwa, Kondoa, Songea (Tanzania); northern region (Uganda); also in Ethiopia, Somalia, Mozambique.

Spilanthes mauritiana   Plate 385

A trailing herb with ovate, dentate leaves and small heads of rather bright, orange-yellow flowers, 8mm (⅓in) across, with noticeable ray florets. It is a common plant in riverside grassland and in lawns in central and western Kenya at altitudes 610–2500m (2000–8200ft); all regions of Tanzania and Uganda; also southern Sudan, Ethiopia, Rwanda, Zaire, south to Zimbabwe, Mozambique. One of five species in East Africa.

Tagetes minuta   Plate 233
Originally an American species but called 'The Khaki Weed' because it came to
South Africa in the Boer War, probably in fodder for mules and horses. It was first
recorded in East Africa in 1925 and probably entered the region in the 1914–18
War. It was at first very luxuriant, so much so that the Kikuyu people, in 1928,
named one of their initiation ceremonies the year of this plant. It is now less
rampant due to pest attacks. It is an erect, strong smelling annual which is often
robust but is very variable in habit with pinnate leaves having elliptic, serrate
leaflets. Its creamy-yellow flower heads, c. 5mm ($\frac{1}{5}$in) across, are grouped in
terminal corymbs. One of three species in East Africa. An abundant and trouble-
some weed in upland farming areas, widespread in central Kenya from the Kitale
area to Nairobi and Narok (Kenya) at altitudes 760–2210m (2500–7250ft); all
regions except Tabora (Tanzania); all regions except Buganda (Uganda).

Taraxacum officinale   Plate 386
A virtually hairless herb with oblong, pinnatifid leaves and solitary yellow flowers c.
25mm (1in) across. It is an introduction from Europe and the only species in East
Africa. Originally known only in the Limuru area in the altitude range 2000–2400m
(6500–7900ft) but has now been found along the 2300m (7500ft) contour in the
Aberdare region as far as upper Gilgil (Kenya); Usambara Mts (Tanzania); no
record in Uganda; also Ethiopia, Burundi, Zaire.

Tarchonanthus camphoratus   Plate 95
This is the grey-leaved, medium-sized bush which the early European newcomers
to Kenya called 'Leleshwa' (the Masai 'Oleleshwa') and associated with good,
disease-free cattle country. It is a much-branched, dioecious shrub which grows to
6m (20ft) high. Its narrow, elliptic leaves have a short stalk and smell of camphor
when crushed. Their margin is entire with the lamina green above and covered in
dense white hairs beneath. The bell-shaped flower clusters form much-branched
panicles of five to twelve grey-white flower heads. The woolly achenes give the
female inflorescence an appearance like cotton wool. Reasonable tobacco pipes
can be made from the roots and the stool shoots provide good knobkerries. It grows
all over the floor of the Rift Valley and in parts of Kajiado and Narok (Kenya). Lake
areas, Maasai, Tanga (Tanzania); northern region (Uganda); also Ethiopia,
Somalia south to Mozambique. Only species in East Africa.

Tithonia diversifolia   Plate 387
A branched, soft shrub with simple to five-lobed, opposite or alternate leaves and a
large head of orange-yellow flowers, 7cm (2$\frac{3}{4}$in) across. It can grow into a large
bush. Introduced into East Africa from Central America, it is now common in west
Kenya and on the western slopes of the Aberdares in hedgerows and waste
ground, at altitudes 1500–2300m (5000–7500ft). It is also recorded in the Nairobi
district (Kenya); lake areas, Maasai, Tanga (Tanzania); Buganda (Uganda); also
widespread in tropical Africa.

VERNONIA
A large genus of about 1000 species, mainly tropical, with 141 species in East
Africa. Leaves alternate, involucre of several rows of bracts; florets all purple,
tubular and hermaphrodite; pappus of small scales outside and bristles within.

Vernonia auriculifera   Plate 579
A large, tall-growing, woody shrub with grey hairs under the ovate, auriculate,
petiolate leaves. Its very large corymb of flower heads, 3–4mm (c. $\frac{1}{8}$in) across, is flat

to slightly rounded, varying in colour from deep purple to medium mauve and fading to a pale violet. A prominent, widespread plant of higher rainfall areas of Kenya at altitudes of 1070–3000m (3500–9850ft) and is often a sign of fertile soil. Recorded in lake areas, Maasai, Tanga, Tabora, Morogoro (Tanzania); all except northern region (Uganda); also Ethiopia, Zaire.

V. aemulans An erect annual covered with soft hairs, often dense, which grows up to 1m (3¼ft) in height with oblanceolate to oblong leaves. Its purple flowers form rather flat, solitary or corymbose flower heads c. 11mm (⅜in) across. It is found in dry bushland and often on the edges of thickets bordering a road in the Embu, Machakos, Kajiado and Nairobi districts (Kenya); Maasai, Tanga, Morogoro (Tanzania); Uganda, no record; elsewhere not identified.

V. brachycalyx   **Plate 580**
A trailing, pubescent climber with thin, wiry stems and ovate to elliptic entire leaves: corymbs terminal of many small purple heads 0.8cm (⅓in) across; achenes sparsely pubescent, four-angled, outer pappus of a few bristles. A showy climber with its purple pappus and florets protruding from the phyllaries long before flowering. The plant is abundant in all dry forest edges; altitude range 900–2400m (3000–8000ft). Recorded throughout Kenya; all regions except Tabora, Morogoro, Songea (Tanzania); all except eastern region (Uganda); also in Ethiopia, Zaire.

V. cinerascens   **Plate 683**
A bushy shrub, densely pubescent when young but becoming glabrous later, with spathulate leaves and loose round-topped terminal corymbs of often subsessile pale purple heads 0.5cm (⅓in) across. Achenes pubescent, eight to ten ribbed; outer pappus of small bristles. Found in dry bushland and common in some areas; altitude range 60–1650m (200–5400ft). Recorded in Magadi and Machakos (Kenya); lake areas, Maasai, Tanga, Mpwapwa, Kondoa (Tanzania); northern region (Uganda); also in Sudan, Ethiopia, Somalia.

V. galamensis (V. pauciflora)   **Plate 777**
A large, erect, usually unbranched annual with elliptic to linear leaves and large terminal sometimes solitary, scattered heads of blue-mauve florets. The phyllaries have a narrow to broad, recurved or spreading green appendage and the achenes are densely covered with soft hairs. It is a very variable, robust annual with a wide ecological range growing in cleared dry woodland or forest, from 800–2200m (2600–7200ft). It does not carry the great mauve-purple corymbose flower head of V. auriculifera but instead has medium-sized heads, c. 2cm (⅜in) across, of mauve-blue florets rather like those of the garden 'Sweet Sultan'. At higher altitudes in montane forest areas, the flower heads are broader and there are broad recurved appendages on the phyllaries, while the dry woodland form has bristle-like phyllaries and narrow heads and flowers. There are intermediates between these two types especially in the Nairobi area. The high altitude form has been given a separate name, V. afromontana. Both forms and intermediates are widespread throughout Kenya in their respective altitude ranges and are recorded in all regions except Mbeya, Iringa (Tanzania); northern and eastern regions (Uganda); also Ethiopia, Malawi, Zimbabwe, Mozambique.

V. galamensis ssp. **galamensis** var. **petitiana**   **Plate 778**
A variety of a subspecies of V. galamensis which is found in northern Kenya, Embu, Machakos, Magadi and the coast hinterland in Kenya and all regions of Tanzania at an altitude range of 750–1500m (350–4900ft). However, there are four varieties of

this subspecies and in addition five other subspecies recorded in East Africa which are only easily identified by botanists.

V. holstii   An erect, weak shrub with ovate serrate leaves which are white-woolly below; heads pale, woolly at base in small terminal corymbs 10mm (⅜in) across; florets white, tinged purple, achenes pubescent, ten-ribbed; outer pappus of short bristles. Altitude range 1000–2040m (3300–6800ft), abundant in the shrub layer of Nairobi forest; otherwise not abundant elsewhere but also recorded in Aberdares and Machakos (Kenya); lake areas, Maasai, Tanga, Mpwapwa, Kondoa (Tanzania); no record in Uganda; also in Malawi.

V. lasiopus   **Plate 581**
An erect, weakly shrubby perennial with ovate, coarsely serrate leaves which are pale-tomentose below, and terminal corymbs of cylindrical heads 1.7cm (1¾in) across; florets pale purple, achenes pubescent, ten-ribbed; outer pappus obscure. Abundant in abandoned cultivation at medium altitudes; altitude range 420–2450m (1400–8200ft), and recorded widely from Elgon and Kitale to Mt Kenya and Embu, Rift Valley and Central Province (Kenya); Maasai (Tanzania); Buganda (Uganda); also in Burundi, Zaire.

V. tufnelliae   **Plate 684**
A pubescent, scrambling or low erect shrub with ovate, often coarsely crenate leaves and large terminal panicles of purple heads, 7mm (¼in) across, achenes pubescent six to seven ridged, outer pappus of very short bristles. Locally common in bushland in western Kenya, rare in the East, and recorded at altitude range 1050–2400m (3500–7875ft) in Tinderet, Aberdares, Mt Kenya, western Kenya, Kisii and Rift Valley (Kenya); lake areas, Tabora, Mbeya, Iringa (Tanzania); all regions except northern (Uganda); also in southern Sudan, Burundi, Zaire.

V. turbinata   **Plate 685**
A tomentose herb from a woody rootstock with simple stems and ovate to elliptic leaves; heads broadly spreading with very numerous phyllaries, usually branched below each head so that these appear to be in diochasia or monochasia, the whole forming a flat-topped inflorescence 1.8cm (1¾in) across; florets purple; achenes sparsely pubescent between the four angles; outer pappus of short broad scales. The involucres over 10mm (⅜in) long. A most distinctive species; altitude range 1500–1860m (5000–6200ft) and mainly found in wooded grassland in western Kenya and Kitale (Kenya); Tanzania, no record; eastern region (Uganda); also in Sudan, Ethiopia.

73. Gentianaceae
THE GENTIAN FAMILY

A medium-sized, almost wholly herbaceous family. It is found mainly in temperate, or even arctic, climates but has some tropical representatives. These plants are almost always hairless, except sometimes for a few hairs on the corolla. Their leaves are opposite, without stipules and usually entire. The cymose inflorescences are formed of four to five regular flowers with a superior ovary of two united carpels. The fruit is usually a capsule with numerous seeds. Forty-five species in eleven genera in East Africa.

Swertia kilimandscharica **Plate 779**
An erect, usually unbranched, possibly short-lived perennial with sessile, lanceolate to oblong, acute leaves and irregular terminal racemes or corymbs of large white to pale blue flowers 2cm ($\frac{4}{5}$in) across. Conspicuous but often local in montane grassland from the bamboo to the alpine zone; altitude range 2300–3900m (7600–13,000ft). Elgon, Cheranganis, Aberdares and Mt Kenya (Kenya); Maasai, Mbeya (Tanzania); western and eastern regions (Uganda). Also in Rwanda, Ethiopia. One of fifteen species in East Africa.

S. usambarensis **Plate 96**
An erect, hairless herb with obovate basal leaves and linear to oblong stem leaves, branching above into a loose corymb of white flowers *c.* 15mm ($\frac{3}{5}$in) across. The species is variable with short or long petals and is common in shallow soils and short montane grassland throughout Kenya at altitudes of 1600–3900m (5250–12,800ft); Usambara Mountains (Tanzania); no record Uganda and elsewhere.

74. Primulaceae

THE PRIMROSE FAMILY

A medium-sized family of herbs found mainly in north temperate regions. Their leaves are simple and lack stipules. Flowers are usually regular, with five petals, nearly always united. Five stamens are placed opposite the petals, the ovary is superior with numerous ovules on a free central placentation and the fruit is a capsule. There are twenty species in East Africa belonging to five genera and nearly all are found at altitudes above 1520m (5000ft).

Anagallis serpens **Plate 686**
A creeping or trailing plant with pink flowers 5–15mm ($\frac{1}{5}$–$\frac{3}{5}$in) across. Twelve species in East Africa. Related to the Pimpernel which grows in the cornfields of Europe. It is common in alpine and subalpine streamside marshes at altitudes 1920–4500m (6300–14,750ft). Found on Mt Elgon, Aberdares, Mt Kenya (Kenya); Mt Kilimanjaro (Tanzania); also in Ethiopia.

Lysimachia volkensii **Plate 687**
A perennial herb, prostrate or erect, stems few to many; leaves subopposite or alternate, sessile, narrowly lanceolate, acute, auriculate at base. Raceme 2–25cm ($\frac{4}{5}$–10in) long, congested at anthesis, lax in fruit, flowers purple, 3–5mm ($\frac{1}{8}$–$\frac{1}{5}$in) long. Three species in East Africa. Found in upland grassland; altitude range 1200–2400m (4000–8000ft). Recorded in Nanyuki, Nyeri, Kericho, Narok, Nairobi (Kenya); Mbulu (Tanzania); Uganda and elsewhere, no record.

75. Plumbaginaceae
THE SEA LAVENDER FAMILY

A rather small family of herbs or shrublets found in most parts of the world, especially in saline areas. Their leaves are alternate and lack stipules. The flowers are regular with a five-toothed, tubular calyx having five, ten or fifteen ribs. The corolla is tubular and often blue or purple. There are five stamens and a superior ovary with one ovule but five styles, or one style with five branches. The fruit is dry. There are eleven species in East Africa belonging to three genera.

Ceratostigma abyssinicum   **Plate 835**
A low, rough shrub with stiff, sharply-pointed leaves and heads of blue flowers *c.* 15mm (⅝in) across. A rare plant, it is found on dry rocky outcrops and scarps in the Northern Frontier and near Isiolo at altitudes of 700–1500m (2300–4900ft) but no further south (Kenya); Tanzania and Uganda, no record; elsewhere Sudan, Ethiopia, Somalia.
NB This is the only African species of a genus confined to the Himalayas and western China.

Plumbago zeylanica   **Plate 97**
A trailing, hairless shrub with ovate leaves and white flowers, *c.* 16mm (⅝in) across, grouped in terminal spikes. It has a tubular calyx with stalked glands and a corolla with a long tube, *c.* 2cm (¾in) long and spreading lobes. It is common in dry bushland throughout Kenya, up to an altitude of 2000m (6600ft) where rainfall is below 400mm (16in) per annum; and is recorded in Maasai, Maswa, Iringa, Zanzibar (Tanzania); western Nile, Teso, Mengo (Uganda); also Ethiopia and Sudan south to Zimbabwe; and is widespread in the tropics.

76. Campanulaceae (including *Lobeliaceae*)
THE HAREBELL or BELL FLOWER FAMILY

A medium sized, mainly temperate climate family of herbs or, rarely, shrublets. Their leaves are nearly always alternate and without stipules. The flowers are usually blue and five in number: they are regular in the subfamily Campanuloideae and zygomorphic in the Lobelioideae. The stamens are separate in the Campanuloideae and connate in the Lobelioideae: the petals united, at least at the base. The ovary is more or less inferior and the fruit a capsule opening by pores or, rarely, a berry. There are eighty species in East Africa belonging to seven genera, nearly all found at altitudes above 1200m (4000ft).

Canarina abyssinica   **Plates 427 & 428**
A dull grey-green climber with a fleshy rootstock and triangular, ovate leaves. Its pendulous, solitary flowers 5–6cm (2–2⅜in) long are orange-red with a five-lobed calyx and a large corolla which is tubular or bell-shaped. This beautiful plant is uncommon but well worth looking for. It is found in wet forests at altitudes of 1620–2130m (5500–7000ft), especially in western and central Kenya; Arusha, Buha (Tanzania); Mbale (Elgon) (Uganda); also Ethiopia, southern Sudan. One other species in East Africa.

C. eminii
Plate 524

An epiphytic or terrestrial, usually glaucous, herb. Root thick, often with a corky surface layer. Stems erect and scandent, pendent up to several metres in length, usually with a fine purplish mottling. Leaf-blades triangular to ovate, up to 10cm (4in) long, acute with cordate to cuneate base, dentate, doubly dentate or double serrate. Corolla funnel-shaped to 7.5cm (3in) long, orange to orange-red with darker venation. Found in upland or riverine forest, epiphytic or among rocks; altitude range 1600–3200m (5300–10,500ft). Very similar to *C. abyssinica* which is not epiphytic, and has a slightly lower altitude range. It also lacks the purplish mottling of *C. eminii* and the leaf blades are triangular to pentagonal. Recorded in Elgon, Cheranganis, Tinderet, Mau, Aberdares, and Mt Kenya (Kenya); Rungwe, Kiwira Forest (Tanzania); Imatong Mts, Mbale (Uganda). Also in Ethiopia, eastern Zaire, Rwanda, Burundi, Malawi.

Cyphia glandulifera
Plate 780

A perennial herb of erect habit stemming from a buried tuber, which grows in shallow soil. Its leaves grow in a rosette at the base. An attractive pink flower with five petals c. 1cm (⅜in) long appears immediately after the rains. It is usually borne on an erect, straight stem, sometimes and especially in the Kedong Valley and on the Rift Valley escarpment, on a twining stem. There is also a much-branched form found generally in dry bushland. Found throughout Kenya except in very dry areas and Nyanza; in northern and central Tanzania; Uganda, not known; also in Ethiopia and Somalia. This is the most northern member of a genus commonest in South Africa. Six more species occur in southern Tanzania.

LOBELIA

Zygomorphic flowers, the corolla split along the upper side with two usually filiform upper teeth and three broader lower ones forming the lower lip; anthers fused around the style. Forty species in East Africa.

Lobelia baumanii
Plate 98

A perennial procumbent or straggling, rarely erect, herb up to 20cm (8in) long, often rooting at lower nodes. Stems ribbed or narrowly winged, more or less pubescent. Leaves with the lamina narrowly to broadly ovate or triangular, acute to acuminate at apex, cuneate or truncate at base, more or less pubescent on both sides but mainly on nerves. Leaves 25–80cm (1–3½in) long. Leaf margin coarsely dentate or serrate, venation especially beneath, prominent. Flowers in lax two- to six- (sometimes to twelve-) flowered shortly pedunculate racemes, bracts linear, sometimes broadest above the middle. Corolla, 13–30mm (½–1½in) long, white, mauve or blue with darker markings in throat, with two longitudinal crests in the mouth of the tube, split to the base at the back. Found in forest margins or forest floors, often on rocks or stream banks in shade; altitude range 800–2400m (2600–7875ft). Recorded in Aberdares, Mt Kenya, Nyambeni Hills (Kenya); Maasai, Tanga, Morogoro, Mpwapwa, Kondoa, Mbeya, Iringa, Songea (Tanzania); Uganda, no record; also Burundi, Zaire, Malawi, Zaire, Zimbabwe, Mozambique.

L. deckenii ssp. keniensis
Plates 582 & 583

A plant up to 3m (10ft) high in flower, suckering from the base. Stem unbranched, hollow with erect inflorescence. Leaves sessile, linear-lanceolate to lanceolate, 16–34cm (6–13½in) long, rounded to acute at apex, densely pubescent above and beneath, margin entire. Inflorescence up to 3m (10ft) tall, dense and cylindrical. Bracts up to 110mm (c. 4½in) long exceed the flowers. Corolla up to 50mm (2in) long, blue to blue-violet, petals united or splitting into lobes. In ssp. *keniensis* the anther tube is hairy on the back. (*L. deckenii* is a much taller plant, up to 8.5m (27ft) high with the corolla split to the base at the back). Found in wet marshland from 3240–4350m (10,500–14,600ft) and recorded only on Mt Kenya (Kenya).

L. deckenii ssp. sattimae   Plate 585

A plant up to 3m (10ft) tall, leaves 5–7.5cm (2–3in) wide, ovate-lanceolate, pubescent on both surfaces. Flower 25–35mm (1–1⅜in) long. Calyx lobes more or less pubescent. Corolla blue, not splitting into lobes but often with two lateral splits, pubescent within, thinly pubescent without. Stamens equalling, or shorter than, the corolla. Found on *Sattima* on the Aberdares in Kenya only and not known elsewhere. Altitude range 3350–3900m (9850–12,800ft). In *FTEA* it is recorded as a subspecies of *L. deckenii*.

NB The photograph is a 'close up' of the flower spike showing the flower corolla, as normally the blue corolla is only visible when standing near the plant and looking up into the spike.

L. duripratii   Plate 584

A mat forming, creeping herb, similar to *L. minutula* but with elliptic leaves narrowing gradually at apex and base and forming loose mats with pinkish flowers raised above leaf level on longer peduncles; corolla 10–14mm (⅜–⅝in) long. An uncommon plant found in wet montane short grassland; altitude range 1675–3070m (5500–10,050ft). Recorded in Elgon, Aberdares, Mt Kenya and Kitale (Kenya); Mbulu – Nou forest (Tanzania); Mbale – Mt Elgon (Uganda); elsewhere, no record.

L. holstii   Plate 688

A stiff perennial with ascending stems and oblanceolate, stalkless leaves. Rather few flowers are borne at the top of a leafless flowering stem; they may be reddish, purple or mauve (but not blue) *c.* 14mm (⅜in) long. It is the most common lobelia, found in rocky places in dry grassland throughout central and eastern Kenya at altitudes of 1500–3350m (5000–11,000ft). Found in Maasai, Tanga, Mpwapwa, Kondoa, Morogoro, Mbeya, Iringa (Tanzania); no record (Uganda); also in Ethiopia, Rwanda, Burundi, eastern Zaire.

L. telekii   Plate 836

A lobelia which is similar to ssp. *keniensis* and which grows to 4m (13ft) in height. It has much narrower leaves than ssp. *keniensis* and its stem has long, hairy, almost feathery, bracts which hang down and tend to hide the small white and purple flowers; flower spike 1.6m (5ft) tall; 15cm (6in) across. It is found in wet, stony ground on Mt Elgon, Mt Kenya and the Aberdares at an altitude of 3050m (10,000ft) or higher (Kenya); Elgon (Uganda); elsewhere, not known.

Wahlenbergia abyssinica (*Lightfootia abyssinica*)   Plate 586

Erect herbs with alternate, simple leaves, and regular flowers with free stamens, corolla *c.* 1cm (⅜in) across. The flowers are either solitary or borne in racemes or corymbs and in most of the twenty-five species which have been recorded in East Africa are white or blue. This very variable species has flowers which are more purple than blue with a corolla 1cm (⅜in) across. Altitude range 1–2700m (3–9000ft) alpine mountain zones to semi-arid areas such as Tsavo West where the specimen illustrated was growing (Kenya); all regions except lake areas and Tabora (Tanzania); Uganda, no record; also Ethiopia, Somalia, Zaire, Zambia, Malawi, Zimbabwe, Mozambique.

W. napiformis **Plate 587**
A perennial or biennial herb from a taproot. Stems usually few, erect up to 0.2–1m (4in to 3ft) tall (sometimes decumbent or straggling), glabrous, hirsute or puberulous. Leaves linear to lanceolate or narrowly elliptic up to 10–80mm (⅖–3in) long, acute, glabrous or pubescent, margin slightly revolute, midrib prominent beneath. Inflorescence leafy, somewhat spiky, sometimes very dense or with flowers, 5–23mm (⅕–1in) long, loosely clustered in the upper leaf axils. Corolla blue, purplish, yellowish or white, split almost to the base in linear lobes 3.5–7.5mm (⅙–⅓in) long. Found in deciduous woodland or grassland, old cultivation, roadsides usually in sandy or rocky soils; altitude range 0–2250m (0–7350ft) and recorded throughout East Africa, except northern Kenya and Morogoro (Tanzania); also Sudan, Ethiopia, south to Zimbabwe, Mozambique.

W. virgata **Plate 99**
A perennial, more or less erect, herb up to 70cm (27in) tall, from a woody taproot. Stems few, glabrous or more or less hirsute at least towards the base, furrowed usually with many erect branches. Leaves few, scale-like, widely scattered on the stem, lanceolate, acute, margin cartilaginous, sparsely denticulate; inflorescence lax. Corolla white 8–10mm (⅓–⅖in) long, slightly tinged bluish or yellow, lobed to about ⅔ length, puberulous inside near the base, glabrous outside. Calyx lobe 1.5–4mm (*c.* ⅙in) long; anthers 2.5–4mm (*c.* ⅙in) long. Found in upland grassland, often in patches of open soil such as eroded places or roadsides; altitude range 1100–2700m (3600–8850ft), and recorded in Elgon, Baringo (Ravine), Tinderet, Nanyuki, Nyeri and Chyulu Hills (Kenya); Maasai, Tanga, Tabora, Mbeya, Iringa (Tanzania); northern region (Uganda); also in Sudan, Ethiopia, Burundi, Malawi, Zimbabwe, Mozambique.

77. Goodeniaceae

Mainly an Australian family with two representatives in East Africa: (*Scaevola plumieri* and *S. taccada*). Leaves alternate, simple and exstipulate. Flowers in axillary cymes, irregular and five-merous, the stamens alternating with the corolla lobes. Ovary inferior, two-celled with one ovule in each, style simple, stigma capitate, surrounded by a fringed cup. Fruit a drupe.

Scaevola plumieri **Plate 100**
A small, decumbent, glabrous shrub up to 1m (3¼in) tall. Leaves obovate, sessile or shortly petiolate. Axils of leaves and bracts woolly or glabrescent. Flowers white, calyx truncate. The corolla tube glabrous outside, densely woolly inside, corolla tube 6mm (¼in) long. A coastal strand plant found in Kenya and Tanzania coastal regions only; Uganda, not known; also in Somalia and Mozambique.

78. Boraginaceae (including *Ehretiaceae*)
THE FORGET-ME-NOT FAMILY

A medium-sized family of herbs, mainly of temperate zones but including a group of mainly tropical trees and shrubs (Ehretioideae). They usually have stiff and bristly hairs and their leaves are simple, nearly always alternate and lacking stipules. The corolla is usually regular, five-lobed and often blue or white. In the two woody genera, *Cordia* and *Ehretia*, which have twenty-nine species in East Africa, the fruit is a drupe surrounded by a persistent calyx. In the ten herbaceous genera, which have about thirty-six species in East Africa, they have two or more, often four, dry nutlets. In all these herbaceous genera, except *Heliotropium*, the ovary consists of four loculi, each with a single ovule, which becomes four single-seeded nutlets, the style arising between them. This distinctive arrangement is found only here and in the Labiatae.

CORDIA
The style is twice forked so there are four separate stigmas.

Cordia africana (*C. holstii, C. abyssinica*)   **Plate 101**
A resplendent forest tree which generally reaches up to 10m (33ft) in height but can occasionally achieve the majesty of 24m (80ft). The stalkless flowers are most decorative, massed in white panicles. Corolla: *c.* 25mm (1in) across. They are shorter than the leaves, white in colour and look as though they are made of paper. The strong ribbed calyx is a soft brown. This tree is widespread in forests at 1040–2100m (3400–6900ft), especially near Meru and Kakamega (Kenya); all regions except southern – Songea (Tanzania); all regions (Uganda); also southern Sudan, Ethiopia, Zaire, Malawi.

CYNOGLOSSUM
Eight species in East Africa. Has a corolla with a short tube more or less closed at the throat by protuberances on the bases of the five spreading lobes; the nutlets bear barbed spines.

Cynoglossum amplifolium (*C. lancifolium*)   **Plate 837**
An erect, perennial herb covered with soft down with petiolate, ovate-elliptic lower leaves and sessile upper ones, a rarer species than *C. geometricum* and found principally near Uplands (Kenya). Leaves scabrid beneath when rubbed towards the apex. The large, bright blue flowers, 2–3mm (*c.* ⅛in) across, are in raceme-like scorpioid cymes. The nutlets are uniformly spiny all over which distinguishes it from *C. lancifolium*, on which they are smooth except for a centre row of spines. Altitude range 2700–3350m (*c.* 9000–11,000ft). Mainly on Aberdares (Kenya); Maasai, Morogoro, Mbeya, Iringa (Tanzania); western, eastern regions of Uganda; also Ethiopia, Rwanda, Zaire, Zimbabwe.

C. coeruleum   **Plate 838**
A trailing species, although sometimes it has a shrubby appearance. It is a rough-feeling perennial with linear leaves arranged in rosettes and small blue flowers 2–3mm (*c.* ⅛in) across. The nutlets are usually spiny all over. It is common all over Kenya in upland grassland at the higher altitudes. Altitude range 1200–3150m (4000–10,500ft). All regions except lake areas, Kondoa and Mpwapwa (Tanzania); eastern region – Jinja, Lake Kioga (Uganda); also Ethiopia.

C. geometricum   Plate 839

An erect herb with entire leaves and bright blue flowers *c.* 8mm (⅓in) across in raceme-like cymes which are coiled during development. The calyx is five-lobed, the corolla has a short tube and five spreading lobes and there are five stamens with short filaments. It is the most common *Cynoglossum* and widespread throughout Kenya in montane forest clearings, along the sides of paths and as a field weed at higher altitudes, 1080–3300m (3600–11,000ft). Found in lake areas, Maasai, Tanga, Tabora, eastern region, Mbeya, Iringa, Njombe (Tanzania); northern region (Gulu), western and eastern regions (Uganda); also Ethiopia, Zaire, Rwanda, Malawi, Zimbabwe.

Cystostemon hispidus (*Vaupelia hispida*)   Plate 840

An erect strigose annual with elliptic leaves and blue flowers 1cm (⅜in) across, fully open, in raceme-like monochasial cymes. Locally common in grassland; altitude range 800–1900m (2600–6250ft) and recorded in Kajiado and especially in the Rift Valley (Kenya); lake areas, Maasai, Shinyanga (Tanzania); Uganda and elsewhere, no record.

Echiochilon lithospermoides   Plate 588

An erect, woody annual with small, stalkless, ovate leaves and pink-mauve flowers *c.* 5mm (⅕in) across. The leaves are an attractive blue-green. Altitude range 1200–1700m (4000–5700ft). It is locally common in dry bushland in the Nanyuki and Kajiado districts (Kenya); Tanzania and Uganda, no record; also southern Ethiopia.

EHRETIA

The style is divided once; the fruit a drupe; the calyx deeply divided.

Ehretia cymosa   Plate 102

A tree which grows up to 18m (60ft) high that is usually found on the edge of forests. Its leaves are ovate, acute and entire and its white, stalkless flowers, 7mm (*c.* ¼in) across, form many-flowered, down-covered, terminal panicles with the corolla not campanulate and three times the length of the calyx. Twelve species in East Africa. This tree is widely distributed in areas of high rainfall, over 1125mm (45in) per annum at altitudes of 1220–1830m (4000–6000ft) (Kenya); all regions of Tanzania; western, eastern and Buganda regions (Uganda); also Ethiopia south to Zimbabwe.

HELIOTROPIUM

Flowers in scorpioid cymes; fruit dry, four-celled, splitting into two or four portions. Fourteen species in East Africa.

Heliotropium steudneri   Plate 103

A perennial herb with elongating spikes of white or creamy-white flowers *c.* 5mm (*c.* ¼in) across which is common almost everywhere in Kenya from 1100–2250m (3500–7400ft), although preferring disturbed dry grassland alongside cut-off drains and old reverted fields. Recorded in lake areas, Maasai, Tanga, Mbeya (Tanzania); northern region – Gulu (Uganda); also Sudan, Ethiopia and Somalia. It is a relative of *H. peruvianum*, the Cherry Pie of gardens in Europe.

H. undulatifolium   Plate 104

A bushy herb with short spikes of crowded, creamy-white flowers *c.* 7mm (*c.* ¼in) across and slightly hairy leaves. It is common in the drier, medium-altitude areas in grassland and along the sides of roads and tracks; altitude range 60–2250m (200–7500ft) (Kenya); lake areas, Maasai, Tanga – one record only Mpwapwa, Kondoa (Tanzania); no record Uganda; also Somalia.

H. zeylanicum (H. subulatum) Plate 234
A spreading hairy, erect perennial herb from a woody rootstock, with elliptic to linear leaves and long spikes of yellow flowers 2mm ($\frac{1}{12}$in) across. All other *Heliotropium* species recorded in the Kenya uplands above c. 1000m (3280ft) have white flowers. Altitude range 60–1710m (200–5700ft). It is locally common in dry bushland in Rift Valley, Machakos and Kajiado (Kenya); all regions except Songea (Tanzania); northern and eastern regions (Uganda); also in Somalia.

79. Solanaceae
THE POTATO, TOBACCO or DEADLY NIGHTSHADE FAMILY

A large family of erect or climbing herbs, shrubs or, very rarely, trees, found throughout the world but especially common in tropical America where *Solanum* alone has over 1000 species. These plants are often poisonous. Their leaves are alternate and lack stipules. Their flowers are regular or slightly irregular with a tubular calyx, four- to five-toothed or lobed, sometimes inflated in fruit, and a four- to five-lobed corolla with the lobes induplicate-valvate. The fruit is a berry or a capsule, usually many-seeded. Sixty-five species in nine genera in East Africa. The so-called Irish Potato, *Solanum tuberosum*, belongs to this family but the Sweet Potato, *Ipomoea batatas*, belongs to the Convolvulaceae.

Cestrum aurantiacum Plate 388
An erect pubescent shrub often up to 3m (10ft) high, with ovate leaves and terminal panicles of orange flowers with long corollas, tube c. 22mm (1in) long, lobe 6mm ($\frac{1}{4}$in) long. Local in disturbed montane forest areas and a garden escape introduced from America. Recorded in Kenya and Tanzania; altitude range 900–2500m (2950–8200ft).

Datura stramonium Plate 105
An erect, hairless annual with ovate, dentate leaves, dichotomously branched, with a white flower c. 8cm (3in) long in the form of a small trumpet at each fork. It is widespread throughout East Africa at 600–2300m (2000–7500ft) and travellers will see it everywhere in Kenya, growing by roadsides and in disturbed patches and old cultivated ground. Its seeds are highly poisonous and can give rise to extreme hallucinations and excessive euphoria. Maasai, Tanga, Mpwapwa, Kondoa and eastern region (Tanzania); western and eastern regions (Uganda); now a weed throughout the world. It is an introduced weed, probably from America, not indigenous to East Africa.

Lycium shawii (L. europaeum) Plate 106
A spiny shrub with narrow, spathulate-obovate, or oblong glabrous, or puberulous leaves up to 2cm ($\frac{3}{4}$in) long. Flowers solitary, on stalks 8mm ($\frac{1}{3}$in) long, calyx shortly tubular and lobed; corolla tube brownish 1.5cm ($\frac{3}{4}$in) long, lobes five 0.8cm ($\frac{1}{3}$in) across, white with a purple tinge, oval, obtuse and ciliate. Fruit (berries) orange or red. Found in dry bush country; altitude range 0–1500m (0–5000ft) in northern and southern districts, the Rift Valley and coast (Kenya); Maasai, Tanga, Mpwapwa,

Kondoa, Mbeya (Tanzania); northern region – Gulu (Uganda); also in Sudan, Ethiopia, Somalia, Malawi, Zambia, Zimbabwe, Mozambique.

Nicotiana glauca
Plate 389
An erect, loose shrub with ovate leaves on long stalks and yellow-orange flowers which have a corolla 35mm (1⅜in) long with a long narrow tube. It is not a truly indigenous plant but an escape from cultivation which is increasingly found wild in Nairobi and the Rift Valley near Naivasha at 1520–2130m (5000–7000ft) (Kenya); Tanzania and Uganda, no record; elsewhere, no record.

N. rustica
Plate 781
An erect, coarse, annual herb up to 1.5m (4¾ft) high, leaves elliptic-lanceolate, fleshy viscid, blade up to 80cm (3in) long. Flowers greenish-yellow 12–17mm (½–¾in) long, 6–8mm (¼–⅓in) across. Found growing in abandoned cultivation and on roadsides throughout Kenya; altitude range 1100–2300m (3600–7550ft). It was the first tobacco grown by colonists in America but has now been superseded by *N. tabacum*, native to South America. Maasai (Tanzania); northern region (Uganda); elsewhere, no record.

N. tabacum
Plate 782
An erect, glandular-pubescent annual with elliptic to ovate leaves and a terminal panicle of white to pink flowers, corolla tube 7cm (*c.* 3in) long, lobes 4cm (1⅜in) across. This is the cultivated tobacco plant of gardens which has escaped and established itself locally. Altitude range 1200–2400m (4000–8000ft). Found in the Cheranganis, Machakos, Nairobi and Kajiado (Kenya); Maasai, Tanga, Tabora (Tanzania); Uganda and elsewhere, no record.

SOLANUM
Herbs, or softly woody shrubs, or small trees, often with stellate hairs; leaves alternate; corolla regular with five spreading lobes; five stamens, often unequal; the anthers often opening by pores; fruit a berry. About fifty species in East Africa, a few of them not native.

Solanum aculeastrum
Plate 589
A large shrub or small tree, up to 6m (20ft) in height; young branches clothed in a short, dense, white, stellate tomentum and armed with robust, usually curved prickles, also on underside of leaves, leaves elliptic, pinnately-lobed or entire, up to 7cm (17in) long, glabrescent above; flowers, white or yellow-white, in lateral umbel-like cymes, stellate-hairy outside, glabrous within, corolla lobe *c.* 1.25cm (⅓in) long. The fruit, a large berry, is globose, 3.75–5cm (1½–2in) diameter, warty, lemon yellow in colour, edible but very bitter. Found in upland forest edges, sometimes used as a hedge plant and widespread at altitude range 1650–2640m (5500–8800ft) (Kenya); all regions except Mpwapwa, Kondoa, Tabora (Tanzania); all regions except northern – Gulu (Uganda); also in Zaire to Zimbabwe, Mozambique.

S. aculeatissimum A soft, tomentose perennial with prickles as well as soft hairs on stems and leaves, and lateral sessile umbels of pale purple flowers *c.* 1.5cm (⅜in) long. Locally common in clearings in montane forest; altitude range 900–2700m (3000–9000ft) and recorded in Elgon, Cheranganis, Mau, Aberdares, Kitale, Machakos and Kajiado (Kenya). It is more common than *S. aculeastrum* which is found in much the same habitat, and which is white-tomentose and coarsely prickly. Maasai, Shinyanga, Tanga, Tabora, Mbeya, Iringa (Tanzania);

northern (Gulu) and western regions (Uganda); also Rwanda and south to Mozambique.

S. anguivi (*S. indicum*)   **Plate 590**
An erect, woody, pubescent herb or shrub with ovate leaves which are sinuate to pinnately lobed; prickles usually on stems and leaves; flowers, 1cm (⅜in) across, mauve to a good purple in small extra-axillary racemes. A variable and widespread plant which is sometimes cultivated for its fruits; altitude range 1300–2700m (4300–9000ft); recorded throughout western, central and eastern districts (Kenya); all regions (Tanzania and Uganda); also in Ethiopia to Mozambique, Zimbabwe.

S. coagulans (*S. dubium*)   **Plate 841**
A much-branched prickly shrub about 40cm (16in) high. The prickles on the branches are slender, needle-like and straight, 6mm (¼in) long. Leaves ovate or ovate-oblanceolate, 6.5cm (2¾in) long, sinuate-lobate, stellate-tomentose on both sides. Inflorescence four- to five-flowered *c.* 12mm (½in) across, corolla violet or rarely white 1.25cm (½in) across. Found in seasonally flooded grassland and near swampy areas; altitude range 60–1620m (200–5400ft). Widespread in Kenya, northern Tanzania and northern region (Gulu) in Uganda. Also in Ethiopia and Somalia.

S. giganteum   A loose shrub with spiny stems and oblanceolate entire leaves and dense almost terminal corymbs of white flowers. Corolla 13mm (½in) across. It is an uncommon plant found in wet montane forests in the Aberdares, Mt Kenya and the Nyambeni Hills from 1500–2250m (5100–7400ft) (Kenya); lake areas, Maasai, Shinyanga, Tanga, Kigoma, Tabora, eastern region (Tanzania); all regions except northern (Uganda); also Ethiopia, Zimbabwe.

S. incanum   **Plate 591**
An erect, felty-haired shrub, commonly known as the Sodom Apple, which often has prickles on its stem and stalks. Its leaves are ovate to lanceolate and entire to sinuate. The blue to mauve flowers are grouped in racemes. Corolla *c.* 13mm (½in) across. It is found all over East Africa in waste ground and along roadsides where the soil has been scraped away or eroded. It is less common over 2300m (7500ft). Also found throughout tropical Africa.

S. nakurense   An erect unarmed herb or shrub from a trailing woody rootstock with broad-elliptic, entire leaves and nearly terminal corymbs of white to pale blue flowers *c.* 8mm (⅜in) across. It is locally common in evergreen upland bushland on Mt Elgon, the Cheranganis, Tinderet, Mau, the Aberdares, Kitale, Kisii, Narok and Rift Valley, from 900–2850m (3000–9350ft) (Kenya); Maasai, Shinyanga, Tanga, Mbeya, Iringa (Tanzania); eastern region – Jinja, Lake Kioga (Uganda); also Ethiopia.

S. nigrum   A soft erect, downy or hairless unarmed annual with elliptic entire or crenate leaves; the inflorescence is extra-axillary and umbellate. The flowers are white, 4mm (*c.* ⅛in) across, and the fruits orange or black. It is a very variable plant which is a common weed in cultivated land below 2100m (7000ft) and grows throughout East Africa from 5–2700m (16–8900ft). Widespread in Tanzania; found throughout tropical Africa. Not found in very dry places.

S. schumannianum **Plate 842**
An erect loose shrub, glabrescent except for the bristly stem, with narrowly elliptic leaves and subterminal corymbs of pale blue flowers *c.* 13mm (½in) across. Locally common in dry montane forest; altitude range 1400–2400m (4600–7875ft); recorded in Aberdares, Mt Kenya and Limuru – Kieni forest (Kenya); Maasai, Shinyanga, Tanga, Tabora, eastern region, Mbeya, Iringa (Tanzania); Uganda and elsewhere, no record.

S. sessilistellatum **Plate 689**
A soft-haired perennial with prickles replacing hairs on its stem and leaves and lateral, almost stalkless umbels of pale purple flowers 27–50mm (1–2in) across. Its leaves are alternate, simple or pinnately lobed, narrowing gradually at the base. It is a high altitude species found in clearings in montane forest at 2390–3050m (7500–10,000ft) in Cheranganis, Elgon, Aberdares, Mt Kenya (Kenya); Tanzania, Uganda, elsewhere, not known.

S. taitense A prickly-stemmed weak and often supported shrub covered in soft hairs with ovate pinnately-lobed leaves and small lateral sessile umbels of one to two white or mauve flowers 10mm (*c.* ⅖in) across. It is locally common in dry *Acacia* bushland in Rift Valley, Magadi and Kajiado from 15–1500m (50–5000ft) (Kenya); lake areas, Maasai, Shinyanga, Tanga (Tanzania); Uganda and elsewhere, no record.

80. Convolvulaceae

THE BINDWEED, MORNING GLORY or SWEET POTATO FAMILY

A medium-sized family consisting mainly of twining plants, found throughout the world, but also including erect herbs, shrublets, shrubs and even trees. Their leaves are alternate, usually without stipules and entire, sometimes palmately lobed and, rarely, pinnate. The flowers are usually regular with the calyx five- (sometimes four-) partite and persistent. The corolla is usually funnel-shaped, unlobed or slightly five-lobed, or rarely, cylindrical. The ovary is superior, uni- to quadrilocular with one to four ovules in each loculus. The fruit may be a capsule or indehiscent and is most often four-seeded. There are 170 species in East Africa belonging to twenty-two genera. They include the *Cuscuta* which, apart from *Cassytha* in the Lauraceae are the only twining parasites found in Africa.

ASTRIPOMOEA

Resembles *Ipomoea* except in its stellate hairs and the stems are usually erect or prostrate, rarely climbing. Ten species in East Africa.

Astripomoea grantii A short-lived perennial up to 1.2m (3½ft) tall with erect or rarely decumbent stems, leaves broadly elliptic or obovate, 6–10cm (2⅖–4in) long and 4–6cm (1⅗–2⅖in) wide, blunt and mucronoate at the apex, narrowly cuneate at the base, mostly rather coarsely tomentose. Flower purple with paler limb or white with purple eye, corolla 2–3.5cm (⅘–1⅖in) long. It is mainly restricted to western Kenya in grassland, bushland and rocky places, often on poor soils; altitude range 1200–1920m (4000–6300ft). Intermediates with *A. hyocyamoides* occur down to 700m (2300ft). It has been recorded in Rift Valley and Nairobi (Kenya); lake areas, Tabora, possibly Mbeya, Iringa (Tanzania); all except northern regions (Uganda); also eastern Zaire.

NB *Astripomoea* can often be seen in great masses along the main Nairobi–Mombasa road from Sultan Hamud to Mtito Andei (Kenya) after the rains where to the casual traveller they may look like great drifts of upright *Ipomoea*. The most widespread species is *A. malvacea*, but *A. lachnosperma* and *A. hyoscymoides* are the two species recorded on the Nairobi–Magadi road and the Nairobi–Mombasa road.

A. hyoscyamoides **Plate 107**
A shrubby short-lived perennial or annual with erect stems, 0.5–2.4m (1½–7½ft) tall; leaves elliptic or elliptic-lanceolate, (rarely obovate-rhomboid) either borne normally on the stem or high up on the peduncles, 2.16cm (⅘in) long and 1.1–6.3cm (⅖–2½in) wide, acute and apiculate at the apex, cuneate at the base, entire or wavy about the middle, rather finely tomentose; corolla white with purple tube, funnel-shaped, 1.8–3.8cm (⅗–1½in) long. Restricted to lower altitudes from 50–1200m (170–4000ft) in desert grassland, bushland and disturbed areas. Recorded in Embu, Machakos and Kajiado (Kenya); lake areas, northern and central Tanzania; elsewhere, not known.

A. lachnosperma **Plate 108**
An annual, stems simple, erect 20–120cm (7¾–47in) tall, floccosely pubescent. Leaf-blade ovate or rhomboid, 3.5–12cm (1⅖–5in) long, acute or rounded at the apex, cuneate or truncate at the base, with margin wavy above the middle but entire below, floccose-pubescent. Flowers in crowded about six-flowered cymes. Corolla white with purple centre up to 2cm (⅘in) long; limb *c.* 2cm (⅘in) diameter. Altitude range 750–2600m (2500–8500ft). Found in *Acacia-Commiphora* deciduous bushland, roadsides and rocky places in dry bush, often in red soil. Recorded in Northern Frontier districts, West Suk, Kajiado (Kenya); Bukoba, Mpwapwà (Tanzania); Karamoja, Bunyoro (Uganda); also in Eritrea, Ethiopia, Sudan.

A. malvacea An extremely variable sub-shrubby perennial with prostrate or erect stems; leaves elliptic to broadly ovate, up to 12cm (4¾in) long and 0.8–9cm (3/10–3½in) wide, acute to rounded at the apex, cuneate to subcordate at the base. Flower rose or mauve (very rarely white). Corolla 2.5–5cm (1–2in) long. Sepals round to lanceolate, 5–10mm (⅕–⅖in) long and very narrow (*c.* 2mm) (*c.* 1/12in). It is widespread in dry grassland and wooded grassland throughout East Africa, also Malawi, Zimbabwe, Mozambique. Altitude range 60–2240m (200–7359ft). It is divisible into a number of poorly defined varieties which are distinctive enough to have been considered as separate species in the past. These varieties are five in number, each having its own habitat range and can be pursued in *FTEA*.

1 Encephalartos tegulaneus, p.18

2 Polygonum salicifolium, p.39

3 Citrullus colocynthis, p.58

4 Coccinia grandis, p.58

5 Combretum exalatum, p.65

6 Dalechampia scandens var. cordofanus, p.82

193

7 **Euphorbia kibwezensis**, p.83

8 **Alchemilla fischeri**, p.86

9 **Alchemilla johnstonii**, p.86

10 **Alchemilla rothii**, p.87

12 **Helinus integrifolius**, p.132

11 **Mucuna gigantea** var. **quadrialata**, p.112

13 Cyphostemma adenocaule, p.132

14 Cyphostemma nieriense, p.133

15 Balanites glabra, p.134

16 Caralluma dummeri, p.144

17 Pergularia daemia, p.148

18 Agathisanthemum bojeri, p.150

19 Acanthospermum hispidum, p.159

21 Lippia carviodora, p.399

20 Justicia betonica, p.393

22 Orthosiphon pallidus, p.405

23 Aneilema brenanianum, p.411

24 Chlorophytum gallabatense, p.422

25 Dipcadi viride, p.423

26 Arisaema mildbraedii, p.425

27 Bonatea steudneri, p.433

28 Habenaria malacophylla, p.437

198

29 Anemone thomsonii, p.19

30 Clematis brachiata, p.19

31 Nymphaea lotus, p.20

32 Cadaba mirabilis, p.25

33 Capparis cartilaginea, p.25

34 Gynandropsis gynandra, p.27

199

35 **Maerua kirkii**, p.28

36 **Farsetia stenoptera**, p.29

37 **Mollugo nudicaulis**, p.36

38 **Geranium aculeolatum**, p.45

39 **Monsonia angustifolia**, p.46

40 **Pelargonium alchemilloides**, p.46

41 Impatiens burtonii, p.48

42 Gnidia subcordata, p.53

43 Commicarpus plumbagineus, p.55

44 Tetracera boiviniana, p.56

45 Passiflora subpeltata, p.57

46 Lagenaria sphaerica, p.59

47 Momordica foetida, p.60

48 Begonia meyeri-johannis, p.62

49 Grewia tembensis
var. **kakothamnos**, p.68

50 Grewia tenax, p.69

51 Grewia truncata, p.69

52 Dombeya burgessiae, p.71

53 **Adansonia digitata**, p.74

54 **Adansonia digitata**, p.74

56 **Hibiscus fuscus**, p.76

55 **Hibiscus flavifolius**, p.76

57 **Triaspis niedenzuiana**, p.81

58 **Bauhinia taitensis**, p.89

59 **Delonix elata**, p.94

60 **Crabbea velutina**, p.389

61 **Ophrestia hedysaroides**, p.113

62 **Clausena anisata**, p.134

63 **Turraea fischeri**, p.135

64 **Turraea mombassana**, p.136

65 **Turraea parvifolia**, p.136

66 Alepidea longifolia, p.139

67 Jasminum floribundum, p.141

68 Acokanthera schimperi, p.142

69 Carissa edulis, p.142

70 Saba comorensis, p.143

71 Kanahia laniflora, p.147

72 Kanahia laniflora, p.147

73 Carphalea glaucescens, p.150

74 Chassalia umbraticola, p.150

75 Conostomium keniense, p.150

76 Conostomium quadrangulare, p.151

77 Feretia apodanthera ssp. **keniensis**, p.151

78 Gardenia ternifolia var. **jovis-tonantis**, p.152

79 Heinsia crinita ssp. **parviflora**, p.152

80 Oldenlandia johnstonii, p.153

81 Pavetta abyssinica, p.154

82 Pavetta stenosepala, p.155

83 Pentas longiflora, p.155

84 Psychotria amboniana, p.156

85 Lonicera japonica, p.157

86 Dipsacus pinnatifidus, p.157

87 Scabiosa austro-africana, p.158

88 Anthemis tigrensis, p.159

89 Athroisma psyllioides, p.160

90 Bidens pilosa, p.161

91 Echinops angustilobus, p.165

92 Echinops hispidus, p.165

93 Eupatorium adenophorum, p.166

94 Helichrysum glumaceum, p.170

95 Tarchonanthus camphoratus, p.178

96 Swertia usambarensis, p.181

97 Plumbago zeylanica, p.182

98 Lobelia baumanii, p.183

99 Wahlenbergia virgata, p.185

100 Scaevola plumieri, p.185

101 Cordia africana, p.186

102 Ehretia cymosa, p.187

103 Heliotropium steudneri, p.187

213

104 Heliotropium undulatifolium, p.187

105 Datura stramonium, p.188

106 Lycium shawii, p.188

107 Astripomoea hyoscyamoides, p.192

108 Astripomoea lachnosperma, p.192

109 Ipomoea garckeana, p.370

110 Ipomoea longituba, p.371

111 Ipomoea spathulata, p.372

112 Craterostigma hirsutum, p.374

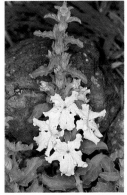
113 Cycnium ajugifolium, p.375

114 Cycnium tubulosum ssp. *tubulosum*, p.376

115 Hebenstretia angolensis, p.377

116 Striga linearifolia, p.378

117 Streptocarpus exsertus, p.380

118 **Barleria acanthoides**, p.387

119 **Barleria argentea**, p.387

120 **Barleria ramulosa**, p.388

121 **Barleria taitensis**, p.388

122 **Crabbea velutina**, p.389

123 **Crossandra friesiorum**, p.389

124 Justicia matammensis, p.394

125 Justicia uncinulata, p.394

126 Mimulopsis solmsii, p.394

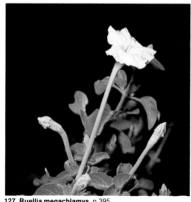
127 Ruellia megachlamys, p.395

128 Thunbergia alata (white form), p.396

129 Thunbergia guerkeana, p.397

130 Chascanum hildebrandtii, p.397

131 Clerodendrum rotundifolium, p.398

132 Priva curtisiae, p.399

133 Aeollanthus zanzibaricus, p.401

134 Becium sp. A, p.402

135 Leucas deflexa, p.403

136 Leucas grandis, p.403

137 Leucas urticifolia, p.404

138 Eriocaulon schimperi, p.415

139 Androcymbium melanthoides, p.417

140 Anthericum cameronii, p.418

141 Anthericum cooperi, p.418

142 Anthericum subpetiolatum, p.419

143 Anthericum suffruticosum, p.419

144 Anthericum venulosum, p.419

145 Chlorophytum bakeri, p.421

147 Chlorophytum tenuifolium, p.422

146 Chlorophytum macrophyllum, p.422

148 Ornithogalum donaldsonii, p.424

149 Trachyandra saltii, p.425

150 Gladiolus ukambanensis, p.428

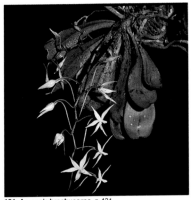

151 Aerangis brachycarpa, p.431

152 Aerangis luteo-alba var. **rhodosticta,** p.432

153 Aerangis thomsonii, p.432

154 Angraecum giryamae, p.432

155 Bolusiella maudiae, p.433

156 Cyrtorchis arcuata, p.433

157 Diaphananthe tenuicalcar, p.434

158 Rangaeris amaniensis, p.440

159 Vanilla roscheri, p.441

160 Ypsilopus longifolia, p.442

224

161 Clematis simensis, p.19

162 Piper capense, p.22

163 Boscia coriacea, p.23

164 Boscia mossambicensis, p.24

165 Cadaba farinosa, p.24

166 Crateva adansonii, p.27

225

167 **Maerua edulis**, p.27

169 **Maerua subcordata**, p.28

168 **Maerua endlichii**, p.27

170 **Maerua triphylla**, p.28

171 **Thylachium africanum**, p.29

226

172 Raphanus raphanistrum, p.29

173 Caylusea abyssinica, p.31

174 Crassula alba, p.33

175 Crassula pentandra var. phyturus, p.34

176 Calyptrotheca somalensis, p.37

177 Phytolacca dodecandra, p.40

178 Cyathula cylindrica, p.42

179 Cyathula orthacantha, p.42

180 Cyathula polycephala, p.42

181 Gomphrena celosioides, p.42

182 Sericocomopsis hildebrandtii, p.43

183 Sericocomopsis pallida, p.43

184 Monsonia longipes, p.46

185 Lawsonia inermis, p.52

186 Protea gaguedi, p.55

187 Oncoba routledgei, p.56

188 Combretum aculeatum, p.65

189 Dombeya kirkii, p.71

190 Dombeya rotundifolia, p.71

192 Abutilon rehmannii, p.75

191 Abutilon grandiflorum, p.74

193 Hibiscus cannabinus, p.76

194 Hibiscus trionum, p.78

195 **Sida ovata**, p.80

196 **Caucanthus albidus**, p.81

197 **Argomuellera macrophylla**, p.81

198 **Croton dichogamus**, p.81

199 **Tragia impedita**, p.85

200 **Tragia insuavis**, p.85

201 **Pterolobium stellatum**, p.94

202 **Crotalaria barkae**, p.100

203 **Acacia brevispica**, p.123

204 **Acacia drepanolobium**, p.123

206 **Acacia mellifera** ssp. **mellifera**, p.123

207 **Acacia senegal**, p.124

205 Acacia mellifera ssp. **mellifera**, p.123

233

208 Albizia anthelmintica, p.124

209 Albizia anthelmintica, p.124

210 Albizia grandibracteata, p.125

234

211 **Maytenus arbutifolia**, p.126

212 **Maytenus senegalensis**, p.126

213 **Pyrenacantha malvifolia**, p.127

214 **Cyphostemma nodiglandulosum**, p.133

215 **Boswellia neglecta**, p.134

216 **Trichilia emetica**, p.135

217 Lepisanthes senegalensis, p.137

218 Lannea alata, p.138

219 Diplolophium africanum, p.140

220 Haplosciadium abyssinicum, p.140

221 Gomphocarpus fruticosus, p.146

222 Gomphocarpus integer, p.146

223 Gomphocarpus semilunatus, p.147

224 Gomphocarpus stenophyllus, p.147

225 Sarcostemma andongense, p.149

226 Gardenia volkensii, p.152

227 Sambucus africana, p.157

228 Conyza pyrrhopappa var. oblongifolia, p.164

237

229 Conyza stricta, p.164

230 Echinops hoehnelii, p.166

231 Helichrysum brownei, p.170

232 Senecio syringifolius, p.176

233 Tagetes minuta, p.178

234 Heliotropium zeylanicum, p.188

235 Hildebrandtia obcordata, p.369

236 Pedaliodiscus macrocarpus, p.382

237 Asystasia schimperi, p.386

238 Barleria eranthemoides, p.387

239 Barleria sp. A, p.387

240 Ecbolium amplexicaule, p.391

241 Lippia javanica, p.399

243 Leonotis africana, p.403

244 Ottelia ulvifolia (with Lemna sp.), p.410

245 Asparagus africanus, p.420

246 Asparagus racemosus, p.421

242 **Lippia ukambensis,** p.399

247 Drimia altissima, p.423

248 Sansevieria intermedia, p.430

250 Tridactyle bicaudata, p.441

249 Polystachya transvaalensis, p.440

251 Tridactyle furcistipes, p.441

252 Ranunculus multifidus, p.20

255 Cleome angustifolia, p.26

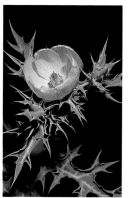

253 Argemone mexicana, p.22

254 Streptopetalum serratum, p.23

256 Kalanchoe citrina, p.34

257 Kalanchoe densiflora, p.34

258 Kalanchoe lanceolata, p.34

259 Sedum ruwenzoriense, p.35

260 Portulaca grandiflora, p.37

261 Portulaca kermesina, p.37

262 Portulaca quadrifida, p.38

263 Talinum caffrum, p.38

264 Linum volkensii, p.43

265 Tribulus cistoides, p.44

266 Tribulus terrestris, p.44

267 Tribulus zeyheri ssp. macranthus, p.44

268 Monsonia ovata, p.46

269 Oxalis corniculata, p.47

271 Coccinia adoensis, p.58

270 Gnidia involucrata, p.53

272 Cucumis sp., p.59

273 Cucumis prophetarum, p.59

274 Momordica boivinii, p.60

275 Peponium vogelii, p.61

276 Ochna holstii, p.62

277 Ochna mossambicensis, p.63

278 Ochna ovata, p.63

279 Hypericum revolutum, p.67

280 Hypericum revolutum, p.67

281 Hypericum roeperianum, p.67

282 Grewia bicolor, p.68

283 Triumfetta brachyceras, p.70

284 Triumfetta flavescens, p.70

285 Hermannia sp. **A**, p.72

286 Hermannia uhligii, p.72

287 Melhania angustifolia, p.72

288 Melhania ovata, p.73

289 Melhania parviflora, p.73

290 Abutilon mauritianum, p.75

291 Hibiscus aethiopicus, p.76

292 Hibiscus ludwigii, p.77

293 Hibiscus lunariifolius, p.77

294 Hibiscus sidiformis, p.77

295 Hibiscus vitifolius, p.78

297 Pavonia sp., formerly called **P. patens**, p.78

296 Pavonia gallaensis, p.78

251

298 Pavonia propinqua, p.78

299 Pavonia zeylanica, p.79

300 Sida cordifolia, p.79

301 Sida 'cuneifolia', p.79

302 Thespesia populnea, p.80

303 Croton megalocarpus, p.82   304 Euphorbia cuneata, p.83

305 Euphorbia graciliramea, p.83   306 Euphorbia kibwezensis, p.83

307 Euphorbia uhligiana, p.84

308 Bauhinia tomentosa, p.89

309 Caesalpinia bonduc, p.90

310 Caesalpinia decapetala, p.90

311 Cassia abbreviata, p.91

312 Cassia afrofistula, p.91

313 Cassia bicapsularis, p.91

314 Cassia didymobotrya, p.92

315 Cassia fallacina, p.92

316 Cassia hildebrandtii, p.92

317 Cassia mimosoides, p.93

318 Cassia occidentalis, p.93

319 Cassia singueana, p.93

320 **Parkinsonia aculeata**, p.94

321 **Tylosema fassoglense**, p.95

322 **Adenocarpus mannii**, p.95

323 Aeschynomene cristata var. pubescens, p.96

324 Aeschynomene schimperi, p.97

325 Crotalaria agatiflora, p.99

326 Crotalaria brevidens var. parviflora, p.100

327 Crotalaria cleomifolia, p.101

328 Crotalaria goodiiformis, p.101

329 Crotalaria lebrunii, p.102

330 Crotalaria massaiensis, p.103

331 Crotalaria mauensis, p.103

332 Crotalaria pycnostachya, p.104

333 Crotalaria recta, p.104

334 Crotalaria retusa, p.104

335 Crotalaria vatkeana, p.105

336 Eriosema montanum, p.107

338 Macrotyloma axillare, p.112

337 Eriosema psoraleoides, p.108

339 Sophora inhambanensis, p.117

340 Acacia nilotica, p.124

341 Acacia seyal, p.124

342 Trichocladus ellipticus
ssp. malosanus, p.126

343 Oncocalyx fischeri, p.129

344 Oncocalyx ugogensis, p.130

345 Cyphostemma orondo, p.133

346 Haplocoelum foliolosum, p.137

347 Pappea capensis, p.137

348 Gomphocarpus kaessneri, p.146

349 Stapelia semota, p.149

350 Anisoppapus africanus, p.159

351 **Aspilia mossambicensis**, p.159

352 **Berkheya spekeana**, p.160

355 **Bidens kirkii** var. flagellata, p.161

353 **Bidens grantii**, p.161

354 **Bidens kilimandscharica**, p.161

264

356 Bidens taitensis, p.161

357 Cineraria deltoides, p.163

358 Conyza hypoleuca, p.163

359 Conyza newii, p.163

360 Crassocephalum mannii, p.164

361 Crassocephalum montuosum, p.164

265

362 Crassocephalum picridifolium, p.164

363 Euryops brownei, p.167

364 Guizotia reptans, p.168

365 Guizotia scabra, p.168

366 Gynura pseudochina, p.169

367 Haplocarpha rueppellii, p.

368 Helichrysum foetidum, p.170

369 Helichrysum kilimanjari, p.171

370 Helichrysum odoratissimum, p.171

371 Helichrysum setosum, p.171

372 Hirpicium diffusum, p.171

373 Launaea cornuta, p.173

374 Launaea hafunensis, p.173

375 Microglossa pyrifolia, p.173

376 Psiadia punctulata, p.174

377 Reichardia tingitana, p.174

378 Senecio keniensis ssp. brassica, p.174

379 Senecio johnstonii ssp. battiscombei, p.175

380 Senecio johnstonii ssp. cheranganiensis, p.175

381 Senecio moorei, p.175

382 Senecio petitianus, p.176

383 Senecio schweinfurthii, p.176

384 Sonchus oleraceus, p.176

385 Spilanthes mauritiana, p.177

386 Taraxacum officinale, p.178

387 Tithonia diversifolia, p.178

388 Cestrum aurantiacum, p.188

389 Nicotiana glauca, p.189

390 Ipomoea obscura, p.372

391 Merremia sp., p.373

392 Alectra sessiflora var. **senegalensis,** p.374

393 Verbascum brevipedicellatum,
p.378

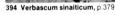

394 Verbascum sinaiticum, p.379

395 Cistanche tubulosa, p.379

396 Markhamia lutea, p.381

271

397 Tecoma stans, p.382

398 Pedalium murex, p.382

399 Pterodiscus ruspolii, p.383

400 Asystasia guttata, p.386

401 Justicia flava, p.393

402 Justicia odora, p.394

403 Thunbergia alata, p.396

404 Thunbergia sp. E, p.396

405 Thunbergia fischeri, p.397

406 Aneilema aequinoctiale, p.411

407 Albuca abyssinica, p.416

408 Bulbine abyssinica, p.421

409 Gloriosa superba, p.423

410 Hypoxis obtusa, p.430

411 Ansellia africana var. nilotica, p.432

412 Eulophia angolensis, p.435

414 Polystachya bella, p.439

413 Eulophia speciosa, p.436

275

415 Kalanchoe glaucescens, p.34

416 Kalanchoe schweinfurthii, p.35

417 Momordica friesiorum, p.60

418 Grewia villosa, p.69

419 Desmodium repandum, p.105

421 Tephrosia holstii, p.118

423 Crassocephalum vitellinum, p.165

420 Erythrina burttii, p.108

424 Emilia coccinea, p.166

422 Acacia kirkii, p.123

277

425 Gynura scandens, p.169

426 Kleinia petraea, p.172

427 Canarina abyssinica, p.182

428 Fruit of **C. abyssinica**, p.182

429 Crossandra subacaulis, p.390

430 Thunbergia gregorii, p.397

431 Leonotis mollissima, p.403

432 Leonotis nepetifolia, p.403

433 Aloe graminicola, p.417

434 Aloe amudatensis, p.417

435 Aloe rabaiensis, p.417

436 Gladiolus natalensis, p.428

437 Platycoryne crocea, p.438

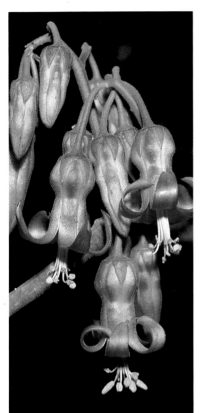

438 Cotyledon barbeyi, p.34

439 Impatiens niamniamensis, p.50

440 Protea kilimandscharica, p.55

441 Opuntia vulgaris, p.62

442 Ochna thomasiana, p.63

443 Hermannia exappendiculata, p.72

444 Sterculia rhynchocarpa, p.73

445 Abutilon hirtum, p.75

446 Hibiscus calyphyllus, p.76

447 Pavonia glechomifolia, p.78

448 Euphorbia heterochroma, p.83

449 Euphorbia schimperiana, p.84

450 Hagenia abyssinica, p.87

451 Cassia grantii, p.92

452 Tamarindus indica, p.94

453 Argyrolobium fischeri, p.97

454 Crotalaria axillaris, p.100

455 Crotalaria cephalotes, p.101

456 Crotalaria deflersii, p.101

457 Crotalaria laburnifolia, p.102

458 Crotalaria lachnocarpoides, p.102

459 Crotalaria natalitia, p.103

460 Crotalaria uguenensis, p.104

461 Crotalaria zanzibarica, p.105

462 Rhynchosia elegans, p.115

463 Rhynchosia holstii, p.115

464 Rhynchosia nyasica, p.115

465 Rhynchosia usambarensis, p.116

466 Sesbania goetzei, p.116

467 Sesbania sesban, p.116

468 Zornia setosa ssp. **obovata,** p.122

469 Englerina heckmanniana, p.129

470 Phragmanthera regularis var. **usuriensis,** p.130

471 Tapinanthus pennatulus, p.131

472 Dodonaea angustifolia, p.136

473 Rhus natalensis, p.139

475 Caralluma tubiformis, p.144

474 Schrebera alata, p.141

476 Ceropegia ballyana, p.145

477 Ceropegia racemosa, p.145

478 Ceropegia seticorona, p.145

479 Ceropegia succulenta, p.145

480 Glossonema revoilii, p.146

481 Pachycarpus rhinophyllus, p.148

482 Helichrysum formosissimum, p.170

483 Helichrysum meyeri-johannis, p.171

484 Helichrysum nandense, p.171

485 Kigelia africana, p.381

486 Spathodea campanulata, p.381

487 Commelina reptans, p.413

488 Gloriosa superba, p.423

489 Gloriosa minor, p.423

490 Kniphofia thomsonii, p.423

491 Ansellia africana, p.432

492 Eulophia clavicornis, p.435

493 Eulophia stenophylla, p.436

494 Eulophia streptopetala, p.436

495 Portulaca foliosa, p.37

496 Impatiens fischeri, p.49

497 Cephalopentandra ecirrhosa, p.57

498 Ochna inermis, p.63

499 Combretum constrictum, p.65

500 Combretum mossambicense, p.66

501 Combretum paniculatum, p.66

502 Terminalia orbicularis, p.66

503 Triumfetta rhomboidea, p.70

504 Hibiscus aponeurus, p.76

505 Hibiscus sp. **D**, p.76

506 **Acalypha volkensii**, p.81

507 **Euphorbia gossypina**, p.83

508 **Euphorbia nyikae** agg., p.84

511 **Emelianthe panganensis**, p.129

510 **Erythrina abyssinica**, p.108

294

509 Erythrina abyssinica, p.108

512 Englerina woodfordioides, p.129

513 Phragmanthera dschallensis, p.130

514 Plicosepalus curviflorus, p.131

515 Tapinanthus oehleri, p.131

516 Adenium obesum (from above), p.142

517 Stathmostelma rhacodes, p.149

518 Pentas parvifolia, p.156

519 Echinops amplexicaulis, p.165

520 Erythrocephalum minus, p.166

521 Kleinia abyssinica, p.172

522 Kleinia gregorii, p.172

523 Kleinia abyssinica
var. **hildebrandtii**, p.172

524 Canarina eminii, p.183

525 Ipomoea hederifolia, p.370

526 Striga asiatica, p.378

527 Crossandra mucronata, p.390

528 Crossandra nilotica, p.390

529 Ruttya fruticosa, p.396

532 Aloe secundiflora, p.417

530 Achyrospermum carvalhi, p.400

531 Salvia coccinea var. **coccinea**,
p.408

533 Aloe volkensii, p.417

534 **Asparagus falcatus**, p.420

535 **Aloe graminicola**, p.417

536 **Boöphone disticha**, p.426

537 **Cyrtanthus sanguineus** ssp. **ballyi**, p.427

538 **Scadoxus multiflorus**, p.427

539 **Gladiolus watsonioides**, p.428

540 Aristolochia bracteata, p.21

541 Hydnora abyssinica, p.21

542 Terminalia brownii, p.66

543 Euphorbia rivae, p.84

544 Euphorbia sp. near **E. stapfii**, p.84

545 Monadenium stapelioides, p.85

546 Ricinus communis, p.85

548 Caralluma speciosa, p.144

547 Tapinanthus ziziphifolius, p.131

549 **Caralluma subterranea**, p.144

551 **Edithcolea grandis**, p.146

550 **Caralluma turneri**, p.145

552 **Huernia aspera**, p.147

553 **Oxystelma bornouense**, p.147

554 Cleome monophylla, p.26

556 Viola abyssinica, p.30

557 Viola eminii, p.30

558 Polygala stenopetala, p.33

559 Pelargonium whytei, p.47

560 Dolichos luticola, p.106

555 Cleome parvipetala, p.26

561 Dolichos oliveri, p.106

562 Millettia usaramensis, p.112

563 Platycelyphium voënse, p.114

564 Tephrosia emeroides, p.117

565 Lythrum rotundifolium, p.52

566 **Vigna frutescens**, p.120

567 **Vigna membranacea** ssp. **membranacea**, p.120

568 **Vigna vexillata**, p.122

569 **Calotropis procera**, p.143

570 **Caralluma russelliana**, p.144

571 **Pachycarpus lineolatus**, p.148

307

572 Oldenlandia friesiorum, p.153

573 Bothriocline fusca, p.162

574 Bothriocline tomentosa, p.162

575 Carduus chamaecephalus, p.162

576 Carduus keniensis, p.162

577 Carduus kikuyorum, p.162

578 Felicia muricata, p.167

579 Vernonia auriculifera, p.178

580 Vernonia brachycalyx, p.179

581 Vernonia lasiopus, p.180

582 Lobelia deckenii ssp. keniensis, p.183

583 Lobelia deckenii ssp. keniensis, p.184

584 Lobelia duripratii, p.184

585 Lobelia deckenii ssp. **sattimae**, p.184

586 Wahlenbergia abyssinica, p.184

587 Wahlenbergia napiformis, p.185

588 Echiochilon lithospermoides, p.187

589 Solanum aculeastrum, p.189

590 Solanum anguivi, p.190

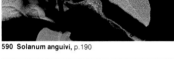

591 Solanum incanum, p.190

592 Ipomoea cicatricosa, p.370

593 Craterostigma plantagineum,
p.375

594 Craterostigma pumilum, p.375

595 Craterostigma sp. nov., p.375

596 Orobanche minor, p.379

597 Streptocarpus caulescens, p.380

599 Sesamum angustifolium, p.384

598 Streptocarpus glandulosissimus, p.380

600 Sesamum calycinum, p.384

601 Acanthus eminens, p.385

602 Blepharis maderaspatensis, p.389

603 Dyschoriste sp. A p.390

604 Dyschoriste.hildebrandtii, p.390

605 Dyschoriste radicans, p.390

606 Dyschoriste thunbergiiflora, p.391

607 Hydrophila auriculata, p.391

608 **Hypoestes aristata**, p.392

610 **Hypoestes triflora**, p.393

609 **Hypoestes forskalei**, p.392

611 **Justicia keniensis**, p.394

612 **Ruellia patula**, p.395

315

613 Thunbergia battiscombei, p.396

614 Thunbergia holstii, p.397

616 Lantana trifolia, p.398

617 Stachytarpheta jamaicensis, p.399

615 Clerodendrum myricoides, p.398

316

618 Aeollanthus repens, p.401

619 Ajuga remota, p.401

620 Erythrochlamys spectabilis, p.402

621 Plectranthus edulis, p.407

622 Plectranthus flaccidus, p.407

623 Plectranthus grandicalyx, p.407

624 Plectranthus igniarius, p.407

625 Plectranthus lanuginosus, p.408

626 Plectranthus zatarhendi, p.408

627 Salvia nilotica, p.409

629 Aneilema petersii, p.412

630 Aneilema spekei, p.412

631 Cyanotis foecunda, p.414

628 Aneilema hockii, p.411

632 Floscopa glomerata, p.414

633 Murdannia simplex, p.415

634 Siphonochilus aethiopicus, p.416

635 Sansevieria suffruticosa, p.430

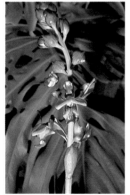
636 Eulophia horsfallii, p.435

637 Polystachya tessellata, p.440

638 Cleome allamannii, p.25

640 Delosperma oehleri, p.36

639 Cleome usambarica, p.27

641 Talinum portulacifolium, p.38

642 Rumex usambarensis, p.40

643 Achyranthes aspera, p.41

644 Amaranthus hybridus, p.41

645 Centemopsis gracilenta, p.41

646 Centemopsis kirkii, p.42

647 Digera muricata, p.42

648 Geranium ocellatum, p.46

649 Oxalis latifolia, p.48

650 Impatiens hoehnelii, p.50

651 Impatiens meruensis ssp. **cruciata,** p.51

652 Epilobium stereophyllum, p.53

653 Commicarpus pedunculosus, p.54

654 Commicarpus pedunculosus, p.54

655 Dissotis or Melastomastrum, sp. p.64

656 Dissotis speciosa, p.64

657 Dissotis senegambiensis, p.65

658 Terminalia prunioides, p.66

659 Euphorbia cryptospinosa, p.82

324

660 Caesalpinia trothae ssp. trothae, p.90

663 Canavalia cathartica, p.98

662 Cadia purpurea, p.97

661 Amphicarpa africana, p.97

664 Canavalia rosea, p.98

665 Canavalia virosa, p.99

666 Galactia argentifolia, p.109

668 Mundulea sericea, p.113

667 Lablab purpurea, p.111

669 Ormocarpum kirkii, p.114

670 Tephrosia interrupta, p.118

671 Tephrosia villosa, p.118

672 Trifolium burchellianum ssp. **johnstonii**, p.118

673 Trifolium rueppellianum, p.119

674 Vatovaea pseudolablab, p.119

675 Catharanthus roseus, p.142

676 Bothriocline calycina, p.162

677 Cirsium vulgare, p.163

678 Crassocephalum sarcobasis, p.165

679 Ethulia scheffleri, p.167

680 Gutenbergia cordifolia, p.168

681 Gutenbergia fischeri, p.168

682 Senecio roseiflorus, p.176

683 Vernonia cinerascens, p.179

330

684 Vernonia tufnelliae, p.180

685 Vernonia turbinata, p.180

686 Anagallis serpens, p.181

687 Lysimachia volkensii, p.181

688 Lobelia holstii, p.184

689 Solanum sessilistellatum, p.191

690 Ipomoea donaldsonii, p.369

691 Ipomoea jaegeri, p.371

692 Ipomoea pes-caprae, p.372

693 Ipomoea wightii, p.373

694 Cycnium cameronianum, p.375

695 Cycnium tenuisectum, p.376

696 Cycnium tubulosum ssp. **montanum**, p.376

697 Cycnium veronicifolium, p.376

698 Cycnium volkensii, p.376

699 Ghikaea speciosa, p.376

701 Acanthus pubescens, p.385

700 Striga gesnerioides, p.378

702 Hypoestes hildebrandtii, p.392

703 Justicia diclipteroides, p.393

704 Lantana camara, p.398

705 Verbena bonariensis, p.400

706 Ocimum fischeri, p.404

707 Orthosiphon parvifolius, p.405

708 Satureia abyssinica, p.409

709 Scutellaria paucifolia, p.409

710 Ammocharis tinneana, p.425

711 Dierama cupiflorum, p.428

712 Romulea fischeri, p.429

713 Satyrium crassicaule, p.440

714 **Clematis brachiata**, p.19

715 **Cleome hirta**, p.26

716 **Hybanthus enneaspermus**, p.30

717 **Polygala abyssinica**, p.31

718 **Polygala amboniensis**, p 32

719 **Polygala sphenoptera**, p.32

720 Kalanchoe pumila, p.35

721 Silene burchellii, p.35

722 Polygonum setulosum, p.39

723 Geranium arabicum ssp. arabicum, p.45

724 Geranium kilimandscharicum, p.45

725 Monsonia senegalensis, p.46

726 Oxalis obliquifolia, p.48

727 Impatiens hochstetteri, p.49

728 Impatiens hochstetteri ssp. hochstetteri, p.49

729 Impatiens nana, p.50

730 Impatiens sodenii, p.51

731 Impatiens tinctoria, ssp. elegantissima, p.51

339

732 **Antherotoma naudinii**, p.64

733 **Grewia lilacina**, p.68

734 **Grewia similis**, p.68

735 **Grewia tembensis** var. nematopus, p.69

736 **Hermannia kirkii**, p.72

737 **Abutilon longicuspe**, p.75

738 Hibiscus cannabinus, p.76

740 Pavonia urens, p.79

741 Urena lobata, p.80

739 Hibiscus pycnostemon, p.77

742 Rubus friesiorum, p.87

743 **Rubus keniensis,** p.87

744 Rubus pinnatus, p.88

745 Rubus steudneri, p.88

746 Caesalpina trothae
ssp. erlangeri, p.90

747 Desmodium salicifolium var. salicifolium, p.106

748 Indigofera nairobiensis, p.110

749 Indigofera schimperi, p.110

343

750 Indigofera volkensii, p.111

752 Trifolium semipilosum, p.119

753 Dichrostachys cinerea ssp. cinerea, p.125

754 Mimosa pudica var. unijuga, p.125

751 Pseudarthria confertiflora, p.115

344

755 Plicosepalus meridianus, p.131

756 Calodendrum capense, p.133

757 Blaeria filago, p.141

758 Gomphocarpus physocarpus, p.147

759 Tenaris rubella, p.149

760 Kohautia caespitosa, p.152

761 Otomeria elatior, p.154

762 Otomeria oculata, p.154

763 Pentas lanceolata, p.155

764 Pentas lanceolata var. **nemerosa**, p.155

765 Pentas zanzibarica, p.156

766 Pterocephalus frutescens, p.157

767 Scabiosa columbaria, p.158

768 Erigeron karvinskianus, p.166

347

769 **Ethulia** sp. A, p.166

770 **Ethulia vernonioides**, p.167

771 **Piloselloides hirsuta**, p.168

772 **Kleinia squarrosa**, p.172

773 **Sphaeranthus cyathuloides**, p.177

774 **Sphaeranthus napierae**, p.177

348

775 Sphaeranthus suaveolens,
p.177

776 Sphaeranthus ukambensis, p.177

777 Vernonia galamensis, p.179

778 Vernonia galamensis ssp.
galamensis var. petitiana, p.179

780 Cyphia glandulifera, p.183

781 Nicotiana rustica, p.189

779 **Swertia kilimandscharica,** p.181

782 Nicotiana tabacum, p.189

783 Ipomoea cairica, p.369

784 Ipomoea hildebrandtii, p.370

785 Ipomoea kituiensis, p.371

786 Ipomoea mombassana, p.372

787 Pseudosopubia hildebrandtii, p.377

351

788 Sopubia karaguensis, p.377

789 Sopubia ramosa, p.377

790 Striga latericea, p.378

791 Josephinia africana, p.382

792 Sesamum alatum, p.383

352

793 Sesamum angolense, p.383

794 Sesamum latifolium, p.384

795 Adhatoda schimperiana, p.385

796 Asystasia charmian, p.386

797 Asystasia gangetica, p.386

798 Barleria spinisepala, p.388

799 Barleria submollis, p.388

800 Hypoestes aristata, p.392

801 Isoglossa punctata, p.393

802 Ruellia patula, p.395

803 Achyrospermum schimperi, p.401

804 Becium obovatum, p.402

805 Geniosporum rotundifolium, p.402

806 Leucas jamesii, p.404

807 Ocimum hadiense, p.405

808 Orthosiphon rubicundus, p.406

809 Orthosiphon suffrutescens, p.406

810 Plectranthus cylindraceus, p.406

812 Salvia merjamie, p.408

811 Plectranthus kamerunensis, p.407

813 **Satureia biflora**, p.409

815 **Stachys aculeata**, p.410

814 **Satureia pseudosimensis**, p.409

816 **Anthericopsis sepalosa**, p.412

817 **Cyanotis barbata**, p.414

357

818 **Murdannia clarkeana**, p.415

819 **Scilla kirkii**, p.424

820 **Crinum macowanii**, p.426

821 **Crinum papillosum**, p.426

822 **Hesperantha petitiana**, p.429

823 Hesperantha petitiana, p.429

824 Delphinium macrocentron, p.19

825 Nymphaea caerulea, p.20

826 Commicarpus helenae, p.54

827 Clitoria ternatea, p.99

828 Crotalaria polysperma, p.104

829 Lupinus princei, p.111

830 **Parochetus** sp. near **P. communis**, p.114

831 **Psoralea foliosa**, p.115

833 **Diodia aulacosperma**, p.151

832 **Vigna unguiculata**, p.121

834 Pentanisia ouranogyne, p.155

835 Ceratostigma abyssinicum, p.182

836 Lobelia telekii, p.184

837 Cynoglossum amplifolium, p.186

838 Cynoglossum coeruleum, p.186

363

839 Cynoglossum geometricum, p.187

840 Cystostemon hispidus, p.187

841 Solanum coagulans, p.190

842 Solanum schumannianum, p.191

843 Convolvulus jefferyi, p.369

844 Jacquemontia tenuifolia, p.373

845 Veronica glandulosa, p.379

846 Barleria ventricosa, p.388

847 Blepharis hildebrandtii, p.388

365

848 Blepharis linariifolia, p.389

849 Brillantaisia nitens, p.389

850 Ecbolium revolutum, p.391

851 Nepeta azurea, p.404

852 Plectranthus barbatus, p.406

853 Plectranthus caninus, p.406

854 Plectranthus laxiflorus, p.408

855 Plectranthus sylvestris, p.408

856 Aneilema pedunculosum, p.412

857 Aneilema somaliense, p.412

858 Commelina sp., p.412

367

859 Commelina albescens, p.413

860 Commelina forskalei, p.413

861 Commelina latifolia, p.413

862 Commelina petersii, p.413

863 Cyanotis arachnoides, p.414

864 Moraea thomsonii, p.429

CONVOLVULUS

Greatly resembles *Ipomoea* but the two stigmas are filiform. Nine species in East Africa.

Convolvulus jefferyi — Plate 843

A perennial climber, stems twining or prostrate, long rather sparingly branched, pilose with adpressed hairs, silvery at first but often drying golden-brown (this applies to the indumentum generally). Leaf blade oblong or elliptic, slightly obovate, wide, rounded or somewhat acute at the apex, cuneate or obscurely hastate-truncate at the base; all the main nerves originating from the base. Length of leaf 0.8–3.5cm ($\frac{1}{3}$–1$\frac{3}{8}$in). The young leaves appear silvery. Flowers two to five in loose bracteate silky-pubescent heads. Corolla mauve or blue 8–10mm ($\frac{1}{3}$–$\frac{2}{3}$in) long. Found in coastal regions; altitude range 0–150m (0–400ft) and recorded at Malindi, Kilifi in Kenya and coast areas of Tanzania, in grassland clearings in dry evergreen forest or on sand dunes by the sea. Uganda and elsewhere, not known.

Hildebrandtia obcordata — Plate 235

A dioecious shrub up to 1m (3ft) tall, branchlets blackish-grey. Leaves fascicled on pubescent-arrested shoots, obovate-spathulate; obtuse or retuse at the apex or deeply incised, cuneate at the base. Flowers cream-white, one to four (female one to three) fascicled on the arrested shoots. Corolla lobes obtuse. Male flower corolla 6–13mm ($\frac{1}{4}$–$\frac{1}{2}$in) long, female flower corolla 6–7mm ($\frac{1}{4}$in) long. Altitude range 750–1470m (2450–4800ft). Found in Northern Frontier areas in dry bush on stony or sandy soil and recorded at Lodwar and South Horr (Kenya); Tanzania, not known; northern region only (Uganda); also in Ethiopia.

IPOMOEA

Herbs or shrubs often twining; corolla broadly funnel-shaped usually purple-pink, less often white; style simple with a big tubular stigma; pollen spinose; fruit an ovoid or globose three- to ten-valved capsule; six to ten seeds, usually four, often pubescent with long hairs. Eighty-nine species in East Africa.

Ipomoea donaldsonii — Plate 690

A shrub, 1–2m (3–6$\frac{1}{2}$ft) tall, with erect or ascending, blackish, purple-brown branchlets which become spine tipped or at least pointed; the young shoots woolly-pubescent. The leaves are borne on short shoots, the blade very small, 5–9mm ($\frac{1}{5}$–$\frac{2}{5}$in) long and 5–14mm ($\frac{1}{5}$–$\frac{3}{5}$in) broad, glabrous above, pubescent beneath, sometimes pubescent on both surfaces. Flowers solitary, axillary; corolla 2–2.8cm ($\frac{4}{5}$–1$\frac{1}{8}$in) long, purple, or white with purple centre (illustrated), silvery-pubescent in the middle areas and broadly funnel-shaped. Altitude range 200–750m (650–2450ft). Found in dry *Acacia-Commiphora* deciduous bushland and recorded only in the Northern Frontier areas such as North Horr and Wajir (Kenya); also Ethiopia, southern Somalia.

I. cairica — Plate 783

A common creeper with dissected leaves which is allied to the Morning Glory and Bindweed of European gardens. Flower *c.* 55mm (2$\frac{1}{4}$in) across, generally a pale mauve-pink, but this can vary to white, with a darker throat. It is found in clearings in forests, swampy grassland, and hedges and on lake shores and waste and cultivated land at medium altitudes, 750–1890m (2460–6200ft). Throughout East Africa; also from Ethiopia to Zimbabwe, Mozambique and throughout tropical Africa.

I. cicatricosa **Plate 592**

This is an unusual *Ipomoea* in that it is a perennial erect shrub, not climbing or trailing, which grows to 1–2m (3–6ft) high. Its stems are covered with short dense down and its ovate or ovate-elliptic leaves, *c.* 7cm (2⅘in) long and 4cm (1⅗in) wide, are hairless above and covered with soft, silky hairs pressed closely against their underside, especially when young. Its cymes are two- to three-flowered and axillary and the purple corollas are funnel-shaped 25–30mm (1–1⅕in) across. It is found in Kenya in semi-arid areas at altitudes of 610–1200m (2000–4000ft); Tanzania and Uganda, no record; also found in Ethiopia and Somalia.

I. garckeana **Plate 109**

A perennial; stems several, bristly-pilose to 1m (3ft) long from a little-branched rootstock, sometimes flowering when stems very short. Leaf-blade orbicular, either deeply tri-lobed with reniform or obovate-orbicular lobes or entire with markedly crenate margin, with a deep sinus at base, and adpressed pilose bristles above, a dense white-cottony tomentum and yellow-bristly nerves beneath. Flowers in few-flowered dense heads. Corolla white with mauve or purple centre or all pink, funnel-shaped up to 3cm (1⅕in) long. Found in dry *Acacia-Commiphora* scrub and deciduous bushland, persisting in grasslands, clearings and by roadsides in secondary vegetation on sandy soils; altitude range 30–350m (*c.* 100–1100ft). Recorded in Kwale, Kilifi, Taita Hills, Mackinnon Road, Sokokwe Forest (Kenya). Elsewhere, Somalia only.

I. hederifolia **Plate 525**

An annual with hairless or sparsely-haired, twining stems. The leaves are ovate or rounded in outline, entire or three-lobed with margins entire, and angular or toothed. Inflorescences are often long and may be few- to several-flowered. The sepals have short bristle appendages and the scarlet corolla is salver-shaped with the tube 28–40mm (1⅛–1⅗in) long and the expanded upper part 20–25mm (⅘–1in) in diameter. A native of tropical America, it is now widely naturalised in Kenya and found in waste places, thickets and forest edges and on cliffs up to altitudes of 1650m (5400ft). It has been recorded in western Kenya, Machakos, Nairobi and Meru and is quite common as an escape at the coast, but not in dry country (Kenya); Shinyanga, Moshi, Lushoto, Zanzibar (Tanzania); Mengo (Uganda); widespread in tropical Africa.

I. hildebrandtii **Plate 784**

A very variable, subwoody plant which grows up to 2.5m (8ft) in height with round to elliptic-oblong leaves which are covered with very fine down beneath and often large. The flowers may be few to many in dense to loose, branched cymes. The bracts and sepals are large; bracts 12–26mm (½–1in) long and 5–14mm (⅕–⅗in) wide and sepals 14–25mm (*c.* ½–1in) long and 5–10mm (⅕–⅜in) wide; corolla purple, white or white with a purple tube and funnel-shaped, 4.5–11.5cm (1⅘–4¼in) long. The seeds have dark, close-lying hairs. Three subspecies have been recognised, one with two varieties.

I.h. ssp. **hildebrandtii** Found in eastern Kenya where it is common in grassland with scattered *Acacia* and *Acacia-Commiphora* deciduous bushland, particularly along the Namanga road in the Narok and Kajiado districts (Kenya), at altitudes 400–1650m (1300–5400ft); lake areas, Maasai, Mpwapwa, Kondoa (Tanzania); Uganda and elsewhere, not known.

I.h. ssp. **grantii** Found in grassland and among scattered trees at 1100–2000m (3500–6500ft). Western Kenya; lake region (Tanzania); all districts of Uganda; also in Zaire.

I.h. ssp. **grantii** var. **mahonii** Very narrow elliptic-oblong leaves. Occurs on Mt Elgon and in the Trans-Nzoia (Kitale) district of Kenya at 1950m (6400ft).

I.h. ssp. **megaënsis** An entirely purple corolla and more silky sepals than the other subspecies, is found in Nanyuki and Rumuruti districts (Kenya), and north of Mega in southern Ethiopia at 610–1850m (2000–6050ft).

I. involucrata A polymorphic species of which three varieties are recognized in East Africa. An exceedingly variable annual or perennial; stems slender, twining, glabrescent to villose up to 8m (26ft) long. Leaf-blade, ovate-cordate, up to 9cm (3½in) long – occasionally 11cm (4⅓in) and 7cm (2⅘in) wide, acute or acuminate at apex, hairy to villous on both surfaces. Inflorescence a dense head enclosed in a large foliaceous boat-shaped involucre. Flowers few to many, very shortly pedicellate; corolla purple, rose, white or white with pink throat, funnel-shaped. Corolla 2–5.5cm (⅘–2⅕in) long, 2–5cm (⅘–2in) wide at mouth, 4–10mm (⅙–⅖in) wide at base. Found in grassland, forest, *Brachystegia* woodland and abandoned cultivated ground; altitude range 100–2700m (328–8850ft) and recorded in western Kenya (Kakamega and North Kavirondo Gulf) and Kisii (Kenya); all regions, Zanzibar (Tanzania); western, eastern regions (Uganda); also throughout tropical Africa and south to Zambia, Zimbabwe.

I. jaegeri   Plate 691
A floriferous, erect shrub which grows to about 60cm (2ft) high with many stems. Its linear-oblong to oblong-oblanceolate leaves are green and slightly hairy above, silvery below. Funnel-shaped flowers are borne singly on short stalks and are white or pink with a darker centre *c.* 5cm (2in) across. This beautiful non-climbing member of the Convolvulus family is common on stony soils, often along roadsides, in the Narok, Rift Valley, Magadi, Machakos, Nairobi and Kajiado areas at altitudes of 910–1700m (3000–5600ft) (Kenya); Maasai, Arusha, Pare (Tanzania); Uganda, no record; also Ethiopia.

I. kituensis   Plate 785
A shrub with suberect or twining pubescent stems up to 6m (20ft) long. Leaf-blade ovate to reniform 3.5–14.5cm (1⅖–5in) long and 3–16cm (1⅖–6⅓in) wide, obtuse, apiculate, acuminate or even bilobed at the apex, cordate at the base, sparsely pubescent or glabrous above, finely pubescent or glabrous beneath; petiole 1–10cm (⅓–4in) long. Flowers few to many in cymes, bracts linear-lanceolate. Corolla 5–8cm (2–3⅛in) long, white, cream or yellow with a purple centre, funnel-shaped, mid petal areas pubescent or pilose, tube narrowed below. Found at altitude range 800–2040m (2600–6700ft) in *Acacia-Combretum* deciduous bushland and recorded in Machakos, Rift Valley, Kibwezi, Taita district (Voi) and coast (Kenya); lake areas, Mpwapwa, Kondoa, Tanga (Tanzania); Uganda, no record; also in Ethiopia, Malawi, Zimbabwe.

I. longituba   Plate 110
A shrub, stems erect or sprawling-decumbent, up to 1m (3ft) long which usually die back annually, tomentose when young. Rootstock tuberous. Leaf-blade ovate, 3–16cm (2⅓–6in) long, 2–12 (⅘–4¾in) wide, subacute or obtuse and mucronate at apex, cuneate or truncate at the base, glabrous or glabrescent above, densely

371

tomentose beneath particularly on the nerves but later often glabrescent. Flowers solitary, clustered at the apices of the shoots. Sepals elongate-elliptic 10–17mm ($\frac{2}{5}$–$\frac{3}{5}$in) long, 5–8mm ($\frac{1}{5}$–$\frac{1}{3}$in) wide, very obtuse, glabrous. Corolla white, opening at night, tube cylindrical and very slender 9–11cm ($3\frac{1}{2}$–$4\frac{3}{4}$in) long, 3–4mm ($\frac{1}{8}$–$\frac{1}{6}$in) wide. Limb salver-shaped 7–9cm ($2\frac{4}{5}$–$3\frac{1}{2}$in) diameter, frilly edged. Found in stony soil or in crevices of rocky outcrops in deciduous bushland and scattered tree grassland; altitude range 1200–2100m (3850–6900ft). Recorded in Nanyuki, Machakos, Magadi and Kajiado (Kenya); Maasai, Mpwapwa, Kondoa, Shinyanga (Tanzania); northern, eastern regions (Uganda); elsewhere, northern Somalia.

NB Since 1960 a leaf-mutation in this species has been found, especially in Tanzania, almost every plant having some of the leaves deeply lobed.

I. mombassana **Plate 786**
An annual or perennial twiner with hairy stems. Its leaves are ovate or ovate-oblong, or elongate-oblong, cordate, cordate-sagittate or subhastate-cordate, rough or hairy. Flower 6cm ($2\frac{2}{5}$in) across. The inflorescence is single- or several-flowered with the funnel shaped corolla purple or white with a purple centre and a narrow tube 3–5cm ($1\frac{1}{8}$–2in) long. This is a lowland species found in dry bushland and *Commiphora* and *Combretum* woodland at altitudes up to 1200m (4000ft) (Kenya); Tanga, Mpwapwa, Morogoro, possibly Zanzibar (Tanzania); no record in Uganda; not known elsewhere.

I. obscura **Plate 390**
A small-flowered *Ipomoea* with an orange, bright yellow, cream or white corolla, always with a purple, crimson or chocolate-brown centre *c.* 25mm (1in) across. It is common in dry or warm areas at 610–2300m (2000–7500ft) over most of Kenya; Tanga, Dodoma, Mpwapwa, Zanzibar (Tanzania); Acholi, Karamoja, Moroto (Uganda); widespread from Ethiopia through Zaire to Zimbabwe, Mozambique.

I. ochracea Almost exactly the same as *I. obscura* but has rather larger flowers, corolla 2.4–4cm (*c.* 1–$1\frac{3}{5}$in) long. It is common over most of Kenya and is often found in forest strips, along river banks, in hot dry country and in *Commiphora* bushland; Mwanza, Mbulù, Uzaramo (Tanzania); Teso (Uganda); also Eritrea, Ethiopia, Zaire.

I. pes-caprae **Plate 692**
A glabrous perennial; stems thick, hollow, creeping 5–30m (16–96ft) long, often forming tangled mats. Leaves held erect, blade suborbicular, quadrangular or elliptic, conspicuously emarginate at the apex, very rarely rounded and entire, usually appearing two lobed; rounded, cuneate or cordate at base. Peduncle erect 3–10cm (*c.* $1\frac{1}{5}$–4in) long, one to many flowered. Corolla funnel-shaped, pink or red-purple 3–5.5cm (*c.* $1\frac{1}{5}$–2in) long with a darker centre. Found in sandy estuaries and sea shores, above high water mark; altitude range 1–1200m (3–3900ft), more rarely on inland lake shores and roadsides. Machakos, Sultan Hamud, Mombasa, Kilifi and Malindi (Kenya); Lake Tanganyika and coastal districts (Tanzania); Uganda, no record; also widespread on the coasts of East and West Africa.

I. spathulata **Plate 111**
A partly erect shrub with twining or scrambling branches which grows up to 2.5m (8ft) long and is covered with grey or yellowish-grey hairs. Its leaves are a medium shade of green, thick and obtuse at the apex. Its flowers, several to many in number, are projected on short, branched cymes, the corolla *c.* 5cm (2in) across is funnel-shaped and white or creamy-white with a darker mauve or purple centre

from which pinkish-mauve rays project. This striking and handsome plant is found in north and central Kenya in districts with warm conditions at 1200–2100m (3900–6900ft); Tanzania, no record; Acholi, Karamoja (Uganda); also Ethiopia. It can easily be grown from cuttings.

I. wightii   Plate 693
A very variable perennial; stems entwining or prostrate up to 4m (13ft) long covered with spreading yellowish hairs. Leaf-blade ovate-cordate up to 10cm (4in) long – ocasionally 13cm (5in), either entire or shallowly to deeply three-lobed with lobes acute and margins entire or crenate, green but pilose above with a very sparse white-cottony tomentum beneath. Flowers in few to many-flowered dense (sometimes lax) heads, very rarely solitary (as in illustration). Corolla magenta or mauve 2–4cm ($\frac{3}{4}$–1$\frac{3}{4}$in) long, glabrous or with some yellow bristles above. Found in open forest and scrub; altitude range 50–2400m (165–7900ft) and recorded in Elgon, western Kenya and Nairobi (Kenya); Mbulu, Lushoto, Uzaramo, Zanzibar (Tanzania); Kigezi, Masaka (Uganda); also Mozambique, Zimbabwe, Malawi.

Jacquemontia tenuifolia   Plate 844
An annual twiner with stems adpressed pilose with silky hairs. Leaf ovate up to 6cm (2$\frac{3}{8}$in) long and wide, acute to acuminate at the apex, acute to cordate at the base, sparingly pilose above and below, or glabrescent. Flowers in dense hairy capitate cymes 2–3cm ($\frac{3}{4}$–1$\frac{1}{4}$in) across, of a ferruginous colour when dry. Corolla blue 1cm ($\frac{3}{8}$in) long, sepals lanceolate, acute, subequal, densely and softly hairy 5–7mm (c. $\frac{1}{4}$in) long. Three Jacquemontia species in East Africa originally placed in Convolvulus but now considered a separate genus on account of the elliptic–long stigmas. Found in dry scrub, grassland and cultivated ground on sandy or rocky soils; altitude range 60–900m (200–2950ft) and recorded in coast areas and Tsavo East (Kenya); Tanga, Morogoro, Mbeya, Iringa, Songea, Zanzibar, Pemba (Tanzania); northern region (Uganda); also in Sudan.

MERREMIA
Differs from Ipomoea in having smooth pollen and a corolla which is yellow, less often white with a red or purple eye. Nineteen species in East Africa.

Merremia sp.   Plate 391
A perennial or annual herb mostly with twining or creeping stems. The flowers are usually cream or yellow with a dark centre and are very similar to those of Ipomoea. The genus is generally widespread in the eastern African region and Merremia species generally occur in semi-arid or rocky conditions. The photograph shows an unidentified species on the east side of Lake Turkana (formerly Lake Rudolph) in Kenya.

M. ampelophylla   A perennial prostrate herb with radiating stems to about 1m (3ft 3in) in length. The leaves are palmately five- to seven-lobed, 2–8cm ($\frac{3}{4}$–c. 3in) long and 3–14cm (1$\frac{1}{8}$–5$\frac{1}{2}$in) wide and usually undulate at margins. It has loose cymes of one to three flowers with primrose-yellow corollas c. 3cm (1$\frac{1}{8}$in) long and brownish-claret centres. It is found mostly in bare places in dry bushland (Kenya), altitude range 500–1000m (1650–3300ft); Maasai, Lushoto (Tanzania); no record in Uganda; elsewhere, no record.

M. pinnata   An annual prostrate or trailing herb about 60cm (23$\frac{1}{2}$in) long with leaves sessile, deeply pinnatifid with eight to twelve pairs of narrow lobes extending almost to the mid-rib about 8mm ($\frac{1}{3}$in) long, 0.5mm wide. There are one to three

COLVOLVULACEAE

flowers 6mm (¼in) long which have a white to yellow corolla 7mm (slightly less than ¼in) long. It is a widespread species in rocky grassland and bushland, especially in sandy soil (Kenya); altitude range 400–2200m (1300–7200ft); Mwanza, Tanga – eastern Usambara, Dodoma (Tanzania); West Nile, Teso, Busoga (Uganda); widespread from Sudan to Zimbabwe, Mozambique.

81. Scrophulariaceae (including *Selaginaceae*)
THE FOXGLOVE FAMILY

A large family of herbs or, rarely, shrubs, found throughout the world. Its leaves are opposite or alternate and without stipules. The flowers are usually zygomorphic with the more or less tubular calyx four- to five-lobed; a gamopetalous corolla; usually four stamens, rarely, two or five, a bilocular ovary with numerous ovules attached to the septum and a long, single style. The fruit is a capsule with numerous minute seeds. Many of the species of *Striga, Cycnium, Alectra* and *Bartsia* are parasites or semi-parasites which draw nourishment from the roots of grasses and, perhaps, other plants. Some species of *Striga* do very serious damage to cereals. 184 species in fifty-two genera in East Africa.

ALECTRA
The only genus in the Scrophulariaceae apart from *Verbascum* which has a yellow corolla with spreading lobes; it has four stamens and pedicels shorter than the calyx. It is semi-parasitic. Thirteen species in East Africa.

Alectra sessiflora var. senegalensis   Plate 392
An erect scabrid-pubescent annual semi-parasite with ovate to lanceolate, dentate leaves, one pair of filaments hairy, and subsessile flowers c. 11mm (½in) long; corolla lobes as broad as long, yellow to orange. Rather variable in leaf shape and locally common in upland forest areas. Altitude range 200–2760m (650–9200ft). Recorded in Cheranganis, Elgon, Tinderet, Mau, Aberdares, Kitale, western Kenya, Kisii, Narok, Machakos (Kenya); Tanga, Mbeya, Iringa, Songea (Tanzania); all regions except northern (Uganda); also south from Sudan to Mozambique and tropical Africa generally.

A. vogelii Similar to *A. sessiflora* var. *senegalensis* with linear to lanceolate leaves and all filaments glabrous. Flower: c. 15mm (⅜in) long. A rare plant found in crops and annual vegetation in dry country; altitude range 970–1335m (3250–4500ft). Recorded in Rift Valley, Machakos, Embu (Kenya); lake areas, Tabora, Mpwapwa, Kondoa, Songea (Tanzania); Uganda, no record; also in Malawi, Zambia, Zimbabwe, West Africa.

CRATEROSTIGMA
Small herbs, non-parasitic; leaves in basal rosettes which can dry out almost completely in drought and recover rapidly with rain; corolla small, blue or white, usually two-lipped. Eight species in East Africa.

Craterostigma hirsutum   Plate 112
A small silky-hairy rosette herb forming mats from thickish rhizomes with erect, elliptic to obovate leaves and long-pedunculate racemes of usually white flowers

1.5cm (⅝in) long. Abundant in shallow soils and seasonally flooded or wet grass-lands; altitude range 350–2250m (1160–7500ft). Recorded almost everywhere in Kenya; lake areas, Maasai, Tabora, Mpwapwa, Kondoa, Mbeya, Iringa (Tanzania); all regions except eastern (Uganda); also Zambia, Zimbabwe.

C. plantagineum   Plate 593
A herb growing from a thick or thin rhizome with a basal rosette of spreading, broad-elliptic and often serrate leaves. Its blue to violet flowers c. 7mm (¼in) across are borne at the end of single stems and resemble violets. Altitude range 1600–2200m (5250–7200ft). It is locally common on shallow soils in open sunny places and dry grassland, except in the very driest areas, over a wide area from Mumias in the west to Nanyuki in the east and from Mt Elgon to Kajiado, and especially common around Nairobi (Kenya); lake areas, Maasai, Tabora (Tan-zania); all regions (Uganda); also Sudan, Ethiopia, Somalia, Malawi, Zimbabwe. It flowers very quickly and profusely as soon as the rains begin.

C. pumilum   Plate 594
Similar in leaf growth to C. plantagineum but is shorter and has long blue to pinkish flowers 13mm (c. ½in) across at the end of single stems. Altitude range 1000–3000m (3300–9900ft) although it grows mainly around 2130m (7000ft) altitude in high dry grassland areas such as those of Mt Elgon, Cheranganis, Tinderet, Aberdares, Mau and Nanyuki (Kenya); Maasai (Tanzania); eastern reg-ion – Jinja, Lake Kioga (Uganda); also Ethiopia, Somalia, Zambia, Zimbabwe. Like the preceding species flowers profusely on the arrival of the rains.

C. sp. nov   Plate 595
A small tufted perennial with the ability of most members of this genus to dry up completely and then revive quickly after rain. It closely resembles C. plantagineum, a rosette herb with a thick or thin rhizome and spreading broad-elliptic often serrate leaves. Flowers bluish to violet, corolla 8mm (⅓in) long. C. sp. nov is found in open places on very shallow soils; altitude range 1300–1600m (4250–5250ft). It has not as yet been clearly described. The photograph was taken in Kajiado district (Kenya).

CYCNIUM
Semi-parasitic herbs with pink or white corollas, with a well developed straight or slightly curved tube much longer than the calyx. Thirteen species in East Africa.

Cycnium ajugifolium (Rhamphicarpa ajugifolia)   Plate 113
A pubescent to tomentose perennial herb from a woody rootstock with ascending stems and small ovate-elliptic coarsely two- to five-toothed leaves; flowers sub-sessile, pale pink or white; corolla tube 3cm (1⅛in) long, lobe 2cm (⅘in) across. An easily identified plant; altitude range 1490–1860m (4900–6200ft), found in stony Combretum woodland soils, and recorded in Aberdares, Rift Valley, Magadi and Machakos (Kenya); Maasai (Tanzania); Uganda and elsewhere, no record.

C. cameronianum (Rhamphicarpa cameroniana)   Plate 694
An erect, although low, annual with down-covered stems and deeply serrate leaves. Its flowers are bright pink c. 25mm (1in) across. It is abundant after rains in dry Commiphora bushland in districts such as Magadi, Machakos and Kajiado (Kenya); at 610–1350m (2000–4500ft). Recorded in Maasai, Tanga, Mpwapwa, Kondoa, Morogoro (Tanzania); Uganda and elsewhere, no record.

C. tenuisectum (*Rhamphicarpa tenuisecta*)   Plate 695
An erect usually glabrescent perennial herb or weak shrub with leaves pinnatisect into linear segments which are triangular in cross-section. This distinguishes it from *C. meyeri-johannis* in which the leaf segments are flat, and which is pubescent and not glabrescent. Corolla tube 16mm ($\frac{2}{3}$in) long, corolla lobe 10mm ($\frac{2}{5}$in) across. It is locally common in grassy marshes; altitude range above 1850m (6000ft) to 3150m (10,500ft) and recorded in Elgon, Cheranganis, Tinderet, Mau, Aberdares, Mt Kenya, Kitale, Rift Valley, and Nanyuki (Kenya); Maasai (Tanzania); all regions except Buganda (Uganda); also rarely in Ethiopia.

C. tubulosum ssp. montanum (*Rhamphicarpa montana*)   Plate 696
Like all *Cycnium* species a semi-parasite which draws nourishment from the roots of the grasses to which it is attached. It is frequently a hairless, erect or ascending perennial herb from a fibrous rootstock with linear-lanceolate, often sparsely-toothed leaves. Its large pink flowers, 4–5cm (2in) across, are borne on individual stalks in a loose raceme and are often only a few in number. It is a very variable species with some tall erect forms with many-flowered racemes, which are found principally in western Kenya. Widespread in Kenya on black cotton grassland soils at 910–2410m (3000–7900ft). It is common after rain in the Masai Mara area and looks like pieces of waste paper dotted across the plains. Recorded in all regions except Songea (Tanzania); all regions (Uganda); also Sudan, Ethiopia, south to Malawi, Zimbabwe, Mozambique.

C. tubulosum ssp. tubulosum   Plate 114
A frequently glabrous erect or ascending perennial herb from a fibrous rootstock with linear-lanceolate often sparsely toothed leaves and often few large white pedicellate flowers in a loose raceme. Found throughout our region on black cotton soils. Corolla tube 14–38mm ($\frac{1}{2}$–1$\frac{1}{2}$in) long. Altitude range 1–2100m (3–6900ft).
   NB Ssp. *tubulosum* has a white corolla, ssp. *montanum* a pink corolla.

C. veronicifolium   Plate 697
An erect annual with pubescent stems and deeply serrate leaves: flowers bright pink. It is very similar to *C. cameronianum*. Corolla tube *c.* 0.2cm ($\frac{1}{12}$in) long, corolla lobe *c.* 1.5cm ($\frac{3}{5}$in) long. Often abundant after rains in dry *Commiphora* bushland and coastal areas; altitude range 0–2100m (0–7000ft) and recorded in Machakos, Magadi, Kajiado and coast (Kenya); Tanga, Morogoro (Tanzania); Uganda and elsewhere, no record.

C. volkensii   Plate 698
An erect weedy perennial up to 120cm (4ft) tall, the stems and leaves covered by stiff hairs. Leaves lanceolate-elliptic 20–30cm (*c.* 8–12in) long, base cuneate, margin coarsely dentate to lobed. Flowers pink. Corolla tube up to 25cm (10in) long, 25mm (1in) across lobes. Found in woodlands, roadsides and rocky outcrops; altitude range 910–2450m (3000–8160ft). Found in all areas except Turkana and coast (Kenya); Maasai, Mpwapwa, Kondoa (Tanzania); no record (Uganda); also Ethiopia.

Ghikaea speciosa   Plate 699
A handsome stiffly erect bushy plant, *c.* 1.5m (4$\frac{1}{2}$ft) tall which is found in dry areas in *Acacia-Commiphora* bushland at 450–1200m (1500–4000ft) and has mauve flowers 2–3cm ($\frac{4}{5}$–1$\frac{1}{5}$in) across. It is the only known species in this genus and has been recorded in north-eastern Kenya and Somalia; also eastern Ethiopia.

Hebenstretia angolensis (*H. dentata* in *UKWF*)   **Plate 115**
A small, erect, wiry shrub with terminal spikes of white and orange flowers 2–3mm
(c ⅛in) across. The only species north of the Zambezi. It is common in rocky
heathland at high altitudes up to 4000m (13,120ft) but can also occasionally be
found in dry grassland at 1700–2450m (5500–8000ft). It has been identified in Mt
Elgon, Cheranganis, Aberdares, Mt Kenya, Rift Valley and Kajiado areas (Kenya);
widespread in Tanzania and Uganda, except Buganda; also Ethiopia, eastern
Zaire, Malawi, Mozambique, Zimbabwe, Zambia, western Somalia.

Pseudosopubia hildebrandtii   **Plate 787**
An erect or prostrate, down-covered, woody herb with linear, acute or obtuse
leaves and loose terminal racemes of purple-pink flowers 15mm (⅝in) across. Four
species in East Africa. It is common in dry bushland in northern and eastern Kenya
at 690–1300m (300–4250ft) and, rarely, up to 1650m (6400ft); Tanga (Tanzania);
northern region – Gulu (Uganda); also Ethiopia, Somalia. This species is variable
and may one day be classified into three or four separate species.

SOPUBIA
Herbs with pink or purple regular corollas, the tube shorter than the calyx; four
stamens. Seven species in East Africa.

Sopubia eminii (*S. trifida*)   An erect scabrid annual with tri-foliate, linear-lobed or
entire leaves and a loose terminal raceme of yellow to white flowers with maroon
centres; corolla tube including lobes 8mm (⅓in) long. The stem is minutely pubescent and not sharply ridged in this species. Locally common in shallow-soil grassland; altitude range 1000–2700m (3280–9000ft) and recorded on Elgon, Tinderet,
Aberdares, in Kitale and Machakos (Kenya); lake areas, Maasai, Tabora,
Mpwapwa, Kondoa, Mbeya, Iringa (Tanzania); eastern region, Buganda (Uganda);
also Zambia.
   NB Though the synonym *C. trifida* has been used in Africa, the true *C. trifida* is
Asiatic.

S. karaguensis   **Plate 788**
An erect pubescent herb with simple linear leaves and terminal woolly spike-like
racemes of pink flowers, corolla including lobes 10mm (⅜in) long. The calyx is
densely woolly on the outside. Locally common in well drained montane grassland;
altitude range 1800–3300m (5900–10,800ft). Recorded on Mau, Tinderet, Aberdares, Mt Kenya and Kajiado (Kenya); lake areas, Maasai (Tanzania); western
region, Buganda (Uganda); also Zambia, Zimbabwe, Swaziland. Two subspecies
are recognised in East Africa; ssp. *karaguensis* and ssp. *welwitschii*.

S. ramosa   **Plate 789**
An erect scabrid (possibly annual) woody herb with simple linear or rarely pinnatifid
leaves and terminal spike-like racemes of purple flowers. The pedicels are always
shorter than the bell-shaped calyx. Corolla with a tube shorter than the calyx and
with five spreading lobes 10mm (⅜in) across. Locally common in wooded grassland;
altitude range 900–2400m (3000–8000ft) and recorded from western Kenya and
Kitale to Rift Valley, Kisii and Kajiado, and on Mau, Mt Elgon and Aberdares
(Kenya); all regions except Mpwapwa, Kondoa (Tanzania); all regions of Uganda;
also Ethiopia, Zaire, Malawi, Zambia, Zimbabwe, Mozambique.

STRIGA
Semi-parasitic or completely parasitic herbs with flowers in a narrow spike; calyx

tubular, corolla zygomorphic with a narrow curved tube. There are thirteen species in East Africa.

Striga asiatica   Plate 526
An erect downy rough-skinned annual root parasite with linear to filamentous leaves and bright crimson flowers *c.* 16mm (⅝in) long and 7mm (*c.* ¼in) across in a terminal spike. This is a conspicuous plant found in upland and dry lowland grassland from sea level to 2300m (7600ft) and recorded throughout East Africa except in dry and arid areas. Especially in western Kenya and in Siaya district it is sometimes a bad parasitic weed on maize and sorghum plants. It is also widespread in tropical Africa.

S. gesnerioides   Plate 700
An erect parasite, usually unbranched and without chlorophyll with scale-like leaves and a spike of mauve to medium purple flowers, corolla tube 8mm (⅓in) long, lobe 4mm (⅛in) long. Locally common in dry bushland; altitude range 1–1600m (3–5250ft). Recorded in western Kenya, Kisii, Rift Valley, Magadi, Machakos and Kajiado (Kenya); all regions (Tanzania); all regions (Uganda); also widespread in tropical Africa.

S. latericea   Plate 790
An erect, densely scabrid, pubescent annual parasite with lanceolate mostly entire leaves and large pink to salmon flowers, corolla tube 2.5cm (1in) long, lobe 2.5cm (1in) across. Altitude range 100–1700m (330–5650ft). Locally common in dry grassland and recorded in Nanyuki, Machakos, Kajiado and Sultan Hamud (Kenya); Maasai, Tanga (Tanzania); Uganda, no record; also in Ethiopia.

S. linearifolia   Plate 116
An erect grey-pubescent annual parasite with scale leaves and white to pale mauve flowers in terminal spikes, with linear corolla lobes. Corolla with a long cylindrical tube 18mm (⅔in) long, 10mm (⅜in) across, sharply bent and often inflated at the middle or above, hairy within and glandular-hairy without; lobes spreading, the three lower ones free from each other and the two smaller upper ones partially fused: stamens included, with one anther cell. Altitude range 600–2100m (2000–7000ft). It is locally common in dry grassland in Rift Valley, Embu, Machakos, Nairobi and Kajiado (Kenya); lake areas, Maasai, Tabora, Mpwapwa, Kondoa (Tanzania); all regions (Uganda); also Ivory Coast to Ethiopia (and Angola).

VERBASCUM
Five stamens (very unusual in Scrophulariaceae) but those species formerly placed in *Celsia* have four. Corolla yellow. Four species in East Africa.

Verbascum brevipedicellatum (*Celsia floccosa*)   Plate 393
An erect, often woody, woolly to glabrescent herb with ovate to lanceolate to oblong leaves and glandular-hairy pedicels and calyx. Flowers yellow *c.* 2cm (⅘in) across. This is an attractive plant found in upland grassland especially on shallow soil; altitude range 1400–3400m (4900–11,330ft) and recorded almost everywhere in Kenya except Machakos and the coast (Kenya); Maasai, Tanga, Mbeya, Iringa (Tanzania); all regions except Buganda (Uganda); also Rwanda, Ethiopia, Zaire. The genus *Celsia* in which it was formerly placed is now held to be not distinct from *Verbascum*.

V. sinaiticum Plate 394

An erect, woolly herb 120–150cm (4–5ft) high, springing from a rosette of large ovate to oblong leaves and bearing simple or branched, terminal racemes of yellow flowers *c.* 1cm (⅜in) across. It is a showy species most common in regions of medium rainfall, especially in wheat lands and along the sides of roads at 1900–2750m (6200–9000ft) and recorded in Tinderet, Mau, Aberdares, Rift Valley, Nanyuki and Timau districts (Kenya); Tanzania and Uganda, no record; also Sudan, Ethiopia.

VERONICA

Herbs with blue flowers; corolla tube very short, the four lobes almost regular; stamens spreading, two; six species in East Africa, all above 1500m (*c.* 5000ft).

Veronica abyssinica A trailing, down-covered herb with ovate, cordate and serrate leaves. It bears two- to five-flowered racemes of blue-mauve flowers 8mm (*c.* ⅓in) across. It is common in upland grassland and forest edges and widespread in Kenya from 1550–3900m (5100–12,800ft); all regions except lake areas of Tanzania; all regions except Buganda, (Uganda); also Ethiopia, eastern Zaire, Malawi.

V. glandulosa Plate 845

A trailing pubescent herb with shortly petiolate, rounded, minutely serrate leaves, and solitary, blue flowers *c.* 10mm (⅜in) across. Locally common in forest zones and the alpine zones; altitude range 2700–4200m (9000–14,000 ft). Recorded in Elgon, Cheranganis, Aberdares, Mt Kenya (Kenya); Maasai, Tanga, Mbeya, Iringa (Tanzania); western, eastern regions (Uganda); also Ethiopia.

82. Orobanchaceae
THE BROOMRAPE FAMILY

A small family of root parasites, found mainly in temperate regions. They are almost devoid of chlorophyll and closely related to the Scrophulariaceae, from which they differ chiefy in the ovary. This is unilocular with the very numerous ovules attached to four parietal placentas. There are four species in East Africa belonging to two genera. Botanists working on the Scrophulariaceae at Kew now hold that the difference between the parasitic members of that family and *Orobanche* are too slight for *Orobanche* to be maintained as a separate family.

Cistanche tubulosa Plate 395

An erect, unbranched spike of yellow flowers *c.* 12mm (½in) across when open, rather like a large hyacinth, which is a parasite of shrubs and trees. Its base is always growing on their roots. It is locally common in dry and open bushland, mainly at low altitudes, 600–1200m (2000–4000ft) and often found springing from the ground in open spaces in Kenya; Pare, Lushoto, Nzega (Tanzania); Uganda, no record; also Ethiopia, Somalia.

Orobanche minor Plate 596

An erect, sparsely branched, root parasite with pale dirty white to purple flowers *c.* 15mm (⅜in) across in terminal spikes and the calyx split above and below the flower. The inflorescence is carried on a long erect peduncle from a base of leaves reduced to scales chiefly near the base of the stem. It is common in cultivated ground, upland grassland, forest edges and is widespread in Kenya though no specimen has been recorded in the Northern Frontier areas and Turkana except one from Moyale, parasitic on maize. Altitude range from 800–2400m (2600–7900ft). All regions, except lake areas (Tanzania); all regions of Uganda; also North Africa.

O. ramosa An erect, sparsely branched parasite with bright blue flowers; corolla up to 15mm (⅜in) long; calyx split only on upper side. An uncommon plant; altitude range 1800–2250m (5900–7400ft), found in upland grassland and recorded in Aberdares and Nairobi (Kenya); Tanzania, Uganda and elsewhere, no record.

NB This European species is possibly not native to East Africa where two varieties, var. *ramosa* and var. *brevispicata* have been recorded.

83. Gesneriaceae
THE AFRICAN VIOLET FAMILY

A medium-sized almost wholly tropical or subtropical, family of herbs or much less often shrubs, climbers or trees. They differ from the *Scrophulariaceae* chiefly in the ovary, which is two-celled below but one-celled above with numerous ovules on two placentas intruding from the central division. Forty-five species in four genera in East Africa.

STREPTOCARPUS
Most easily recognized by the long narrow capsule whose two valves twist spirally on dehiscence. Twenty-one species in East Africa. More common in Tanzania than in Kenya and does not occur in very dry areas.

Streptocarpus caulescens   **Plate 597**
A soft, trailing pubescent herb with ascending fleshy stems bearing ovate-elliptic entire petiolate leaves and loose panicles of richly violet and purple flowers, corolla *c*. 18mm (¾in) long, with a conspicuous lower lip; capsule glabrous. Altitude range 900–2100m (3000–6900ft). Locally common in shady wet forest especially along streamsides. Only recorded in Chyulu and Taita Hills (Kenya); Maasai, Tanga, Morogoro, Mbeya, Iringa (Tanzania); Uganda and elsewhere, no record.

S. exsertus   **Plate 117**
A rare plant which is only known to occur on two basement complex mountains in northern Kenya where it is found in moist shady crevices at 1430–1520m (4700–5000ft). Flower *c*. 7mm (¼in) long. It was first discovered in 1963 and described scientifically in 1971. The basement complex mountains support a number of plants which are different from those found on the more prominent volcanic mountains, not only because the soils are more sandy and poorer in certain minerals but also because they existed long before the volcanoes appeared. The specimen illustrated is shown in a pot because when first located on Ol Lolokwe it was not in flower and was, therefore, transplanted and grown on until the white flower could be photographed.

S. glandulosissimus   **Plate 598**
A soft, trailing pubescent herb with ascending fleshy stems bearing ovate-elliptic entire petiolate leaves and loose panicles of richly violet and purple flowers 2.6cm

(1in) long with a conspicuous lower lip. The pedicels are noticeably more hairy than in *S. caulescens* which it resembles. Altitude range 1900–2700m (6300–9000ft). Locally common in shady wet forest especially along streamsides and recorded in Aberdares, Mt Kenya and Machakos (Kenya); Maasai, Tanga, Morogoro, Mbeya, Iringa – one specimen only from Mulindi (Tanzania); Ruwenzori Mts, Kigezi (Uganda); also Rwanda, Burundi, eastern Zaire.

84. Bignoniaceae

A medium-sized family of tropical trees, climbers and shrubs, most common in America. Their leaves are nearly always opposite, usually pinnate, less often palmate or simple and sometimes end in tendrils. The corolla tube of the zygomorphic flowers is bell-shaped, funnel-shaped or tubular. The stamens usually number four and the ovary is superior, bi-locular and has numerous ovules. The fruit is a capsule or drupe. There are thirteen species in East Africa belonging to eight genera. They include the Nandi Flame Tree and the Jacaranda (introduced from Brazil).

Kigelia africana (*K. aethiopica*)   Plate 485
A low-branched tree, commonly known as the Sausage Tree, which grows to 9m (30ft) in height. Its leaves are paired and opposite, the elliptic-oblong leaflets, usually seven to nine in number, are rounded at the base and 6.25–15cm (2½–6in) long. The unpleasantly scented flowers have a trumpet shaped corolla up to 12cm (4½in) long, the inside reddish or maroon, the outside pale with reddish lines. The fruit hangs down like a long sausage – hence the tree's popular name. It is widely spread in warm and wet savannah country and along rivers in dry areas up to altitudes of 1830m (6000ft). Found throughout East Africa; also Ethiopia, Zaire, south to Zimbabwe, Mozambique.

Markhamia lutea (*M. hildebrandtii, M. platycalyx*)   Plate 396
A shrub or tree up to 10m (33ft) high. Leaves 22–50cm (*c.* 8–20in) long, seven to eleven leaflets, stalked, ovate-oblong, mucronate, base cuneate. Flowers yellow, corolla tube 6cm (2⅜in) long, 4cm (1⅜in) across. Occasionally up to 18m (60ft) high and girth of 4m (13ft). Found in treed bushland and grassland; altitude range 1000–2040m (3300–6800ft) and recorded in Rift Valley, Central Province and western Kenya (Kenya); lake areas, Maasai, Tanga, Tabora (Tanzania); western region and Buganda (Uganda); also Zaire, Rwanda, Burundi.

Spathodea campanulata (*S. nilotica*)   Plate 486
A tree up to 18m (60ft) high. Bark pale grey, somewhat rough and scaling at the base of the bole. Leaves pinnate, opposite or in threes, leaflets usually nine to thirteen, ovate to ovate-oblong, acutely acuminate, pubescent below. Flower buds brown, tomentose, containing much water which squirts out when squeezed. Flowers showy, crimson or flame, edged with yellow, 9–13cm (3½–5in) long with crispate lobes, borne in short dense terminal corymbose racemes; calyx recurved, corolla widely trumpet shaped, the whole like an open chalice. A variety with saffron-ochre coloured flowers is sometimes planted ornamentally. Indigenous to forest in western Kenya, Uganda and Zaire; altitude range 1500–1975m (5000–6500ft), but now widely planted as an ornamental tree and commonly known as the Nandi Flame.

Tecoma stans   **Plate 397**
An erect shrub to 4m (13ft) tall, leaves unequally pinnate, five to eleven leaflets, lanceolate, apex acuminate, base cuneate with toothed margin. This is a garden plant not native to Africa and must not be considered an indigenous flower. Flowers yellow, corolla tube up to 5–6cm (2–2⅜in) long, 3.5cm (*c.* 1⅜in) across. Sometimes called Yellow Elder. Altitude range 950–2200m (3200–7400ft).

85. Pedaliaceae

Annual or perennial herbs, or, rarely, shrubs, covered, at least in the young parts, with four-celled mucilage glands easily recognized as white dots, which become slimy when wet; leaves exstipulate, opposite (upper ones sometimes alternate) or fasciculate on short branches in shrubs or trees; flowers usually solitary in axils of leaves or bracts that are similar to leaves; pedicels generally with two nectarial glands at the base; flowers bisexual, zygomorphic, sometimes spurred; corolla sub-bilabiate or sub-equally five-lobed; four stamens, the fifth often represented by a staminode; two anther-cells, ovary superior; style filiform, very long exceeding the anthers; stigma two-lobed; fruit very variable, often with emergences such as wings or apical horns. Most species of this family live in the arid zones of Africa, and some behave as weeds. Sixteen species in eight genera in East Africa.

Josephinia africana   **Plate 791**
A low shrub, or semi-decumbent woody herb, up to 130cm (51in) high; branches opposite, dark brown, densely crisped-pubescent to pilose when young, becoming glabrous. Leaves pale green, blade obovate, lobulate or coarsely sinnate-dentate to 2.5cm (1in) long, rounded at the apex, cuneate at base, pubescent and glandular on both sides, more densely so below, becoming glabrous. Corolla 2.5–4cm (1–1⅜in) long, mauve, to pale pink, spotted with black inside, thinly pubescent and glandular, limb 2–3.5cm (¾–1⅜in) diameter; the central lobe of lower lip suborbicular to transverse-elliptic 1.5–2cm (⅜–¾in) across. Stamen with a tuft of hairs at base of filaments. Fruit indehiscent, globose, covered with stout spines. Altitude range 100–650m (328–2100ft). Found in dry *Acacia-Commiphora* and semi-desert scrub and on the margins of Sisal plantations. Recorded in the Northern Frontier (El Wak) to Voi, Taita Hills (Kenya); elsewhere, southern Somalia only.

Pedaliodiscus macrocarpus   **Plate 236**
An annual herb, procumbent or ascending to 0.6m (1¾ft) high, with opposite leaves. Leaf-blade angular, acute and sinuate up to 8cm (*c.* 3in) long and 2cm (*c.* ¾in) wide, petiole about 2.5cm (1in) long. Flowers, solitary, axillary, *c.* 18mm (¾in) long; corolla tube up to 15mm (⅝in) long, yellowish-white with brownish purple lines inside. Fruit with four short spines. Found in open *Acacia-Commiphora* scrubland, grassy savannah and coastal sandy dunes; altitude range 50–1000m (164–3280ft). Originally this species was thought to be endemic in coastal areas on the Kenya–Tanzania border but it is now widespread in coastal areas and inland up to its altitude range. Recorded from Somalia to Tanzania. The only species in this recently described genus which is hardly distinct from Pedalium.

Pedalium murex   **Plate 398**
An erect, spreading or subprostrate, sparsely glandular annual herb 12–75cm

(5–30in) high. Leaves elliptic, obovate or oblong, sometimes fleshy, to 5cm (2in) long, coarsely dentate particularly in the upper half, rounded or truncate at apex. Flowers pale primrose yellow, corolla tube 2–2.5cm ($\frac{4}{5}$–1in) long; limb 1.5–2cm ($\frac{3}{5}$–$\frac{4}{5}$in) across. Fruit indehiscent, four-angled with four spines. This species is a saline salt indicator in and around limestone in short grass in the coastal belt and in old sisal plantations. Altitude range 0–450m (0–1475ft). Recorded in Mombasa district (Kenya); Rufiji District, Mafia Island, Zanzibar (Tanzania); and in Ethiopia and Somalia. The leaves can be eaten as a vegetable. The only species in the genus in East Africa.

Pterodiscus ruspolii   Plate 399
Plant with a fleshy base, 4–8cm (1$\frac{3}{5}$–3$\frac{1}{5}$in) long and 0.5–2cm ($\frac{1}{5}$–$\frac{4}{5}$in) diameter, from which up to twenty stems arise which are erect or suberect, 4–20cm (1$\frac{3}{5}$–c. 8in) long. Leaves variable, usually long petiolate; blade obovate, elliptic or ovate, rounded at apex, cuneate at base, thinly to densely glandular below, glabrescent above, margins entire or undulate. Flowers bright yellow to orange, sometimes with a red or purple centre spot, opening two to three at a time. Corolla tube straight or slightly curved 1.6–3cm ($\frac{3}{5}$–1$\frac{1}{5}$in) long, 3–4mm ($\frac{1}{8}$–$\frac{1}{6}$in) across, glandular without, pubescent with multi-cellular hairs within, especially in the upper part of throat; lobes 0.5–1cm ($\frac{1}{5}$–$\frac{2}{5}$in) long, 1–1.5cm ($\frac{2}{5}$–$\frac{3}{5}$in) across. Fruit, indehiscent, four-angled without spines. Found in open semi-desert scrub and grassland in dry sandy or rocky ground and alluvial soil; altitude range 150–1100m (500–3500ft). Recorded on Central Island – Lake Turkana, Isiolo (Kenya); Tanzania and Uganda, no record; also in Sudan, Ethiopia, Somalia.

SESAMUM
Annual or perennial herbs; flowers pink or purple, solitary in the leaf axils; fruit an oblong, grooved capsule, beaked at apex; seeds numerous, often winged. Five species in East Africa, one of them, *S. indicum*, 'Simsim' of great value as an oil seed crop.

Sesamum alatum   Plate 792
An erect herb 20–90cm (rarely 150cm) high (8–36in (58in)) high, stem simple or sparsely branched, sulcate, glabrous. Leaves generally heteromorphic, opposite or rarely alternate; lower leaves long-petiolate 2–7cm ($\frac{4}{5}$–2$\frac{4}{5}$in) long, palmately three- to five-foliolate or partite; lobes lanceolate to narrowly linear-lanceolate; broad central lobe longest, cuneate at the base, acute or rounded at apex; margins entire or undulate, glabrous; upper leaves usually simple, linear-lanceolate to finely linear, and attenuate into a long petiole. Flowers pink or purple, sometimes red, spotted within. Calyx deciduous. Corolla long, 2–3cm ($\frac{4}{5}$–1$\frac{1}{5}$in), thinly glandular and pilose outside with white multi-cellular hairs. A plant of semi-desert grassland on river banks or near springs; altitude range 600–900m (1950–2950ft) and recorded in Northern Frontier areas, Lake Turkana, Turkwell Valley and South Horr (Kenya); Tanzania and Uganda, no record; also in Sudan, Ethiopia, Zimbabwe, Mozambique.

S. angolense   Plate 793
A shrubby annual or sometimes perennial herb 0.8–3m (2$\frac{1}{2}$–10ft) tall. Leaves subsessile, or shortly petiolate, elliptic to narrowly oblong, margins entire, more or less inrolled, upper surface glabrescent, lower surface tomentose. Flowers pink to purple or pale mauve, with deeper markings; lobes 5–10mm ($\frac{1}{5}$–$\frac{2}{5}$in) long, 2mm ($\frac{1}{12}$in) broad; corolla 3.5–7cm (1$\frac{3}{5}$–2$\frac{4}{5}$in) long, 2–3cm ($\frac{4}{5}$–1$\frac{1}{5}$in) wide at throat. Found in grassland, by roadsides, in abandoned cultivation and along river valleys;

altitude range 360–2350m (1200–7700ft) and recorded in Tinderet, western Kenya, Kisii, Embu and Nairobi (Kenya); lake areas, Tabora, Morogoro, Songea, Mbeya, Iringa (Tanzania); Buganda (Uganda); also in Zaire, Malawi, Zambia, Zimbabwe.

S. angustifolium
Plate 599

An erect or sometimes spreading, simple or branched herb, 30–180cm (1–6ft) in height, stems subquadrangular, grooved, pubescent to thinly pilose, becoming glabrescent. Leaves sessile, subsessile or lower ones sometimes shortly petiolate, narrowly linear to linear-lanceolate, 2–12cm ($\frac{4}{5}$–4$\frac{3}{4}$in) long, margin entire, (rarely undulate), thinly pubescent to glabrous above, usually densely glandular below, cuneate at base, acute or subacute; (rarely rounded) at apex. Flowers pink, red, mauve or purple; corolla 2–4cm ($\frac{3}{4}$–1$\frac{3}{4}$in) long, 1–2.3cm ($\frac{2}{5}$–1in) wide at throat; calyx lobe 5–9mm ($\frac{1}{5}$–$\frac{1}{3}$in) long. Found in cultivated and waste areas, the gardens of small homesteads, roadsides and short grassland; altitude range 5–2000m (16–6560ft). Often cultivated as a vegetable for medicinal purposes and for the oil in the seeds. Recorded in central and southern Kenya and throughout Tanzania and Uganda. Also in Zaire, Zimbabwe, Malawi, Mozambique.

S. calycinum
Plate 600

An erect herb generally simple (only strong specimens are branched and then sometimes woody at the base), 30–90cm (12–36in) high; leaves sessile or subsessile, narrowly linear to linear-lanceolate 2–12cm ($\frac{4}{5}$–4$\frac{3}{4}$in) long and up to 1cm ($\frac{2}{5}$in) broad, margins entire, sometimes the lower leaves coarsely and irregularly toothed. Flower pink to purple, often spotted within; corolla 2–3.5cm ($\frac{4}{5}$–1$\frac{3}{8}$in) long and 1–1.8cm ($\frac{2}{5}$–$\frac{3}{4}$in) in diameter, at the throat. Found in grassland and waste land and also in cultivated areas; altitude range 600–2040m (2000–6700ft), and recorded in Aberdares, Kitale, western Kenya, Nanyuki, Embu and Machakos (Kenya); all regions of Tanzania and Uganda; also in Zaire, Malawi, Zambia. Zimbabwe.

S. latifolium
Plate 794

An erect herb 60–120cm (2–4ft) high; stems quadrangular, sulcate, more or less densely pubescent with brownish hairs. Leaves generally heteromorphic; lower ones large, long-petiolate, ovate-cordate or three-lobed, cordate at base; upper leaves smaller ovate to ovate-lanceolate, subtruncate or cuneate at base, finely to coarsely serrate on margin, acuminate at apex, pubescent on both sides especially on upper leaves, both surfaces. Flowers pale pink or pinkish mauve. Bracteoles conspicuous, pale brown, rather membraneous, narrowly lanceolate, pubescent. Corolla glandular outside, thinly pubescent 2.5–2.8cm (c. 1in) long, throat 1cm ($\frac{2}{5}$in) wide. Altitude range 300–1300m (1000–4200ft). Locally common among rocks in semi-desert scrub. Recorded in Northern Frontier areas, Lake Turkana, Tana River and Baringo (Kenya); Tanzania, no record; Karamoja (Uganda); also Sudan, Ethiopia.

86. Acanthaceae

A large tropical family of herbs, shrublets or, rarely, shrubs with a few warm temperate representatives. Their leaves are opposite, without stipules, nearly always simple, usually entire and usually containing dark crystalline bodies called cystoliths. The bracts are often conspicuous in the inflorescence. There are four or five sepals, free or slightly united, a zygomorphic corolla, usually five-lobed, and two or four stamens. The ovary is superior, bi-locular and usually has two (although sometimes one or three) ovules per loculus. The style is terminal and often bilobed. The fruit is a capsule, usually containing about four flat seeds. A few genera with more numerous ovules and seeds form a transition to the *Scrophulariaceae*. 390 species in fifty-six genera in East Africa.

ACANTHUS

Stiff herbs or softly woody shrubs with prickly leaves and bracts; flowers large. Five species in East Africa.

Acanthus eminens   Plate 601

A woody herb which grows to a height of 3m (10ft). Its large thistle-like leaves are opposite, oblong-elliptic and deeply pinnatifid or lobate with spiny margins. They may be up to 30cm (12in) long and 15cm (6in) wide, although they can be only half this size. Royal blue flowers c. 5cm (2in) long. Found in Kenya at 1830–2770m (6000–9100ft) covering large areas in cedar and allied forest; Tanzania, no record; eastern region (Uganda); also southern Sudan – Imatong Mts, Ethiopia.

A. pubescens (A. arboreus in KTS)   Plate 701

Much taller than *A. eminens*, up to 6m (20ft) in height and more vigorous. Its inflorescence is rose, pink or magenta c. 35mm (1¾in) across. It is found in western Kenya at 1125–1800m (3700–6000ft); lake areas, Tabora (Tanzania); all except northern regions (Uganda); also Ethiopia, Burundi, eastern Zaire. *A. arboreus* is now considered to be confined to the Yemen only.

Adhatoda schimperiana (*Justicia schimperiana*)   Plate 795

An erect shrub up to 2.5m (8ft) tall. Leaves opposite, elliptic, entire, cuneate at base, glabrous c. 13cm (c. 5in) long and 4cm (1⅜in) wide. Inflorescence a terminal thyrsus, ovary conspicuous. Flowers c. 2cm (¾in) long, white with a dark purple throat, each contained in a bract c. 1.5cm (⅜in) long which has a prominent scarious margin. Found in coastal areas and inland on rocky slopes, light forest and abandoned cultivation; altitude range 30–1750m (100–5800ft). It is also grown as an ornamental hedge plant and garden shrub. Recorded at the coast and Taita Hills (Kenya); Pare Mountains (Tanzania); Uganda, no record; also in Ethiopia, Somalia, Eritrea.

Anisotes parvifolius

A many-stemmed woody shrub up to 3m (10ft) high. Bark grey with scattered lenticels. Leaves obovate, glabrous to 2.5cm (1in) long. The flowers, c. 5cm (2in) long, sessile, one to three together, in axillary clusters, yellowish-green at base and brick-red above. Altitude range 5–760m (16–2500ft), found in relict patches of coastal evergreen forest and edges of *Acacia-Commiphora* bushland. Recorded in Meru National Park but also grown ornamentally in Nairobi (Kenya) and Tanga (Tanzania).

ASYSTASIA

Herbs or weak shrubs with flowers in spikes; corolla funnel-shaped with five equal lobes; four stamens; four seeds. Twelve species in East Africa.

Asystasia sp. A

A trailing herb, or weak shrub, with glabrous, ridged stems and linear scabrid leaves. The inflorescence is a terminal dense spike of yellow-green flowers, corolla 20mm ($\frac{4}{5}$in) long. Altitude range 900–1900m (2950–6250ft). It is a rare plant of the Rift Valley grasslands but can be found between Kedong and Olorgesaille (Kenya); Musoma only (Tanzania); Uganda and elsewhere, not known.

NB This species is Sp 'A' in *UKWF* but recorded as Sp. 'B' at Kew.

A. charmian **Plate 796**
An erect, weak herb or shrub from a woody rootstock with scabrid four-angled stems and ovate-lanceolate leaves; flowers white, with mauve or purple spots, in loose terminal spikes, corolla tube *c.* 2cm ($\frac{4}{5}$in) long, lobe 1cm ($\frac{2}{5}$in) wide. Altitude range 600–1200m (2000–3900ft). An uncommon species in dry bushland and recorded in Machakos and Loitokitok (Kenya); Maasai, Tanga, Mpwapwa, Kondoa (Tanzania); Uganda and elsewhere, no record.

A. gangetica **Plate 797**
A trailing perennial, pubescent or glabrescent, with ovate leaves, rounded or cordate at base and one-sided racemes of white and pale purple flowers; corolla tube 2cm ($\frac{4}{5}$in) long, lobe 1.5cm ($\frac{3}{5}$in) across. Altitude range 0–1850m (0–6500ft). Common at the coast and western Kenya in secondary grassland but rare elsewhere, although recorded in Rift Valley and Embu (Kenya); all regions of Tanzania and Uganda; also widespread in tropical Africa.

A. guttata **Plate 400**
A perennial herb with a rather woody rootstock and ascending stems. Corolla *c.* 24mm (1in) long. Found in drier areas in *Acacia-Commiphora* open bushland and in moister areas in grassland; altitude range 350–1600m (1150–5250ft). Recorded in North-east Frontier areas, Turkana, Nairobi, Machakos, Embu, coastal dry areas (Kenya); Maasai (Tanzania); northern, western regions (Uganda); also eastern Ethiopia, Somalia.

A. laticapsula A pubescent to tomentose perennial from a woody rootstock with ascending stems bearing subsessile oblong leaves, narrowed to the very short petiole; flowers white with pale purple markings in very loose racemes; corolla tube 2.5cm (1in) long, lobe 2cm ($\frac{4}{5}$in) across. Locally common in grassland especially in black cotton soil in Central Province but also recorded in Aberdares, Magadi, Machakos, Kajiado, Nairobi and Embu (Kenya); Maasai (Tanzania); Uganda, no record; also Somalia.

A. schimperi **Plate 237**
An erect, or when old decumbent, pubescent annual, (rarely perennial) with obovate to elliptic leaves and short dense terminal spikes of white flowers; corolla less than 14mm (*c.* $\frac{1}{2}$in) long, palate often spotted with green: bracts lanceolate, acute, longer than the calyx. Abundant at medium and lower altitudes as a weed of arable land and pathsides. Altitude range 550–2000m (1800–6500ft). Recorded in Aberdares, Kitale, western Kenya, Kisii, Baringo, Rift Valley, Embu, Machakos and Nairobi (Kenya); all regions except Mbeya, Iringa, Songea (Tanzania); all except northern regions (Uganda); also Ethiopia, Somalia.

BARLERIA

Herbs or shrublets often spiny; calyx of four lobes, the upper and lower, large and broad; the lateral ones linear and smaller; fertile stamens two with two much smaller staminodes also present. Fifty species in East Africa. As well as those described here there are many other species of *Barleria* in East Africa at low and medium altitudes with white, yellow or blue flowers. They are difficult to classify and much work still needs to be done on them.

Barleria acanthoides   **Plate 118**
A small, low growing shrub having elliptic to oblong, spathulate leaves with markedly-toothed spines, often as long as the leaves, which spring from the point where the leaf joins the stem. The white flowers, often single, open at night from a long cylindrical tube c. 4cm (1¾in) long; c. 2cm (¾in) across. They are pollinated by moths with long tongues. In the morning they turn blue-black in colour and die when the sun becomes hot about 11.00 hours. This delightful species grows in dry scrub, bushland and semi-arid grassland, often in rocky places and generally at altitudes of 60–1550m (200–5100ft) in the Narok, Baringo, Magadi, Machakos and Kajiado districts (Kenya); Maasai, Tanga (Tanzania); northern region – Gulu (Uganda); also Sudan, Ethiopia, Somalia.

B. sp. A   **Plate 239**
A small, much branched, spiny shrub with subsessile, elliptic obtuse leaves and quadrifid interpetiolar spines. Flowers orange in dense spiny heads, bracts narrowly obovate with a long apical spine; outer calyx segments broadly elliptic with a very long apical spine; corolla lobe 2cm (¾in) across, tube 2.5cm (1in) long; stamens almost as long as the corolla with anthers 3–4mm (⅛in) long. The capsule is conic, 1.5cm (⅝in) long. Found in dry bushland and rocky places; altitude range up to 1050m (3500ft). Recorded in Magadi (Kenya). This is still an obscure species and more information is needed, especially on its habitat.

B. argentea   **Plate 119**
A much-branched perennial or under-shrub 10–30cm (4–12in) high with no spines. Stems grey-pubescent. Leaves oblong or narrowly elliptic, cuneate at base, subsessile up to 3.5cm (1¾in) long. Inflorescence, 1.8cm (c. ¾in) long, single- to tri-flowered axillary and scattered on the branches, pale mauve to lilac with markings on the throat. Widespread in arid and semi-arid areas; altitude range 96–1800m (320–5900ft) throughout Kenya; Lushoto (Tanzania); Karamoja (Uganda); also in Sudan, Ethiopia and Somalia.

B. eranthemoides   **Plate 238**
A small, much-branched, spiny shrub with almost stalkless, elliptic leaves and spines between the stalks. The flowers are yellow to orange in dense, spiny heads c. 18mm (¾in) across. The corolla tube is cylindrical and narrow with a subequally five-lobed limb. It is found in dry grassland and bushland at 150–1800m (500–5900ft) in Narok, Baringo, Magadi, Machakos and Kajiado districts and in all drier areas (Kenya); Maasai, Tanga (Tanzania); northern region – Gulu (Uganda); also Ethiopia, Somalia, Malawi, Mozambique.

B. micrantha   An erect or semi-scandent herb with shortly petiolate, rather small elliptic obtuse leaves; one to three flowers in the leaf axils, not in terminal heads; outer calyx segments broadly elliptic with toothed margins. Corolla tube c. 2.6cm (1in) long, lobe c. 2.5cm (1in) across, pale blue or lavender, rarely white. Found in woodland or thicket, rarely in grassland; altitude range 5–2100m (16–7000ft) and recorded in Baringo, Narok, Rift Valley, Nanyuki, Embu, Machakos and Nairobi (Kenya); (a form with exceptionally large flowers occurs in the forest and woodland areas of the Nairobi and Eastern Upland areas); lake areas, Maasai, Tanga (Tanzania); all regions except northern (Uganda); also Burundi.

B. ramulosa **Plate 120**

An erect. much branched, spiny, perennial, hairy herb up to 2m (6½ft) tall; leaves opposite, obovate; spines whitish and paired on the stem. Bracts spiny. Flowers sky blue to white; corolla lobes 3cm (1⅕in) long, 2cm (⅘in) across. Found on sandstone ridges and rocky bushland; altitude range 15–1800m (50–6000ft). Widespread in Kenya; Tanzania and Uganda, no record; also in southern Somalia.

B. spinisepala **Plate 798**

A low growing, much-branched, woody perennial herb with almost stalkless, elliptic, mucronate leaves and pinnatisect spines between the stalks. Its solitary flowers are axillary with a spiny-margined calyx and a pale blue corolla *c.* 2cm (⅘in) across. It is night-flowering and by midday the corolla has dropped. It is found in dry grassland at 1500–2150m (4900–7000ft) rarely at lower altitudes especially in northern Kenya and the eastern Maasai country – Kajiado district (Kenya); Maasai (Tanzania); Uganda and elsewhere, no record.

B. submollis **Plate 799**

An erect or semi-prostrate herb which sometimes roots at the nodes. Its leaves are obtuse and rounded at the base. Its blue flowers are axillary, corolla *c.* 15mm (⅗in) across and grow in clusters of one to three. It is found in savannah and bushland at 900–1350m (3000–4500ft) in Kenya; Maasai, Tanga, Mpwapwa, Kondoa, Morogoro (Tanzania); northern region (Uganda); elsewhere, not known.

B. taitensis **Plate 121**

A bushy subshrub up to 50cm (20in) high with rusty-coloured indumentum, growing from a woody rootstock. Leaves greyish beneath, dark green above. Flowers white, tinged with blue at the tip. Corolla tube *c.* 3cm (1⅕in) long divided into five lobes each 2cm (⅘in) long. Two stamens. Found in dry *Acacia-Commiphora* bushland and rocky hills; altitude range 375–1050m (1250–3500ft). Common in Kitui, Machakos and Tsavo West and East National Parks (Kenya); Tanga (Tanzania); Uganda and elsewhere, no record.

B. ventricosa **Plate 846**

A scandent herb with subsessile, elliptic, subacute leaves, attenuate below; flowers in the axils of the upper leaves congested into a head, but axillary cymes usually present also; outer calyx, segments elliptic, entire, yellow-haired; corolla medium to large, 20×15mm (⅘×⅗in), blue. Capsule ellipsoid, two-seeded. Found in forest undergrowth; altitude range 1100–2400m (3600–7900ft). Widespread in East Africa and from Ethiopia to Mozambique.

BLEPHARIS

Leaves in whorls of four; unequal sized calyx, four-cleft, the upper segment much larger than the lower; corolla with a short tube and a three- to five-lobed lower lip, the upper lip absent; four stamens, capsule three-seeded. Twenty-four species in East Africa.

Blepharis hildebrandtii **Plate 847**

A perennial, much branched, usually prostrate herb, forming a dense mass on the ground or sometimes climbing on thickets to 1m (3ft) high. Leaves narrowly elliptic to linear-oblong up to 35mm (1⅖in) long and 10mm (⅖in) wide. Flowers, pale blue to purple, sessile, axillary and often solitary with spiny bracts, corolla 2.5cm (1in) long. Found in wooded grassland among lava rocks and stony ground; altitude range 100–2160m (330–7200ft). Recorded in Embu, Machakos, Kajiado, Narok, coast hinterland, Taita Hills (Kenya); Maasai, Tanga (Tanzania); Uganda, no record; also in Ethiopia, Somalia.

B. linariifolia
Plate 848

A prostrate annual plant with stalkless, unequally indented, spine-toothed leaves. Its elongated terminal spikes, short at first, bear bright blue flowers *c.* 18mm (¾in) long. It is found in open spaces in dry thornbush and grassland in north-eastern and southern Kenya at altitudes of 140–1400m (450–4600ft), especially in the Northern Frontier and near Voi (Kenya); Maasai, Tanga, Mpwapwa, Kondoa, Mbeya, Iringa (Tanzania); northern region – Gulu (Uganda); also Sudan, southern Ethiopia, Somalia.

B. maderaspatensis
Plate 602

Erect or prostrate herbs with unequal, elliptic, usually entire-margined leaves and axillary solitary or clustered flower spikes, each bearing a single pale blue terminal flower, corolla 12–26mm (½–1in) long; upper bracts of the spike rounded above with recurved tips and reflexedly scabrid bristles; the lower stamen filaments with a slender tooth almost as long as the anther. A common weed of grassland and bushland but not widespread from 1–2700m (3–9000ft) in Kenya. There is a subspecies *B. maderaspatensis* ssp. *maderaspatensis* with a protruding upper calyx segment which occurs in coastal regions (Kenya); also regions except Mbeya, Iringa (Tanzania); also throughout tropical Africa south to Mozambique, Zimbabwe.

Brillantaisia nitens
Plate 849

An erect, much-branched, perennial herb, growing to 2m (6½ft) high, with broadly ovate, acuminate, evenly serrate leaves, narrowing sharply below into the winged petiole and rarely cordate. The flowers, *c.* 26 mm (1in) long, are in a long, narrow panicle with the upper bracts elliptic to oblanceolate and with large blue-purple corollas. It is found in western Kenya from Kericho to Kitale in forest undergrowth at 1650–2200m (5400–7200ft); Tabora (Tanzania); western region and Buganda (Uganda); also eastern Zaire. Ten other species in East Africa.

Crabbea velutina
Plates 60 & 122

A low, tufted herb with short petiolate oblong-elliptic leaves: flowers 20–25mm (⅘–1in) across, white to pale lilac, with a yellow patch on lower lip, opening in the early evening and dying the next morning. Found in bush and grassland; altitude range 450–1800m (1475–5900ft) and recorded in Kisii, Baringo, Rift Valley, Machakos, Nairobi and Kajiado (Kenya); all regions except Tabora, Songea (Tanzania); all regions except Buganda (Uganda); also Ethiopia, Malawi, Mozambique, Zimbabwe, Botswana.

CROSSANDRA

Herbs; flowers in dense strobilate spikes; corolla with a long linear tube, the limb split above to give a single three- to five-lobed lip; four stamens. Ten species in East Africa.

Crossandra friesiorum
Plate 123

Generally a straggling plant with small white flowers 17–21mm (*c.* ¾in) across found in dense shade in forest, or damp forest undergrowth, up to altitudes 1220–1500m (4000–5000ft); Aberdares, Kajiado (Kenya); Maasai, Tanga (Tanzania); Uganda and elsewhere, unknown.

ACANTHACEAE

C. mucronata
Pale orange to red flowers 18–26mm (c. ¾–1in) across. Found in dry areas up to 1800m (6000ft) in Kenya; Maasai, Tanga (Tanzania); northern region – Gulu (Uganda); also Ethiopia, Somalia, Zimbabwe.

C. nilotica
Plate 528
A short, erect, sometimes straggling, branched herb with elliptic-lanceolate leaves and spikes of red or apricot flowers, inflorescence c. 35mm (1⅜in) across. It is found in partial shade in wooded grassland and dry bushland and occasionally in olive forest at 1070–2400m (3500–8000ft) in Tinderet, Kisii, Rift Valley, Narok and Baringo districts (Kenya); lake areas, Tabora (Tanzania); all regions of Uganda; also Ghana to Ethiopia, Zaire, Zambia.

C. subacaulis
Plate 429
A low growing plant with leaves crowded almost into a rosette. The apricot to orange, or even red, spikes of closely-knit flowers c. 5cm (2in) across spring from the leaves, only a few inches or centimetres above the ground. It grows in savannah country, open grassland and on rocky slopes up to 1690m (5500ft) in the Nairobi, Machakos, Narok and Kajiado districts and is fairly common on stony slopes in the Maasai Mara area (Kenya); lake areas, Maasai, Tanga, Morogora, Songea (Tanzania); northern and western regions (Uganda); also Sudan, Zaire.

C. stenostachya   Yellow flowers 10–12mm (⅜–½in) across. Found in grassland and wet places in arid areas at altitudes up to 910m (3000ft) in the Machakos district (Kenya); Maasai, Tanga (Tanzania); northern region – Gulu (Uganda); elsewhere, no record.

C. tridentata   Similar to C. friesiorum but found up to altitudes of 2450m (8000ft) in Aberdares, Kajiado (Kenya); Maasai, Tanga, Morogoro (Tanzania); Uganda and elsewhere, no record.

DYSCHORISTE
Herbs or small shrubs; flowers in axillary cymes; calyx lobes about as long as the tube; corolla contorted; four stamens; capsule four-seeded. Eight species in East Africa.

Dyschoriste sp. A
Plate 603
A wiry shrub with obovate leaves, rounded at apex, flowers blue-purple, rarely more than six at the nodes. Corolla tube 2.5cm (1in) long, lobe 2.4cm (c. 1in) long. Local in wooded grassland; altitude range 600–1800m (1950–5900ft), especially near Thika and recorded also in Embu, Machakos and Nairobi (Kenya). Though this species is recorded in UKWF and at the Herbarium, Nairobi, there is no record of it at Kew and details are limited.

D. hildebrandtii
Plate 604
An erect, densely glandular, pubescent herb or low shrub with ovate to obovate, slightly crenate leaves and rather loose pedunculate cymes of mauve to greenish-purple flowers, 22mm (c. 1in) long, 15mm (⅜in) across. Locally common in dry wooded grassland at 900–1600m (2950–5250ft). Baringo, Embu, Machakos, Kajiado, Chyulu Hills (Kenya); Tanzania, Uganda and elsewhere, unknown.

D. radicans
Plate 605
A pubescent or glabrescent trailing herb with elliptic to obovate leaves and few to

many flowers c. 20mm ($\frac{4}{5}$in) long, 8mm ($\frac{1}{3}$in) across, sessile in leaf axils: corolla pale purple to mauve. Common in disturbed grassland at altitude range 1080–2400m (3600–8000ft) and widespread throughout Kenya; lake areas, Maasai, Tanga, Tabora, Mbeya, Iringa (Tanzania); all regions (Uganda); also Sudan, Ethiopia, northern Somalia, Zaire, Rwanda, Burundi, Zambia, Botswana.

D. thunbergiiflora   **Plate 606**
A much-stemmed, woody shrub to 2m (6ft) high, sparsely pubescent. Leaves obovate, obtuse, attenuate at base to 3cm (1$\frac{1}{5}$in) long. Flowers axillary, 5cm (2in) long, one- to four-flowered, rather lax monopodial cymes. The calyx divided half way into linear teeth. Corolla tube 2.8cm (1$\frac{1}{10}$in) long; lip 2.3cm ($\frac{9}{10}$in) long; purple with dark markings in the throat. Found in open bushland and riverine wooded grassland; altitude range 270–1950m (900–6500ft). Recorded in Samburu, Kitui, Machakos, Meru National Park, Cheranganis, Nairobi, Tana River District (Kenya); elsewhere, not known. Grown in Nairobi Arboretum as an ornamental bush.

ECBOLIUM
Three stamens, two seeds; five species in East Africa.

Ecbolium amplexicaule   **Plate 240**
A stiff bushy herb 1–3m (3–10ft) tall; leaves oblong, sessile with broad basal lobes embracing the often axillary cone-like spikes; bracts large, green, often bracteoles minute; calyx with five lobes; corolla a strange greenish-blue, with a very narrow tube c. 20mm ($\frac{4}{5}$in) long, and a limb c. 30mm (1$\frac{1}{5}$in) across, which is two-lipped, the upper lip entire, the lower with three broader lobes; two stamens with elliptic anthers divergent at base but equal in length. Found in dry bushland and Nyika areas; altitude range 1–1000m (3–3280ft), in Central Province and coast areas (Kenya); Tanga, Morogoro, Songea (Tanzania); Uganda and elsewhere, no record.
  NB There is a pubescent form of *E. amplexicaule* which has been named *E. subcordatum* but it is doubtful whether it is a distinct species.

E. revolutum (*E. hamatum*)   **Plate 850**
A small shrub with ovate to elliptic, acute or rounded leaves and blue or occasion-ally white, flowers c. 12–16mm (c. $\frac{1}{2}$–$\frac{3}{5}$in) across, in spikes up to 8cm (3in) long. It has minute down on all its parts, although the leaves are almost hairless. It is locally common in fine soils in dry bushland and has been recorded in Magadi, Machakos and Kajiado districts and in Tsavo East National Park (Kenya); lake areas, Maasai, Tanga, Mpwapwa, Kondoa (Tanzania); northern region – Gulu (Uganda); else-where, no record.

HYGROPHILA
Corolla two-lipped; the upper lip hooded; the lower lip three-lobed; four stamens; capsule with numerous seeds. Eleven species in East Africa.

Hygrophila auriculata   **Plate 607**
An erect, sparingly branched, annual herb with square stems and shortly petiolate elliptic leaves; flowers in axillary sessile clusters, each with a few stout spines and oblong-elliptic bracts; corolla bluey-mauve, pinkish or white c. 25mm (1in) long. Found in swamps and open bushland; altitude range 50–2100m (165–6900ft). Kitale, Western Kenya, Kisii, Rift Valley and Machakos (Kenya); all regions of Tanzania and Uganda; also Senegal to Ethiopia, Zaire, Malawi, Mozambique.

ACANTHACEAE

H. sp. A An erect branching herb up to 1.5m (4¾ft) with softly pubescent, elliptic, subsessile leaves much reducing in size in the inflorescence. Flowers large pale-mauve or purple 3.5cm (1⅜in) long. Found in wet grassland and swamps, and wet places in forest; altitude range 350–1500m (2800–5000ft), only in western Kenya.

H. pobeguinii An erect, branched, glabrous annual with narrowly oblanceolate sessile leaves and small mauvish flowers 15mm (⅝in) long in sessile axillary clusters. Found in damp grassland and ditches; altitude range 750–1600m (2450–5250ft), and recorded only in Kisii, and western Kenya (Kenya); Songea (Tanzania); western region of Uganda; also Zaire, West Africa.

H. spiciformis A large, straggling or bushy herb with shortly petiolate or sessile elliptic leaves and spiciform or interrupted terminal leafy inflorescences of mauve or purple flowers, corolla 25mm (1in) long. Occasional plants occur with very narrow leaves but these are not distinct. Found in woodland, thickets, forest and damp grassland; altitude range 1560–2800m (5200–9300ft) and recorded in Tinderet, Aberdares, Kitale, Narok, Machakos and Nairobi (Kenya); lake areas, Maasai, Mpwapwa, Kondoa, Mbeya, Iringa (Tanzania); Uganda, no record; also Ethiopia, Somalia, Mozambique.

HYPOESTES
Flowers borne between a pair of bracts which are connate, at least at their base; corolla two-lipped, the upper lip reflexed; two stamens, each with a single cell; capsule four-seeded. Eight species in East Africa.

Hypoestes aristata   Plates 608 & 800
Rather similar to *H. forskalei* with lanceolate leaves and axillary whorls of white, pink or mauve flowers 13mm (*c.* ½in) long; 6mm (*c.* ¼in) across, which are neither as close together nor as dense as those of *H. forskalei*. It is found in forest, thicket or in the margins of relict forest patches in most parts of Kenya at altitudes 1250–2710m (4100–8900ft); all regions except lake areas, Songea (Tanzania); all regions except eastern – Jinja, Lake Kioga (Uganda); also Ethiopia, Malawi, Zimbabwe, Mozambique.

H. forskalei (*H. verticillaris*)   Plate 609
A very variable, straggling or erect, perennial herb with elliptic leaves. The flowers, 14mm (½in) long, borne in the axils of the peduncle, are pale mauve streaked with pink, purple or white, or sometimes all white. Because it is so variable it can be found in a wide range of habitats in bushland, dry grassland, forest edges and clearings from 10–2740m (30–9000ft) in Kenya; all regions of Tanzania and Uganda; also widespread in tropical Africa (also South Africa).
   NB The second photograph shows an unusual deep pink form.

H. hildebrandtii   Plate 702
A virgately-branched tussock herb up to 45cm (18in) high with a conspicuous grey appearance. Leaves oblong, or narrowly elliptic, obtuse, up to 10cm (4in) long. Inflorescence axillary, running into a narrow terminal panicle; spikelets mostly in unilateral cymes up to 4cm (1⅜in) long. Corolla pale pink, 10mm (*c.* ⅜in) long, limb 5mm (⅕in) long; faint dark spots at base of upper lip. Found in grassland and open areas in *Acacia-Commiphora* bushland, rocky hillsides and in thickets; altitude range 570–1800m (1900–6000ft). Recorded in Samburu, Isiolo, Meru, Tsavo East and West, Nanyuki, Baringo (Kenya); Tanzania and Uganda, no record; also in Ethiopia, northern Somalia.

H. triflora   **Plate 610**
A straggling annual herb, very variable in size with petiolate elliptic leaves and usually three white or pale mauve flowers 2.5cm (1in) long, in pedunculate, axillary umbels, or solitary; calyx segments subacute; corolla tube widening slightly upwards, the corolla limb two-lipped with upper lip reflexed and the lower lip broader and spreading; two stamens. Found in forest undergrowth or on forest edges; altitude range 1650–3050m (5500–10,000ft) and recorded on Elgon, Mau, Aberdares, Mt Kenya and in western Kenya and Embu (Kenya); all regions except Songea (Tanzania); all regions except Buganda (Uganda); also Ethiopia, Rwanda, Malawi.

Isoglossa punctata (*I. oerstediana*)   **Plate 801**
A trailing pubescent herb with petiolate ovate-elliptic leaves which are subsessile below the inflorescence: inflorescence simple or more usually branched, of spike-like racemes of white, pink-spotted flowers 10mm (⅜in) long. Twelve other species in East Africa. Altitude range 1350–2400m (4500–8000ft). Locally common in montane rain forest undergrowth and recorded in Elgon, Tinderet, Mau, western Kenya, Kericho and Machakos (Kenya); Maasai, Tanga (Tanzania); all regions except Buganda (Uganda); also Ethiopia.

JUSTICIA
Sepals shortly fused at base; corolla two-lipped, pubescent outside, the upper lip hooded, the lower lip three-lobed; two stamens, with two anther cells set one above the other, the lower cell tailed; capsule four-seeded. About fifty species in East Africa.

Justicia betonica   **Plate 20**
A weakly erect or trailing, glabrous to pubescent herb from a woody rootstock, leaves elliptic, often with undulate margins, flowers white with red guidelines, corolla tube c. 12mm (½in) long, c. 7mm (¼in) across. A variable and widespread plant; altitude range 400–1900m (1300–6200ft). Forms from wet forest have large pubescent leaves and pale green bracts, while those from riversides in drier areas have conspicuously white and green bracts, and smaller glabrous or pubescent leaves. Recorded throughout Kenya; all regions except Tabora, Tanga (Tanzania); all regions of Uganda; also Sudan, Ethiopia, south-western Zaire, Malawi.

J. diclipteroides   **Plate 703**
A sparsely pubescent, trailing herb which roots at the nodes. It has ovate leaves and scattered purple to pink flowers c. 8mm (⅓in) across in the upper axils. It is a common species in evergreen forest edges in eastern Kenya, found at 1220–2130m (4000–7000ft) in eastern Mau, Aberdares, Narok, Nanyuki, Embu, Machakos, Nairobi and Kajiado districts (Kenya); Maasai, Tanga (Tanzania); Uganda and elsewhere, no record. The common upland form around Nairobi has tightly downward curved stem hairs and in dry bushland there is a form with spreading, mixed glandular and eglandular stem hairs.

J. flava   **Plate 401**
A trailing or erect, downy, woody herb with ovate, acute leaves and crowded terminal spikes of yellow flowers c. 6mm (¼in) across subtended by oblong to lanceolate bracts. A very variable species, common in a variety of open habitats and over a wide ecological range and found almost everywhere in its habitat in Kenya up to an altitude of 2200m (7200ft); all regions of Tanzania and Uganda; also Senegal to Ethiopia, Somalia, Malawi, Mozambique.

J. keniensis **Plate 611**

A trailing herb with ascending stems and a sparse pubescence of spreading hairs, leaves ovate-elliptic, rounded at apex, often subsessile; flowers often rather regular in the upper axils and apparently spicate, pink or pale mauve, rarely white or deep purple; corolla 5mm (⅕in) long, limb 4mm (⅙in) top to bottom. Locally common within and at the edge of montane forest; altitude range 1800–2800m (3280–9200ft) and recorded in Elgon, Cheranganis, Mau, Aberdares, Rift Valley, Mt Kenya and western Kenya (Kenya); Tanzania, Uganda and elsewhere, no record.

J. matammensis **Plate 124**

A hairy annual with ascending or erect stems and elliptic to lanceolate leaves; spikes usually four-flowered of white campanulate flowers; corolla 5mm (⅕in) long. Locally common in sandy soils in disturbed bushland; altitude range 5–1500m (16–4900ft). Recorded in Embu, Machakos, Kajiado, Magadi (Kenya); Tanzania, no record; eastern region – Jinja, Lake Kioga (Uganda); also Sudan, Ethiopia, Zaire, Malawi, Zimbabwe, Mozambique.

J. odora **Plate 402**

An erect shrub, pubescent or glabrous, with subsessile suborbicular to oblong to obovate leaves. Sessile yellow flowers in groups of one to three in the upper axils. The corolla, 6mm (¼in) long, limb 11mm (⅖in) top to bottom, two-lipped, pubescent on the outside with a two-lobed posterior hood-like lip which covers the stamens and a three-lobed spreading anterior lip. The anterior part of the mouth of the corolla tube is wrinkled and grooved. This is a common and very variable shrub of dry stony bushland; altitude range 5–1600m (16–5250ft); found over a wide area from Baringo to Nanyuki, Embu, Magadi, Machakos, Kajiado and Rift Valley (Kenya); Maasai (Tanzania); Uganda, no record; also Sudan, Ethiopia, Somalia.

J. uncinulata **Plate 125**

A herb from a woody rootstock with trailing stems and elliptic to almost orbicular leaves; the species is, however, very variable in its leaf size, and shape, and pubescence. Most forms have elliptic leaves and some long spreading stem-hairs outside the two lines of pubescence. Flower 6mm (¼in) across lips. Found in grassland, mainly on black cotton soils; altitude range 290–2500m (960–8350ft), in all districts of Kenya from the west to Machakos in the east; all regions except Tabora, Songea (Tanzania); Uganda, no record; also Ethiopia.

MIMULOPSIS

Flowers in racemes of cymes; corolla broadly funnel-shaped from the base with five almost equal lobes; four stamens, each with two anthers, one anther of each anterior anther twisted; capsule six to eight seeded. Five species in East Africa.

Mimulopsis solmsii **Plate 126**

A trailing, woody herb often covered with long reddish hairs and with ovate, crenate or serrate leaves. Corolla tube *c.* 3cm (1⅕in) long, lobe *c.* 2.5cm (1in) across, pale blue to yellowish with purple guide lines within. An abundant herb of the forest floor in some areas; altitude range 1650–2550m (5500–8500ft) and showing the phenomenon of mass-flowering every five to nine years, after which it may be difficult to find until it increases again. Recorded in Aberdares, Mau, Tinderet and Elgon (Kenya). Maasai, Tabora, Morogoro, Mbeya, Iringa (Tanzania); all regions except northern (Uganda); also Ethiopia, Zaire, Zambia.

M. alpina Similar to *M. solmsii* but without the reddish hairs and with a condensed spike-like raceme of mauve flowers. The leaves are also less markedly crenate or serrate. Corolla tube 3cm (1⅕in) long, lobe 0.3cm (⅛in) across, usually mauve with yellow guide lines and an orange patch on the lower side. Altitude range 1800–3150m (6000–10,500ft). The distribution and habitat are similar to those of *M. solmsii* but it has been recorded rather more widely in Cheranganis, Mt Kenya and western Kenya (Kenya); Tanzania and Uganda, no record; also in Rwanda.

Phaulopsis imbricata A down-covered, trailing herb with ascending stems bearing elliptic leaves which gradually narrow at the base and apex. The flowers are small and form dense, one-sided, lateral or terminal spikes with white corollas over 8mm (⅓in) long. One of five species in East Africa. It is common on the floor of drier forests and in evergreen woodland everywhere in Kenya at altitudes of 1520–2450m (5000–8000ft); all regions except Songea (Tanzania); all regions of Uganda; also throughout tropical Africa except the driest areas.

RUELLIA
Bracts foliaceous; corolla tube cylindric below, campanulate above, the limb subequally five-fid; four stamens; seeds numerous. Ten species in East Africa.

Ruellia megachlamys   Plate 127
A tall, woody, much branched, perennial to 2m (6½ft) tall, with broadly ovate, petiolate leaves; flowers solitary, axillary, sessile and white. The corolla tube is very long, between 8–11cm (3–4⅖in) in length, expanding at the throat only; the limb is 30mm (1⅕in) across. Altitude range 600–1650m (1950–5400ft). Found in dry *Acacia, Commiphora* and *Grewia* bushland and recorded in Narok, Magadi and Kajiado (Kenya); lake areas, Maasai (Tanzania); northern and eastern regions (Uganda); also Ethiopia. The corolla opens at dusk or during the night and falls before noon of the following day.

R. patula   Plates 612 & 802
A much branched, semi-erect or erect herb with petiolate, ovate-spathulate, obtuse or acute leaves and pinkish-lilac flowers in subsessile axillary clusters of one to three; corolla *c.* 12–25mm (½–1in) long but very variable, 8–15mm (⅓–⅗in) across; calyx small with linear-lanceolate lobes. This is a very variable species and two forms can be recognized. One has short strigose hairs usually intermixed with glandular ones and occurs chiefly in semi-arid areas and dry bushland (e.g. Baringo, Magadi and Kajiado in Kenya). The other is a more bushy often creeping plant with numerous long, fine multicellular hairs mixed with the short strigose ones on the young shoots and petioles; glandular hairs frequently present as well. This form is found in wetter districts of Kenya and at slightly higher altitudes ranges 1–2200m (3–7200ft). Lake areas, Maasai, Tanga, Mpwapwa, Kondoa, Morogoro (Tanzania); northern region (Uganda); also Sudan, Ethiopia, Somalia, south to Zimbabwe, Mozambique.
R. patula is badly in need of further research by botanists; the species is ill defined and very diverse and though two forms are given above, it is probably wiser at this stage to regard it as polymorphic.

R. prostrata A much branched, woody herb with petiolate, sparingly pubescent, ovate-elliptic leaves with obtuse to acuminate tips and acuminate bases. The flowers are in sessile axillary clusters of one to three, with petiolate elliptic obtuse bracteoles and calyx with five subequal long linear lobes: corolla pinkish-mauve to white with a campanulate tube *c.* 20mm (⅘in) long, linear at the base and a subequally five-lobed limb 30mm (1⅕in) across. Found generally in open bushland or forest and widespread in Kenya at altitudes of 300–1700m (1000–5600ft); all regions (Tanzania); all regions except Buganda (Uganda); also Ethiopia, Eritrea, Malawi, Mozambique.

Ruttya fruticosa **Plate 529**
A shrub which can grow up to a height of 3m (10ft) but is often smaller. Its leaves are entire, ovate or elliptic and up to 5cm (2in) long. The markedly two-lipped flowers are coppery red with a splash of black in the throat *c.* 2cm (⅘in) long. The only species of this small genus in East Africa, it is recorded over most of central, southern and northern Kenya in moderately dry bushland and forest margins, especially on rocky ground, at 610–1825m (2000–6000ft); lake areas, Maasai, Mpwapwa, Kondoa (Tanzania); Uganda, no record; also in Ethiopia, Somalia. It is commonly cultivated as an ornamental shrub and a yellow variety is also grown in gardens.

THUNBERGIA

Flowers enclosed at the base by two large, partially connate, bracteoles hiding the calyx which is composed of ten to twenty linear lobes; corolla, tubular and widened where the four stamens are inserted; limb subequally five-lobed; capsule, broadly triangular with four seeds. Thirty-seven species in East Africa.

Thunbergia alata **Plates 128 & 403**
A climbing or trailing plant, popularly known as 'Black-eyed Susan'. Its slightly hairy leaves are triangular to lanceolate or ovate. The flowers *c.* 4cm (1⅗in) across, often borne in considerable numbers, are usually orange but sometimes local forms are red, white or yellow. They have a purple centre and tube, this is usually very dark in colour, leading to the common name. It is found up to an altitude of 2740m (9000ft) in bushland, thicket and secondary grassland throughout East Africa usually in partial shade. It prefers wetter, higher altitude zones for full vigour and can then often be seen covering or half covering a large bush. Also found throughout tropical Africa especially in eastern areas.

T. battiscombei **Plate 613**
An erect shrub, rarely climbing except in semi bush shade or woodland, which has large lilac flowers *c.* 3cm (1⅕in) across with an orange or yellow throat; corolla 4.5cm (1⅘in) long, mouth of tube 1.4cm (*c.* ⅝in) wide. It frequents savannah and grassland at 1070–2300m (3500–7500ft) in Mt Elgon, Kitale and Kisii districts (Kenya); Tanzania, no record; all regions except Buganda (Uganda); also Sudan, Zaire.

T. elliotii A trailing, pubescent or densely hairy, herb with oblong-triangular petiolate leaves narrowing abruptly into a petiole, broadly winged in the upper half and naked below; flowers golden-yellow to orange, solitary on long peduncles; corolla tube 2.2cm (⅞in) long, lobe 2.8cm (1⅛in) across. Found in upland grassland; altitude range 1500–2850m (5000–9500ft), usually appearing after burning and recorded in Cheranganis, Tinderet, Kitale, western Kenya and Narok (Kenya); Maasai (Tanzania); northern region (Uganda); elsewhere, not known.

T. sp. **E** **Plate 404**
A trailing, pubescent to tomentose, herb with ovate or broadly lanceolate, densely tomentose, petiolate leaves; solitary orange flowers with a blackish purple throat;

corolla tube 3cm (1⅕in) long, lobe 5cm (2in) across. Found on stony ridges and rocky places in grassland; altitude range 1850–2750m (6000–8000ft) and recorded in Aberdares, Rift Valley and Kajiado (Kenya); elsewhere, not known.

T. fischeri   **Plate 405**
A procumbent or erect, white-tomentous herb with elliptic to obovate or oblong, subsessile or shortly petiolate, leaves and solitary or paired, pedicillate pale lemon yellow flowers, corolla tube c. 15mm (⅝in) long, c. 15mm (⅝in) across. Found in upland grassland from 1200–2600m (4000–8500ft) throughout Kenya; lake areas, Maasai (Tanzania); Uganda and elsewhere, no record.

T. gregorii   **Plate 430**
A trailing herb which has orange hairs on its stems and peduncles. The leaves are broadly lanceolate-triangular and it bears solitary deep orange flowers c. 45mm (1⅘in) across on long stalks. It is apparently very local and is found in upland grassland at 1800–2300m (5800–7500ft) in Kisii, Machakos, Kajiado and Nairobi and especially in the Ngong Hills (Kenya); Maasai, Tabora, Mbeya, Iringa (Tanzania); Uganda, no record; also Ethiopia.

T. guerkeana   **Plate 129**
A climber with white tubular flowers c. 10cm (4in) long which open at night and are presumably visited by long-tongued moths. The ten- to twelve-lobed calyces form whitish-green, star-like structures which are hidden in the bud by two large bracteoles, as in all species of *Thunbergia*. These are clearly seen in our illustration. It is common in most dry bushland areas at altitudes of 400–1100m (1300–3600ft) in Kenya; Tanga (Tanzania); Uganda, no record; also Ethiopia, Somalia.

T. holstii   **Plate 614**
A medium-sized, bush-like shrub with lovely trumpet-shaped, solitary flowers c. 25mm (1in) across, which are bluish-purple with a yellowish centre. It grows in profusion in wooded grassland and bushland up to an altitude of 1500m (5000ft) and is common in Magadi, Embu, Nairobi, Machakos and Kajiado districts, and can be seen to perfection along the Ngulia mountain range in Tsavo West (Kenya); lake areas, Maasai, Tanga (Tanzania); Uganda, no record; also Somalia.

87. Verbenaceae
THE TEAK FAMILY

A medium-sized family of mainly tropical trees, shrubs or herbs. Their leaves are usually simple, opposite or whorled and lack stipules. The calyx is five-lobed and more or less tubular, the corolla zygomorphic (sometimes obscurely so) and the stamens number four. The ovary of two fused carpels is two- to four-locular with one ovule in each loculus, the style is terminal and the fruit divides into two or more parts. 123 species in East Africa, of which forty-five are trees and shrubs. They belong to thirteen genera (two alien).

Chascanum hildebrandtii   **Plate 130**
A perennial herb from a woody rootstock which has long-stalked, obovate to elliptic leaves and spikes of white flowers c. 25mm (1in) long. It is common in some areas of dry *Commiphora* or *Combretum* woodland, especially in sandy or disturbed

places at altitudes of 14–1800m (45–5900ft) in the Baringo, Magadi, Nanyuki, Embu, Machakos and Kajiado districts, the Tsavo National Parks and widespread in the Northern Frontier (Kenya); Maasai, Tanga, Morogoro (Tanzania); northern region – Gulu (Uganda); also south-eastern Ethiopia, Somalia.

CLERODENDRUM

Shrubs or woody climbers with opposite or whorled leaves and a tubular five-lobed corolla; fruit a globose drupe with four stones. Sixty-two species in East Africa.

Clerodendrum myricoides   Plate 615

A shrub growing to about 2.5m (8ft) in height with almost stalkless leaves, arranged in whorls around the stem, ovate to elliptic with acute apex, deeply-toothed margin and cuneate base. Its irregular flowers, c. 15mm (⅝in) across, grouped in few-flowered cymes, form a terminal panicle. The calyx is sparsely hairy or hairless with rounded lobes, obtuse and erect. The very short corolla tube has white or pale blue, obovate upper lobes and slightly longer lower lobes which are dark blue. This shrub is found in bushland and forest margins at 1500–2400 (5000–8000ft) in all except the driest areas of Kenya; all regions of Tanzania and Uganda; also Sudan, Ethiopia, Somalia, Zaire, Zambia, Zimbabwe.

C. rotundifolium   Plate 131

A shrub with densely down-covered twigs which grows to 2.5m (8ft) in height. Its leaves are opposite or ternate, ovate to suborbicular, downy, and up to 15cm (6in) long and broad, with margins entire or crenate, base rounded or cordate. Its regular, white flowers form loose, few-flowered, long-stalked terminal cymes. The calyx is 12mm (½in) long and the slender corolla tube 76mm (3in) long. It is found in the wetter districts of Meru, Kericho, Mt Elgon, Nandi and Sotik at 1200–2150m (4000–7000ft) (Kenya); lake areas, Maasai, Tanga, Mpwapwa, Kondoa, Morogoro (Tanzania); all regions of Uganda; also eastern Zaire.

LANTANA and LIPPIA

Aromatic stiff herbs or softly woody shrubs with small flowers in dense clusters. They can only be distinguished by the fruits which are two-celled drupes in Lantana and two hard dry mericarps in Lippia. Five species of Lantana, six species of Lippia in East Africa.

Lantana camara   Plate 704

A herbaceous shrub with opposite or ternate, roughish, stalked leaves. It has prickly stems and rather showy, large, pinkish-mauve flowers, c. 3mm (⅛in) across, which can also bear touches of orange and white. It is certain to be noticed in all average or above-average rainfall areas at 5–1800m (15–6000ft), pushing its way through the bush and forming large, dense thickets. This is an introduced species and often a noxious weed and is sometimes known as the Curse of India. Widespread in Kenya, Tanzania and Uganda; also spreading throughout Africa.

L. trifolia   Plate 616

A scrambling herbaceous shrub up to 3m (10ft) high with hispid stems. Leaves ternate, occasionally opposite on weak, lateral growths, ovate to lanceolate, 1.25–10cm (½–4in) long and 6mm–3.75cm (¼–1½in) wide, margin closely crenate-serrate, wrinkled and rough above, pubescent or tomentose below. Flowers pink, mauve or rarely white in spikes, 1.5cm (⅜in) across head, at first globose, then oblong. Fruits purple. Found almost everywhere, altitude range 1–1850m (3–6000ft), in open bushland, Acacia bushland, forest edges and paths (Kenya);

Tanzania and Uganda, widespread; also in Ethiopia and tropical Africa.

Lippia carviodora   Plate 21
A softly woody, very aromatic shrublet, up to 1m (c. 3ft) tall with white flowers,
2–3mm ($\frac{1}{12}$–$\frac{1}{8}$in) across, among broad papery green bracts in small compact spikes.
Found in dry areas, altitude range c.1–1100m (c. 1–3600ft), and recorded both
west and east of Lake Turkana, and in Samburu and Meru National Parks, rarely
along the Galana River and in drier parts of the coast regions (Kenya); also
south-eastern Ethiopia, Somalia.

L. javanica   Plate 241
An erect, down-covered shrub with lanceolate to oblong leaves which usually has
more than four narrow spikes to each node. The white flowers, 2mm (c. $\frac{1}{12}$in) across,
are on pedunculate, crowded spikes 6mm ($\frac{1}{4}$in) across; the calyx small, two- to
four-lobed and two-keeled. The corolla has four white or cream lobes and the
stamens are included in the corolla tube. The underside of the leaves is covered
with dense white down. It is widespread throughout the upland areas of Kenya at
1280–2200m (4200–7200ft) and abundant in disturbed places and rocky soils in
dry woodlands; all regions except Tabora (Tanzania); eastern region – Jinja, Lake
Kioga (Uganda); also Ethiopia, Zaire, south to Zimbabwe, Mozambique, and tropical Africa.

L. ukambensis   Plate 242
Very similar to L. javanica, with white flowers, but is rough, not downy, on the
underside of the leaves. Flower head 12mm (c. $\frac{1}{2}$in) across; flower 3–4mm (c. $\frac{1}{8}$in)
across. It is an abundant invader of disturbed places and rocky soils in dry woodland; altitude range 1300–2200m (4250–7200ft). Throughout Kenya; lake areas,
Maasai, Tanga, Mbeya, Iringa (Tanzania); Uganda and elsewhere, not known.

Priva curtisiae   Plate 132
An erect, pubescent shrub with oblong to obovate leaves and long unbranched
racemes of pale flowers; corolla tube c. 1cm ($\frac{3}{8}$in) long, limb 2–3mm ($\frac{1}{8}$in) across;
calyx in fruit globose, hardly beaked above. The original type specimen was
collected by an American visitor, Mrs A. Curtis in 1923. The flowers are pinker than
in the illustration. Locally common in dry country; altitude range 900–1800m
(2950–5900ft), and recorded in Kisii, Narok, Baringo, Rift Valley, Machakos,
Magadi, Nairobi and Kajiado (Kenya); lake areas, Maasai (Tanzania); Uganda, no
record; also in Ethiopia.
   NB A white form of this species is quite common in Kenya.

P. cordifolia   An erect pubescent herb from a woody rootstock with oblong to ovate
leaves, petiolate, the petiole over half as long as the lamina, with long, unbranched
racemes of pale pink flowers, c. 1cm ($\frac{3}{8}$in) long. It is very similar to P. curtisiae, but
the latter has subsessile leaves; the petiole is less than a quarter of the lamina, and
the calyx in fruit, globose and hardly beaked above, whereas, in P. cordifolia it is
wider than long, with an apical beak. Found in dry, sandy Commiphora bushland;
altitude range 135–2250m (450–7500ft). Recorded in Machakos, Kajiado and
Kibwezi (Kenya); lake areas, Tanga, Morogoro (Tanzania); eastern region,
Buganda (Uganda); elsewhere, throughout tropical Africa.

Stachytarpheta jamaicensis   Plate 617
An annual with subprostrate habit, woody at the base up to 1m (3ft) high. Leaves
ovate to oblong, c. 5cm (2in) long and 2.5cm (1in) wide, coarsely toothed, cuneate

at base. Flowers royal blue, c. 4mm (⅛in) long, sunk in deep depressions in the axils; bracts appressed; spike up to 30cm (12in) long. Often a weed in coconut plantations. Found only in purely coastal regions; altitude range below 1500m (c. 5000ft). One of three species in East Africa, all alien and originally from America. Shimba Hills and Kilifi (Kenya); Dar University campus (Tanzania).

S. urticifolia A sub-shrub growing to 1m (3ft) high with forked branches and almost four-angled shoots. Leaves ovate to ovate-oblong up to 3.5cm (1⅜in) long and 4cm (1⅜in) wide, decurrent and deeply toothed. Flowers deep blue sunk into deep depressions in the axils; bracts very narrow; spike up to 45cm (18in) long; corolla lobe c. 3mm (⅛in) long, 10mm (⅜in) across; tube 9mm (⅓in) long. A native of South America, it is grown in Kenya as an ornamental hedge on roadsides; altitude range 0–1650m (0–5500ft). Recorded as an escape at Diani on sand and coral, in Kwale at forest edges near the shoreline (Kenya); Dar-es-Salaam, Tanga, Lushoto, Muheza (Tanzania); no record in Uganda.

Verbena bonariensis   Plate 705
An erect, often robust, downy annual which often attains a height of 2m (6½ft). It has stalkless, oblong, serrate leaves and carries large terminal corymbs of short spikelets with violet-purple flowers, c. 4mm (c. ⅛in) across. Found along the sides of roads and on the edges of forest at altitudes 1620–2440m (5500–8000ft), it is seen mainly east of the Mau Escarpment, except in the Tinderet area (Kenya); Maasai, Tanga (Tanzania); Uganda and elsewhere, no record.

88. Labiatae (Lamiaceae)
THE DEAD NETTLE, MINT OR SAGE FAMILY

A large family of usually aromatic herbs, shrublets or shrubs found in both temperate and tropical countries. Their leaves are opposite, rarely with entire margins, and usually aromatic, containing oil glands which, under a lens, can often be seen as dots. They have quadrangular stems and a tubular calyx which is often zygomorphic. The corolla is nearly always zygomorphic and nearly always two-lipped. There are four stamens, or two in a few genera, either arched up under the lip in the more temperate genera, such as *Leonotis*, *Leucas*, *Nepeta*, *Salvia* and *Satureia* or bent downwards in the lower lip in the tropical *Plectranthus* and related genera. They have an ovary with four one-seeded portions surrounding the base of the style, which become four nutlets in the fruit. 288 species in thirty-eight genera (*Plectranthus* fifty-two species) in East Africa.

ACHYROSPERMUM
Low shrubs or herbs; flowers in spike-like inflorescences; calyx ten-nerved with five almost equal teeth; corolla bi-labiate. Seven species in East Africa.

Achyrospermum carvalhi   Plate 530
An erect, soft shrub, covered with short, soft hairs below the elliptic, acute and attenuate leaves and bearing short racemes of bright red, long-tubed flowers, corolla c. 15mm (⅜in) long. It is a rare plant found at 1600–2100m (5250–6900ft) altitudes and was recorded only on Mt Kenya until the specimen illustrated was discovered in the Mathews Range (Kenya); Tanga, Morogoro (Tanzania); Uganda, no record; also Malawi, Zimbabwe, Mozambique.

A. schimperi

Plate 803

A stiff, erect, tomentose herb with broad-elliptic, acute leaves and dense terminal spikes of flowers, the pink corolla, c. 5mm ($\frac{1}{5}$in) long, hardly exceeding the large calyx. Stems with spreading hairs; bracts of racemes rounded, mucronate; calyx tube curved with oblique mouth. Locally common in wet streamsides in partial shade within the montane forest; altitude range 1600–4000m (5250–13,100ft). Recorded in Elgon, Cheranganis, Mau, Aberdares and Machakos (Kenya); Maasai (Tanzania); western and eastern regions (Uganda); also in Ethiopia, north-eastern Zaire, Rwanda.

A. parviflorum

A crisped-pubescent herb, or weak shrub with elliptic acute leaves and small pink flowers, corolla 5mm ($\frac{1}{5}$in) long, in dense racemes borne terminally on lateral branches. Stems with appressed brisk hairs, bracts of racemes acute; calyx tube with a straight mouth. Altitude range 1500m (5000ft). Locally common in the shade of lowland and middle-altitude forest but only recorded from Kakamega forest in western Kenya.

AEOLLANTHUS

Subsucculent herbs or shrublets; flowers in spikes, cymes or dense clusters; calyx truncate, hardly lobed two-lipped and circumscissile at the base in fruit; corolla has a bent tube and two lips; stamens four, declinate. Fourteen species in East Africa.

Aeollanthus repens

Plate 618

A trailing, pubescent, soft, fleshy shrublet with sessile, oblong or oblanceolate, distantly dentate leaves and ascending leafless peduncles. Inflorescence of one or more spikes (often on groups), bracts with a conspicuous raised gland at the apex; corolla 10cm (4in) long, pale lilac. Common on shallow soils or in rock crevices in the lower forest and wooded grassland zones; altitude range 1500–2700m (5000–9000ft). Widespread throughout Kenya; lake areas, Maasai, Tanga, Morogoro (Tanzania); all regions of Uganda; also in southern Sudan, eastern Zaire, Rwanda, Burundi.

A. zanzibaricus

Plate 133

A much-branched undershrub to 1m (3ft) high with rather fleshy stems. Leaves are petiolate, broadly ovate, up to 3.5cm (1$\frac{2}{5}$in) long, obtuse at apex, broadly cuneate or subtruncate at base with obscurely crenate margins. The panicle very sparse and the spikes very lax, the longest up to 13cm (5in) long, calyx subcylindrical, circumscissile above the base. Flower colour white with mauve streaking; corolla 6mm ($\frac{1}{4}$in) long. Found in open, gently eroded slopes in *Acacia* bushland; altitude range 240–450m (800–1500ft). Recorded in coast areas of Kenya and Tanzania; also in southern Somalia.

Ajuga remota

Plate 619

An erect, often rhizomatous, pubescent herb with lanceolate, coarsely toothed leaves and small subsessile axillary pale blue flowers. Calyx bell-shaped, five-toothed; corolla tube 0.9cm ($\frac{2}{5}$in) long, lips 0.5cm ($\frac{1}{5}$in) across, with very small upper lip and much larger lower lip. Stamens four, the lower pairs longest. The species as a whole is found throughout East Africa and recorded in almost every district. Common in disturbed areas in grassland; altitude range 1100–2600m (3600–8600ft). A mountain form, more strictly rhizomatous, with a rosette of leaves at ground level, also occurs and may later be given specific status. It is found on the Aberdares and Mt Kenya (Kenya). Also southern Sudan – Imatong Mts, eastern Ethiopia, north-eastern Zaire, Rwanda.

LABIATAE

BECIUM

Terminal racemes of clusters of flowers; calyx zygomorphic with a large upper tooth, obsolete lateral teeth and two lower teeth; corolla bilabiate; stamens four, declinate. Eleven species in East Africa.

Becium sp. A · Plate 134

An erect, often woody annual with elliptic to lanceolate, acute, pubescent leaves and long interrupted racemes of white to pale pink flowers 18mm (¾in) across. Found in dry rocky country and recorded in Kisii, Magadi, Embu, Machakos, Kajiado (Kenya); Tanzania, Uganda and elsewhere, no record. More information is required on its habitats.

B. obovatum · Plate 804

An erect or trailing, down-covered or hairless herb or wiry shrub which grows from a woody rootstock or rhizome. Its leaves are oblong, obovate or ovate and rounded at the base or at the apex. It bears head-like inflorescences of white or pale pink flowers, c. 16mm (⅝in) long, including the stamens. Common in upland grassland, appears to grow where drainage is poor and is very variable. It has been recorded at 300–2400m (1000–7750ft) over most of East Africa; also Ethiopia, Malawi.

ERYTHROCHLAMYS

Related to *Ocimum* with declinate stamens. Two species in East Africa.

Erythrochlamys spectabilis · Plate 620

An erect, downy shrub with oblong-lanceolate, almost stalkless leaves and simple terminal racemes of purple flowers; corolla c. 10mm (⅜in) long, 5mm (¼in) across. The calyx becomes very enlarged and conspicuous, and bright red in fruit, c. 1cm (⅜in) across. Found mostly below 1000m (3200ft) and is common in disturbed dry sandy bushland, although not in the very driest areas. Machakos, Embu and Northern Frontier districts, and especially common in the Voi-Kibwezi area (Kenya) at 300–1350m (1000–4500ft); Tanga (Tanzania); no record in Uganda; also Ethiopia, Somalia.

Geniosporum rotundifolium (*G. paludosum*) · Plate 805

Similar to *Ocimum*. A stout, erect perennial herb from a woody rootstock, branching above, up to 1.2m (c. 4ft) high. Stems densely pubescent. Leaves shortly petiolate ovate to narrowly ovate, slightly crenate on margins. Inflorescence composed of dense terminal cylindrical racemes up to 7.5cm (3in) long, consisting of small pinkish flowers subtended by large white or mauve-tinged bracts at the base of the racemes; individual flower 5mm long; c. twenty in each whorl. Found in open, damp grassland at high altitudes, marshy areas, grazed hilltops, riverine forest and arable land; altitude range 1150–2775m (3500–9250ft). Recorded in Turkana, Elgon, Kitale, Cheranganis, western Kenya, Kisii (Kenya); Morogoro, Tabora, Mpwapwa, Kondoa, Songea (Tanzania); northern, western regions, Buganda (Uganda); widespread in tropical Africa.

LEONOTIS

Erect, stiff herbs or softly woody shrubs; flowers in dense globular masses at the upper nodes; calyx zygomorphic with eight spine-tipped teeth; corolla orange or white-yellow, densely hairy above; stamens four, arcuate. Nine species in East Africa.

Leonotis africana   **Plate 243**
An erect, pubescent or woolly annual or short-lived perennial herb with suborbicular leaves, truncate at base and pale white, cream or yellow flowers. The leaves are often wider then 4cm (1⅜in) and the flowers carried in few dense globular masses at the upper nodes. The corolla tube, 2.5cm (1in) long, exceeds the calyx and is densely hairy, as is the upper lip; lower lip marcescent (withering but persistent). Pollen deposited on bristly terminal hairs of the upper lip of the corolla ready to be brushed off by bird pollinators. Altitude range 1500–1800m (5000–6000ft).
   NB This genus is now under revision by botanists, and *L. africana* is now provisionally classified as conspecific with *L. nepetifolia*.

L. mollissima   **Plate 431**
An erect, woody herb or shrub which sometimes reaches tree-like proportions. Its leaves are woolly, ovate and cordate, and its orange, or occasionally white, flowers, *c.* 25mm (1in) long, are grouped in one to three terminal spherical masses. This is the common *Leonotis* above 1950m (6500ft), where it can be seen at the side of roads, in disturbed places and often in montane forest in Kenya; although its overall altitude range is 1200–2600m (3900–8500ft), it is rare in the lower altitudes, where it tends to be supplanted by *L. nepetifolia*. Both are much favoured by sunbirds. All regions of Tanzania; eastern region and Buganda (Uganda); also Zambia, Malawi, Zimbabwe, Mozambique.

L. nepetifolia   **Plate 432**
A down-covered, tall-growing, erect, woody annual with long petiolate leaves and orange flowers, *c.* 25mm (1in) long, grouped in spherical masses at intervals up the stem. It is the common *Leonotis* at lower altitudes, found all over Kenya up to 2100m (7000ft) almost as a weed; all regions of Tanzania; all regions except Buganda (Uganda); also Ethiopia south to Zimbabwe, Mozambique.

LEUCAS
Related to *Leonotis* but usually smaller and less erect; corolla always white; calyx ten-toothed. Thirty species in East Africa.

Leucas deflexa   **Plate 135**
A perennial herb, shortly hairy, on stems to 1.5m (4½ft) tall. Leaves are oblong-lanceolate to 8cm (3⅛in) long, narrowed to the base, distinctly crenate, slightly hairy. Inflorescence globose, very dense; flower head *c.* 2cm (⅘in) across; bracts as long as the calyx, rigid, linear and ciliate. Calyx very deflexed, hairy with deltoid teeth; corolla very small, very hairy, white with orange anthers. Found in high forest areas; altitude range 1575–2550m (5230–8500ft). Recorded in Kakamega, Aberdares, Elgon, Chyulu Hills and Maasai Mara (Kenya); all regions except lake area (Tanzania); all regions except northern (Uganda); also in Ethiopia, north-eastern Zaire, Rwanda.

L. grandis (*L. mollis*)   **Plate 136**
A very similar but much more common and widespread species. More densely covered with short, soft hairs than *L. urticifolia*. Flower *c.* 3mm (⅛in) across. It prefers wetter and colder conditions and is especially noticeable in the Machakos district (Kenya); abundant in Maasai, scarce in Tanga (Tanzania); Uganda and elsewhere, no record.

L. jamesii   **Plate 806**
An erect, pubescent shrub with oblanceolate to linear leaves and clusters of white

flowers, c. 1.2cm ($\frac{1}{2}$in) long, in most upper axils; calyx regular with short, blunt teeth, persistent. An uncommon plant found in dry bushland; altitude range 450–1700m (1500–5660ft). Recorded in Nanyuki (Kenya); Tanzania and Uganda, no record; also in Ethiopia, Somalia.

NB Not found south of latitude 0°25 north.

L. masaiensis (*L. venulosa*)   Many trailing or climbing stems and obovate to elliptic leaves, and is covered in coarse, strong hairs. Flower c. 2mm ($\frac{1}{12}$in) across. Common in black cotton soils, altitude range 1300–3000m (4250–9800ft), especially near Nairobi (Kenya); Maasai (Tanzania); eastern region (Uganda); elsewhere, not known.

L. urticifolia   Plate 137
An erect, woolly, often powdery, short-lived herb or shrub, with ovate-elliptic leaves and rather round clusters of hairy, white flowers, c. 3mm ($\frac{1}{8}$in) across, up the stem; flower clusters c. 25mm (1in) across. It is a common flower on old cultivated land, hut sites and disturbed ground generally in dry country in the Nanyuki, Embu, Kajiado and Northern Frontier districts at altitudes of 150–2100m (500–6900ft) (Kenya); Maasai (Tanzania); no record in Uganda; also Sudan, Ethiopia.

NEPETA

Calyx fifteen-ribbed, five-toothed; corolla two-lipped; stamens four, arcuate. One species only in East Africa.

Nepeta azurea   Plate 851
An erect, down-covered perennial with lanceolate, cordate leaves and a terminal, spike-like inflorescence of purple-blue flowers, c. 2cm ($\frac{4}{5}$in) across. It often grows on the edges of forest and along the grassy banks of roads, making an arresting sight when in full flower. It is found in areas of medium to heavy rainfall at altitudes of 1800–3600m (5900–11,800ft) on Mt Elgon, the Cheranganis, Mau, Aberdares, Mt Kenya and the Kisii Hills (Kenya); Maasai (Tanzania); eastern region (Uganda); also Ethiopia, northern Somalia.

OCIMUM

Flowers in rather dense terminal racemes; calyx zygomorphic with a large upper lobe which is decumbent upon the tube and four lower teeth; corolla bilabiate; stamens four, declinate. Nineteen species in East Africa.

Ocimum fischeri (*Hemizygia fischeri*)   Plate 706
A shrubby, tomentose, perennial herb with numerous stems to 75cm (30in) high. Leaves linear-lanceolate, acute or subobtuse, entire, narrowing to the base, pubescent above, tomentose beneath, up to 45mm (c. 2in) long, sage-scented. The flowers, c. 13mm ($\frac{1}{2}$in) long, are enclosed in conspicuous cordate, acuminate bracts which are twice as long as the calyx. Corolla pale mauve. Found in dry *Acacia-Commiphora* bushland and in clearings in grassland; altitude range 250–450m (830–1500ft). Recorded in Machakos, Tsavo East and West, Taita Hills, Kwale, Galana Ranch (Kenya); Mkomazi Game Reserve (Pare), Mpanda (Tanzania); Uganda and elsewhere, no record.

O. sp. A   A rhizomatous herb with ascending stems and subsessile, ovate-elliptic leaves, racemes simple, terminal, similar to those of *O. kilimandscharicum*, but more slender. Fruiting calyx 0.5cm ($\frac{1}{5}$in) long. It is mentioned here because though locally abundant in black cotton and waterlogged swamp soils it is found only around Nairobi and in one area of northern Mt Kenya. Altitude range 1500–2490m (5000–8300ft).

O. hadiense   Plate 807
An erect shrub with sparsely pubescent or glabrous, shortly petiolate, lanceolate to elliptic leaves and large pale purple flowers, 1cm (⅜in) across lip, in terminal, usually simple racemes of rather distant whorls; hairs of the inflorescence and calyx often tinged with purple. A locally common plant in dry *Commiphora* bushland; altitude range 60–780m (200–2600ft). Recorded in Nanyuki, Machakos and Tsavo West (Kenya); Tanzania and Uganda, no record; also in Sudan, Ethiopia, Somalia.

O. kilimandscharicum   An erect, branching, pubescent shrub with ovate to elliptic leaves and simple terminal racemes of rather distant whorls of small white to pinkish flowers, 0.5cm (¼in) across lip. A common plant of rocky ground in the evergreen wooded area of upland Kenya, altitude range 120–2430m (400–7300ft), and recorded in lake areas, Maasai, Tanga, Mpwapwa, Kondoa, Mbeya, Iringa (Tanzania); eastern region (Uganda); elsewhere, not known.

O. lamiifolium   An erect, robust, branching shrub with pubescent to tomentose ovate-acute leaves and white or very pale purple flowers in compound or simple terminal racemes. Fruiting calyx *c.* 0.8cm (*c.* ⅓in) long. Locally common in montane forest edges and disturbed ground, altitude range 1500–2700m (5000–9000ft), and recorded in Cheranganis, Tinderet, Mau, Aberdares, Mt Kenya, Elgon and Kisii (Kenya); lake areas, Maasai, Tabora, Mbeya, Iringa (Tanzania); all regions (Uganda); also Rwanda, eastern Zaire, Ethiopia.

O. suave   An erect shrub with long-petiolate, ovate, serrate leaves and terminal paniculate racemes of small, dirty white flowers, buds often with reddish-purple hairs. Fruiting calyx 0.5cm (¼in) long. Common in disturbed ground in the upland forest areas, altitude range 600–2400m (2000–8000ft), and recorded throughout East Africa; also Sudan, Ethiopia, Somalia, Zaire, Zambia, Malawi, Zimbabwe.

ORTHOSIPHON
Herbs or shrublets with rather small flowers in whorls of six in terminal racemes; calyx zygomorphic with an enlarged upper lobe; corolla with a straight or slightly bent tube, bilabiate; stamens four, declinate. Thirteen species in East Africa.

Orthosiphon pallidus   Plate 22
A short-lived perennial, much-branched from the base, forming a dense clump up to 40cm (16in) high. The stems are short, usually pubescent. Leaves shortly petiolate, small, ovate, obtuse at apex, crenate at margins, cuneate at base, usually pubescent on both sides. Flowers in few-flowered whorls, forming a lax terminal raceme, up to 13cm (5in) long; corolla 10mm (⅜in) long, greenish-white or dull purple; fruiting calyx 6mm (¼in) long. Found in eroded gullies in flash flood plains with sandy soils in open *Acacia* bushland; altitude range 425–1500m (1400–4900ft). Recorded in north-eastern frontier areas, Cheranganis, Embu, Meru, Machakos, Kajiado, Narok (Kenya); Tanga (Tanzania); not known in Uganda; also in Eritrea, Somalia.

O. parvifolius   Plate 707
A pubescent herb with a tuft of erect stems from a small woody rootstock, bearing subsessile, petiolate, oblong to elliptic to linear, leaves and terminal inflorescences

of pinkish flowers, 1.5cm (⅜in) long; corolla tube about twice as long as calyx at anthesis. A common plant of shallow soil and seasonally flooded grassland in upland dry forest regions; altitude range 210–2040m (700–6800ft). Recorded in Narok, Nanyuki, Embu, Machakos, Kajiado and Nairobi (Kenya); lake areas, Maasai, Tanga, Mbeya, Iringa (Tanzania); northern region (Uganda); also in southern Somalia.

O. rubicundus   Plate 808
An erect, pubescent herb or weak shrub with obovate to ovate leaves, frequently attenuate at base into the short petiole. Flowers in conspicuous terminal reddish-mauve racemes, corolla mauve, 11mm (⅜in) long. Calyx reddish-purple. A fairly common plant of wooded grassland, especially in western Kenya, altitude range 450–1600m (1475–5250ft); recorded in Elgon, Cheranganis, Tinderet, Kitale and Machakos (Kenya); all regions except lake area (Tanzania); all regions except Buganda (Uganda); also in Zaire, Zambia, Malawi, Zimbabwe, Mozambique.

O. suffrutescens   Plate 809
A sparsely pubescent, erect herb or weak shrub; leaves obovate to ovate, tending to attenuate into the petiole at base. Flowers pale mauve or pinkish, c. 12mm (½in) long, in rather loose terminal racemes. A rather variable plant of open and wooded grassland, especially in drier regions and extending to the coast; altitude range 60–1700m (200–5700ft). Recorded in western Kenya, Narok, Machakos, Kajiado (Kenya); lake areas, Maasai, Tanga, Mpwapwa, Kondoa, Morogoro, Songea (Tanzania); all regions except Buganda (Uganda); also in Somalia, Burundi, Zaire, Zambia.

PLECTRANTHUS
Terminal racemes, or panicles, of whorled flowers; calyx zygomorphic with an enlarged upper lobe; corolla with a sharply bent tube, a flat upper lip and a deeply concave lower lip; stamens four, declinate. Fifty-three species in East Africa. More than thirty-two species recorded in Kenya.

Plectranthus barbatus   Plate 852
An erect, soft, downy shrub which is sometimes tree-like. It has ovate to ovate-elliptic, fleshy leaves and terminal racemes of large, bright blue flowers, c. 2cm (⅘in) long. It is an occasional plant in upland bushland in Kenya and is often used by the Kikuyu people as a quick-growing hedge plant. Found in lake areas, Maasai, rarely Tanga, Tabora, Morogoro (Tanzania); all regions of Uganda; also Zaire, southern tropical Africa.

P. caninus   Plate 853
A low, fleshy plant with ascending stems which bear elliptic to cuneate leaves and dense uninterrupted, terminal, spike-like racemes of bright blue or violet flowers, c. 12mm (½in) long, with apiculate bracts which are longer than the flowers. It has a strong and unpleasant smell. Found in disturbed, dry, rocky country at altitudes 1520–2300m (5000–7500ft) and widespread in Kenya; lake areas, Maasai, Tabora, Mpwapwa, Kondoa (Tanzania); northern and eastern regions (Uganda); also Ethiopia, Rwanda, Burundi, Zambia, Zimbabwe, Zaire.

P. cylindraceus   Plate 810
A down-covered, fleshy, scrambling shrub with elliptic to obovate leaves and sparsely-branched, densely-haired, spike-like racemes of small, powder blue flowers; inflorescence c. 1cm (⅜in) across. It is locally common in dry, rocky

bushland at altitudes of 610–2070m (2000–6600ft). Kitale, Baringo, Rift Valley, Nanyuki, Voi, Machakos, Nairobi and Kajiado (Kenya); lake areas, Maasai, Tanga, Mpwapwa, Kondoa (Tanzania); no record Uganda; also Ethiopia, Zaire.

P. edulis   **Plate 621**
A pubescent annual or short-lived perennial, with trailing stems rooting at the nodes and ascending inflorescences; leaves elliptic to broad-ovate, serrate; flowers in crowded whorls, bright blue with dark blue hair bases; corolla *c.* 10mm (⅜in) long but variable in size. Frequently found in upland forest regions, altitude range 1500–1900m (4900–6200ft), especially in the bamboo zone where this has been disturbed. Two forms are recorded, with large and small flowers respectively. The leaf shape is also variable. Recorded in Elgon, Cheranganis, Tinderet, Mau, Aberdares, Mt Kenya and Kitale (Kenya); lake areas, Maasai, Mbeya, Iringa (Tanzania); western and eastern regions (Uganda); also in Ethiopia, eastern Zaire.

P. flaccidus   **Plate 622**
A weak, erect and variable annual up to 30cm (1½ft) high with blue flowers; corolla 9mm (⅓in) long. Found in shady places in bushland and forest. Recorded in northeastern Kenya, Shimba Hills, coast (Kenya), altitude range 1–50m (3–164ft); Maasai, Tanga, Morogoro, Zanzibar (Tanzania), altitude range 1–2400m (3–7875ft); Uganda, no record; also Zambia.

P. grandicalyx   **Plate 623**
A short-lived perennial, aromatic herb with the main stem unbranched, up to 1.8m (*c.* 6ft) high. Leafy branches more or less semi-succulent, woody, shortly glandular papillose and hirsute. Leaves elliptic to ovate-elliptic up to 10.5cm (*c.* 4in) long and 9.5cm (3⅜in) wide, apex obtuse to rounded, margin crenate, especially in upper half, bark cuneate. Inflorescence a compact, whorled spike up to 12cm (5in) long; calyx large and purple; corolla blue, tube *c.* 9mm (⅓in) long, upper lip 12mm (½in) long, 9mm (⅓in) broad. Found on the edge of forest, on shallow soils on rocky outcrops and among rocks; altitude range 1600–3180m (5350–10,300ft). Recorded in Northern Frontier areas, Cheranganis, Tinderet, coast hinterland (Kenya); Tanzania, no record; northern region (Uganda); also in Sudan, Ethiopia.

P. igniarius (*Coleus igniarius*)   **Plate 624**
An erect shrub with tomentose, obovate or orbicular leaves which fall before the production of the terminal inflorescences of unbranched, rather long racemes; flowers bright blue, 15mm (⅜in) long, with a white upper lip. The calyx with a few woolly hairs inside the mouth in fruit. Found in dry rocky country, altitude range 520–2000m (1730–6650ft), and recorded in Machakos, Baragoi and western Kenya (Kenya); Tanzania and Uganda, not known; also Ethiopia, northern Somalia, Sudan – Red Sea Hills.
   NB A conspicuous feature of this species is the succulent stem.

P. kamerunensis   **Plate 811**
A tomentose or pubescent, weak, erect shrub or scrambler with ovate leaves and branched or simple inflorescence of pink to pale purple and white flowers; corolla tube *c.* 9mm (⅓in) long, each lip *c.* 9mm (⅓in) long. Found throughout the montane forest area from 1500–2950m (4900–9800ft) (Kenya); Maasai (Tanzania); Uganda, no record; also in Zaire.

P. lanuginosus   **Plate 625**
A pubescent, trailing, subsucculent herb with orbicular to wide-elliptic to ovate leaves and terminal simple racemes of rather tightly whorled bright blue flowers; corolla 1cm (⅜in) long, 0.5cm (¼in) across lips. Found in dry upland grassland, where it is very local in occurrence, altitude range 900–2400m (3000–8000ft), and recorded in Elgon, Aberdares and Kajiado (Kenya); Maasai, Tanga (Tanzania); eastern region (Uganda); also in Ethiopia, Zaire.

P. laxiflorus (*P. albus*)   **Plate 854**
An erect, or decumbent, pubescent herb with ovate cordate leaves and a very loose inflorescence of paired triflorate pedunculate cymes of pink or pale purple flowers, *c.* 12mm (½in) long, at the nodes. Common in disturbed ground on wet montane forest, altitude range 1000–3000m (3280–9850ft), and recorded in Aberdares, Mt Kenya and Limuru district (Kenya); Maasai, Tanga, Morogoro, Mbeya, Iringa (Tanzania); western region (Uganda); also Rwanda, Burundi, Zaire.

P. sylvestris   **Plate 855**
A hairless, erect, sparsely-branched herb with ovate, acuminate leaves and bright blue flowers with white spots on the upper lip which are grouped in inflorescences that are usually branched. Flower corolla *c.* 1cm (⅜in) long. It is common in disturbed ground at the higher levels of montane forest, especially where there is bamboo, at altitudes of 2300–2750m (7500–9000ft) on Mt Elgon, Tinderet, Mau, the Aberdares and Mt Kenya (Kenya); Maasai, Tanga, Tabora, Mbeya, Iringa (Tanzania); western and eastern regions (Uganda); also Zaire, Malawi.

P. zatarhendi (*P. hadiensis*)   **Plate 626**
A trailing, pubescent, subsucculent perennial with ascending stems and long petiolate, coarsely serrate, orbicular leaves; flowers lilac or purple in terminal, sparsely-branched racemes; corolla *c.* 5mm (¼in) long. A plant found in disturbed rocky places in dry evergreen woodland; altitude range 1100–1900m (3600–6200ft). Recorded in Aberdares, Narok, Baringo, Rift Valley and Nairobi (Kenya); lake areas, Maasai, Tabora (Tanzania); western and eastern regions (Uganda); also in Ethiopia, northern Somalia.

SALVIA
Corolla two-lipped; stamens two, arcuate, each with two anthers separated by a long connective. Two native species in East Africa.

Salvia coccinea var. **coccinea**   **Plate 531**
An erect annual with ovate, cordate leaves and conspicuous red flowers, *c.* 15mm (⅜in) across. It is an escape from fardens but is now found growing wild in disturbed places from 1600–1800m (5250–5900ft) in the Nairobi and Mt Elgon areas (Kenya); Maasai, Tanga, Morogoro, Mbeya, Iringa (Tanzania); Uganda and elsewhere, no record. It was originally a native of America.

S. coccinea var. **lactea**   A white variety of the same species as the preceding plant. It is also sometimes found in the wild as an escape from cultivation in Kenya, although in Tanzania, Uganda and elsewhere there is no record.

S. merjamie   **Plate 812**
An erect, loosely hairy perennial which springs from a rosette of leaves and a thick, woody taproot. Its leaves are oblong and often lobed. Its pale purple flowers, *c.* 1cm (⅜in) long, form dense racemes. It is locally common in grassland at 2440–4130m

(8000–13,500ft) in Kenya, especially where burning is a common practice; northern Tanzania volcanic areas and Kilimanjaro (Tanzania); no record in Uganda; also Ethiopia.

S. nilotica   Plate 627
A hairy, rhizomatous herb with white, pink or purple flowers in branching and open racemes; corolla c. 1cm (⅜in) long. Its leaves are pinnatifid and obovate with a hairy texture. The commonest *Salvia* at 1830–3690m (6000–12,100ft), widespread in East Africa at these altitudes. Found in Kenya; Maasai, Tanga, Mbeya, Iringa (Tanzania); western and eastern regions (Uganda); also Ethiopia, eastern Zaire, Rwanda, Zimbabwe.

SATUREIA
Calyx with thirteen nerves or ridges, five-toothed, corolla pink or purplish; stamens four, arcuate. Eight species in East Africa.

Satureia abyssinica   Plate 708
A pubescent herb with many ascending, unbranched stems from a woody rootstock, bearing broad-ovate, elliptic, petiolate leaves and terminal racemes of pale purple flowers; corolla tube 2cm (⅜in) long, lips 0.5cm (¼in) across. Altitude range 2100–2750m (7000–9000ft). Not uncommon in woodland in Elgon, Cheranganis, Tinderet, Mau, Aberdares, Mt Kenya, Kitale, western Kenya, Machakos and Kajiado (Kenya); Maasai, Tanga, Morogoro (Tanzania); northern, eastern regions (Uganda); also Sudan, Ethiopia, northern Somalia.

S. biflora   Plate 813
An erect, woody herb with elliptic to orbicular, entire leaves and axillary clusters of two to twenty pink flowers, c. 7mm (¼in) long. It is a widespread and common species in upland dry grassland; altitude range 1800–3350m (6000–11,000ft). Kenya; all regions except Mpwapwa, Kondoa (Tanzania); all regions except Buganda (Uganda); also Ethiopia, northern Somalia, Rwanda, Zaire. The species includes an alpine form with the lower calyx teeth twice as long as the upper, which was formerly classified as *S. biflora*, and the lowland form formerly known as *S. punctata*, but they have been classified now as one.

S. pseudosimensis   Plate 814
A hairy shrub with weakly branching, ascending stems from a woody base. Its leaves are ovate to rounded and almost stalkless. Its purple or purplish-pink flowers, c. 1cm (⅜in) long, form dense axillary clusters. It is common in clearings and at forest edges, mostly in the upper limits of montane forest and within the heath zone at altitudes of 1700–3500m (5600–11,500ft). Kenya; Maasai, Mbeya, Iringa (Tanzania); all regions except Buganda (Uganda); also Ethiopia, Zaire, Malawi.

Scutellaria paucifolia   Plate 709
An erect, pubescent herb from a woody rootstock, usually less than 50cm (20in) tall, with the ovate leaves on separate shoots, not numerous on flowering branches; calyx zygomorphic with a flat dorsal scale, closed after flowering. Flowers purple, mauve or rarely white, c. 16mm (⅜in) long, 6mm (¼in) across lips. Altitude range 1200–1950m (4000–6500ft). Two other species in East Africa. Locally common in short grassland in western areas, Elgon, Kitale, Mumias and Kisii (Kenya); all regions except Tanga (Tanzania); northern and eastern regions (Uganda); also in Zaire, Burundi, Zambia, Malawi, Zimbabwe.

LABIATAE

STACHYS
Flowers in terminal racemes of whorls; calyx with ten nerves and five equal teeth; corolla white, pink or purple, two-lipped; stamens four, arcuate. Four species in East Africa.

Stachys aculeata   **Plate 815**
A trailing, or creeping, tomentose herb with ascending stems and heart-shaped, cordate, acuminate leaves with stiff hairs on upper surface and more or less glabrous below. Calyx, 0.5cm (¼in) long, minutely glandular only; flowers, 1.5cm (⅝in) long, darker purple or pink with purple marking. Found in wet montane forest edges, altitude range 2100–3400m (7000–11,330ft), and recorded in Elgon, Mau, Aberdares, Mt Kenya, Machakos and Limuru – Kieni forest (Kenya); Kilimanjaro (Tanzania); western and eastern regions (Uganda); also in Ethiopia.

NB *S. aculeata* is a variable species; four of its forms in Kenya were at one time treated as separate species which cannot be maintained now that the full range of varieties is known.

Tinnea aethiopica   An erect, or straggling, pubescent shrub with elliptic, coarsely toothed leaves and paired flowers; the flower, *c.* 2cm (⅝in) long, with a red calyx and black corolla. Note the very curious sculptured fruit inside the inflated calyx. Common in all upland forest edges; altitude range 30–2310m (100–7700ft). Five other species in East Africa, mostly in southern Tanzania. Recorded in almost all districts and at the coast in Kenya; all regions of Tanzania and Uganda; also in Sudan, Somalia, Zaire.

NB The genus is named after Madame Tinne, a Dutch woman who discovered the plant in Sudan where, soon afterwards, she died of a fever.

MONOCOTYLEDONS

89. Hydrocharitaceae

Aquatic herbs with alternate or opposite, usually stipulate leaves. Flowers in clusters within usually bifid spathes; bisexual or unisexual, regular, sepals three, free; petals nought to three, free; stamens three to twelve, with short filaments. Ovary inferior, single-celled. Twenty-three species in three marine and five freshwater genera in East Africa.

Ottelia sp. A   Only recorded in western Kenya, it is similar to *O. ulvifolia*, but the spathe, 7cm (*c.* 3in) long, has no lateral wings, the flower axis is elongated and the flowers borne well above the opening of the spathe. Altitude range *c.* 1550–2000m (5000–6500ft). Six other species in East Africa.

O. ulvifolia   **Plate 244**
A rooted, aquatic herb with a rosette of submerged, or floating, elliptic leaves and conspicuous yellow flowers held above the water surface. The spathe, *c.* 5cm (2in)

long, with two lateral wings; flower axis hardly elongated and the flowers borne one at a time at the mouth of the spathe, which is bifid and pedunculate. Altitude range 1160–2700m (3900–9000ft). Locally common in pools on Elgon and Tinderet, and in Kitale, western Kenya, Embu and Nairobi districts (Kenya); all regions except Tanga (Tanzania); all regions of Uganda; also Sudan, Ethiopia, south to Zimbabwe, Mozambique.

90. Commelinaceae

A moderately-sized family of mainly tropical herbs. Their leaves are alternate with sheathing bases. There are three sepals, which may be free or united, and three delicate and deliquescent petals, one often smaller than the other two, which last only one day. Some of their six stamens may be reduced to staminodes. They have a superior two- to three-locular ovary and the fruit is usually a compartmented capsule. 111 species in eleven genera in East Africa.

ANEILEMA
Inflorescence a terminal thyrse; sepals three, equal; petals three, free, the upper two large and clawed, the lower one smaller; stamens six, the upper two or three reduced to staminodes, the lower three fertile or the centre one reduced; fruit a two-valved capsule. Twenty-seven species in East Africa.

Aneilema aequinoctiale   Plate 406
A herb with trailing stems with hooked hairs and large yellow flowers, c. 23mm (c. 1in) across. It is found in forests, forest edges and occasionally along roadsides, from 600–1800m (2000–6000ft). Recorded in the Aberdares, Mt Kenya, Nyambeni Hills, Embu, Machakos, Nairobi and Kajiado (Kenya); all regions except lake areas (Tanzania); western region, Buganda (Uganda); also Ethiopia, widespread south to Zimbabwe, Mozambique.

A. brenanianum   Plate 23
A rhizomatous perennial herb with thick and fleshy stems, erect to ascending, occasionally straggling in bushes, sometimes becoming woody, up to 1m (3ft) in length. Leaves linear-lanceolate up to 10cm (4in) long and 2cm ($\frac{4}{5}$in) wide. Inflorescence a terminal thyrse 5cm (2in) long. Flowers 8mm ($\frac{1}{3}$in) across, boat-shaped, petals white to pale mauve, filaments yellow. Found in open *Acacia* bushland on sandy soils among rocks; altitude range 1450–1700m (4800–5700ft). Recorded in Kajiado, Narok (Kenya); Maasai (Tanzania); elsewhere, not known.

A. hockii   Plate 628
A herb with tufted ascending decumbent stems with hooked hairs and large mauve to blue flowers, c. 16mm ($\frac{5}{8}$in) across, in shape rather like a small pansy, carried in pairs (sometimes in threes) opposite to each other on a long thin peduncle. It is common in grassland but also occurs in bushland and on rocky hills at lower altitudes and is recorded in the Aberdares, Narok, Magadi, Embu, Machakos, Nairobi and Kajiado (Kenya), at 500–1700m (1600–5600ft); all regions except Tabora (Tanzania); no record, Uganda; also Zaire.

COMMELINACEAE

A. pedunculosum   Plate 856
A small herb with a small dense inflorescence often with long hairs on the axis and
blue flowers c. 0.4cm (⅛in) across with violet-margined sepals. A fairly common
plant of upland forest, altitude range 1800–2700m (6000–9000ft), and recorded
everywhere in its ecological zone (Kenya); lake areas, Maasai, Tanga, Morogoro,
Songea (Tanzania); Uganda, no record; also in Zaire.

A. petersii   Plate 629
An annual with erect stems, or perennial with long decumbent stems, with a small,
hairy, few-flowered inflorescence of white to pale mauve flowers, c. 8mm (⅓in)
across. Found in bushland, altitude range 5–1875m (16–6250ft), and recorded in
Machakos, Kajiado, Vipingo (Kenya); Maasai, Tanga, Morogoro, Songea, Mafia Is.
(Tanzania); western region (Uganda); also southern Sudan, Mozambique.

A. somaliense   Plate 857
A straggling, more or less semi-succulent herb, sometimes rooting at the nodes, up
to 25cm (10in) high. The roots are fleshy and fascicled with short fusiform tubers.
Upper leaves up to 11cm (4⅜in) long and 4cm (1⅜in) wide, ovate, acute at apex and
base sessile on the leaf sheath. Inflorescence a terminal panicle 6×3cm (2⅔×1⅓in),
with main axis straight. Flowers small, pale lilac, 5mm (⅓in) across. An uncommon
plant of roadsides and under bushes; altitude range 750–1400m (2500–4700ft).
Recorded in Northern Frontier areas in Kenya, Somalia and Ethiopia only.

A. spekei   Plate 630
A short-lived perennial with erect to scandent stems and a dense elongate inflorescence of pink flowers, 9mm (⅔in) across. Found in wet savannah, and as a weed in
cultivated land, altitude range 1000–2000m (3280–6560ft), and recorded in Kitale,
western Kenya, Kisii and Baringo (Kenya); lake areas, Maasai, Tabora, Mpwapwa,
Kondoa, Mbeya, Iringa (Tanzania); all regions of Uganda; also in Zaire.

Anthericopsis sepalosa   Plate 816
A small herb with a basal rosette of leaves and large flowers with three equal petals.
The flowers are occasionally white but usually either a very pale blue or tinged with
blue; petals c. 25mm (1in) long. It has underground root tubers, and, like other
Commelinaceae, comes up quickly after rain and affords useful grazing before the
grasses are available. One species only in the genus. It occurs in grassland at
altitudes of 15–1620m (50–5300ft) and sometimes in woodland in Embu,
Machakos and Kajiado at medium altitudes. It is also common in dry bushland such
as the Northern Frontier district and the Tsavo National Parks (Kenya); Maasai,
Tanga, Mpwapwa, Kondoa, Mbeya, Iringa, Songea (Tanzania); Uganda, no record;
also in Ethiopia, Somalia, Malawi, Zimbabwe, Mozambique.

COMMELINA
Resembles *Aneilema* except that the short cymose inflorescences are enclosed
until the flowers open within folded spathes. Fifty species in East Africa. All flower
sizes in *Commelina* are approximate. See Plate 858.

Commelina africana   A more or less prostrate spreading herb with yellow flowers;
corolla tube c. 8mm (⅓in) across, spathe c. 2.5mm (1in) long. Very variable.
Recorded at altitude range 10–2400m (33–7875ft) throughout tropical Africa and
south to Natal. Widespread in East Africa.
   NB This species has twelve varieties.

C. albescens
Plate 859

A small herb with erect or ascending branches and the folded edges of the spathes strongly curved; the flowers are a pale pinkish-purple, rarely (possibly never) blue, 20mm (⅘in) across. This is a plant of dry grassland and bushland; altitude range 100–1300m (328–4250ft). It usually occurs in drier situations than *C. erecta*, but the two may occasionally be found together. Recorded in Magadi, Machakos, Kajiado and Loitokitok (Kenya); lake areas, Maasai (Tanzania); northern region (Uganda); also in Ethiopia, Somalia.

C. benghalensis
Flowers bright blue, *c.* 15mm (⅜in) across, and a climbing or erect habit. It thrives in the damper areas of cultivated or disturbed patches of land and has a wide altitude tolerance, from 10–2200m (33–7200ft). Found over a wide area of Kenya; Tanzania and Uganda, all regions; also Ethiopia, Somalia, south to Zimbabwe, Mozambique.

C. erecta
A herb with tufted, erect or ascending stems, the folded edge of the spathe straight or slightly curved (cf. *C. albescens*), the flowers, *c.* 2.5cm (1in) across, blue with the paired sepals fused, the paired petals with very short claws and the middle petal filiform. A fairly common plant in grassland and bushland, altitude range 210–1530m (700–4600ft). Kisii, Narok, Rift Valley, Magadi, Embu, Machakos and Kajiado (Kenya); all regions except lake areas, Tabora, Songea (Tanzania); Uganda, no record; also Ethiopia, Eritrea, Mozambique.

C. forskalei
Plate 860

A small, trailing herb which roots at the nodes. Its very narrow leaves usually have undulate margins and its flowers are blue, *c.* 12mm (*c.* ½in) across. It is a plant of grassland and bushland, most common below 910m (3000ft), and recorded in Nyambeni, Baringo, Machakos and western Kenya from 10–1650m (33–5400ft); all regions of Tanzania; northern region (Uganda); also Sudan, Ethiopia, Somalia.

C. latifolia
Plate 861

Flowers darker blue than *C. benghalensis* and broader, stronger leaves. *c. 17mm (c.* ⅝in) across. It is also common in cultivated or disturbed ground and where cut-off drains keep the ground moist, from 1–2400m (3–7900ft) in Kenya; all regions of Tanzania (one specimen only from Zanzibar); western region, Buganda, (Uganda); also Sudan, Ethiopia, Zaire, Rwanda.

C. petersii
Plate 862

An erect or scrambling herb with large acuminate spathes and bright, deep blue flowers, *c.* 2.5cm (1in) across, anthers of stamens entirely yellow. Found in dry grassland, bushland, savannah and occasionally at forest edges; altitude range 210–1530m (700–4800ft). Recorded in Baringo, Embu, Machakos, Kajiado and Nanyuki (Kenya); Maasai, Tanga, Mpwapwa, Kondoa, Mbeya, Iringa, Morogoro (Tanzania); Uganda, no record; also Ethiopia, Eritrea, Mozambique.

C. reptans
Plate 487

A herb with erect branches when young, and twisted, linear-lanceolate to lanceolate leaves, margins undulate, and yellow flowers, 2–2.5cm (¾–1in) wide. The stems loop and twist along the ground, rooting at the nodes; spathes 16–27mm (⅝–1in) long on stalks 1–7.5cm (⅜–3in) long. Found in seasonally swampy grassland and boggy soils, altitude range 1500–2530m (3000–8400ft): and recorded on Mt Kenya, Nanyuki, Machakos, Nairobi, Kajiado, Magadi, Narok, Rift Valley, Aber-

COMMELINACEAE

dares and Kitale (Kenya); lake areas, Maasai (Tanzania); all regions of Uganda; also in southern Ethiopia – Mega Mt.

CYANOTIS
Flowers subsessile in dense clusters more or less enclosed in spathaceous bracts; sepals and petals three, equal, united into tubes; stamens six, all fertile and equal filaments with long beaded hairs. Ten species in East Africa. The flowers of all seven species of *Cyanotis* recorded in Kenya are usually blue and white or pink. It is characteristic of all species to have some long hairs on the filaments.

Cyanotis arachnoides
Plate 863

A perennial herb with decumbent branches, a woody indumentum and often reddish leaves. Flowering shoots up to 25cm (10in) long, arising from a creeping perennial stem of which the internodes are completely covered by the leaf-sheaves; flower clusters at three to five nodes per shoot; stalked flower clusters usually present in addition to the sessile ones. Colour of flower bluish-purple, 4–5mm ($\frac{1}{6}$–$\frac{1}{5}$in) across. It is common on rocky outcrops, altitude range 1650–2450m (5400–8000ft), and recorded in Tinderet, Aberdares, Mt Kenya, Kitale, Narok, Nanyuki, Machakos, Nairobi and Kajiado (Kenya); Usambara Mts (Tanzania); Uganda, no record; elsewhere, not known.

C. barbata
Plate 817

An erect-stemmed, common annual which springs from small bulbs or rhizomes, with a spherical flower cluster at the end of the stem; flower *c.* 6mm ($\frac{1}{4}$in) across. The specimen illustrated is a rare white-mauve form. This flower is usually found in grassland, sometimes in shallow soil over rocks, altitude range 1650–3200m (5400–10,500ft), in districts ranging from Mt Elgon and the Cheranganis to Kitui, Mumias and Kisii (Kenya); lake areas, Maasai, Tabora, Mbeya, Iringa (Tanzania); all regions of Uganda; also Sudan, Ethiopia, Somalia, Zaire, Malawi, Zimbabwe, Mozambique.

C. foecunda
Plate 631

An annual or short-lived perennial with weakly erect, many-noded, flowering shoots becoming decumbent with age. Flowers mauve-purple, 4mm ($\frac{1}{6}$in) across. A common species usually growing among rocks in grassland, bushland or at forest edges; altitude range 200–2100m (650–6900ft). Widespread from east to west in Kenya and from Kitale to Kajiado (Kenya); Tanzania, no record; all regions except Buganda (Uganda); elsewhere, no record.

Floscopa glomerata
Plate 632

A herb with decumbent stems, clasping leaves and a dense terminal thyrse of small purple or bluish-white flowers, *c.* 5mm ($\frac{1}{5}$in) across, with pink to purple sepals. Found along watercourses and standing water in forests or in full sun; altitude range 1350–2160m (4500–7200ft). Seven other species in East Africa. Cheranganis, Kitale, Tinderet, Loita Hills, Aberdares, Machakos and Nairobi (Kenya); all regions except Tanga, Morogoro (Tanzania); all regions of Uganda; also Ethiopia, Malawi.

MURDANNIA

A terminal panicle of more or less regular flowers; sepals three, free, equal; petals three, free, equal or nearly so; stamens six, fertile, three opposite to the sepals; staminodes three, opposite to the petals. Capsule three-valved. Six species in East Africa.

Murdannia clarkeana   Plate 818

Has bluish-mauve flowers, *c.* 12mm ($\frac{1}{2}$in) across, and is found in temporarily waterlogged land on thin soil over rocks in grassland; altitude range 1600–1770m (5250–5800ft). It is common around Nairobi but rare elsewhere in Kenya; all regions except Mpwapwa, Kondoa (Tanzania); all regions of Uganda; also southern Sudan, Ethiopia, southern Somalia, Zaire south to Zimbabwe, Mozambique.

M. semiteres   A much smaller herb than *M. simplex*. It has tufted, erect stems and tiny, blue to mauve flowers, *c.* 6mm ($\frac{1}{4}$in) across. It grows at the edge of temporary pools in rocky formations at 1520–1820m (5000–6000ft) but is confined to western Kenya and even there is rare; lake areas, Mpwapwa, Kondoa (Tanzania); eastern region only (Uganda); also Rwanda, Burundi, Zaire, Zambia.

M. simplex   Plate 633

A hairless herb with erect and ascending stems and lavender to bluish-mauve flowers, *c.* 15mm ($\frac{3}{4}$in) across. Tends to open in the afternoon. It is found in swamps, grassland, rocky places and almost everywhere except really dry areas at altitudes of 14–2100m (45–6900ft) in Kenya; all regions (including Zanzibar) of Tanzania and Uganda; also Sudan, Ethiopia, Somalia, Zaire south to Mozambique.

91. Eriocaulaceae

Herbs of wet places with simple linear leaves and unisexual flowers in pedunculate bracteate heads; flowers very small, monoecious, regular; sepals and petals three, in separate whorls; stamens up to six, ovary of three carpels with three linear stigma. Fruit in three-seeded capsule. Twenty-five species in two genera in East Africa.

Eriocaulon schimperi   Plate 138

A densely tufted, perennial herb with numerous bluntly tipped, linear-tapering leaves and white heads, *c.*10mm ($\frac{3}{8}$in) across, on long scapes. Locally common in marshes in the upper bamboo and heath zones; altitude range 1950–3450m (6500–11,500ft). Recorded in Elgon, Mau, Aberdares, Cheranganis, Mt Kenya (Kenya); Morogoro, Mbeya, Iringa (Tanzania); western region (Uganda); also Ethiopia, Rwanda, Burundi, Zaire, Malawi.

92. Zingiberaceae
THE GINGER FAMILY

Herbs with aromatic fruits and roots, with alternate, distichous, ligulate, pinnate-veined entire leaves; flowers in terminal racemes or spikes of cymes, zygomorphic, bisexual, bracteate; sepals three, usually stiff and scarious; petals three, larger than the sepals, the posterior often the largest, an anterior enlarged petaloid lip present within the petals; stamens one, ovary inferior. Thirty-seven species in four genera in East Africa.

Siphonochilus aethiopicus (*Kaempferia aethiopica*)   **Plate 634**
A tuberous rooted, erect herb with three to seven large, elliptic to oblanceolate leaves, produced after the tuft of large delicate yellow and purple flowers are produced; petals 2.8–5.5cm (1½–2½in) long. Fruits red. Locally common in dry, sandy bushland, altitude range 390–1830m (1300–6000ft), especially near Kibwezi and recorded also in Kajiado (Kenya); all regions except Tanga (Tanzania); all regions except northern – Gulu (Uganda); also in southern Sudan, Ethiopia, south to Mozambique, Zimbabwe; all savannah regions of tropical Africa.

93. Liliaceae
THE LILY FAMILY

A large, cosmopolitan family of perennial herbs or, less often, of woody climbers. Their flowers are usually regular and mostly in racemes with the perianth in two similar petaloid whorls of three and nearly always six stamens, usually free. The ovary is superior and three-locular, the style usually single, occasionally threefold, and the fruit a capsule or, less often, a berry. In classifying the *Liliaceae* the underground storage organs are important. Some genera such as *Ornithogalum* and *Scilla* have bulbs, others, such as *Bulbine*, have corms, while others, including *Anthericum* and *Chlorophytum*, have swollen roots. 240 species in twenty-four genera in East Africa.

Albuca abyssinica (*A. wakefieldii*)   **Plate 407**
A robust plant up to 1m (3¼ft) or more tall, from an ovoid bulb produced into a neck which is sometimes fibrous; the leaves are variable, folded and often twisted with ciliated margins; often undulate in smaller forms of the plant. The flowers are bell-shaped, c. 16mm (⅝in) across, never opening fully, rather widely spaced on the peduncle and yellowish-green in colour with a darkish stripe down the middle of each perianth segment and the margins paler (yellowish). This is the commonest *Albuca* throughout East Africa from 10–2500m (30–8200ft). It is a very variable species, found also in Sudan, Ethiopia, widespread in tropical Africa.

ALOE
Stout herbs, softly woody shrubs or small trees with massive succulent toothed leaves which exude a yellow latex when cut; flowers yellow, orange or red, sometimes with some green, in stiff axillary simple or branched racemes; bracts present, perianth segments united to form a tube below, more or less equal; fruit a many-seeded capsule. Sixty species in East Africa.
Elephants are fond of aloes and can be observed eating them with relish. Where the

aloes grow in abundance it is an indication that the elephant has been driven away or shot out for a time.

Aloe graminicola   Plates 433 & 535
A small aloe with a rosette of triangular leaves with serrate edges. The orange-red flowers are borne on a branching head rounded in shape at the end of a long stem. Inflorescence 25–30cm (10–12in). It is often common in dry, sandy grassland and around Naro Moru in north-east and central Kenya; Tanzania and Uganda, no record; also southern Ethiopia.

A. amudatensis   Plate 434
A small aloe with a rosette of white-spotted, triangular leaves and solitary heads of pink to coral flowers on long peduncles; inflorescence c. 55cm (c. 22in) tall. Very similar to A. graminicola but uncommon, apparently confined to northern areas above 910m (3000ft) in Kenya; Tanzania, Uganda and elsewhere, not known.

A. lateritia
A simple panicle of green and orange or red flowers and a sessile rosette of white-spotted and streaked leaves. Inflorescence c. 110cm (43in) tall. It is an upland woodland species found up to altitudes of 2100m (7000ft) and appears to intergrade with A. graminicola (Kenya); Maasai, Tanga, Mbeya, Iringa, Songea (Tanzania); Buganda (Uganda); also Rwanda, Zaire.

A. rabaiensis   Plate 435
A thicket-forming aloe with dense shrub-like growth and dull green, hardly crowded leaves. Its bright orange-red flowers are grouped in four- to seven-branched terminal panicles. Inflorescence c.60cm (24in) tall. It is locally common in rocky ground at altitudes 90–1890m (3000–6200ft) in Nairobi, Tinderet, Aberdares, Rift Valley, Machakos and Kajiado (Kenya); doubtful in Maasai (Tanzania); Uganda, no record; also southern Somalia.

A. secundiflora   Plate 532
A large, fleshy herb with a rosette of green, unspotted, more or less glossy leaves at ground level and a much-branched panicle of red flowers. All, or nearly all the flowers are turned to one side of the inflorescence branch on which they are borne. Flowers c. 35mm (1⅜in) long; inflorescence 100cm (3¼ft) tall. It is a common aloe, growing in several types of soil and often confined to rocky areas where elephant pressure was or is high. It is found in fairly dry areas, altitude range 700–1800m (2300–5900ft), in Kitale, Baringo, Rift Valley, Magadi, Nanyuki and Kajiado districts (Kenya); lake areas, Maasai, Tanga, Mpwapwa, Kondoa (Tanzania); Uganda, no record; also southern Sudan, southern Ethiopia.

A. volkensii   Plate 533
A tall, single-stemmed or, occasionally, branched tree growing up to 6m (19ft) high. It has dull, grey-green leaves in a terminal rosette and much-branched panicles of red flowers; perianth segments 35mm (1⅜in) long; inflorescence 80cm (c. 32in) tall. It is common in rocky bushland, altitude range 900–2300m (3000–7500ft), in Narok and Kajiado districts (Kenya); lake areas, Maasai, Tanga (Tanzania); western region (Uganda); also Rwanda. Aloes sometimes vary considerably from place to place, sometimes as a result of hybridization, and, therefore, present even experienced botanists with difficulties in identification.

Androcymbium melanthoides   Plate 139
A small, erect herb up to 30cm (12in) high from a dark brown corm; stem leaves

narrow, few. Inflorescence an ebracteate spike, *c.* 4cm (1⅝in) across involucre; perianth persistent; tube short, campanulate or cylindric; segments equal spreading with two glands above the base; stamens inserted at base of perianth segments, filiform; anthers oblong, versatile; styles three, stigmatose at apex, persistent. Found in rocky soils and evergreen bushland and woodland; altitude range 1500–3000m (5000–9850ft). The only species in East Africa. Recorded in Elgon, Cheranganis, Tinderet, Aberdares, Mt Kenya, Kitale, Rift Valley, Nanyuki, Kajiado (Kenya); lake areas, Maasai, Tanga (Tanzania); northern, eastern regions (Uganda); also Ethiopia, Eritrea, Malawi, Mozambique.

ANTHERICUM
Herbaceous perennials, the above-ground part ephemeral, rhizomatous and often with root tubers but not bulbous; perianth open, rotate of six free white tepals with a median dark line which may appear only when the tepals dry; fruit subglobose with small irregularly angled seeds. Twenty-two species in East Africa.

Anthericum angustifolium Very similar to *A. gregorianum* but less robust. The leaves narrowly linear, glabrous and longer than the pedicels. The flowers are few, white and star-like, 1cm (⅜in) across, on pedicels which are much longer than the peduncle which is often hidden in the leaf rosette. It occurs in clumps (gregariously); altitude range 1550–2650m (5200–8800ft), in similar conditions to *A. gregorianum*, but appears to be confined to the area from Elgon to the Aberdares (Kenya).

A. cameronii   Plate 140
A glabrous herb with a horizontal fibrous rhizome and thin wiry roots with distant tubers. The leaves distichous, linear to linear-lanceolate, variable in breadth and length, folded or flat, bases sheathing with irregular purple markings just below ground level, scape flattened, narrowly winged, rachis usually zigzagging between axils. Flowers, white, *c.* 2cm (¾in) across, in groups of one to three, with a very faint broad median stripe on each segment. Pedicels articulated near base. An attractive lily found in highland grasslands often on rocky slopes; altitude range 1000–2200m (3300–7500ft), flowering just after first rains and recorded in Elgon, Cheranganis, Tinderet, Kitale, Kisii, Narok and Baringo (Kenya); all regions except Tanga (Tanzania); all regions (Uganda); also in Sudan, Rwanda, Burundi, Zaire, Malawi, Zambia.

A. cooperi   Plate 141
A small plant from a horizontal, knobby rhizome covered with fibrous remains of old leaf cases and producing many thin stringy roots with some scattered tubers near their tips. Leaves distichous, erect or falcate, linear to lanceolate, variable in length and breadth, usually folded, glabrous or papillate on the prominent ribs with entire margins. Inflorescence usually simple and congested near the apex, scape compressed, narrowly winged, bracts dark or white and membraneous, pedicels short up to 10mm (⅜in) in fruit, articulated below the middle and angular or flattened. Flowers one- to three-nate, 20mm (¾in) across, white with a green to red-brown median stripe per segment; capsule globose, bluntly three-angled, about 8mm (⅓in) in diameter, slightly indented at the apex with many transverse ridges. A common lily of grasslands, black cotton soil or shallow soils overlying rocks; altitude range 600–2100m (1950–6900ft), flowering after the first rains, often after fires have burnt the grass, in Cheranganis, Kitale, Aberdares, Magadi, Nairobi, Nanyuki, Machakos and Kajiado (Kenya); lake areas, Maasai, Tanga, Tabora, Mbeya, Iringa (Tanzania); Uganda, no record; also Burundi, Malawi, Zambia, Zimbabwe.

A. gregorianum   A robust plant with canaliculate, fleshy, linear-lanceolate leaves, ciliated at margins and with a distinct 5–15cm (2–6in) long peduncle bearing stiffly erect, spreading pedicels up to 4cm (1⅜in) long. The flowers, *c*.1.3cm (½in) across, white with three-veined green median stripe on each segment, bracts white, membraneous. This is a pretty lily of highland grasslands and shallow soils overlying rocks; altitude range 900–1950m (3000–6500ft), appearing soon after first rains and recorded in Aberdares, Mt Kenya, Nanyuki, Machakos, Nairobi and Kajiado (Kenya); Maasai (Tanzania); not known in Uganda; also in southern Ethiopia.

A. subpetiolatum   **Plate 142**
A small plant from a horizontal moniliform rhizome with short, fleshy roots tapering from a thickened base, without tubers; the outermost two or three leaves are small and curved, the inner leaves up to 30cm (12in) long, much narrowed and petiole-like (stalk-like) in their lower half, flat or usually folded, margin minutely ciliate, the peduncle shortly hairy. The inflorescence is somewhat lax and usually congested near the apex, perianth segments white, not conspicuously striped in fresh material. Flower 1cm (⅜in) across. The pedicels are short, *c*.6mm (¼in) in length. This is a delicate lily found in grasslands and woodlands; altitude range above 850m (2800ft). Widespread in Kenya; the photograph was taken at Emali; all regions of Tanzania except Songea; all regions of Uganda; also Sudan, Ethiopia, south to Zimbabwe.

A. suffruticosum   **Plate 143**
Plant with erect or prostrate, eventually branched, aerial stems usually about 2.5cm (1in) thick or more, and covered with stiff fibres from old leaf bases, leaves distichous, grass-like, borne at the apices. Inflorescence simple or branched, flowers white with a greenish or brown median stripe. Perianth segments *c*.12mm (½in) long. This remarkable lily is quite unlike any other species in the genus and is easily identified by its thick aerial stems. Found in rocky outcrops in predominantly coastal areas, also on coral outcrops; altitude range 1–1800m (3–6000ft). Up country it has only been recorded from the hills at Ulu, the furthest inland record in Kenya; lake areas, Tanga, Morogoro (Tanzania); Uganda and elsewhere, not known.

   NB The thick aerial stems of this species correspond to the rhizomes of other species and are sometimes called aerial rhizomes.

A. venulosum   **Plate 144**
A small, robust plant from a horizontal knobby rhizome covered with fibrous remains of old leaf bases and producing many thin, stringy roots with some scattered tubers near their tips. Leaves distichous, erect or falcate, linear to lanceolate with conspicuous, hairy, often undulate and raised margins; leaf bases without any markings. Scape glabrous except for hairy wings. Inflorescence lax and rachis often visible between fascicles of flowers. Flowers white; perianth segments *c*. 11mm (½in) long. Similar to *A. cooperi* but less robust, leaves only minutely hairy at margins, inflorescence congested, pseudocapitate, rachis very short, sometimes zigzagging. Found in grasslands, open woodlands; altitude range 600–1500m (2000–5000ft). Mostly recorded along Thika–Kangundo and Thika–Sagana roads and along Tsavo River (Tsavo National Park) (Kenya); Tanzania, Uganda and elsewhere, not known.

ASPARAGUS

Usually perennial, woody, much-branched, more or less climbing plants, often spiny. True leaves reduced to scales or spines; modified stems (cladodes) carry out the function of leaves; flowers numerous, small, yellow or greenish; fruit a single- to several-seeded berry. Twenty-two species in East Africa.

Asparagus africanus
Plate 245

A glabrous to pubescent, much-branched, armed, woody climber with fibrous roots and smooth or slightly grooved, somewhat zigzagging, grey-brown to greenish stems, branches usually solitary at each node, with a tendency to pubescence, usually spreading but often reflexed in pubescent forms; cladodes fascicled, ascending to spreading, needle-like, straight or slightly arcuate; spines present on the stem and larger branches; flowers white, 6–7mm (¼in) across, axillary and terminal, stalks articulated below the middle; berry globose, fleshy, red and single-seeded. This is a frequent plant of forest edges and bushy wooded areas where it climbs up to 3m (10ft) in height, but it also occurs in open vegetation, where it forms low bushes up to 1m (3ft) in height, or can be found scrambling among rocks, and in drier areas. Altitude range 1–2500m (3–8200ft), occasionally to 3400m (11,150ft). Widespread in Kenya; all regions of Tanzania; western, eastern regions of Uganda; also Sudan, Ethiopia, Zaire south to Zimbabwe, Botswana.

Asparagus buchananii
A glabrous, much-branched, armed, woody climber with tortuous and often strongly zigzagging, smooth stem and branches which are very variable in colour; branchlets lacking spines spreading to ascending; cladodes in fascicles of six- to eight-angled, terete or grooved, needle-like, slightly arcuate; spines well developed up to 4cm (1¾in) long or more on the main stems, dorsally flattened towards the base and usually reflexed. Flowers white, solitary, 4mm (⅛in) across; pedicel with variable articulation and ovary stalked. The berries are red and fleshy, one- to two-seeded. Easily recognized by its stout, extremely pungent, strongly reflexed spines, which are characteristically flattened at the base. A frequent climber in forest but also found scrambling over bushes in open country, often appearing after early rains; altitude range 1–2300m (3–7500ft). Widespread throughout Kenya; all regions of Tanzania; all regions of Uganda except Buganda; also in southern Somalia, Malawi, Zimbabwe, Mozambique.

A. falcatus
Plate 534

A much-branched, glabrous climber or scrambler with tortuous, smooth, pale stems and spreading branches which are usually solitary, cladodes flattened, linear, straight or falcate, dark green, fascicled; flowers cream to white, 3mm (⅛in) across. Very fleshy red berry, usually single-seeded. Found in upland forests and woodlands, but sometimes scrambling on bushes in drier areas; altitude range 5–2000m (16–6550ft). Mau, Aberdares, Mt Kenya, Kisii, Narok, Rift Valley, Machakos and Nairobi (Kenya); Tanzania, Uganda and elsewhere, widespread.

NB This species is classified at Kew under the title A. aethiopicus/falcatus complex. At a later date it may be classified into two definite and different species.

A. flagellaris (A. nudicaulis)
An erect-to-climbing, armed, woody perennial with tortuous, grooved, often greenish stems and terete, solitary branches; branchlets often well defined, mostly solitary; cladodes fascicled, needle-like, terete, numerous, stiffly erect and mostly longer than the internodes on vegetative branches. Easily recognized by the conspicuous white spurs at the base of the fascicles of the cladodes which lie in the axils of the spines. Cladodes very few or absent on flowering shoots but numerous on fruiting or vegetative shoots. Flowers, white,

0.4cm (⅛in) across, in axillary pairs, sometimes single or fascicled, pedicel articulated near the base. Fleshy orange berry, single-seeded. Found in dry areas, sometimes scrambling over rocks; altitude range 640–2100m (2100–7000ft). Elgon, Kitale, western regions, Kisii, Baringo and Machakos (Kenya); all regions of Tanzania except Maasai; all regions of Uganda; also Sudan, Ethiopia, Zaire, Rwanda, Burundi, Malawi, Mozambique.

A. racemosus   Plate 246
A glabrous woody climber or scrambler with twining, usually grooved and yellowish stems; the branches and branchlets spreading to ascending, solitary at nodes; spines pungent, short 3–6mm (⅛–¼in) long, brownish to grey; flowers white, 0.5cm (⅛in) across, solitary and paired laterally, but more numerous terminally on short 2–3mm (1/12–⅛in) pedicels, and articulated near or at the middle. The berry is globose, red and single-seeded. A widespread species of drier areas and forest margins; altitude range 240–2880m (800–9600ft). Elgon, Mau, Aberdares, Narok, Baringo, Rift Valley, Machakos and Amboseli (Kenya); all regions of Tanzania except lake areas, Mpwapwa, Kondoa; all regions of Uganda; also in Sudan, Ethiopia, Somalia, Zaire, Zambia.

Bulbine abyssinica   Plate 408
An erect plant which grows from a vertical rhizome with many fleshy roots. The leaves spring upwards from a rosette at the base. Flower c. 8mm (⅓in) across. Tufts of long yellow hairs on the filaments make its bright yellow or sulphur flowers look puffy. A widespread lily of the grassland areas, generally found above 1220m (4000ft). Two other species in East Africa. Common in many parts of Kenya; all regions of Tanzania except Morogoro; all regions of Uganda; also southern Sudan, Ethiopia, south to Zimbabwe.

CHLOROPHYTUM
Resembles *Anthericum*, but the seeds are large, flat and rounded. Fifty-six species in East Africa.

Chlorophytum bakeri   Plate 145
A small plant from an erect, shortly fibrous rhizome with roots swollen, fleshy and often shortly furry; leaves in an ascending rosette, progressively larger, narrow, glabrous, half folded and wavy at margins. Inflorescence a dense subspicate raceme, usually simple and short up to 30cm (12in) tall; bracts usually projecting beyond the very short pedicillate white flowers, small and bell-shaped, with exserted stamens. Flower spike 5cm (2in) long, 1cm (⅜in) across. A graceful, fairly common herb of grassland and open woodlands appearing after first rains. Altitude range 420–2100m (1400–7000ft). Widespread (Kenya); lake areas, Maasai, Tanga, Tabora, Mbeya, Iringa (Tanzania); northern region of Uganda; elsewhere, not known.

C. blepharophyllum
Broad and long leaves, the lower ends of which tightly clasp the flower stalk. The flowers, borne on one to three short branches, and close together, are white in colour with a greenish-brown stripe on the perianth. Inflorescence 8–10cm (3–4in) long; perianth segment 7mm (c. ⅓in) long. Locally common in burnt grassland; altitude range 600–2100m (2000–7000ft). Especially common in Mt Elgon area, and widespread from there to Mumias, Narok, Baringo, Kitale and the Cheranganis (Kenya); all regions of Tanzania but doubtfully at coast; all regions of Uganda; also Sudan, Ethiopia, south to Zimbabwe.

LILIACEAE

C. gallabatense Plate 24
Grows from a short, compact rhizome with many long, narrow roots which bear widely-spaced, small tubers. Its flowers are greenish-white and grow in a crowded raceme on loose branches up the stalk. Inflorescence 12–16cm (4⅘–6in) long; perianth segment 5mm (⅕in) long. In the afternoons they tend to be fully reflexed. Fairly frequent in grasslands, open woodlands and shallow soils, appearing after the first showers of rain; altitude range 130–2100m (430–7000ft). Higher Elgon, Mau and Aberdares, on or above 2130m (7000ft), Kitale, Kisii, Baringo, Nanyuki and Machakos districts (Kenya); lake areas, Tabora, Mpwapwa, Kondoa, Mbeya, Iringa, Songea (Tanzania); northern and eastern regions of Uganda; also southern Sudan, Ethiopia, southern Somalia, Zambia, Zimbabwe.

NB One or two specimens are recorded in the Songea region well below the normal altitude range.

C. macrophyllum Plate 146
A handsome plant which grows from a vertical or horizontal rhizome with many thick, fleshy roots which carry ovoid tubers. It has broad, slightly thick, hairless leaves which are broadly lanceolate, wavy and crisped at margins, narrowing above the base. The inflorescence is up to 30cm (12in) tall, the raceme dense, usually simple with white flowers up to 1.5cm (⅗in) across, 12mm (½in) long, in fascicles up to five in number. The lower bracts are long, project beyond the flowers and are blackish as they dry off. Found on black cotton soil in grassland or open bushland, with flowers opening a few at a time; altitude range c. 1350–1800m (c. 4400–6000ft). Narok, Machakos and Kajiado districts, common in the Ngong and Athi plains areas near Nairobi (Kenya); all regions of Tanzania, sometimes found near the coast at lower-than-normal altitudes; Uganda, not known; also Senegal to Ethiopia, Angola to Zimbabwe, Mozambique.

C. micranthum Small, greenish-white flowers which grow from a small rhizome. It is commonly seen in burnt grassland, flowering after the first showers of rain. Inflorescence c. 12mm (½in) long; perianth segment c. 5mm (⅕in) long. Kitale district (Kenya); lake areas, Morogoro (Tanzania); all regions of Uganda except Buganda; also southern Sudan (possibly a form of C. gallabatense).

C. tenuifolium Plate 147
A fairly large plant with a densely fibrous rhizome and delicate, lanceolate, half-folded leaves in a rosette ascending from the base. Its white flowers, c. 28mm (1⅛in) across, are usually solitary, also, rarely, in pairs. Locally common (Kenya) in black cotton soils and seasonally wet grasslands, generally at altitudes of 100–1650m (300–6400ft); Tanga – Usambara Mts (Tanzania); Uganda, no record; also northern Somalia; never recorded in true coastal areas.

DIPCADI
Bulbous plants; flowers in a simple central raceme, brown or green in colour; the three outer tepals have long, curved, tapering tips. Five species in East Africa.

Dipcadi arenarium A slender plant 10–35cm (4–14in) tall with very narrow linear leaves, often dilated and clasping at the base and rarely more than 25cm (10in) long; inner segments of the perianth narrow and conspicuously pointed. The flowers are an unusual brownish-green colour, and 15mm (⅗in) long. This is a small, graceful lily of grasslands, often on seasonally wet shallow soils overlying rocks and black cotton soil; altitude range 800–1800m (2600–6000ft). Kitale, Narok, Rift Valley, Machakos and Nairobi (Kenya); lake areas, Maasai (Tanzania); northern region of Uganda; also in Burundi.

NB The records for this species are not very reliable and it may well have a wider range.

D. viride   Plate 25
A hairless plant from 10–60cm (4–24in) in height, with linear to linear-lanceolate shiny, flaccid and indistinctly veined leaves which are variable in size. The shiny scape is terete and sometimes arcuate at the base. The flowers, c. 14mm ($\frac{2}{3}$in) long, are green with a yellowish or khaki tinge, and the tips of the outer segments are curved outwards. The capsule is oblong in outline and about 1cm ($\frac{2}{5}$in) long. It is a common but variable species often found in wetter areas of grasslands and in bushland from 1200–2000m (4000–6500ft). Kitale, Baringo, Rift Valley, Embu, Machakos and Nairobi (Kenya); all regions of Tanzania; all regions of Uganda except eastern; also Ethiopia, Somalia, south to Zimbabwe, Mozambique.

Drimia altissima (*Urginea altissima*)   Plate 247
A bulbous herb flowering before the leaves, flowers whitish to greenish sometimes marked reddish-brown to purplish; bracts pouched or spurred on the back; perianth segments 6–9mm ($\frac{1}{4}$–$\frac{1}{3}$in) across, all similar and united for lower third or quarter; the free parts linear-spathulate and slightly hooded at the top. The stamens are inserted at top of the perianth-tube and the capsule is oblong-ovoid; seeds black, papery and hairy. The plant is poisonous. Altitude range 1–2100m (3–6900ft). Found in all regions of Kenya, Tanzania and Uganda; also in Sudan, Ethiopia, Somalia, Zaire south to Zimbabwe, Mozambique. Five other species in East Africa. All species are imperfectly known and require further study.

Gloriosa superba (*G. simplex*)   Plates 409 & 488
A most spectacular flower which grows vigorously from a V-shaped tuber, seeds itself easily and has been known to climb up to 5m (16ft) in height in upland forest. The tips of the lanceolate leaves act as tendrils. The flower is c. 75mm (3in) across, generally brilliant red, with the perianth segments reflexed, but it is also often striped with yellow or yellow and green. It is widespread below an altitude of 2530m (8300ft) and is sometimes called 'The Flame Lily'. A particularly beautiful variant often grows at lower altitudes, pale yellow in colour with a mauve to purple stripe. The variant is fairly widespread in Tsavo West National Park and can also be found in the Samburu district (Kenya); all regions of Tanzania and Uganda; also Ethiopia, Madagascar, widespread in tropical Africa.

NB Recently a beautiful white-flowered *Gloriosa* has been found in southern Somalia which may be a form of *G. superba*.

G. minor   Plate 489
Smaller than *G. superba*, being under 50cm (1$\frac{1}{2}$ft) tall, and has narrower leaves and perianth segments. It grows in low-lying dry areas of Kenya; Tanzania and Uganda, no record; also Ethiopia, Somalia.

Kniphofia thomsonii   Plate 490
Related to the Red Hot Poker of European gardens. An erect herb from a fibrous, sometimes branched, irregular rhizome with leaves up to 100cm (39in) long and a dense to lax raceme. The flowers, up to 3cm (1$\frac{1}{5}$in) long, are elongate and trumpet-shaped and range in colour from yellow to a flame red. Found along streams and in marshy places; altitude range 1000–1600m (3300–5250ft). There is a dry area form which has shorter racemes and distinctly keeled leaves, the apices of which are sometimes triangular in section. The wet area form is more robust with flat

leaves. Elgon, Mau, Cheranganis, Tinderet, Aberdares, Kitale, Baringo and Rift Valley (Kenya); Maasai, Mbeya, Iringa (Tanzania); northern, eastern regions of Uganda; also Ethiopia, Burundi, Zaire.

ORNITHOGALUM

Bulbous plants; flowers usually white and open with the tepals spreading. Three species in East Africa.

Ornithogalum donaldsonii (*Albuca donaldsonii*)   **Plate 148**
A robust plant growing up to 1m (3ft) or more in height from a large bulb which is 8cm (3in) across. Its large flowers are white to cream, their outer segments having a green median stripe, and borne on long, erect to ascending pedicels. The green tepals form a bell-shaped flower and are c. 15mm (⅝in) long. A frequent plant in grassland and bushland at 520–1000m (1700–3250ft). Especially along Mombasa road near Ulu and in the Machakos district (Kenya); Maasai, Tanga (Tanzania); Uganda, no record; also Ethiopia.

O. gracillimum   A small, graceful plant growing to 5–20cm (2–8in) in height from a small bulb which is up to 1cm (⅜in) across. It has a few small and loosely-arranged white flowers, 3–7mm (⅛–¼in) long, which appear after the first rain. It is found in grassland and shallow soils overlying rocks at altitudes 1800–2700m (5900–8850ft). Upland areas of Kenya; Tanzania, no record; northern and eastern (Mt Elgon) regions of Uganda; elsewhere, not known.

O. tenuifolium (*O. ecklonii*)   Long, linear-lanceolate leaves with the lamina usually folded and clasping at the base, and the margins often inrolled on the upper half. Its young conical raceme is dense with bracts projecting beyond the buds, thus as the white flowers open they make the raceme become rather lax. Its perianth segments have a broad green median stripe and white margins. Flower c. 15mm (c. ⅜in) across; perianth segment 1cm (⅜in) long. The leaves are highly poisonous. Aberdares, Rift Valley, Machakos, common around Nairobi (Kenya); all regions of Tanzania; western region, Buganda (Uganda); also in Ethiopia, Somalia, Zaire south to Zimbabwe, Mozambique.
   NB Named as *O. longibracteatum* in *UKWF*.

SCILLA

There are sixteen species in East Africa, placed in *Scilla*, but the whole group is now under revision and it is likely that some or all of them may be assigned to other genera.

Scilla kirkii   **Plate 819**
A low-growing plant, with ovate to sword-shaped leaves, which springs from a large bulb. Flowers are carried on an upright stalk, generally blue or purple. This attractive lily grows seasonally in wet soils and appears after rains; also common in most dry areas at altitudes of 9–1750m (30–5750ft). Mainly in the Magadi, Machakos, Nairobi and Kajiado areas (Kenya); all regions of Tanzania except Tabora, Songea; Uganda, no record; also Ethiopia, Somalia.

S. indica   Very similar to *S. kirkii*, with blue, or sometimes purple, flowers, c.1cm (⅜in) long, but is less robust. It is possible that both species will eventually be classed as one. Widespread in Kenya at higher altitudes; Maasai, Tabora, Morogoro, Mbeya, Iringa, Songea (Tanzania); all regions except eastern Uganda; also southern Sudan, Ethiopia, Malawi, Zambia, Zimbabwe.

Trachyandra saltii   **Plate 149**
A grass-like plant with many thin, but fairly stout roots. Its thread-like to linear leaves gradually dilate into a tubular, membraneous base. In Kenya its axillary inflorescence is in the form of a simple, many-flowered raceme with one bract per flower and single pedicels. The single flowers, *c.* 11mm ($\frac{2}{3}$in) across, usually open in the afternoon. They are white with a greenish to dark brown median stripe per segment. This is a very variable and adaptable species: three distinct forms have been recorded in Kenya. It is small in dry conditions, robust in wetter ones and found at altitudes of 880–2130m (2900–7000ft). Three other species in East Africa, which resemble *Anthericum*. Aberdares, Narok, Nanyuki, Machakos, Nairobi and Kajiado (Kenya); lake areas, Maasai, Tabora, Mpwapwa, Kondoa, Mbeya, Iringa, Songea (Tanzania); all regions except eastern Uganda; also Angola to Mozambique.

94. Araceae

Rhizomatous or cormous herbs with distichous or spiral reticulately veined, often cordate, leaves; flowers small, unisexual or bisexual, regular, sessile on a spike and enclosed in an often attractive spathe. Perianth of six parts present or absent, two to eight stamens, ovary superior, or immersed in the spike. Usually with few basal or apical ovules. Fruit a berry. Thirty-nine species in fifteen genera in East Africa.

Arisaema mildbraedii   **Plate 26**
A cormous dioecious herb with two to three erect five- to eleven-foliolate leaves and lateral entire leaflets borne on branching petioles, with a central peduncle bearing a tubular green and white spathe. The appendage of the spike is cylindrical and green just exceeding the tube of the spathe. Spathe 7–23cm (2$\frac{4}{5}$–9in) long; tube 4–10cm (1$\frac{3}{5}$–4in); pistillate spadix 3–5cm (1$\frac{1}{5}$–2in) long. Locally common in wet montane forest edges; altitude range 1400–2500m (4600–8200ft). Five species in East Africa. Elgon, Aberdares, Nyambeni Hills and Kitale (Kenya); Tanzania, no record; eastern region of Uganda; also Zaire, Rwanda, Burundi.

95. Amaryllidaceae
THE DAFFODIL or SNOWDROP FAMILY

A medium-sized, widespread family of herbs. More or less linear leaves rise from the bulb – the plant's storage organ. Inflorescence an umbel subtended by bracts and borne on a leafless stalk springing from the bulb, or, rarely, a solitary flower. The perianth is of six petaloid segments, free or united into a tube below, often with a corona. There are six stamens and an inferior, three-locular ovary. Fruit is a capsule or berry. Twenty-three species in seven genera in East Africa.

Ammocharis tinneana   **Plate 710**
A bulbous herb with a spreading fan of thick leaves around the base. The inflorescence consists of about twenty long-tubed flowers opening out at their ends from a

common peduncle and ranging in colour from pink to red. Perianth tube 6–10cm (2⅔–4in) long. It is locally common in dry bushland or wooded grassland at 350–1350m (1150–6000ft). Narok, Baringo, Magadi, Lower Embu and Kajiado districts (Kenya); lake areas, Maasai, Mpwapwa, Kondoa, Morogoro, Mbeya, Iringa (Tanzania); northern and eastern regions of Uganda; also Sudan, Ethiopia, Somalia, Rwanda south to Botswana.

A. angolensis (*A. heterostyla*) Similar plant to *A. tinneana*. It has fewer flowers, which are pink, not red; perianth tube 4–8cm (1⅗–3in) long. Found in rocky bushland. Western Kenya; Tabora (Tanzania); eastern region of Uganda; also Zambia.

Boöphone disticha   Plate 536
A herb with a large bulb which annually produces a fan of leaves and a dense umbel of dull red flowers; perianth *c.*3cm (1¼in) long. Their pedicels lengthen and spread when in fruit to become stiff and straight so that the entire fruiting inflorescence can break away and roll over the ground, distributing the seeds in the process. The bulb is poisonous to cattle and the name comes from the Greek for 'ox-killer'. It is a good example of a so-called 'tumble-weed' and is locally common in rocky grassland at 1520–2440m (5000–8000ft). The only species in East Africa. Mt Elgon, Cheranganis, Tinderet, Narok, Baringo, Rift Valley, Nairobi and Kajiado districts (Kenya); Maasai, Tabora, Mpwapwa, Kondoa, Morogoro, Mbeya, Iringa (Tanzania); northern and eastern regions of Uganda; also Zaire, Mozambique, Zambia.

CRINUM
The largest genus of the *Amaryllidaceae* in East Africa may be recognized by the perianth tube being much widened distally, so that it becomes bell-shaped. The species are difficult to distinguish and in the past several have been called *C. kirkii*.

Crinum macowanii   Plate 820
A large bulbous plant with thick, heavy, dull grey-green leaves which spring out from the ground. Its long tubular flowers are white with pink stripes, earning it the popular name of the Pyjama Lily. Perianth lobes *c.* 3cm (1¼in) long; perianth tube *c.* 10cm (4in) long. It is fairly common in open grassland and survives along roadside verges at altitudes of 500–2700m (1700–9000ft). Widespread in Kenya; lake areas, Maasai, Tabora, Morogoro, Mbeya, Iringa, Songea (Tanzania); northern, eastern regions of Uganda; also Sudan, Ethiopia, Somalia, Zaire, Malawi, Zambia, Zimbabwe.

NB A rare albino form with a faint green midrib exists and may be seen on the edge of Ngorongoro Crater in Tanzania.

C. papillosum   Plate 821
A bulb up to 12cm (5in) in diameter, often with a distinct neck. Leaves more or less spreading on the ground, strap-shaped, very variable in length without midrib or keel, ciliate; one to two scapes, 10–30cm (4–12in) long, produced with the leaves or before. Spathe-valves lanceolate, drooping at anthesis. Two to twelve flowers per inflorescence, sessile or with pedicels up to 2.5cm (1in) long. Perianth tube 8–14cm (*c.* 3–5½in) long, segments 6–14cm (2⅔–5½in) long. Perianth tube brownish-green, only slightly curved; segments white, with a very pale pink flush down the centre, linear to narrowly lanceolate, acuminate, the inner ones slightly broader than the outer, all coming together to a funnel; tips only slightly reflexed at anthesis. Filaments white, declinate, anthers yellow and curved. Fruit dull yellow when ripening. Found in deciduous bushland, valley or wooded grassland, common in disturbed places; altitude range 450–1100m (*c.* 1500–3600ft). Kitui,

Kajiado, Tsavo National Park (Kenya); lake areas, Maasai, Tanga, Mbeya, Iringa (Tanzania); Uganda, no record. Also in Zambia.

Cyrtanthus sanguineus ssp. **ballyi**   **Plate 537**
An erect herb with linear strap-shaped leaves and a funnel-shaped, bright red perianth with one to three flowers together; perianth 5–10cm (2–4in) long. Locally common in stony grassland; altitude range 1630–1950m (5400–6500ft). One of two species in East Africa. Sometimes a good display in the Nairobi Game Park but, although no exact record can be made, there are probably not more than 3000 plants in Kenya. It is, therefore, an endangered species and should on no account be disturbed or collected from its habitat. Tanzania, Uganda and elsewhere, not known (ssp. *wakefieldii* recorded also in Morogoro, Songea, in Tanzania).

C. sanguineus ssp. **salmonoides**   Resembles ssp. *ballyi* but has solitary, or occasionally two, pink to orange flowers, perianth 7–9cm (2¾–3½in) long. It has been found near the Ngong Hills, up to 1950m (6500ft) altitude and in the Kajiado district (Kenya). Tanzania, Uganda and elsewhere, not known (ssp. *wakefieldii* recorded also in Morogoro, Songea in Tanzania).

Scadoxus multiflorus (*Haemanthus multiflorus*)   **Plate 538**
The magnificent red flowers of this lily appear with the first rains and before its thick, upright leaves appear. They are carried on a single, long, thin stem, as many as 150 making up a single head, and become pinkish as they fade, giving the appearance of a gigantic shaving brush. It is widespread in rocky places, riverine forest and open grassland and often found growing in the shade of trees or on the edges of large antheaps at altitudes up to 2700m (9000ft). It is popularly called the Fire Ball Lily. A slightly different form, which prefers a more arid habitat, can be seen on Mt Marsabit (Kenya) in the forest zone, carpeting the ground for hundreds of square metres. The individual flowers are slightly more widely spaced and redder than in the other form and do not present such a strong impression of a shaving brush. The bulbs of both forms are often very deeply placed in the soil. Inflorescence 14–19cm (5½–7½in) acrss, Altitude range 1–2700m (3–9000ft). Found throughout East Africa except in the driest regions; also in almost all parts of tropical Africa. Three other species in East Africa.

96. Iridaceae
THE IRIS FAMILY

A medium-sized, mainly temperate family of herbs, most numerous in South Africa and South America. Their rootstock is a corm, rhizome or, rarely, a bulb, and their leaves are narrowly linear, basal or on the stem. The regular or zygomorphic flowers have a petaloid perianth and are often tubular below with six segments. There are three stamens and an inferior ovary. The fruit is a capsule. There are fifty-eight species in East Africa, belonging to twelve genera, but they are rarely found below 1000m (3300ft) altitude.

ARISTEA
Rhizomatous with leaf-like bracts; perianth blue, without a tube, of six equal segments. Seven species in East Africa, all above 1200m (c. 4000ft).

Aristea alata   An erect, tufted herb with numerous fans of short, stiff leaves at the base and an erect, branching inflorescence of clusters of blue flowers; the stem is flattened with narrow wings. Flower c. 9mm (⅓in) across. Locally common in high-land wet grassland from 1700–3700m (5600–12,100ft). Elgon, Cheranganis, Tinderet, Mau, Aberdares, Kitale and Kisii (Kenya); Maasai, Tanga (Tanzania); Uganda, no record; also Zaire, Zambia, Malawi, Zimbabwe, Ethiopia.

A. angolensis   An erect herb with rather few very long leaves at base, bearing an erect, leafy stem with sessile clusters of blue flowers; the stem is flattened but not winged. It also does not have the numerous fans of short, stiff leaves at the base as in *A. alata*. Flower c. 13mm (½in) across. It is locally common in wet grassland from 1700–2500m (5600–8200ft). Western regions, Elgon, Tinderet, Aberdares and Kitale (Kenya); Tanga, Tabora, Mbeya, Iringa (Tanzania); Uganda, no record; also Zaire, Zambia, Malawi, Zimbabwe.

Dierama cupiflorum (*C. pendulum*)   **Plate 711**
A robust, densely-tufted perennial, growing from a rhizomatous rootstock with laterally flattened linear leaves and branched panicles of delicate, nodding and short, tubular, pinkish-purple flowers, c. 25mm (1in) across. Common in high-altitude grassland from 2400–3900m (7900–12,800ft) in Kenya. All regions of Tanzania except Songea; eastern region (Mt Elgon) of Uganda; also southern Ethiopia, Malawi, Zimbabwe.
   NB The species found in East Africa is *D. cupiflorum* (*UKWF D. pendulum*). The true *D. pendulum* is a Southern African species not known in East Africa.

GLADIOLUS
Erect herbs whose globose corms have a fibrous covering; perianth zygomorphic with a long curved tube; anther and stigma connivent under the upper segment. Twenty species in East Africa.

Gladiolus natalensis   **Plate 436**
One of the ancestors of the cultivated garden gladiolus, this is similar to the *G. primulinus* garden varieties which have been evolved by plant breeders. Its flowers are borne on a long, erect stem and are markedly hooded. They range from yellowish-brown to orange in colour and are often streaked or flecked with brown. Flower c. 2cm (⅘in) across. It is a common plant in grassland from 1200–3050m (4000–10,000ft) but rarely found above that higher altitude. A local species, G. sp. 'A', with yellow flowers streaked with orange, is found in rocky, wooded grassland in western Kenya. Widespread in East Africa and south to South Africa.
   NB This species may eventually be reclassified into more than one.

G. ukambanensis (*Acidanthera candida, A. ukambanensis*)   **Plate 150**
An erect herb springing from a round corm with a fibrous covering. Its long white flowers are beautifully scented, c. 35mm (1⅖in) across, and have a tube 10cm (4in) long. It flowers copiously in years of good rainfall but is capricious in its flowering, in some years being abundant and in others rather scarce. It is found in stony grasslands at altitudes of 610–2100m (2000–7000ft), but it is not common. Machakos district (Kenya); lake areas, Maasai, Tanga (Tanzania); Uganda and elsewhere, not known.

G. watsonioides   **Plate 539**
The finest of the East African gladioli. Its flowers are bright red, with a curved perianth tube 30–40mm (c. 1½in) long. It grows only at high altitudes in stony soils of

the alpine and subalpine regions from 3050m (10,000ft) and higher. Aberdares and Mt Kenya (Kenya); Mts Kilimanjaro, Meru only (Tanzania); Uganda and elsewhere, not known.

Hesperantha petitiana
Plates 822 & 823

A small herb with subulate leaves and single or spiked pink to pale mauve flowers; perianth, 20mm (¾in) long, with a yellow spot in the throat, regular, with a tube and six equal segments. Three stamens, alternate with the three stigmas. Seeds globose, the corm is covered with scales. Locally common in subalpine and alpine stony grassland; altitude range generally 3000m (9800ft) upwards. The only species in East Africa. Elgon, Aberdares and Mt Kenya (the photograph was taken at 3040m (10,000ft) on the Aberdares) (Kenya); Maasai (Kilimanjaro), Mbeya, Iringa, Songea (Tanzania); eastern region of Uganda; also southern Sudan, Ethiopia, Malawi, Zimbabwe.

Moraea carsonii   An erect herb with narrow leaves and white-spotted, blue flowers, pediciliate in a panicle; it is similar to *M. thomsonii* but the bracts differ in size, the outer often subtending a pedicel, and smaller. Flower *c.* 20mm (¾in) long. Flowers mostly pedicillate in a panicle, whereas in *M. thomsonii* the bracts are all similar and flowers sessile on a spike. Found locally in stony grassland at medium altitudes and more common in western Kenya than *M. thomsonii*. Altitude range 1950–2100m (6500–7000ft). Elgon, Kitale and western Kenya, whereas *M. thomsonii* extends east to Nairobi, Aberdares, Mt Kenya, Nanyuki (Kenya); Tabora, Mbeya, Iringa (Tanzania); northern, eastern regions of Uganda; also southern Sudan, Zambia. One of nine species in East Africa.

M. thomsonii
Plate 864

An erect herb with narrow leaves and spikes of white-spotted blue flowers, *c.* 30mm (1¼in) across. A pretty, iris-like plant found locally in stony grassland at medium altitudes – 1200–3300m (3850–10,700ft). Cheranganis, Tinderet, Aberdares, Mt Kenya, Kitale, western Kenya, Nanyuki and Nairobi (Kenya); Maasai, Tabora, Mpwapwa, Kondoa, Morogoro, Mbeya, Iringa (Tanzania); northern regions of Uganda; also southern Sudan (one record only), Ethiopia, Malawi, Zambia, Zimbabwe, Mozambique.

Romulea fischeri
Plate 712

A member of the Iris family with single, star-like, mauve or pale purple flowers, *c.* 22mm (⅞in) across. It grows in wet upland and alpine stony grassland in all the higher-altitude areas above 1830m (6000ft) in Elgon, the eastern Cheranganis and eastern Tinderet and above 2130m (7000ft) in western Cheranganis, western Tinderet, the Plateau, Mau, Aberdares, Loita Hills and northern and western slopes of Mt Kenya (Kenya); on the south and east slopes of Mt Kenya it is found from 1520m (5000ft) upwards; Tanzania, no record; northern, eastern regions of Uganda; also Ethiopia. Three other species in East Africa.

R. keniensis   Similar to *R. fischeri* in appearance but has smaller flowers. Perianth *c.* 25mm (1in) long. Grows in stony wet soils, especially alongside streams, in the alpine zones of Mt Kenya and the Aberdares (Kenya); Mt Kilimanjaro (Tanzania); Uganda and elsewhere, not known.

97. Agavaceae

Rhizomatous herbs, shrubs or trees with woody stems and spiral or distichous linear to ovate-elliptic leaves; flowers in racemes, bisexual or rarely unisexual, regular, perianth with a cylindrical tube and six spreading lobes, six stamens, ovary superior or inferior, with a few axile ovules in each of the three cells. Fruit a capsule or berry. Thirty-four species in two genera in East Africa.

Dracaena afromontana A spindly shrub or tree usually up to 3.6–9m (12–30ft) high but occasionally reaching 12m (40ft). Stems much branched, usually only 2.54–5cm (1–2in) but sometimes as much as 30cm (12in) thick. Branches drooping, leaves linear and laxly disposed up to 30cm (12in) long and 3.75cm (1½in) broad, very dark green in colour. Flowers white, tinged with red outside in lax terminal panicles up to 30cm (12in) long. Berries small, 8–12mm (⅓–½in), spherical and red when ripe. Found in the lower layers of mountain forest and widespread from 1500–2400m (5000–8000ft) throughout East Africa.

Sansevieria intermedia (*S. volkensii*)   **Plate 248**
A stoloniferous perennial with stiff, usually straight, cylindrical, scarcely variegated leaves and a terminal unbranched raceme of white, and dirty reddish flowers, 3.5cm (1½in) long. Locally common in dry, rocky bushland; altitude range 200–2000m (650–6650ft). Narok, Rift Valley and Machakos (Kenya); Maasai, Tanga (Tanzania); Uganda and elsewhere, no record.

S. suffruticosa   **Plate 635**
An erect, bushily branching herb arising from a creeping rhizome up to 75cm (30in) high. Seven to eighteen leaves to a growth, usually irregularly directed, up to 60cm (24in) long, cylindrical and with a concave channel extending to a very acute, hard, spine-like point. The flower stem 40cm (*c.* 16in) long with twenty-five flowers in a cluster at intervals along the rachis, whitish or greenish-white, sometimes with a reddish tinge outside. Perianth *c.* 3.5cm (1⅜in) long. Found in shallow soils overlying rocks, on rocky outcrops and in thickets; altitude range 1450–1890m (4800–6300ft). Rift Valley, Naivasha, Narok, Embu, Machakos (Kenya); lake areas and Maasai (Tanzania); Uganda and elsewhere, not known.

98. Hypoxidaceae

A small family of perennial herbs found mainly in the Southern Hemisphere. The rootstock is in the form of a fibrous rhizome or corm and the leaves are basal, sheathing below. The star-like perianth has six segments, usually six stamens and an inferior ovary. Found at all altitudes up to 3050m (10,000ft) but never in really dry areas. Eight species in East Africa in two genera.

Hypoxis obtusa   **Plate 410**
A perennial plant which grows from a corm and has narrow, strap-like, recurved leaves. Its yellow flowers, *c.* 15mm (⅜in) across, are held upright and open on a long, thin stalk or scape. It is common in burnt grassland and the moister parts of

shallow soils at altitudes of 910–2100m (3000–7000ft). Throughout Kenya, except possibly in the west; all regions of Tanzania and Uganda; also Ethiopia, Malawi, Zambia, Zimbabwe, Mozambique.

H. villosa Similar to *H. obtusa* but with smaller flowers; perianth 11mm (⅜in) long. It is found in much the same districts and occasionally in black cotton soils, especially near Nairobi (Kenya); all regions of Tanzania and Uganda; elsewhere, see *H. obtusa*.

H. multiflora Dense or loose racemes of large yellow flowers which tend to centre themselves in the middle of upright or semi-erect, broad, linear-lanceolate leaves which spring from a largish corm. Locally common in burnt grassland in Kitale, Elgon and the Cheranganis (Kenya); all regions of Tanzania and Uganda; elsewhere, see *H. obtusa*.

NB *H. obtusa* is a complex and variable species; in *UKWF*, *H. villosa* and *H. multiflora* are recorded as separate species but the opinion of botanists today is that they should be included in *H. obtusa*.

99. Orchidaceae
THE ORCHID FAMILY

A very large family, mainly of epiphytic and tropical plants but also with numerous terrestrial species, many of which are temperate. They are almost absent from dry tropical areas. They are herbs with rhizomes, root tubes or leaves swollen at the base to form pseudo-bulbs. Their flowers are zygomorphic, the perianth having two whorls of three, the outer either sepaloid or petaloid, the inner petaloid. The middle petal differs from the other two and forms a lip. Often either the lip or the dorsal sepal is spurred. One or two stamens unite with the style to form the 'column'. Pollen becomes stuck together in waxy masses called pollinia. The ovary is inferior, and the fruit is a capsule containing innumerable minute seeds. The terrestrial orchids are much commoner in the southern highlands of Tanzania than further north. Of the seventeen genera and 166 species of the tribe Orchideae found in East Africa, all are found in these southern highlands, whereas only eighty species in eleven genera are found in the Kenya highlands. In all there are in the Orchidaceae 696 species in seventy-one genera in East Africa, of which 427 species in twenty-nine genera are recorded in Orchidaceae, Parts 1 and 2 of *FTEA*.

AERANGIS
Epiphytic with racemes of white flowers with long tubular spurs. Twenty species in East Africa.

Aerangis brachycarpa   Plate 151
Stem woody, usually short, leaves dark green, borne close together in a fan; flowers pale green when opening becoming white or with pink tinges, and the petals reflexed. Flower 4–6cm (1¾–2⅜in) in diameter; spur 4–6cm (1¾–2⅜in) long. It differs from *A. flabellifolia* in the length of spur; that of *A. flabellifolia* at 12–15cm (5–6in) long being more than twice as long as in *A. brachycarpa*. In addition, in *A. brachycarpa* only the petals are reflexed, whereas in *A. flabellifolia* all the perianth parts are reflexed. Found in rather dry highland forest and bush, usually in deep shade; altitude range 1675–2300m (5500–7500ft). Mau, Aberdares, Mt Kenya, Rift

Valley, Machakos and Nairobi (Kenya); Maasai, Tabora (Tanzania); northern and eastern regions of Uganda; also in Ethiopia, Zambia.

A. luteo-alba var. **rhodosticta** **Plate 152**
A small, almost stemless plant with six to twelve thick green leaves up to 12cm (5in) long, usually less than 1cm ($\frac{2}{5}$in) wide. Inflorescence with four to twenty creamy-white flowers, rather flat, and up to 3cm (1$\frac{1}{5}$in) in diameter, 30mm (1$\frac{1}{5}$in) long when open, with a bright red (sometimes yellow) column at the centre. Found only in shady positions, usually near water in warm, moist localities generally attached to branches and twigs of shrubs; altitude range 1300–2100m (4250–6900ft). Mt Kenya, Nyambeni Hills, western regions, Kisii, Narok, Embu, Machakos (Kenya); lake areas, Tabora (Tanzania); western and eastern regions, Buganda (Uganda); also Sudan, Ethiopia, Zaire.

A. thomsonii **Plate 153**
Stem stout, woody, 15–60cm (6–24in) long with very thick aerial roots; leaves deep green, hard and leathery; flowers pure white, six to twelve per raceme, all perianth parts strongly reflexed, spur distinctly thickened towards the tip. Tepals 25–30mm (*c.* 1in) long; spur *c.* 100–150mm (4–6in) long. Altitude range 1500–2100m (4900–6900ft). Common in highland forests, usually above 2150m (7000ft) on the trunks of tall trees and recorded everywhere in this habitat (Kenya); Maasai, Tanga (Tanzania); eastern region of Uganda; also in Ethiopia, Zambia.

Angraecum giryamae **Plate 154**
A robust epiphyte orchid up to 1m (3ft) long with a stout woody stem which emits many pencil-like long roots. Leaves strap-shaped up to 70cm (27in) long and 50cm (20in) wide, elliptic, strong and leathery, rounded at the apex and slightly serrate. Inflorescence is borne on the leafless parts of the stem. Sepals and petals equal, pale green, the spur slightly curved, the lip white. The flowers, strongly scented, open in succession from the base of the spike and the plant remains in blossom for several weeks. Sepals and petals 3–4cm (1$\frac{1}{5}$–1$\frac{3}{5}$in) long; spur 4–5cm (*c.* 1$\frac{3}{4}$in) long; inflorescence up to 80cm (31in) long. Altitude range 0–900m (0–3050ft). Found in coastal regions anchored to well-shaped coral rock cliffs or on trees and in coastal hinterlands (Kenya); Tanga, Morogoro, Pemba Island (Tanzania); Uganda and elsewhere, not known. Twenty-one other species in East Africa.

Ansellia africana (*A. gigantea*) **Plates 411 & 491**
An erect, very variable, epiphytic plant 50–125cm (20–50in) tall. Pseudobulbs fusiform or cylindric; slender, slightly tapering above 10–50cm (4–20in) long, covered by papery sheaths and leaf bases when young. Eight to ten leaves, in apical half of pseudobulb, narrowly lanceolate, acute or rarely obtuse, 15–20cm (6–8in) long. Inflorescence laxly thirty- to forty-flowered, much branched. Flowers more or less heavily blotched with dark maroon. Petals elliptic, rounded at apex, slightly shorter and broader than sepals; 1.6–2.8cm (*c.* $\frac{3}{5}$–1$\frac{1}{8}$in) long, 0.5–1.1cm ($\frac{1}{5}$–$\frac{2}{5}$in) broad; lip 1.4–2.2cm ($\frac{3}{5}$–*c.* 1in) long. Lip three-lobed, broad, bearing two to three longitudinal keels in centre. Side lobes erect, rounded in front, mid-lobe orbicular to obovate, retuse or obtuse with undulate margins. An epiphyte, but sometimes found on rocks in open woodland, wooded grassland or on *Hyphaene* palm trees. Altitude range 0–2200m (0–7200ft). Western Suk, Kajiado (Nguruman Hills), Kilifi (Kenya); Seronera, Tanga, Ulanga, Rukwa (Tanzania); West Nile, Bunyoro, Mbale – Elgon (Uganda); throughout tropical Africa to South Africa.

NB *A. africana* is a very variable species; one of the varieties which occurs in East Africa has been called var. *nilotica*, which has spots varying in size but always brown, usually small and distinct.

Bolusiella maudiae (*B. imbricata*) **Plate 155**
A very small, indeed minute, epiphyte with short, thin roots and stemless, or with a woody stem to 5cm (2in) long, leaves fleshy, flattened in a vertical plane, 1–3.5cm ($\frac{2}{5}$–1$\frac{2}{5}$in) long. Inflorescence usually arising below and longer than the leaves to 7cm (*c.* 3in) long with many minute white flowers partially hidden by dark brown bracts, pedicels very short and lip three-lobed. Sepals less than 4mm ($\frac{1}{6}$in). Altitude range 0–1800m (0–6000ft). Generally found on twigs and branches in warm, humid situations at lower altitudes throughout region. Two other species in East Africa.

Bonatea steudneri **Plate 27**
A robust herb which grows to 25–125cm (10–50in) in height bearing ten to twenty leaves and six to thirty green and white flowers. Its bracts are leafy, shorter than the pedicel with ovary; the lip claw is 15–30mm ($\frac{3}{5}$–1$\frac{1}{5}$in) long then divides, the middle lobe is linear and usually bent sharply backwards from the middle, the side lobes much longer, 25–85mm (1–3$\frac{2}{5}$in), and the spur usually 1–2cm ($\frac{2}{5}$–$\frac{4}{5}$in) long and usually twisted. Found in bush, scrub and grassland at the edge of thickets, by roadsides and in rocky places at 1000–2400m (3300–8000ft) altitudes. Widespread in Kenya; Musoma (Serengeti), Lushoto (Tanzania); Karamoja, Busoga, Mubende (Uganda); also Sudan, Eritrea, Somalia, eastern Zaire, Zambia, Zimbabwe. One of six species in East Africa.

Cyrtorchis arcuata **Plate 156**
A robust epiphytic orchid, 30–50cm (12–20in) high. The stem round, woody and covered with dry sheaths of shed leaves. Leaves distichous eight to sixteen, tongue-shaped, glossy, stiff with divided tips up to 22cm (9in) long and 4cm (1$\frac{3}{5}$in) wide. The inflorescence is from the axil of the leaf on the growing part, usually two or more. The racemes stand horizontally or arch slightly, as long or longer than the leaves, each with eight to twelve flowers. Flowers, 3–5cm (1$\frac{1}{5}$–2in) diameter; spur 3–5cm (1$\frac{1}{5}$–2in) long; they tend to be larger in highland districts compared with coastal specimens. Petals short, lip broader than the sepals; spur conical, slightly bent. Flowers greenish-white to pure white, fading to an attractive apricot or orange. Delightfully fragrant. Found in coastal and highland forests throughout East Africa, altitude range 60–2280m (200–7500ft). Also Ethiopia, Burundi, Malawi, Zambia. Nine other species in East Africa.

Diaphananthe fragrantissima An epiphytic plant with a woody stem which attaches itself to the branches of tall trees. The flowers are whitish-green and attached to the leafless stem in groups of two to four individual flowers. Flower *c.* 15mm ($\frac{3}{5}$in) across; spur 7mm (*c.* $\frac{1}{4}$in) long. It grows within the forest zone (Kenya) at altitudes of 1070–1500m (3500–5000ft). Lake areas, Tanga, Morogoro (Tanzania); all regions of Uganda except northern; also Sudan, Ethiopia, south to Zimbabwe, Mozambique. One of twenty-five species in East Africa.

D. pulchella Similar to *D. fragrantissima*, but with longer flowers, which are semi-transparent, a darker green and arranged in groups of six to eight. Flower *c.* 12mm (*c.* $\frac{1}{2}$in) across; spur *c.* 10mm ($\frac{2}{5}$in) long. It is found in dry forests at altitudes of 1350–2100m (4500–7000ft). Mt Elgon, Aberdares, Machakos districts (Kenya); Maasai, Tanga, Tabora, Mbeya, Iringa, Songea (Tanzania); all regions of Uganda except western; also Malawi, Zambia.

D. rutilla Often insecurely attached to its host tree by short aerial roots with larger roots hanging free. Its leaves are rather leathery and touched with purple. Dingy, greenish-purple flowers densely arranged, 4mm ($\frac{1}{6}$in) across; spur c. 6mm ($\frac{1}{4}$in) long. Widespread in forested areas at altitudes of 200–2100m (700–7000ft). Mau, Aberdares, Mt Kenya, Mumias, Kisii, Machakos, Nairobi area (Kenya); Maasai, Tabora, Mbeya, Iringa, Songea (Tanzania); western region, Buganda (Uganda); also Malawi, Zambia, Zimbabwe, Mozambique.

D. tenuicalcar   **Plate 157**
A straggling, untidy plant with long aerial roots entangled among the many branching pendent stems. Inflorescence with only three to four white flowers, each having a spur at least 2–5cm ($\frac{4}{5}$–2in) long; perianth 5mm ($\frac{1}{6}$in) long; spur (very slender) 22mm (c. 1in) long. Found in montane forests and on savannah trees, altitude range 2100–2400m (7000–8000ft) (Kenya); Tanzania, no record; western region of Uganda; also Ethiopia.
    NB D. tenuicalcar is very similar to the two following species.

D. subsimplex, which has thirteen to fifteen flowers, semi-transparent with the lip more or less quadrate, wider at the apex than at the base. It has a wider altitude range than D. tenuicalcar, from 1700–2400m (5500–8000ft).

D. xanthopollina, which has generally longer and narrower leaves and longer inflorescences; flowers yellow with a bright yellow anther cap, lip much broader than long and obscurely three-lobed at its apex. Found in riverine forest at 1100–1675m (3500–5500ft) and only recorded in Kisii in western Kenya.

Disa erubescens Flowering stems from 30–90cm (12–36in) high with bracts shorter than the very distinctive, large, orange, red or deep scarlet flowers, c. 18cm (c. $\frac{3}{4}$in) across. The dorsal sepal is slightly incurved but not really hooded and spurred at about the middle. The spur projects backwards or slightly upwards, and the petals are bi-lobed with the lip narrowly linear and 1mm (less than $\frac{1}{24}$in) broad. Found in short upland grassland, particularly where drainage is poor and in swamps from 1400–2600m (4500–8500ft). Elgon, the Cheranganis, Tinderet, Mau, Kitale and Kisii (Kenya); Tabora, Morogoro, Mbeya, Iringa, Songea (Tanzania); northern and western regions of Uganda; also Sudan, Zaire, Malawi, Zambia. Twenty-six other species in East Africa.

D. hircicornis Flowering stem from 30–85cm (12–33in) in height, with dense inflorescence; sixteen- to many-flowered; the lowermost bracts often overtopping the pale pink to purple flowers. The dorsal sepal is curved forward and narrowly conical and in turn narrows into a short slender spur, which is usually curved round like the horn of a goat. The petals are entire and erect with a linear-spatulate lip. Flower c. 12mm ($\frac{1}{2}$in) across. Found in wet grassland and swamps, often near streams, from 950–2600m (3200–8500ft). Cheranganis, Tinderet and Kitale (Kenya); lake areas, Mbeya, Iringa, Songea (Tanzania); northern region of Uganda; also Sudan, Zaire, Malawi, Zambia, Zimbabwe.

D. scutellifera Flowering stems 25–75cm (10–30in) high. The inflorescence is densely many-flowered; the lowermost bracts overtopping the pink flowers; dorsal sepal erect, convex and spurred below the middle. The petals are erect and bi-lobed, in the upper part with the lip pendent and linear. Flower c.10mm ($\frac{2}{5}$in) across. Found in damp grassland and grassy, rocky slopes from 1800–2400m (6000–8000ft). Elgon, Tinderet, Mau, Aberdares and Mt Kenya (Kenya); Tanzania, no record; Karamoja (Uganda); also Sudan, Ethiopia.

D. stairsii A terrestrial or, rarely, epiphytic herb with slender, hairy roots but no tubers; the inflorescence is often cylindrical rather than dense; the lower bracts longer than the pink to wine-red flowers with the dorsal sepal erect, convex and hooded with a pendent spur below the middle. The petals are entire with a ligulate lip 2–3mm (⅛in) broad. Flower c. 20mm (⅘in) across. Always found above 2700m (9000ft) in grassland, moorland and rocky areas. Elgon, the Cheranganis, Aberdares and Mt Kenya (Kenya); Arusha (Mt Meru), Kilimanjaro, Uluguru Mts (Tanzania); Toro (Ruwenzori Mts), Kigezi, Elgon (Uganda); also Zaire.

EULOPHIA

Terrestrial herbs with creeping underground stems which frequently produce pseudobulbs resembling those of many epiphytic genera in *Orchidaceae*. The inflorescence is produced separately from the leafy shoots; flowers yellow, red or brown with short spurs. *E. petersii*, which occurs near El Wak in Kenya, survives on a rainfall of 250mm (10in). Seventy species in East Africa, and twenty-six in Kenya alone.

Eulophia angolensis   Plate 412

Rhizome subterranean, cylindrical and sometimes branched; leaves narrowly lanceolate, inflorescence laxly four- to twenty-flowered, sepals reflexed, yellowish-brown, slightly longer than the much broader yellow petals, lip yellow with three to five lamellae and greyish-purple markings. Inflorescence up to 1m (3ft) tall. Found in swampy ground. Altitude range 0–2300m (0–7500ft); rare below 1000m (3250ft) in Kenya, but occurs on Zanzibar and Pemba Island. Tinderet, Aberdares, Kitale, Kisii, western regions and Nairobi (Kenya); all regions except Maasai, Tanga (Tanzania); all regions of Uganda; also Sudan, Ethiopia, south to Zambia, Mozambique; no record, Zimbabwe.

E. clavicornis (*E. violacea*)   Plate 492

A terrestrial herb with the leaf-bearing shoot standing next to the flower-bearing stem; the leaves absent to fully developed at flowering time, 5–20cm (2–8in) long. One or both petals of the flower and sometimes the lip are fused to the side of the column and sometimes distorted, white, tinged pale pink to pale blue. Side lobe veins gradually curving away from the centre line of the lip. Column foot almost absent. Lip 9–18mm (⅓–¾in) long; sepal (odd) 9–18mm (⅓–¾in) long. This is a widespread grassland orchid in South Africa, which occasionally extends into the equatorial area. It would appear to have a wide altitude tolerance, probably 1000–2300m (3000–7500ft), but is rare in Kenya. The photograph was taken in the Chyulu Hills (Kenya). Report any findings in Kenya to the Herbarium at the Kenya National Museum, Nairobi. Maasai, Mbeya, Iringa, Songea (Tanzania); Uganda, no record; also in Ethiopia, Malawi, Zambia, Zimbabwe, Mozambique.

E. horsfallii (*E. porphyroglossa*)   Plate 636

A robust orchid growing from a subterranean rhizome with leaves plicate to a height of 1m (3¼ft) and a width of 15cm (6in), the peduncle rising to 1–3m (3–10ft). Its flowers are large, the bronze-purple sepals reflexed, the petals longer than broad and mauve, often white on the inner surface. The lip is distinctly three-lobed, with several rows of tall lamellae on the middle lobe. Flower c. 4cm (1⅜in) across. It grows in swamps and at river edges up to altitudes of 2400m (8000ft). Mainly in north-west, western and central Kenya; all regions of Tanzania except lake areas, Maasai, Mpwapwa, Kondoa; all regions of Uganda except northern; also Zaire, Malawi, Zambia, Zimbabwe, Mozambique. Not found below 1000m (3280ft) in Kenya, but recorded in Mafia and Zanzibar Island and Dar-es-Salaam (Tanzania).

E. speciosa (E. wakefieldii)   Plate 413

Rhizome subterranean, linking aerial pseudobulbs which are spindle-shaped, bearing groups of thick, leathery leaves with serrate margins at the apex. Inflorescence a panicle, sepals reflexed, small and green, petals orbicular and entirely bright yellow, with reddish veins. Lip 15mm (⅝in) long; raceme 30–45cm (12–18in) long. (In E, stenophylla, which is rather similar, the petals are yellow with a grey inner surface.) Found in seasonally wet grassland and poor rocky soils; altitude range 0–2100m (0–7000ft). Kitale, Kisii, Machakos and near the coast – Taru desert (Kenya); all regions of Tanzania, Zanzibar; all regions of Uganda except eastern; also Zaire, Malawi, Zambia, Zimbabwe.

E. stenophylla   Plate 493

A herb with ovoid pseudobulbs at or above ground level. Its leaves are usually less then 2cm (⅘in) wide and are well developed at the time of flowering. The flowers are not more then 25mm (1in) in diameter, and have yellow petals with a grey inner surface, the lip yellow with purplish veins, and the sepals are green overlaid with brown. It is usually found in bush or among rocks with some shade at altitudes of 610–1830m (2000–6000ft). Nairobi, Narok and the Rift Valley near Nakuru (Kenya); Maasai (Tanzania); northern region of Uganda; elsewhere, not known.

E. streptopetala (E. paivaeana)   Plate 494

A terrestrial herb with ovoid pseudobulbs above the ground, leaves well developed at the time of flowering, 4–10cm (1¾–4in) wide; inflorescence a raceme, sepals greenish, heavily overlaid with brownish-purple, reflexed. Petals yellow, lip pale yellow with side lobes heavily streaked with purple; central lobe with reflexed sides and bright yellow lamellae in the centre; spur 1.5mm ($\frac{1}{16}$in) long. Found in forests, bush and grassland often among rocks; altitude range 1200–2100m (4000–7000ft). Widespread in East Africa in its ecological zone. In Kenya the plants belong to the ssp. borealis. All regions of Tanzania and Uganda; also Sudan, Ethiopia, south to Zimbabwe, Mozambique.

HABENARIA

Terrestrial herbs with erect terminal racemes of green and/or white flowers with slender spurs. More than 113 species of Habenaria are recorded in East Africa. Only a few, therefore, can be noted here; each species tends to be selective in its altitude range and habitat, which may help in identification.

Habenaria altior   Stem 20–95cm (7¾–37in) long, bearing nine to thirteen linear or lanceolate leaves. Flowers seven to many, suberect, green and white; dorsal sepal elliptic, laterals larger, obliquely obovate. Petal lobes lanceolate, the anterior slightly longer and broader than the posterior; lip three-lobed almost from the base, side lobes about two-thirds the length of the middle lobe and a little broader. Spur swollen in the apical half. Inflorescence 4–25cm (1¾–10in) long; spur 15–22mm (¾–1in) long. Found in grassland, especially near streams and in forest glades; altitude range 1800–3300m (5900–11,000ft). Elgon, Cheranganis, Tinderet, Mau and Aberdares (Kenya); Mt Kilimanjaro (Tanzania); Uganda, no record; also Zaire.

H. bracteosa   A terrestrial herb up to 20–80cm (7¾–31in) high, bearing five to ten lanceolate or oblong-lanceolate leaves. Flowers green or yellowish-green, many; lip three-lobed from near the base, side-lobes a little longer than the middle lobe, spur slender. Inflorescence 5–50cm (2–20in) long; lip 3–8mm (⅛–1⅓in) long; spur 15–28mm (¾–1in) long. Found in grassy glades in mountain forest and heath zones; altitude range 2200–3600m (7200–12,100ft). Elgon, Cheranganis, Mau and Mt

Kenya (Kenya); Maasai (Mt Kilimanjaro), Mbulu (Mt Hanang), Uluguru Mts (Tanzania); eastern region – Moroto Mt and Elgon (Uganda); also in Sudan, Ethiopia.

H. attenuata Stem 15–20cm (6–7¾in) high, bearing up to twenty green flowers in a single spiral row; lip three-lobed nearly to the base, the middle lobe longer and broader than the spreading side lobes with a slender spur. Dorsal sepal *c.* 3–3¾mm (*c.* ⅛in) long, laterals 3–4mm (⅛–⅙in) long; total length of lip, including claw, *c.* 4mm (⅙in); spur (pendent) 10–16mm (⅖–⅗in) long. Found in upland grassland among bracken and in conifer plantations, selective in altitude range of 2100–2600m (6900–8500ft). Mau (at Londiani Railway Station) (Kenya); Tanzania, no record; Mbale district (Uganda); also in Ethiopia, Zaire.

H. eggelingii A terrestrial herb, stem up to 1.2m (40in) high, bearing six to twelve lanceolate, acute leaves. Flowers green, many; lip three-lobed from the middle, middle lobe longer and broader than side lobes; spur swollen in apical part. Inflorescence up to 56cm (22in) long; spur 5–6.5mm (⅕–¼in) long; lip 4–6mm (⅙–¼in) long. Found in damp, shady places in upland rain-forest and moor, often in gullies; altitude range 2400–3800m (7900–12,750ft). Elgon, Aberdares and Mt Kenya (Kenya); Tanzania, no record; western region – Kigezi, Mt Muhavura (Uganda); also eastern Zaire.

H. macrantha Stem 20–50cm (7¾–20in) high, bearing five to seven lanceolate to ovate-lanceolate leaves. Flowers two to nine, green or whitish-green; dorsal sepal erect, 2–2.6cm (⅘–1in) long, sepals and petals papillose and ciliolate. Lip glabrous, three-lobed, side lobes longer than middle lobes, diverging but more or less incurving with six to ten narrow threads on the outer margin. 3cm (1⅕in) long, This species is found in upland grassland, and moorlands among *Erica arborea*; altitude range 2600–3040m (8500–10,000ft). Aberdares (Kenya); Tanzania, no record; Elgon (Uganda); also Ethiopia.

H. malacophylla **Plate 28**
Terrestrial herb with fleshy, tuberous roots, stem 30–100cm (12–40in) high, bearing ten to nineteen lanceolate, rather soft leaves. Flowers green, many, dorsal sepal elliptical-ovate, laterals lanceolate, anterior lobe of petal longer and narrower than posterior, curving upwards; lip three-lobed almost from the base, lobes linear, side lobes longer than middle lobe, spur thicker in the middle than at either end. Bracts distinctly shorter than the flowers. Inflorescence 8–34mm (⅕–1⅖in) long; spur 9–18mm (⅓–¾in) long. Flowers green and/or white. Found in upland rain-forest and grassland in forest; altitude range 1250–2450m (4000–8000ft). Elgon, Mau, western regions and Kajiado (Kenya); Maasai, Morogoro, Mbeya, Iringa (Tanzania); all regions of Uganda except northern; also Ethiopia, Zaire, Malawi, Zambia, Zimbabwe.

H. peristyloides A terrestrial herb, stem 10–80cm (4–31in) high, bearing four to nine lanceolate, oblanceolate or linear-lanceolate leaves. Flowers, green, many; lip with broad cordate base, three-lobed in the apical two-thirds, the middle lobe about twice as long as the side lobes; spur cylindrical. Inflorescence 5–30cm (2–12in) long; lip 7–12mm (¼–½in) long; spur 1.5–3mm (1/18–⅛in) long. Found in short, upland grassland, marshes and open scrub; altitude range 1800–2550m (5900–8450ft). Elgon, Tinderet, Mau, Aberdares, Kitale and Kisii (Kenya); Mbeya, Iringa (Tanzania); western, eastern regions of Uganda; also Sudan, Ethiopia, Zaire.

H. petitiana Stem10–100cm (4–40in) high, bearing seven to fourteen ovate or broadly lanceolate leaves, base clasping the stem. Flowers very small, green or yellow-green and many; lip almost as broad as long, three-lobed in the apical half; side lobes usually longer than the middle lobe; spur almost globose. Inflorescence up to 28cm (11in) long; petals *c.* 3mm ($\frac{1}{8}$in) long, *c.* 1.5mm ($\frac{1}{16}$in) broad; lip 2.5–4mm (*c.* $\frac{1}{8}$–$\frac{1}{6}$in) long. Found in short grassland and forest edges; altitude range 1500–3000m (4900–10,150ft). Elgon, Cheranganis, Mau, Aberdares, Mt Kenya and Nyambeni Hills (Kenya); Maasai, Tanga, Mbeya, Iringa (Tanzania); all regions of Uganda except Buganda; also in Ethiopia, Zaire.

H. vaginata Stem 10–50cm (4–20in) high, with one or two ovate or orbicular leaves at or near the base and a few sheaths on the upper part. Six to many flowers, curving outwards, green; lip three-lobed from near the base, side lobes a little shorter and narrower than the middle lobes, spur slightly swollen in the middle. Inflorescence 4–20cm (1$\frac{3}{5}$–7$\frac{1}{2}$in) long; spur 1.7–2.7cm ($\frac{3}{5}$–1$\frac{1}{10}$in) long; petals (entire) 3.5–5cm (1$\frac{2}{5}$–2in) long, 1.5cm ($\frac{3}{5}$in) broad. Found in short, damp grassland and forest edges; altitude range 1500–2700m (4900–8850ft). Elgon, Tinderet, Mau, Aberdares, Narok and Nairobi (Kenya); Tanga (Tanzania); Uganda, no record; also in Ethiopia.

Microcoelia guyoniana A small to robust plant with thicker roots and white flowers larger than *M. smithii*. This genus has no leaves, photosynthesis taking place in the roots. The perianth parts are wider and the anther cap yellow or brown. The spur is conical with the apex yellowish, greenish or brownish. Flower *c.* 4mm ($\frac{1}{6}$in) across. Found in dry forest and bush from 1500–2000m (5000–6500ft). Kitale, western Kenya, Kisii, Narok, Baringo, Rift Valley and Nairobi (Kenya); lake areas, Tanga, Mbeya, Iringa (Tanzania); western region, Buganda (Uganda); also Sudan, Ethiopia, Zaire, Zambia. One of fourteen species in East Africa.

M. smithii A tiny, almost minute plant with very thin roots. Flowers, *c.* 3mm ($\frac{1}{8}$in) across, white, with the spur about the same length as the lip, and often tinged with green or pink at the tip; the perianth parts are often rather narrow. Found in dry forest and bush from 300–1800m (1000–6000ft). Coastal forests, Nairobi (Kenya); Maasai, Tanga (Tanzania); Uganda and elsewhere, not known.

Platycoryne crocea **Plate 437**

A terrestrial herb, glabrous except for the roots; tubers ellipsoid or almost globose, densely tomentose up to 18mm ($\frac{3}{4}$in) long. Stem erect, often somewhat flexuous, slender, terete or angled, with a tuft of leaves at the base and several more scattered along its length. Leaves five to twelve, sometimes up to sixteen, the lowermost sometimes reduced to a sheath, the lower ones, three to eight, forming a tuft, linear or linear-lanceolate, suberect or variously spreading, the largest not more than 8cm (3$\frac{1}{5}$in) long, the upper ones at intervals on the stem and shorter than those at the base. Inflorescence short, *c.*2.5cm (1in) long, densely two- to six-flowered (sometimes to nine). Flowers suberect or curving outwards, yellow or orange. Petals erect, 4.5–10.5cm (2–4in) long, but much curved; lip 5–12mm ($\frac{1}{5}$–$\frac{1}{2}$in) long. Found in grassland; altitude range 0–360m (0–1200ft); ssp. *montis-elgonis*: 1200–2350m (3900–7600ft), ssp. *ochrantha*: 600–1400m (2000–4400ft) and in areas near the coast at low altitudes. Shimba Hills and Msambweni (Kenya); no record, Tanzania or Uganda; ssp. *montis-elgonis* has been recorded in Elgon and Cheranganis (Kenya); Karamoja and Mbale (Uganda); ssp. *ochrantha* is recorded in Rungwe district (Tanzania). Five other species in East Africa.

POLYSTACHYA

Epiphytic, usually with pseudobulbs and erect, often branched, inflorescences of rather small flowers which are somewhat pouched at the base, but not truly spurred. Eighty-seven species in East Africa.

Polystachya adansoniae Pseudobulbs narrow and uniformly swollen, bearing two to four linear or narrowly elliptic leaves; inflorescence simple, flowers white or greenish-white, 7mm ($\frac{1}{4}$in) across; tepals with acuminate, sometimes purplish tips. Common and widespread in relatively dry situations on *Acacia* spp. etc. Altitude from 1500–2100m (5000–7000ft) (Kenya); Morogoro, Songea (Tanzania); northern region – West Nile and Toro (Uganda); also Zaire, Zambia, Malawi, Zimbabwe, Mozambique.

P. bella **Plate 414**
An epiphytic orchid; pseudobulbs, oval in shape and laterally compressed, bearing two to six ligulate dark green leaves; the inflorescence simple, bearing large, orange-yellow pubescent flowers, 23mm (*c.* 1in) across. Found high up in forest trees from 1800–2100m (6000–7000ft). Mau and Kisii (Kenya); elsewhere, not known.

P. caespitifica ssp. **latilabris** Pseudobulbs thin and upright to 5cm (2in) high in a dense tuft; leaves coriaceous linear; inflorescence simple, five- to eight-flowered, usually shorter than the leaves. Flowers, *c.* 11mm ($\frac{2}{5}$in) across, white with yellow and mauve markings on the lip with mauve anther cap. Found in forest from 2100–2400m (7000–8000ft). Widespread in Elgon, Cheranganis, Mt Kenya, Aberdares, Mau and Kisii (Kenya); Maasai – Mt Meru (Tanzania); Uganda and elsewhere, not known.

P. campyloglossa Pseudobulbs short, almost spherical, bearing two to three oblanceolate leaves; inflorescence bearing two to five large flowers, 17mm ($\frac{3}{4}$in) across; sepals variable in colour from greenish-yellow to reddish-brown, each with a white lip. Widespread and found in cool forests often in dry areas from 1500–2700m (5000–9000ft) (Kenya); Maasai (Tanzania); northern and western regions of Uganda; also in Malawi.

P. cultriformis Pseudobulbs conical, very variable in size, 2–20cm ($\frac{4}{5}$–7$\frac{3}{4}$in) long; leaves oblanceolate and often undulate. Inflorescence paniculate, bracts small; flowers white, yellow, pink, mauve or purple, *c.* 10mm ($\frac{2}{5}$in) across; sepal 4–8mm ($\frac{1}{6}$–$\frac{1}{3}$in) long; petal and lip 3.5–7.5mm ($\frac{1}{6}$–$\frac{1}{3}$in) long. A very common orchid, often in forest near rivers or along riverside banks from 300–2400m (1000–8000ft). Widespread (Kenya); Maasai, Tanga, Morogoro, Mbeya, Iringa (Tanzania); all regions of Uganda except northern; also Ethiopia, Zaire, Burundi, Malawi, Zimbabwe.

P. spatella Pseudobulbs slender, slightly enlarged at the middle, leaves lanceolate. Flowers *c.* 9mm ($\frac{1}{3}$in) across, yellowish-green; sepals and petals rounded at the tips or mucronate; lip brighter yellow than other parts, column mauve. Common and widespread in highland forests from 1800–2550m (6000–8500ft) (Kenya); Maasai (Tanzania); western and eastern regions of Uganda; also in Zaire.

P. stricta (*P. benettiana*) Pseudobulbs long and slender bearing four to six elliptic or lanceolate, pointed leaves. Inflorescence paniculate, flowers yellowish-green, or whitish-green with some purple streaks on the lip. Petal 6–8mm ($\frac{1}{4}$–$\frac{1}{3}$in) long; lip 7.5–10mm ($\frac{1}{3}$–$\frac{2}{5}$in) long. Widespread and found in light shade in drier forests from

1500–2100m (5000–7000ft) (Kenya); Tanga, Tabora (Tanzania); western region, Buganda (Uganda); also Zaire.

P. tessellata Plate 637
An epiphytic herb with pseudobulbs 5–10cm (2–4in) long, slightly swollen towards the base. Leaves thin, elliptic to elliptic-oblong, up to 5cm (2in) broad; inflorescence paniculate with many small greenish or yellowish sometimes mauve-streaked flowers. Petal 1–2.6mm ($\frac{1}{24}$–$\frac{1}{10}$in) long, 0.5mm wide; lip 2–3mm ($\frac{1}{12}$–$\frac{1}{8}$in) long, 1.7–2.5mm ($\frac{1}{15}$–$\frac{1}{10}$in) wide. Found in riverine forest throughout East Africa; altitude range 500–1800m (1650–5900ft). Shimba Hills (Kenya); Lushoto, Korogwe, Rungwe, Lindi (Tanzania); Bunyoro, Masaka, Mengo (Uganda); also in southern Sudan, Ethiopia south to Zimbabwe and Mozambique.

P. transvaalensis Plate 249
An epiphyte with long and slender pseudobulbs which bears four to six elliptic, thickened leaves with rounded tips. Its inflorescence is paniculate with yellowish-green or reddish-green sepals and paler, spathulate petals with the lip nearly white and purple-spotted. Flower c. 15mm (c. $\frac{3}{5}$in) across. It is found in highland forest in Kenya at altitudes of 1520–3050m (5000–10,000ft); Maasai, Tanga, Morogoro, Mbeya, Iringa (Tanzania); all regions of Uganda except Buganda; also Burundi, Zambia, Malawi, Zimbabwe.

Rangaeris amaniensis Plate 158
Stems elongated and often branched, bearing two rows of short, leathery leaves, near the tip, and very thick, robust roots. Inflorescence usually longer than the leaves, bearing five to twelve flowers. Lip lanceolate with obscurely rounded or quadrate lobes in the lower part. Flower c. 20mm ($\frac{4}{5}$in) across; spur 8–15cm ($3\frac{1}{5}$–6in) long. Found in dry forest areas; altitude range 1350–2100m (4425–6900ft). Widespread in Kenya; lake areas, Maasai, Tanga, Mpwapwa, Kondoa, Morogoro (Tanzania); northern region of Uganda; also southern Ethiopia, Malawi, Zimbabwe. Three other species in East Africa.

SATYRIUM
Terrestrial orchids with tubers and erect stems. Easily recognized because each flower has two spurs or occasionally four; though, very rarely, the spurs may be absent. Thirty-seven species in East Africa.

Satyrium cheirophorum Flowering stem from 25–70cm (10–27in) in height, bearing six to ten leaves with the two to three near the base much larger than the others. The inflorescence is cylindrical with ten to many pale or bright pink flowers and slender spurs from 10–18mm ($\frac{2}{5}$–$\frac{3}{4}$in) long. Flower c. 24mm (1in) across. Found in damp or poorly drained upland grassland from 1500–2600m (5000–8000ft). Mau, Aberdares, Kisii and Nairobi (Kenya); Mbeya, Iringa, Songea (Tanzania); Uganda, no record; also Malawi, Zimbabwe, Mozambique.

S. crassicaule Plate 713
A terrestrial herb, glabrous except for the roots; rootstock short and thick, roots numerous in a dense tuft, slender, pubescent. Stem erect, slender to robust; terete, leafy along its entire length. Leaves eight to thirteen, lower ones spreading or somewhat erect in a tuft, broadly lanceolate to ligulate or narrowly ligulate from 8–48cm (c. 3–19in) long, the upper ones smaller, sheath-like, pressed close to stem, lanceolate and acute. Inflorescence cylindrical, 5–37cm (2–14$\frac{1}{2}$in) long, densely many-flowered. Flowers spreading or curved upwards, pink to mauve

(rarely white); petals 4–7mm ($\frac{1}{6}$–$\frac{1}{3}$in) long. Found in damp grasslands, or swamps, especially by streams, sometimes in running water, also grasslands on edge of or in glades of montane and bamboo forest; altitude range 1050–3150m (3450–10,300ft). Kitale, western regions, Limuru (Kenya); western Usambara Mts, Mbeya, Songea (Tanzania); Kigezi, Elgon, Mengo (Uganda); also Sudan, Ethiopia, Zaire, Malawi, Zambia.

S. sacculatum Flowering stem from 30–120cm (12–48in) in height, with thirteen to seventeen sheathing leaves, and a sterile shoot up to 7cm (2–3in) high bearing three to six leaves. Inflorescence is cylindrical and densely flowered; flowers many, *c.* 15mm ($\frac{3}{8}$in) across, orange-yellow to red (flame colour) and rarely white, with the margins of the petals ciliate. Spurs are 8.5–10.5mm (*c.* $\frac{2}{5}$–$\frac{1}{2}$in) long, usually with a pair of very short spurs in front. Found in short grassland and amongst scattered bushes from 1500–2500m (5000–8300ft). Elgon, Tinderet, Mau, Aberdares, Mt Kenya and Rift Valley (Kenya); lake areas, Tabora, Mbeya, Iringa, Songea (Tanzania); all regions of Uganda except Buganda; also Sudan, Ethiopia, Rwanda, Zaire, Malawi, Zambia.

S. schimperi Flowering stem from 15–60cm (6–24in) in height, bearing five to seven leaves and a narrow cylindrical inflorescence of nine to many greenish or yellowish-green flowers, *c.* 10mm (*c.* $\frac{3}{8}$in) across. All petals with a papillose margin and the spurs slender and 5–8mm ($\frac{1}{5}$–$\frac{1}{3}$in) long. Found in upland grassland often among rocks from 2100–2900m (7000–9500ft). Cheranganis, Tinderet, Mau and Aberdares (Kenya); Tanzania, Uganda, not known; also Ethiopia, Zaire.

TRIDACTYLE
Epiphytes with long, straggling stems, often many together in an untidy clump, leaves linear or ligulate, unequally bilobed at the apex, often thick or fleshy. Inflorescence very short or elongated; sepals and petals often slightly recurved, sepals longer than petals, lip nearly always bilobed; spur as long or longer than the tip. Twenty-five species in East Africa.

Tridactyle bicaudata   Plate 250
Stems woody, elongated bearing ligulate-linear leaves near the tips; inflorescence many-flowered, below and among the leaves; flowers yellowish or greenish, fading to brown, 10–13mm ($\frac{2}{5}$–$\frac{1}{2}$in) diameter; side lobes of lip as long or longer than the middle lobe and divided with many narrow hair-like lobes at their tips. Common in dry forest areas in Kenya from the coast to the highlands at medium altitudes; altitude range 1500–2100m (5000–7000ft); north-eastern region, Zanzibar (Tanzania); eastern region and shores of Lake Victoria (Uganda); also in Burundi, Zaire and Zambia.

T. furcistipes   Plate 251
Stems woody, elongated, usually erect, bearing linear-ligulate leaves and many-flowered inflorescences. Flowers *c.* 10mm ($\frac{2}{5}$in) long, greenish-white or creamy, fading to ochre; lateral lobes of lip triangular, entire or slightly fimbriate at apex, much shorter than middle lobe. Found in highland forest; altitude range 2100–2550m (7000–8500ft). Cheranganis, Tinderet, Aberdares and Mau (Kenya); Maasai (Tanzania); northern region of Uganda; elsewhere, not known.

Vanilla roscheri   Plate 159
A terrestrial liane of indeterminate length, lacking green leaves but with brown membranous vestigial leaves, *c.* 3cm (1$\frac{1}{5}$in) long. The stems are succulent and

terete with two shallow channels on either side and roots arising at the nodes. Inflorescence terminal or axillary with peduncles up to 20cm (7¾in) long, bearing up to thirty-five spirally-arranged, cream-white flowers. Found in coastal bushland, mangrove swamps, coral rocks and open evergreen scrub inland; altitude range 0–750m (0–2500ft). Kwale (Taru Desert), Arabuko-Sokokwe Forest (Kilifi) (Kenya); Lushoto, Tanga, Uzaramo, Dar-es-Salaam, Zanzibar (Tanzania); Uganda, no record; also in Mozambique. Three other species in East Africa.

NB The only orchid genus in East Africa which is a liane; in *V. roscheri* the leaves are reduced to scales.

Ypsilopus longifolia   **Plate 160**
A pendent epiphyte with short pendent stems, leaves few, 5–23cm (2–9in) long, very long and narrow (grasslike), arising from the woody stem. Inflorescence arising below the leaves, two-to eight-flowered, flowers white, 1.5cm (⅝in) diameter, spur 4cm (1⅜in) long, sepals and petals lanceolate, petals slightly smaller than the sepals. Widespread in dry forest; altitude range 1200–2300m (4000–7600ft). Mau, Aberdares, Nanyuki, Mt Kenya and Nairobi (Kenya); Tanga, Tabora, Mbeya, Iringa, Songea (Tanzania); Uganda, no record; also in Malawi, Zambia, Zimbabwe. Three other species in East Africa.

Further Study

The plants of East Africa are studied at the following institutions, whose staff, in so far as their other duties permit, are always glad to help with enquiries.

Kenya: The East African Herbarium, P.O. Box 45166, Nairobi (part of the National Museum)
Tanzania: The National Herbarium of Tanzania, Tropical Pesticides Research Institute, P.O. Box 3024, Arusha; The Botany Department, University of Dar-es-Salaam, P.O. Box 35060, Dar-es-Salaam
Uganda: The Botany Department, Makerere University, P.O. Box 7062, Kampala

East African plants are also actively studied at the following institutions, whose staff, however, as they are committed to the study of the whole world flora, cannot normally devote much time to purely local problems:

Europe: The Royal Botanic Gardens, Kew, Richmond, Surrey, TW9 3BQ, England
America: Missouri Botanic Garden, 2345 Tower Grove Avenue, St Louis, MO 63166, U.S.A.

The following books are helpful: *The Flora of Tropical East Africa*, obtainable from Kew and the East African Herbarium
The Mountain Flowers of Southern Tanzania (1932), P. J. Cribb & C. P. Leedal (Balkema, Rotterdam)
Environmental History of East Africa, A. C. Hamilton (Academic Press)
Some Common Flowering Plants of Uganda, E. M. Lind & A. C. Tallantire (Oxford University Press)
Upland Kenya Wild Flowers, A. D. Q. Agnew (Oxford University Press)
Kenya Trees & Shrubs, I. R. Dale & P. J. Greenway (Buchanan's Kenya Estates, 1961) (a second edition is being prepared at the East African Herbarium)

The last two or three are now out of print but second-hand copies are occasionally sold through the East African Herbarium.

LEAF AND FLOWER FORMS

PARTS OF A FLOWER

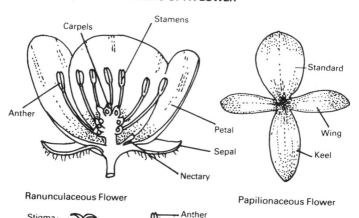

Ranunculaceous Flower

Papilionaceous Flower

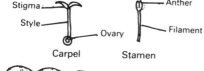

Carpel

Stamen

Ovary superior. Sepals, petals and stamens below the ovary *(Hypogynous)*.

Ovary superior. Sepals, petals and stamens around the ovary *(Perigynous)*.

Ovary inferior. Sepals, petals and stamens above the ovary *(Epigynous)*.

Irregular flower

Violaceous flower

Rubiaceous flower

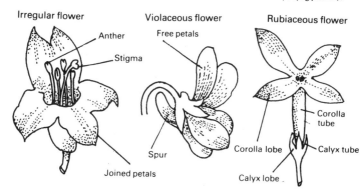

FORMS OF INFLORESCENCE

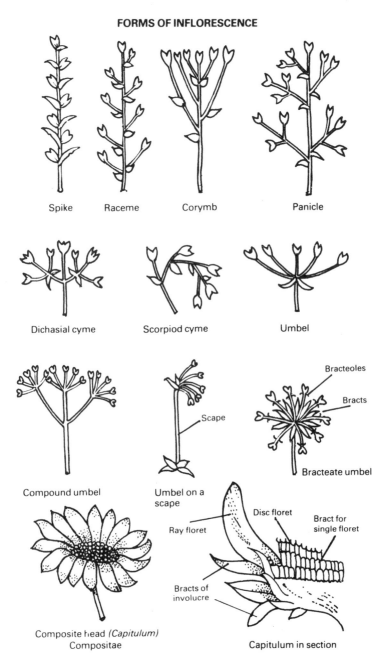

Spike   Raceme   Corymb   Panicle

Dichasial cyme   Scorpiod cyme   Umbel

Compound umbel

Umbel on a scape

Scape

Bracteoles

Bracts

Bracteate umbel

Composite head *(Capitulum)*
Compositae

Ray floret

Disc floret

Bract for single floret

Bracts of involucre

Capitulum in section

LEAF FORMS AND ARRANGEMENTS

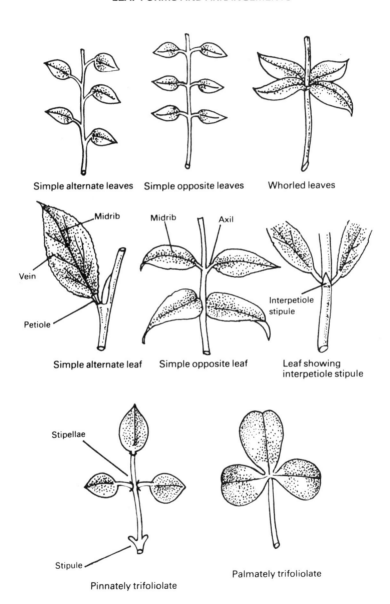

Simple alternate leaves   Simple opposite leaves   Whorled leaves

Midrib

Vein

Petiole

Simple alternate leaf

Midrib   Axil

Simple opposite leaf

Interpetiole stipule

Leaf showing interpetiole stipule

Stipellae

Stipule

Pinnately trifoliolate

Palmately trifoliolate

LEAF FORMS AND COMPOUND LEAVES

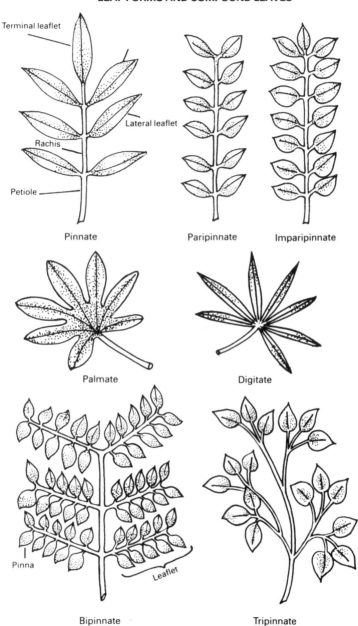

Terminal leaflet

Lateral leaflet

Rachis

Petiole

Pinnate

Paripinnate

Imparipinnate

Palmate

Digitate

Pinna

Leaflet

Bipinnate

Tripinnate

LEAF SHAPES

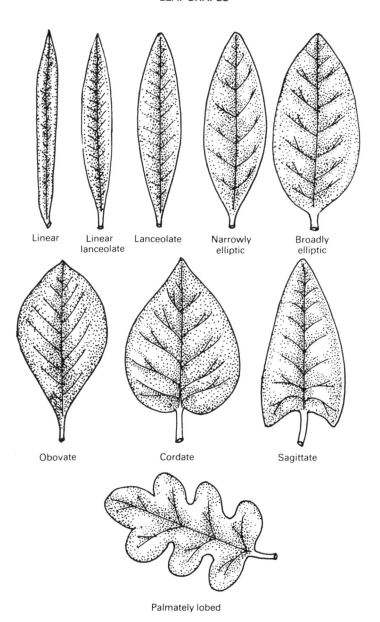

Linear

Linear lanceolate

Lanceolate

Narrowly elliptic

Broadly elliptic

Obovate

Cordate

Sagittate

Palmately lobed

LEAF SHAPES

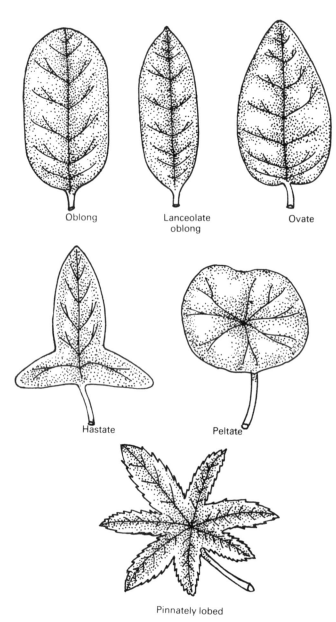

Oblong

Lanceolate
oblong

Ovate

Hastate

Peltate

Pinnately lobed

LEAF TIPS

Emarginate   Apiculate   Mucronate   Caudate (or Cuspidate)

LEAF BASES

 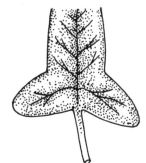

Cuneate   Auriculate

LEAF MARGINS

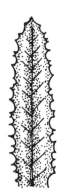   

Doubly dentate   Pinnatifid   Pinnatilobed   Pinnatipartite

LEAF TIPS

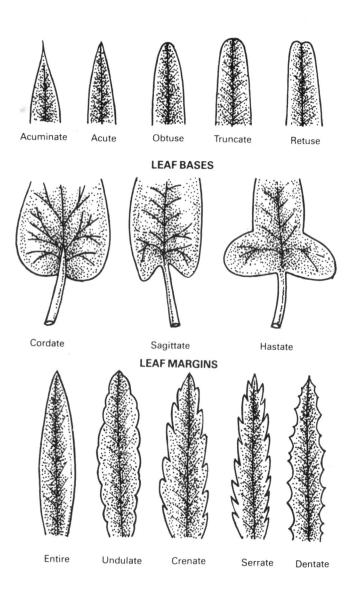

Acuminate   Acute   Obtuse   Truncate   Retuse

LEAF BASES

Cordate   Sagittate   Hastate

LEAF MARGINS

Entire   Undulate   Crenate   Serrate   Dentate

GLOSSARY
of Botanical Terms

Abaxial Away from the axis, the opposite of adaxial.

Abscissed Separated actively.

Acaulescent Becoming stemless or nearly so.

Achene Dry, single-seeded fruit.

Actinomorphic Regular. May be divided into equal parts in many ways. The opposite of zygomorphic.

Acu- Sharply-pointed.

Aculeate Armed with prickles or thorns.

Acuminate Narrowed at the tip so that the sides are concave (see p. 450).

Acute Sharply-pointed but not tapered (see p. 450).

Adaxial Nearest the axis, the opposite of abaxial.

Adventitious Used of buds or roots produced elsewhere than the axils of leaves, the extremities of branches or at nodes.

Alternate Neither opposite nor whorled, alternating along the stem (see p. 445).

Amplexicaul Stem clasping, as when base of leaf is dilated and embraces the stem.

Annual Plant living for one year or less; shallow-rooted and never woody.

Anther Part of the flower producing pollen (see p. 443).

Anthesis The time when the flower is fully opened.

Apiculate Ending in a short, sharp point (see p. 449).

Appressed Pressed closely against, but not joined to, the surface.

Arcuate Arched, upwards.

Aril An appendage covering, or partly enclosing the seed and arising from the stalk (funicle) of the seed.

Ascending Growing or climbing upwards.

Awn Long, bristle-like appendage.

Axil The upper angle between the stem and the branch or leaf growing from it (see p. 445).

Axillary Rising from an axil.

Baccate Having the form of a berry.

Biennial Plant living two years, usually only flowering in the second year.

Bifurcate Forked into two branches or parts.

Bilabiate Divided into two lips as when two or three lobes of the calyx or corolla stand separate from the others, forming an ·pper and lower lip.

Bipinnate When the pinnae of a pinnate leaf are themselves pinnate (see p. 446).

Bract A small, leaf-like organ or modified leaf, especially one with a flower or inflorescence growing from its axil (see p. 444).

Bracteole Small, usually scale-like bract on or close to the calyx of a flower, above the bract.

Bulbil Small bulb-like organ near the base of leaves or in place of flowers which break off to form new plants.

Caespitose Growing in dense tufts.

Calcareous Chalky, or lime-bearing.

Calyx Outer (usually green) protective envelope of a flower consisting of free or united sepals (see p. 443).

Campanulate Bell-shaped.

Canescent White or greyish, due to the presence of numerous short, white hairs.

Capitate Gathered into a compact cluster or head.

Capitulum A compact cluster of usually sessile flowers as in daisies.

Carpel Female reproductive organ, consisting of ovary, style and stigma; carpels may be fused to form a single pistil.

Caudate With a tip drawn out into a long, tail-like point (see p. 449).

Caulescent With a leaf-bearing stem aboveground.

Ciliate With a fringe of hairs along the edge.

Chamae Dwarf, or low growing.

Ciliolate Minutely ciliate.

Cleistogamous When fertilization occurs within the unopened flower (e.g. tet nsHViola1).

Composite Belonging to the daisy family, Compositae.

Compressed Flattened lengthwise, either side to side (laterally) or from front to back (dorsally).

Conical Cone-shaped.

Connate When parts of the same series are so closely connected that they cannot be separated without tearing.

Connivent Converging, especially used of parts nearer together towards their tips rather than below.

Contorted Twisted, used mainly of petals.

Convolute Rolled lengthwise with margins or sides curling.

Cordate Heart-shaped with basal lobes rounded and a notch between them (see pp. 447, 450)

Coriaceous Leathery.

Corolla The petals as a whole, especially when joined (see p. 443).

Corona A crown-like circle of living appendages between corolla and stamens as in Passiflora.

Corymb An inflorescence or flower form in which branches or pedicels start from different points, but reach approximately the same level to give a more or less flat top.

Crenate Edged with rounded notches (see p. 450).

Crenulate Edged with very small teeth or notches.

Crispate Curled or waved.

Cucullate Hooded.

Cuneate Wedge-shaped; cuneate leaves are attached at the narrow end (see p. 449).

Cuspidate Abruptly tipped with a short, sharp point.

Cyclic Having the leaves or petals in whorls.

Cyme An inflorescence in which the first flower to open is the terminal bud of the main stem, and subsequent flowers develop from lateral buds below it, or as terminal buds of lateral stems.

Declinate Curved downwards.

Decumbent Lying flat with tip growing upwards.

Decussate In pairs borne at right angles to the next pair immediately above or below.

Dehisce To burst open, as in seed vessels.

Deliquescent When the main stem is lost in many branches. Also becoming pulpy when dying.

Dentate Having a toothed edge (see p. 449).

Depressed Flattened as though pressed from above.

Descending Growing downwards.

Dichotomous Branching by repeated division into equal parts.

Dicotyledon Plant having two embryonic seed leaves and leaves with net-like veins (cf. Monocotyledon).

Dioecious Flowers unisexual; the male and female flowers on different plants.

Distal Furthest from the axis or point of attachment.

Distichous Regularly arranged, one above the other, in two opposite rows, one on each side of the stem.

Drupe Fleshy fruit with a stone enclosing the seed as in cherry, peach, olive and plum.

Eglandular Without glands.

Elliptic Shaped like an ellipse.

Elongate Drawn out.

Emarginate Having a notched tip or edge (see p. 449).

Endosperm Storage tissue within the seed which nourishes the embryo and often surrounds it.

Entire Having an uninterrupted margin or edge, without teeth or lobes.

Ephemeral Transitory, short-lived as with many annuals.

Epicalyx A ring of sepal-like bracts just below the true sepals.

Epipetalous Borne on the petals.

Epiphyte Plant growing on another plant but not deriving nourishment from it (as distinct from a parasite which also grows on another plant but obtains nourishment from it).

Exstipulate (estipulate) Without stipules.

Facultative Able to exist under more than one set of environmental conditions.

Falcate Curved like a scythe or sickle.

Fascicle Cluster.

Fasciculate Clustered.

Ferruginous Rust-coloured.

-fid Divided into parts or lobes (e.g. trifid, cleft with three parts).

Filament Stalk of a stamen.

Filiform Thread-like.

Fissile Tending to split.

Flexuose Full of bends, zig-zag.

Floret Small flower, especially one forming part of a larger head or cluster (see p. 444).
  Disc floret Florets near the centre of a head or capitulum, their petals usually forming a tube.
  Ray floret Florets at the margin of the capitulum, their petals usually forming a strap.

Floriferous Bearing flowers.

Flower The reproductive organs of a plant and the envelope which protects them (see p. 443).

Fluted With deep, vertical channels.

-foliate Bearing leaves.

-foliolate Bearing leaflets (as trifoliolate = bearing three leaves).

Follicle A pod consisting of a single carpel opening usually only along the inner (i.e. ventral) suture to which the seeds are attached.

Form A division of a species subordinate to a variety, having trivial differences (such as colour) from other forms of the species.

Free Not united.

Fugacious Falling or fading early; soon cast off.

Fusiform Spindle shaped, thick, but tapering towards each end.

Glabrous Hairless.

Glabrescent Becoming glabrous (hairless) or nearly so.

Glaucous Covered with a waxy or powdery bloom, as on a plum or cabbage leaf. Also, dull grey-green or blue-green in colour.

Globose Spherical.

Glomerate Completely clustered.

Glomerule A small, compact cluster.

Glutinous Sticky.

Gymnosperm Plant bearing its seeds naked on the surface, often arranged on cones or below fern-like leaves.

Gynoecium The pistil; the female part of the flower consisting of, when complete, ovary, styles and stigmas.

Gynophore A stalk supporting the gynoecium, and formed by the elongation of the receptacle.

Habit General appearance and manner of growth.

Halophyte A plant that thrives on salty soil or in salty conditions.

Hastate Having a pointed tip and two outward pointing lobes at base (from the Latin for a spear, *hasta*) (see p. 448).

Head Mass of sessile or subsessile flowers grouped on a common receptacle or support.

Herbaceous Soft, not woody.

Hetero- More than one kind; diverse, various.

Heterocarpous Diversely fruited or seeded.

Heteromorphic Of more than one shape or form.

Heterophyllous Diversely leaved.

Hilum The point of attachment of a seed to its stalk.

Hispid Bristly pubescent, or covered with stiff, bristly hairs.

Hypo- Under.

Hypoglaucous Glaucous underneath.

Imbricate Overlapping, especially of flower buds in which one sepal or petal is wholly internal and one wholly external, the others overlapping at the edge only.

Incised Having sharply and deeply indented edges.

Indehiscent Remaining closed when ripe.

Indumentum Covering of hair, scales, wax etc.

Induplicate Bent or folded inwards with the edges touching but not overlapping.

Inflorescence The flowering part of a plant and the arrangement of the flowers upon it.

Interpetiolar Between petioles.

Involucral Like or resembling a ring of bracts, belonging to an involucre.

Involucre Whorl of bracts surrounding the base of a flower or a flower cluster.

Irregular flowers Those in which the parts of the

calyx or corolla are dissimilar in size or shape including (i) asymmetric flowers which cannot be divided into two equal parts and (ii) zygomorphic flowers which are bilaterally symmetric and may be dissected in only one plane so that the two halves are mirror images or exactly the same.

Keel (i) The lower part of the flower of a member of the Pea family in which two petals combine to conceal the stamens and style (see p. 443). (ii) A projecting ridge.

Laciniate Jagged or slashed and divided into long, slender, irregular taper-pointed segments or indentations, like a fringe.

Lamina Flat blade of a leaf or petal.

Lanate With soft, entangled, woolly hairs.

Lanceolate Spear-shaped, narrowly long, oval and pointed (see p. 448).

Lax Loose, not compact.

Leaflet A single division of a compound leaf.

Lenticels Corky spots or breathing pores on the bark.

Lenticellate Having corky spots or breathing pores in the bark.

Liane Woody climber.

Ligulate Strap-shaped, provided with a strap-shaped appendage (especially used of ray florets of many Compositae).

Ligule The thin membraneous appendage at the top of the leaf sheath of grasses or the limb of ray flowers in Compositae.

Limb Main branch, of a tree; or the upper spreading part of a petal or corolla where this differs from the narrow erect claw or tube below.

Linear Long and very narrow with almost parallel edges, as in grass leaves.

Lobe Division of a leaf, perianth or anther. Lobed margins usually having large rounded teeth and shallow notches or sinuses.

Lobulate Divided into little lobes.

Locular Compartmented.

Medifixed Attached by the middle.

Membraneous Thin, dry, flexible and generally translucent.

Mericarp Part of a fruit which splits into one-seeded indehiscent portions, such as one of the halves of the fruit of Umbelliferae.

Moniliform Necklace-shaped, like a string of beads.

Monocotyledon Plant with only one embryonic seed leaf and leaves with parallel veins and flowers with parts in threes.

Monoecious Flowers unisexual, the males and females on the same plant.

Mucronate Terminating in a sharp point.

Multicolor Many colours.

Navicular Boat-shaped.

Nerve A vascular bundle in a leaf, usually appearing as a projecting ridge or line on the undersurface, often starting from the midrib and diverging or branching throughout the blade; the smaller lines, ribs or branches are veins.

Nitophilous Shiny-leaved.

Node Joint, point on a stem or branch at which a leaf or further branch is produced or borne.

Oblanceolate Having a broad round apex and a tapering base.

Oblique Slanting, unequal-sided.

Oblong With sides more or less parallel and a

rounded apex, twice to six times as long as broad (see p. 448).

Obovate Like the longitudinal section of an egg, with the narrow end at the base (see p. 447).

Obtuse Blunt or rounded at the tip (see p. 450).

Ochreous Pale yellow-brown or ochre-coloured.

Odd-pinnate Pinnate with an odd terminal leaflet.

Orbicular Flat with a circular outline.

Ovate Shaped like the longitudinal section of an egg, with the broader end at the base (see p. 448).

Ovule Grain-like body containing the egg cell which, after fertilization, develops into the seed.

Pachyphyllous Thick-leaved.

Palmate Divided into lobes, like the outspread fingers of a hand.

Pandurate Fiddle-shaped.

Panicle A compound raceme, a (usually) pyramidal inflorescence into which the axis is divided into several branches, bearing flowers, the lower branches being longer and blossoming earlier than the upper ones.

Papillate Having minute, nipple-like protuberances.

Papillose Covered with minute, nipple-like protuberances.

Pappus Tuft or ring of hairs or scales round the fruits of the plants of the family Compositae which aids dispersal by the wind.

Parasite A plant which grows on another and derives its nourishment from it.

Parietal Having ovules attached to the walls.

Paripinnate Pinnate with an even number of leaflets. i.e. without a terminal leaflet.

Parted Not quite divided; used of simple leaves divided almost to the midrib or to the base of the blade.

Pedate Resembling palmate, but the side-lobes further divided.

Pedicel Stalk bearing an individual flower of an inflorescence.

Pedicellate Provided with a pedicel (stalk).

Peduncle Common stalk of an inflorescence or the stalk of a single flower which is the only inflorescence of that plant.

Pedunculate Having a peduncle or growing from one.

Pendulous Hanging down, suspended.

Peltate Of a leaf, of which the stalk is attached to the undersurface of a leaf instead of to the edge.

Pentamerous Five-merous or with five parts, from penta = five.

Perennial Living for more than two years.

Perianth Outside part of a flower, consisting of calyx or corolla or both, used when it is difficult to distinguish between the calyx and corolla.

Perigynous Having a concave or flat receptacle, on whose rim the calyx, corolla and stamens are borne.

Persistent Remaining attached to the plant after the normal time of falling off.

Petaloid Petal-like.

Petiolate Having a petiole or stalk.

Petiole Stalk by which a leaf is attached to a plant.

Petiolule Stalk of a leaflet.

Phyllaries Bracts forming the cup or involucre of a composite flower head.

Pinna (*pl.* pinnae) Primary division of a pinnate or bipinnate leaf.

Pinnate Having leaflets growing on each side of a common stem or rhachis (see p. 446).

Pinnatifid Having the margin of a leaf cut or cleft and reaching less than half way to the midrib (see p. 449).

Pinnatilobed Having the margin of a leaf cut or cleft and reaching more than or half way to the midrib (see p. 449).

Pinnatipartite Pinnately divided almost to the midrib.

Pinnativeined Where on an entire leaf, the veins are pinnate, i.e. opposite to each other side of the midrib.

Pistil Female reproductive part of a flower.

Placentation The way ovules are attached to an ovary.

Plumose Feathered, having long, fine hairs on either side.

Precocious Flowering before the leaves are open.

Procumbent Lying along the surface of the ground.

Prostrate Synonymous with procumbent.

Protandrous With anthers shedding pollen before stigmas are mature.

Proximal Nearest to the axis or point of attachment.

Puberulous Minutely pubescent.

Pubescent Covered with short soft hairs or down.

Punctiform Dot-like in form.

Punctulate Minutely dotted.

Pustulate With slight, pimple-like swellings.

Pyriform Pear-shaped.

Raceme Inflorescence in which the flowers are borne on pedicels or stalks along an unbranched stem, or axis, the lower flowers opening first (see p. 444).

Racemose Having the characteristics of, or being like, a raceme.

Rachis The axis of an inflorescence or of a compound leaf (see p. 446).

Ranked Arranged in rows; three-ranked – three rows.

Ray (i) Floret on the margin of the flower head of members of the family Compositae when different from those of the centre. (ii) Radiating branch of an umbel.

Re- Bent abruptly backwards (see reflexed).

Receptacle The basal part of a flower to which calyx, corolla, stamens and carpels are attached.

Recurved Bent backwards or downwards.

Reflexed Bent markedly or abruptly backwards.

Regular Symmetrical – actinomorphic.

Reniform Kidney-shaped.

Repand Used of an uneven or wavy margin with shallow undulations; slightly sinuate.

Revolute Used of margins rolled back to midrib.

Rhachis See Rhachis.

Rhizome Root-like, thickish stem, normally creeping under, or half in and out of the ground, which sends rootlets down and from which branches, stems, leaves and flowering shoots rise upwards.

Riparian Along river and stream sides and banks.

Rosette Dense cluster of leaves resembling, in their arrangement, the even spacing of petals in a double rose.

Rotundate Intermediate between orbicular and oblong.

Saccate Pouched.

Sagittate Arrow-shaped (see p. 447).

Saprophyte A plant which grows on dead or rotten leaf matter.

Scabrid Scabrous.

Scabrous Rough to the touch, covered with small hard projections.

Scale A specialized leaf or bract, especially the protective covering of a bud, not resembling a leaf but more like a small plate-like covering.

Scandent Climbing.

Scape Leafless flower stalk, springing from the root.

Scarious Thin and dry, not green.

Sclerophyllous Hard-leaved, having much fibre and a thick wall.

Scorpioid Having the main stem curled during development.

Scrambler Plant which produces long weak shoots with which it grows over, and covers other plants.

Sepal One of the separate parts of the calyx of a flower (see p. 443).

Septate Divided by one or more partitions.

Septum Partition.

Sericeous Silky.

Serrate Toothed like a saw, with regular pointed teeth, pointing upwards and outwards (see p. 450).

Serrulate Minutely serrate.

Sessile Without a stalk.

Setaceous Bristle-like.

Setose With bristles.

Setulosus Full of small bristles.

Sheath Protective covering.

Simple Unbranched or undivided.

Sinuate Uneven or wavy, with rather marked deep curves or undulations.

Spathe Large bract enclosing the inflorescence or flower cluster of a plant, especially of any or several members of the Lily tribe.

Spathulate Having a narrow base and a broad, rounded apex.

Spicate Arranged on a spike, or like a spike.

Spiciform In the form of a spike.

Spike An inflorescence or arrangement of flowers with the flower sessile (without a stalk) along an unbranched axis or stem, the lower flowers opening first.

Spinose Covered with spines or thorns.

Spinulose Tending to be covered with very small spines.

Spur Slender, usually hollow extension of part of an individual flower, usually containing nectar sought by visiting pollinators (see p. 443).

Stalk Supporting stem.

Stamen Male organ of a flower, consisting of pollen sacs (anthers) and usually a stalk (filament) (see p. 443).

Staminal Pertaining to a stamen (e.g. staminal tube); staminal column – the tube column formed by stamens united by their filaments.

Staminode A sterile or abortive stamen or its homologue, without its anther.

Standard Large posterior petal of a papilionaceous flower; it is the outside petal in the bud (see p. 443).

Stellate Star-shaped.

Stem Main axis of a plant.

Stigma Terminal part of the ovary where pollen is received (see p. 443).

Stipe The stalk of a carpel or pistil.

Stipel Stipule at the base of a leaflet; not of a leaf.

Stipellate Provided with stipels.

Stipitate Supported on a special stipe (stalk) as for an ovary (e.g. Capparaceae).

Stipular Of, or belonging to stipules – like stipules in character.

Stipulate Provided with stipules.

Stipule Leaf-like or scale-like appendage of a leaf, usually at the base of the stalk – petiole (see p. 443).

Stolon Slender horizontal stem that grows along the surface of the soil and propagates by producing roots and shoots at the nodes or tips, a 'runner'.

Striate Marked with fine parallel lines, grooves or ridges.

Strigose Covered with appressed bristles.

Sub- Nearly, slightly or under, as in many compound words (e.g. subsessile, subacute – somewhat acute; subentire – having a very slightly uneven margin).

Subtend Hold or extend underneath (of a bract, stem etc.); to have growing in its axil, to enclose or embrace.

Subulate Awl-shaped.

Subumbelliform Nearly or almost in the form of an umbel.

Suffrutex An undershrub, usually producing erect, leafy and flowering shoots from a woody underground stock each year.

Suffruticose Somewhat shrubby.

Sulcate Grooved.

Suture A line of junction, or seam of union, commonly used of the line of opening of a carpel.

Style Narrowed upper part of a pistil bearing the stigma.

Tendril A thread-like projection by which a plant may attach itself to a support.

Tepal A segment of the perianth where the inner and outer petals look alike.

Terete Cylindrical, or tapering and round in cross-section.

Terminal Borne at the end (of a branch, stalk etc.).

Ternate Arranged in whorls or clusters of three.

Tetra Signifies four.

Throat Mouth of the corolla tube.

Thyrse A panicle with the secondary and ultimate axes cymose.

Tomentellous Shortly tomentose.

Tomentose Densely covered with short soft hairs.

Tooth Short projection on the margin of a leaf, especially if sharp and pointing outwards.

Tube Long hollow cylinder, especially used of the lower, often long portion of the calyx or corolla (see p. 443).

Tumid Swollen.

Umbel Inflorescence in which the divergent pedicels or peduncles spring from the same point as in the spokes of an umbrella.

Valvate (i) With margins meeting but not overlapping. (ii) Opening into valves, like double doors meeting edge to edge.

Variety Division of a species.

Venation Arrangement of the veins on a leaf or leaflet.

Verticil Circular arrangement of parts about an axis, especially leaves round a stem.

Vexillary Near the standard (vexillum) of a papilionaceous flower.

Vibratile Quivering, easily shaken.

Villose Shaggy with long weak hairs.

Villous See Villose.

Virgate Slim, straight or erect.

Viscid Sticky or glutinous.

Whorl Group of three or more similar parts arranged in a circle about an axis which may be a pedicel, peduncle or stalk.

Wing (i) Any flat membraneous expansion. (ii) One of the two lateral petals of a papilionaceous flower.

Zygomorphic Having only one plane along which it can be dissected so that the two halves are mirror images of each other.

INDEX

Scientific family names are in **bold**; common names are in ordinary type; scientific, generic and specific names are in *italics*. References to text pages are in ordinary type and to plates in **bold** type. Synonyms are listed with a reference to the name under which they are described.

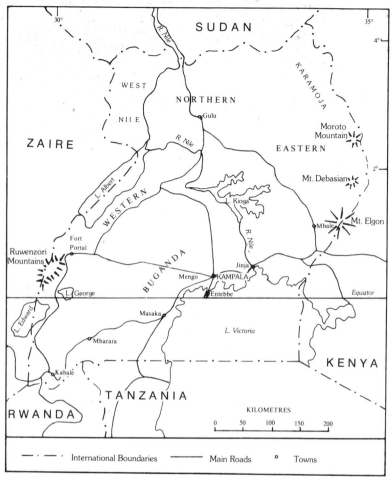

UGANDA